D1266087

A HISTORY OF
TECHNOLOGY

A HISTORY OF
TECHNOLOGY

EDITED BY

CHARLES SINGER · E. J. HOLMYARD

A. R. HALL and TREVOR I. WILLIAMS

ASSISTED BY

Y. PEEL · J. R. PETTY · M. REEVE

VOLUME IV

THE INDUSTRIAL REVOLUTION

c 1750 TO *c* 1850

1958

OXFORD UNIVERSITY PRESS

NEW YORK and LONDON

Oxford University Press, Amen House, London E.C.4

GLASGOW NEW YORK TORONTO MELBOURNE WELLINGTON
BOMBAY CALCUTTA MADRAS KARACHI KUALA LUMPUR
CAPE TOWN IBADAN NAIROBI ACCRA

THE LIBRARY OF SCIENCE EDITION FIRST PUBLISHED 1958
REPRINTED BY ARRANGEMENT WITH OXFORD UNIVERSITY PRESS
MANUFACTURED IN THE UNITED STATES

PREFACE

THE present volume covers a period of exceptional, indeed unique, importance in the history of technology, for within it occurred what is generally known as the Industrial Revolution. That title is not altogether apt, for it suggests changes more sudden and violent than in fact took place; the varying dates that historians assign to this period of rapid change themselves suggest that neither its beginning nor its end is susceptible of sharp definition. Nevertheless, the hundred years from 1750 to 1850 with which we are here concerned saw technological developments that profoundly affected the whole pattern of civilization, first in Britain, then in continental Europe and in the North American continent, and ultimately in much of the rest of the world. During this period man's relationship to natural resources became utterly changed.

Britain, as the cradle of the new inventions and technical innovations, and for the time the undisputed industrial leader of the world, necessarily figures largely throughout this volume. By 1850 the end of her supremacy in a number of fields was within sight, but the story of the successful challenges that other countries made to British industrial leadership, and of the complex factors that made them possible, belongs to the next and final volume of our work. For that volume, too, we reserve all discussion of the profound economic and social changes that resulted from this tremendous technological progress.

In 1750 the industrial state, as now understood, did not exist, although, as our previous volume made clear, the foundations for it had been well laid. Britain was then essentially an agricultural and mercantile nation. Napoleon could refer to England as 'a nation of shopkeepers', but by 1815 Britain, and Britain alone, was so far industrialized as to deserve the title of the workshop of the world. By 1851 she could stage the Great Exhibition, which brought together a profusion of machinery, and of the products of machinery, unimaginable in 1750.

But the wide use of power-driven machinery, although a basic factor in the Industrial Revolution, was not all-important. The application of science to technology played an increasingly effective part. Science did not become a major force in industry as a whole until after our present period, although it had become significant even in the seventeenth century. Nevertheless, as the final chapter in this volume shows, the transition from craft-mystery to science as a basis of technology was becoming increasingly evident. While many branches of technology were virtually unaffected by the ferment of new scientific ideas, some were receptive of them. Thus the chemical industry (ch 8), which was closely linked with textile manufacture, made increasing use of the new theoretical ideas of the age; the development of the steam engine (ch 6) owed much to Black's conception of the idea of latent heat; and the making of optical glass for special purposes was rendered possible by researches such as those of Faraday at the Royal Institution. Again, the safety lamp, an invention of profound significance for the increasingly important coal-mining industry (ch 3), was the direct fruit of laboratory investigation, while instruments for navigation and map-making—important factors in the great expansion of shipping that was an essential concomitant of industrial development—were based upon new scientific discoveries as well as upon improved craftsmanship.

That the seeds of the Industrial Revolution lay dormant for many years before they sprang into such prodigious growth in Britain was no chance event but the natural consequence of several factors. Britain not only had inventive genius and commercial enterprise, but was in fact the only country in a position to take great material advantage of the opportunities of the age. The wars that tore Europe in the second half of the eighteenth century and continued into the first part of the nineteenth, had indeed borne heavily upon her. But her commitment in terms of man-power was always relatively small and she had always retained command of the seas. With the latter went the wealth conferred by freedom to trade without restriction in any part of the world—to import the raw materials vital for the new industries and to export the manufactured products. Coal and iron ore she had in abundance and conveniently situated within her own frontiers. Britain emerged potentially wealthy from the wars that impoverished the rest of Europe.

Though the main initiative in these changes was with Britain, other European countries, especially France, made notable contributions, and we can also glimpse in this volume the beginnings of the tremendous developments that were to take place in North America. The revolution in thought that established chemistry as a formal science, with all that this subsequently entailed, was mainly of French origin. Moreover, the violent political changes of the French Revolution—shocking though their excesses were—disseminated new conceptions of individual freedom that played their role also in the Industrial Revolution. With no liberty to change employment or to seek other centres of work by the new modes of transport, with no belief that the existing order was susceptible of radical change, the growth of the new industrial towns would have been impossible. Countries that remained feudal also remained technologically backward.

Editorially, the tremendous increase in the pace of discovery and application has presented great problems of selection. Our first volume covered the whole of technological history before 500 BC; the second, the following two millennia. In the third volume the principal technological events of no more than two and a half centuries could be recounted, and for the present one the span is virtually but a hundred years. Even so the limitation of space has obliged us to omit altogether, or to discuss but briefly, many interesting topics. We have sought throughout to follow the main lines of evolution and to avoid the by-ways and blind alleys, however tempting their exploration may be. To those who find the absence of particular topics disappointing, we can but say that they could have been included only at the cost of displacing other material of at least comparable importance. While the main span of the volume is the period 1750 to 1850 we have had frequent occasion, as in earlier volumes, to interpret the time-frontiers elastically, and to look backward or forward in order to avoid artificial breaks in the thread of discussion.

A further editorial difficulty—which we have found still more acute in the preparation of our fifth and final volume—lies in the rapidly increasing complexity of the subject. As long as ideas and machines remain relatively simple—springing from common experience and fertile imagination rather than from specialized knowledge—the nature of new inventions is relatively easily expounded. We now, however, enter a period in which there is an acceleration in the complexity of machines and in the use of processes depending upon less familiar principles and concepts. Detailed explanation is often not feasible without interrupting the discourse and occupying space essential for discussion of other topics. We are grateful to our authors for the trouble they have taken in seeking a compromise between these two opposing obligations, and for their guidance in selecting appropriate illustrations for their chapters. Those who wish for more detailed accounts than it is possible to give here will find them in the works cited in the bibliographies at the end of each chapter.

We have again some changes in our staff to record. Mrs A. Clow left us at the end of 1956, and we are glad to take this opportunity of acknowledging her assistance in the collection of illustrations for many of the chapters of this volume. Mrs E. Harrison remained with us until virtually all the material for this volume had gone to press, but has now taken up another appointment, and we are happy to put on record our appreciation of her painstaking work over nearly three years. To the other members of our team—Mrs D. A. Peel, Miss J. R. Petty, Miss M. Reeve, and Miss J. V. Woodward—we once again express our thanks. It is perhaps not easily comprehended how great an amount of meticulously careful work, other than editorial, is entailed in such a project as this. We must also acknowledge part-time help given by Mrs S. Withers in collecting material for illustrations and bibliographies for this volume. The work has demanded close collaboration between editors and publisher and we should like to put on record our appreciation of the patient co-operation of the staff of the Clarendon Press.

As with earlier volumes, much recourse has had to be made to large libraries and we once again express our thanks to the officials concerned. We have mainly relied on the British Museum Library, the Bodleian Library, the Cambridge University Library, the library of Imperial Chemical Industries Limited, the London Library, the Patent Office Library, the Science Library, and the library of the Warburg Institute. As previously, Mr D. E. Woodall has been responsible for most of the drawings, and we much appreciate the trouble he has taken in meeting our rather exacting requirements. The indexes were prepared by Miss M. A. Hennings. The list of abbreviations was compiled by Mr F. H. Ayres.

Finally, we would again express our warm appreciation of the patronage of Imperial Chemical Industries Limited, without which this project, now near completion, would never have been started. In this connexion we must in particular thank Sir Walter Worboys, a director of the Company, for his unfailing support and encouragement.

CHARLES SINGER
E. J. HOLMYARD
A. R. HALL
TREVOR I. WILLIAMS

CONTENTS

ILLUSTRATIONS AND TABLES

'The Forge' by James Sharples (1825–93). The artist was a self-taught painter and almost the whole of his working life was spent in engineering workshops at Bury and Blackburn. This painting, 52 in × 38 in, was his principal work and was completed in 1847. Sharples then taught himself to engrave on steel, and during the years 1849–59 made an engraving of 'The Forge'. This brought him fame, and many thousands of copies were sold. Reproduced by courtesy of the Sharples family FRONTISPIECE

TEXT-FIGURES*

1. PART I. AGRICULTURE: FARM IMPLEMENTS *by* OLGA BEAUMONT *and* J. W. Y. HIGGS

1. PART II. AGRICULTURE: TECHNIQUES OF FARMING *by* G. E. FUSSELL

2. FISH PRESERVATION *by* C. L. CUTTING

* The names at the end of entries are those of the artists who drew the illustrations.

4. PART I. EXTRACTION AND PRODUCTION OF METALS: IRON AND STEEL

by H. R. SCHUBERT

4. PART II. EXTRACTION AND PRODUCTION OF METALS: NON-FERROUS METALS by F. W. GIBBS

5. POWER TO 1850 *by* R. J. FORBES

13. PRECISION MECHANICS *by* MAURICE DAUMAS

14. MACHINE-TOOLS *by* K. R. GILBERT

15. BUILDING AND CIVIL ENGINEERING CONSTRUCTION *by* S. B. HAMILTON

16. PART I. SANITARY ENGINEERING: WATER-SUPPLY *by* J. KENNARD

16. PART II. SANITARY ENGINEERING: SANITATION *by* J. RAWLINSON

17. ROADS TO *c* 1900 *by* R. J. FORBES

18. PART I. CANALS: INLAND WATERWAYS OUTSIDE BRITAIN *by* ROGER PILKINGTON

18. PART II. CANALS: INLAND WATERWAYS OF THE BRITISH ISLES *by* CHARLES HADFIELD

19. SHIP-BUILDING *by* GEORGE NAISH

20. CARTOGRAPHY *by* R. A. SKELTON

PLATES

ABBREVIATIONS OF PERIODICAL TITLES

(AS SUGGESTED BY THE WORLD LIST OF SCIENTIFIC PERIODICALS)

Agric. Hist.	Agricultural History. Agricultural History Society. Washington
Amer. Mach., N.Y.	American Machinist; Magazine of Metalworking Production. New York
Ann. Sci.	Annals of Science. A quarterly Review of the History of Science since the Renaissance. London
Apothekerztg, Berl.	Apothekerzeitung. Standeszeitung deutscher Apotheker. Berlin
Arch. Eisenhüttenw.	Archiv für das Eisenhüttenwesen. Fachberichte des Vereins Deutscher Eisenhüttenleute und des Max-Plank Instituts für Eisenforschung. (Ergänzung zu 'Stahl und Eisen'.) Düsseldorf
Archaeol. Rev.	Archaeological Review. London
Beitr. Gesch. Tech. Industr.	Beiträge zur Geschichte der Technik und Industrie. Jahrbuch des Vereins Deutscher Ingenieure. Berlin
Bijdr. Gesch. Overijssel	Bijdragen tot de Geschiedenis van Overijssel. Zwolle
Bull. Instn Metall.	Bulletin of the Institution of Metallurgists. London
Bull. Soc. industr. Mulhouse	Bulletin de la Société industrielle de Mulhouse. Mulhouse
Chron. méd.	La Chronique médicale. Revue de médicine scientifique, littéraire et anecdotique. Paris
Civ. Engng, Lond.	Civil Engineering and Public Works Review. London
C.R. Acad. Sci., Paris	Comptes Rendus hebdomadaires des Séances de l'Académie des Sciences. Paris
Discus	Discus. Imperial Smelting Corporation Ltd. Bristol
Econ. Hist.	Economic History. A Supplement to Economic Journal. Royal Economic Society. London.
Econ. Hist. Rev.	Economic History Review. Economic History Society. Cambridge.
Edgar Allen News	Edgar Allen News. Allen, Edgar and Co. Ltd. Sheffield
Edinb. new phil. J.	Edinburgh New Philosophical Journal. Edinburgh
Emp. Surv. Rev.	Empire Survey Review. London
Engineer, Lond.	Engineer. London
Expositor	The Expositor. An illustrated Recorder of Inventions, Designs, and art Manufactures. London
Fmrs' Mag.	Farmers' Magazine. London
Geogr. J.	Geographical Journal. Royal Geographical Society. London

Hist. Acad. R. Sci.	Histoire de l'Académie royale des Sciences avec les Mémoires de Mathématique et Physique. Paris
Ill. Lond. News	Illustrated London News. London
Imago Mundi	Imago Mundi. A Review of early Cartography. Stockholm
Industr. text.	Industrie textile. Paris
Ingenieur, 's Grav.	De Ingenieur. The Hague
Iron Coal Tr. Rev.	Iron and Coal Trades Review. London
J. Chem. u. Phys.	Journal für Chemie und Physik. Nuremberg
J. Inst. Navig.	Journal of the Institute of Navigation. London
J. Paris	Journal de Paris. Paris
J. R. agric. Soc.	Journal of the Royal Agricultural Society (of England). London
J. Soc. Bibl. nat. Hist.	Journal of the Society for the Bibliography of Natural History. London
J. Soc. chem. Ind., Lond.	Journal of the Society of Chemical Industry. London
Mariner's Mirror	Mariner's Mirror. Journal of the Society for Nautical Research. London
Mechanic's Mag.	The Mechanic's Magazine. London
Mém. Acad. Sci. Sav. étrang.	Mémoires de Mathématique et de Physique présentés à l'Académie Royale des Sciences par divers Savants [étrangers]. Paris
Mem. Manchr lit. phil. Soc.	Memoirs and Proceedings of the Manchester Literary and Philosophical Society. Manchester.
Milit. Engr, Wash.	Military Engineer. Society of American Military Engineers. Washington
Min. Proc. Instn civ. Engrs	Minutes of Proceedings of the Institution of Civil Engineers. London
Nature, Lond.	Nature. London
Nieuwe Verh. proefonderv. Wijsbeg.	Nieuwe Verhandelingen. Bataafsch Genootschap der proefondervindelijke Wijsbegeerte. Rotterdam
Obsns Phys.	Observations sur la Physique, sur l'Histoire naturelle et sur les Arts. Paris
Phil. Mag.	Philosophical Magazine; a Journal of theoretical, experimental and applied Physics. London
Phil. Trans.	Philosophical Transactions of the Royal Society. London
Post Man	Post Man and the historical Account. London
Proc. Amer. Soc. civ. Engrs	Proceedings of the American Society of Civil Engineers. New York
Proc. Instn civ. Engrs	Proceedings of the Institution of Civil Engineers. London
Repert. Arts Manufact.	The Repertory of Arts and Manufactures. London
Road Tar	Road Tar. British Road Tar Association. London

Schweiz. Z. Strassenwesen	Schweizerische Zeitschrift für Strassenwesen und verwandte Gebiete. Solothurn
Sci. Amer. Suppl.	Scientific American Supplement. New York
Strasse	Strasse. Berlin
Struct. Engr	Structural Engineer. Institution of Structural Engineers. London
Suisse horlog.	La Suisse horlogère. La Chaux-de-Fonds
Surveyor, Lond.	Surveyor and Municipal and County Engineer. London
Tijdschr. Inst. Ing. 's Grav.	Tijdschrift van het Koninklijke Instituut van Ingenieurs te 's Gravenhage. The Hague
Trans. Instn Min. Engrs	Transactions of the Institution of Mining Engineers. London
Trans. Instn wat. Engrs	Transactions of the Institution of Water Engineers. London
Trans. Newcomen Soc.	Transactions. Newcomen Society for the Study of the History of Engineering and Technology. London
Trans. roy. Soc. Edinb.	Transactions of the Royal Society of Edinburgh. Edinburgh
Trans. Soc. Arts	Transactions of the Society [afterwards Royal Society] of Arts. London
Univ. Mag. Knowledge Pleasure	Universal Magazine of Knowledge and Pleasure. London
Verkündiger	Der Verkündiger, oder Zeitschrift für die Fortschritte und neuesten Beobachtungen, Entdeckungen und Erfindungen in den Künsten und Wissenschaften. Nuremberg
Wat. Pwr	Water Power. London
Yale J. Biol. Med.	Yale Journal of Biology and Medicine. New Haven
Z. öst. Ing.- u. ArchitVer.	Zeitschrift des österreichischen Ingenieur- u. Architektenvereins. Vienna

I

PART I

AGRICULTURE: FARM IMPLEMENTS

OLGA BEAUMONT AND J. W. Y. HIGGS

I. INTRODUCTORY

THE century from 1750 to 1850 saw considerable activity and expansion in British agriculture. The new interest in farming under the influence of the great improvers; the opportunity to adopt new ideas resulting from enclosure; the continually increasing population leading to additional demands for food; better means of communication; and the stimulus of the Napoleonic wars, all led to great developments in farming techniques (ch I, pt II). More effective equipment was invented and brought into use, and ideas which had been put forward many years earlier found practical expression for the first time. Without any doubt the main incentive to advance in Britain was to be found in enclosure; machinery or equipment that would have been worthless on strips could be used effectively on the new commercial farms. In the rest of Europe, where enclosure lagged behind that in this country, the introduction of new equipment was slower and was confined to the larger estate-farms.

Although changes in the farmer's implements had become inevitable, the actual time of the change was to some extent conditioned by contemporary industrial progress. In 1750 most tools used by the farmer were made either locally by the village blacksmith or carpenter or, in a cruder form, by the farmer himself. In 1850 the equipment of the farm was coming in ever increasing quantities from the factories of industrial Britain. The village craftsman worked largely in wood and wrought iron, whereas the factory was able to make use of new materials and techniques. Cast iron, for example, because of its cheapness of manufacture and its durability, quickly replaced not only wrought iron but wood. Many of the leading manufacturers of agricultural machinery of the nineteenth century developed from the more enterprising craft-establishments of the eighteenth century. Despite the advantages of manufactured goods, however, the farmer continued to remain faithful to the craftsman for some implements until well into the twentieth century, and although much equipment was bought from the big firms some continued to be made in the village (vol III, ch 5).

A time-lag of up to a century could occur between the invention of a machine and its adoption for general use. The small tenant-farmer, even with his land consolidated, often lacked the capital to change to more advanced methods and had of necessity to continue to use old-style implements. During the period now under review, however, the big landowners and the farmers with capital never hesitated to take advantage of the great technical changes of the times. In fact, the changes in the equipment available between the beginning and the end of the period amounted to no less than a revolution. A countryman living on one of the more progressive farms between 1770 and 1850 might have witnessed a complete transformation of farming during his lifetime. The factory-made plough would have replaced the one made locally; seed formerly broadcast would be sown in rows by drills and the plants hoed by horses; intricate machines would have replaced the sickle or scythe for harvesting and the flail for threshing.

II. CULTIVATING IMPLEMENTS

Important developments in the design and construction of ploughs took place in the eighteenth and nineteenth centuries. The Rotherham plough (plate 2 A), built according to principles brought from Holland, was smaller and lighter than older ploughs and required fewer draught-animals. It was a swing-plough with a curved mouldboard which turned the earth well over, but the main innovation was a rearrangement of the parts of the main frame involving the substitution of a triangle for the quadrilateral of the seventeenth-century plough and earlier forms. This change was the first significant development in plough design in the eighteenth century.

The Rotherham plough was widely used in the northern and eastern counties of England. It inspired men such as John Arbuthnot and James Small to consider principles of plough design and to discuss in books the relative merits of the various ploughs in use. They produced plans, tables, and detailed descriptions from which ploughs could subsequently be built. James Small introduced the Rotherham plough into Scotland about 1767, and his book 'A Treatise on Ploughs and Wheeled Carriages' (1784) has an important place in the history of plough design. Competition between designers was intensified by the offer of premiums by the Royal Society of Arts, founded in 1754.

The close of the eighteenth century and beginning of the nineteenth century is the period during which the change from wooden ploughs to iron ploughs occurred. The mouldboard of the Rotherham plough was of wood partly covered with an iron plate. It also had an iron coulter and share. In 1763 James Small brought out the Scotch swing-plough, an improvement on the Rotherham with a wrought iron beam and handles. While working at a foundry at Norwich in 1785, Robert Ransome, founder of the firm of that name, took out a patent for hardening cast iron shares. Four years later he established a factory at Ipswich and patented chilled cast iron shares. The under surface of the share was cooled more quickly than the upper surface, thus making one side harder than the other and the share self-sharpening. Shares had previously been filed in the

FIGURE 1—*Crosskill's clod-crusher.*

field or taken back to the forge for sharpening. When chilled cast iron shares came into use a permanently sharp edge was ensured. The principle of manufacture of self-sharpening shares is still the same today.

A third important patent was taken out by Ransome in 1808; this was for a plough-frame of iron to which standardized replaceable parts could be fitted. This plough was constructed in such a way that it could be taken to pieces with ease and fresh parts substituted for those worn or broken. Since that time no very radical changes have been made in the principles governing the construction of horse ploughs.

It must not be assumed that the ideas of Ransome and other prominent ploughwrights were at once adopted throughout Great Britain. In the mid-nineteenth century, every available type of implement was in use from the *caschrom*[1] in the west of Scotland to the Rotherham and other improved forms of general purpose ploughs. By 1840 Ransomes were making as many as eighty-

[1] A tool used by Highlanders for cultivating stony ground. The word is Gaelic.

six distinct types of plough in order to suit the requirements of local markets. Some village craftsmen continued to produce implements of traditional regional design long after manufacturers were making all-metal ploughs. Throughout the northern counties variations of the Rotherham plough were important, but in Kent and Sussex a turnwrest (plate 2B) plough was widely used. This was an old form of the one-way plough and had been little altered in basic design

FIGURE 2—*Coleman's patent expanding lever harrow: a mid-nineteenth century zigzag harrow.*

over a period of 300 years. At the end of the furrow the mouldboard was removed and replaced on the other side, so that the plough could return down the same furrow.

Changes in other cultivating implements were equally important. Some entirely new equipment was introduced in addition to improvements in the design of old implements. Rollers were originally made of wood or stone, but smooth cast iron rollers appeared in the early nineteenth century. When constructed in two sections rotating independently, such rollers had less tendency to pull the plants out of the soil in turning on the headland. Later, rollers were manufactured consisting of a number of cast iron wheels mounted closely together on an axle to permit independent movement of each segment. Rollers were used both for consolidation of the soil and for breaking down the clods. The heaviest varieties were known as clod-crushers. The famous Crosskill clod-crusher of 1841 (figure 1) consisted of numerous serrated disks on a central axle.

Harrows were made in many sizes and weights. They were square, triangular, or rhomboidal in shape. In some places iron tines had replaced wooden spikes as early as the sixteenth century, and soon after 1800 frames also came to be made of iron. Finally the zigzag form of harrow was invented. This design overcame the troublesome swinging from side to side which had impaired the efficiency of early harrows. The distance between tines was reduced and individual tines were less likely to become clogged. Zigzag harrows (figure 2) were made up of two or more sections attached to a bar; the form patented by Armstrong in 1839 was the prototype of modern tined harrows.

Increased population at the end of the eighteenth century and the need for additional home-grown food supplies during the Napoleonic wars made the cultivation of new land imperative and led to the invention of a number of heavy implements capable of deep penetration. Previously, several ploughings had sufficed. Cultivators, which came into use at that time, were built more heavily than harrows and were often mounted on wheels. They had strong curved tines capable of stirring the land to a considerable depth. After 1850 tines mounted on springs which imparted a vibrating action were introduced.

III. SOWING IMPLEMENTS

Jethro Tull's seed-drill, invented in 1701, and made public in his book 'Horse-Hoing Husbandry' in 1731, was not only the first practical drilling machine produced in England but the first important step towards the elimination of manual labour in farm operations in Britain. Tull (1674–1741) made a number of varieties of his drill. The type for sowing wheat may be considered typical. It sowed three rows at a time and was drawn by one horse. After 1780 many other varieties of drill were produced, but some were not very successful. James Cooke's drill, brought out in 1782 and later improved, was the real ancestor of the modern machine. A feature of this drill was the use of gears instead of belts and chains to turn the dropping-mechanism. Improved forms of Cooke's drill were the most important type in England in the early nineteenth century. They formed the basis for Salmon's Bedfordshire and Smyth's Suffolk drill, which were first produced about 1800.

Drilling was not widely adopted until long after Jethro Tull's death, and even then the use of drills was limited to larger farms. The surveys made by the first Board of Agriculture reveal that at the turn of the nineteenth century progress in drilling was greatest in Norfolk and Suffolk. Travelling drills went from Suffolk into the midlands to serve scattered farms. Arthur Young noticed that the use of drills was most widespread on lighter soils. Drilling spread gradually into grain-growing areas as the number of machines available increased. John Morton, writing in his 'Cyclopedia of Agriculture' in 1851, remarked: 'Drilling corn . . . is steadily progressing in every district of England where high farming and improved cultivation prevail.'

Early drills were designed for sowing light, small seeds such as sainfoin, but machines were later produced that could be adjusted to sow most sizes of seeds. Drills or spreaders with special mechanisms were used for distributing manure and artificial fertilizers. The Suffolk corn and manure drill built by the Smyth brothers was probably the first combined commercial drill on the market. Other contemporary improvements included the invention of different mechanisms

FIGURE 3—*Garrett's general purpose cup-feed drill.*

for adjusting sowing rates. The leading manufacturers in Britain in the mid-nineteenth century were Garrett (figure 3), Smyth, and Hornsby. Seed was conveyed from the dropping-mechanism to the ground by pipes which were normally made of loose, telescoping, metal sections. In 1850 Hornsby invented indiarubber seed-pipes.

The horse-hoe was introduced by Jethro Tull early in the eighteenth century. He tried to impress upon farmers the necessity for cleaning between rows of crops, and it was to simplify the work of hoeing that he advocated the use of mechanical drills which sowed seeds in parallel rows. James Sharp's catalogue, published in 1777, showed a horse-hoe very similar to Tull's original design. It had three blades and was intended for use with a drill-plough. By 1830 hoes were being made in a wide variety of forms. They often hoed only one row at a time, but some types possessed several rows of blades, and could hoe a number of rows of crop in one operation.

IV. HARVESTING IMPLEMENTS

Before the introduction of mechanical reaping, more labour per unit was required for harvesting than for any other task on the farm. It was customary to hire extra labour every year to harvest the crops. Many reaping machines were invented in England and America between 1780 and 1850. The mechanisms brought into use were many and varied, but few of the machines were successful. The first patent for a reaping machine in England was issued to Joseph Boyce in 1800. For cutting, his machine used a series of scythes projecting from a circular disk. James Smith of Deanston in Perthshire adopted a circular

FIGURE 4—*Patrick Bell's reaping-machine.*

cutter which operated horizontally; this design was first tested in 1811. John Common submitted a reaper for a prize offered by the Royal Society of Arts in 1812.

The first really successful reaper was brought out in 1826 by Patrick Bell of Forfarshire (figure 4). The cutting apparatus consisted of a series of scissors which worked with a clipping action, and the grain was brought on to the cutter by sails. Later the now universal knife and cutter-bar principle was used in Bell's machine. His reaper was pushed by horses and not pulled behind them. It was exhibited in Scotland and awarded a prize of £50 by the Highland and Agricultural Society. It came into use in Scotland, but was not at first in sufficient demand to justify manufacture on a commercial scale.

The first reaper to be generally adopted was invented in America by Cyrus McCormick in 1831 (figure 5), when he was only twenty-two. Cutting was done by a knife and cutter-bar and the machine was pulled, not pushed. McCormick's reaper, together with a design by another American, Hussey, and also one of

Bell's, aroused much interest at the Great Exhibition in 1851. Trials were frequent after this date, and both Bell's reaper and that of the American design came into wider use.

In the eighteenth century little was done to assist haymaking by mechanical means. Throughout the British Isles hay was made entirely with hand tools before 1850, and methods were not revolutionized until the latter half of the nineteenth century. The earliest mechanical invention in connexion with haymaking was the horse-rake, which appeared early in the nineteenth century. It consisted of long metal teeth placed a short distance apart and mounted on a framework with wheels. When pulled along, this simple device gathered up loose

FIGURE 5—*Cyrus McCormick's American reaping-machine.*

hay; it has altered little in general design since its first introduction. The use of a lever by which the tines could be raised and the hay freed at regular intervals was an effective improvement.

A simple haymaking machine or tedder was designed by Robert Salmon of Woburn about 1800. It consisted of an axle with wheels at each end; attached to the axle were a series of iron tines which scattered the hay in all directions. It can be considered the forerunner of the present day haymaker and was remarkably similar to the rotary tedder now in use.

In England contemporary agriculturists thought in terms of arable rather than pastoral farming. Consequently the mowing machine, which replaced the scythe in the late nineteenth century, developed as a by-product of the invention of corn harvesters. Mowing machines left hay in straight swaths and therefore made easier the invention of machinery for tedding and collecting.

V. THRESHING MACHINERY

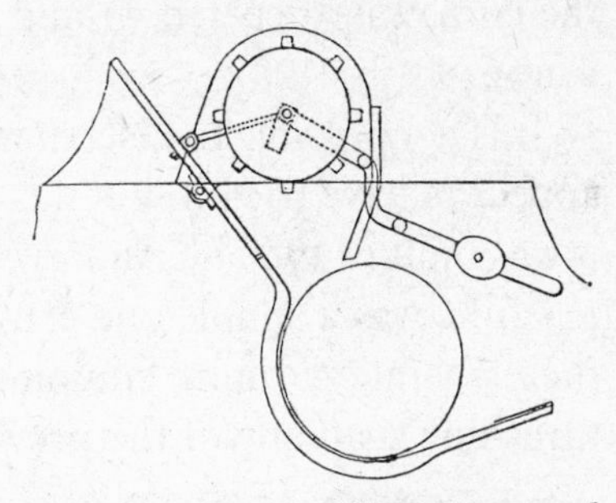

FIGURE 6—*A section of Fison's drum guard, showing the drum and concave principle.*

Attempts to produce a device that would reduce the time and labour involved in the arduous work of flailing were made as early as the seventeenth century, but few of the machines produced were of any value. Many of them, in fact, worked on the flail principle. In 1732 Michael Menzies, for example, invented and patented a machine which consisted of a number of flails on a shaft operated by water-power in such a manner that they struck grain laid out on the floor beneath them. Another method, tried by William Winlaw, consisted of a rubbing-mill, not unlike a corn-mill in action; the corn had first to be pulled by hand through a comb in order to free the ears from the straw. The method which was ultimately successful, and which was to become universal, was that employing the drum and concave (figure 6). A metal or wooden drum was made to rotate at speed inside a fixed concave with only a small clearance between the two;

FIGURE 7—*Garrett's improved threshing machine (section).* c *1851.*

the corn was then fed in and the grain removed by the rubbing action of the drum.

It is not possible to discern who first thought out this principle, for many people appear to have tried it, but it is clear that the first successful machine embodying it was built in 1786 by Andrew Meikle of the East Lothians of Scotland. Meikle's machine was a simple one consisting of drum and concave only; it had none of the elaborate cleaning equipment of later days. It did a more successful job of threshing than any of the previous devices, and the result was not only that his machines were in great demand in Scotland and on the border, but that other manufacturers began producing machines embodying the same idea. These machines were generally driven by water or by horses, but sometimes by hand. The most common type was driven by four horses walking round a central geared wheel from which the drive was transmitted by shafting to the thresher. So great were the advantages of the machine over the flail that its use spread rapidly. A survey of the reports to the Board of Agriculture reveals that many were at work on farms by the early years of the nineteenth century. For example, Bailey and Culley, in their survey of Northumberland in 1805, state that threshing machines were then coming into general use. Arthur Young, in his Norfolk survey of 1804, described several different types of threshing machines then working in the county. It is fair to say that, by the middle of the nineteenth century, machine threshing (figure 7) had become the normal method on all larger farms and on many small ones.

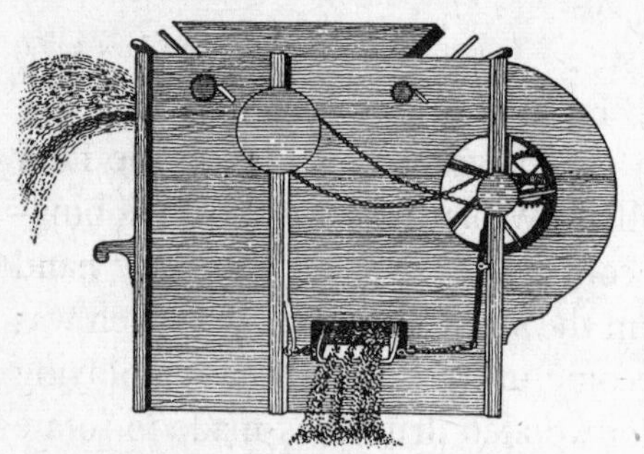

FIGURE 8—*Winnowing machine. Late eighteenth century.*

The grain had still to be separated from the chaff by hand, and in 1750 the most advanced tool for the purpose was a crude implement consisting of a central axle and arms to which sacks were attached. By 1777 James Sharp, a London manufacturer, was selling a self-contained winnowing machine (figure 8) very similar to many still in common use on farms today. A fan within the machine was rotated by a handle which also oscillated some cleaning sieves. Corn and chaff were thrown into the top of the machine, which cleaned the grain and delivered it into a sack.

From this stage it was not difficult to combine the functions of threshing and cleaning in one machine, and such a piece of equipment is said to have been produced at Thetford, in Norfolk, as early as 1848. Numerous other devices were added after 1850, such as rotary grading screens for sorting the corn. As a result the threshing machine grew into the rather complex mechanism that we know today. With the advent of the steam-engine it became possible for it not only to be steam-driven but also to be hauled from farm to farm by the engine. In the late nineteenth century few but the largest farms would own their threshing equipment. Most farms would use the services of a contractor, who would visit them with his travelling 'drum'.

VI. BARN EQUIPMENT

Barn equipment included chaff cutters, root cutters, linseed-cake crushers, and grinding mills. Forage crops and roots, such as turnips, mangolds, and swedes, had become increasingly important after 1750, and numerous different machines were produced to prepare them for consumption.

FIGURE 9—*Ransome and May's chaff cutter.*

Early chaff cutters consisted of a three-legged wooden trough with a knife at the end which was used with a guillotine action. In 1794 James Cooke brought out a design which may be considered the prototype of modern chaff cutters. It consisted of a rectangular trough along which straw was moved by hand. As the straw reached the end of the trough it was cut by blades attached to a wheel. Ransome and May's chaff cutter is shown in figure 9.

The root slicer developed in the same period, but not so rapidly. One form, consisting of a lever hinged to a trestle, appeared after 1800. This implement acted by downward pressure of the lever on to knives fitted to the trestle. Rotary root cutters, consisting of fluted rollers or incised disks placed under a hopper, appeared after 1830.

The equipment in the barns of large farms was very elaborate by 1850, and remained so until the end of the nineteenth century. Contemporary accounts of farm buildings are illustrated with pictures that include the huge barns which the wide variety of barn machinery made necessary. All this machinery would be driven from shafting by a stationary steam-engine.

Agriculture in Great Britain was gradually mechanized in the late eighteenth and early nineteenth centuries and the foundations were laid for the developments of the late nineteenth and twentieth centuries. The progress made in technology and industry after 1750 was followed by the gradual use of machinery in agriculture, which assisted all the operations of the farming year. This machinery, though opposed by workers and treated with indifference by less enlightened farmers, played an important part in the movement for increasing productivity and helped the practice of farming to go hand in hand with scientific developments. Credit for most of the inventions made before 1850 must be given to Britain, but after 1850 America and the countries of the British Empire began to play an increasingly important part.

BIBLIOGRAPHY

BEECHAM, H. A. and HIGGS, J. W. Y. 'The Story of Farm Tools.' Young Farmers' Club Booklet, No. 24. Evans, London. 1951.

FUSSELL, G. E. 'The Farmer's Tools, 1500–1900.' Melrose, London. 1952.

LOUDON, J. C. 'An Encyclopaedia of Agriculture' (5th ed.). London. 1844.

MORTON, J. C. 'A Cyclopedia of Agriculture.' London. 1855.

PASSMORE, J. B. 'The English Plough.' Oxford University Press, London. 1930.

Ploughing scene, eighteenth century.

I

PART II

AGRICULTURE: TECHNIQUES OF FARMING

G. E. FUSSELL

BEFORE 1750 farmers in the countries of western Europe had already begun to break away from the age-old traditional methods, but most arable land was still cropped under the ancient rotation of winter corn, spring corn, fallow. The livestock grazed on the wild grass pastures of the waste, on the fringes of the woodland, on the fallow, and on the stubble after harvest. During the winter they subsisted on a little hay and the straw of the corn-crops, often supplemented by leaves and branches of trees and vines.

The cattle did not fare well. Only small numbers—and those of inferior breeds—could be kept. The mid-eighteenth century farmer lacked two things: adequate feed for his stock and consequently adequate manure for his crops. The result was that crop-yields were low, and animals and their products were small.

The great problem was to increase supplies of animal feed for use in winter. In some of the earliest printed books on farming, didactic writers in many countries had recommended the cultivation of fodder crops, but with little immediate result, and it is now difficult, if not impossible, to determine where such crops were first grown. In the mid-seventeenth century clover (*Trifolium* spp) and turnips were already well established in the district between Antwerp and Ghent, and clover was grown in north Italy. In France some sainfoin (*Onobrychis viciifolia*) was grown, and perhaps in southern Spain some lucerne (*Medicago sativa*). Buckwheat (*Fagopyrum esculentum*) was important in most continental countries for both man and beast. From Flanders, clover spread southward into Germany and westward into England. By the mid-eighteenth century, clover, sometimes mixed with ryegrass (*Lolium perenne*), was grown in many parts of England, and the so-called Norfolk four-course rotation (p 18) was spreading through the country.

The introduction of fodder crops called for new implements, or improved implements, and created the need for the seed-drill (p 5) and the horse-hoe (plate 2 C and p 6). It also enabled more animals to be kept, and more manure and livestock-products to be produced. Having these things to hand the farmer was obliged to consider the best and most economical way of using them. He had to employ his supply of organic manure to the best advantage for his crops, and his supply of feeding-stuffs to produce the maximum improvement in his animals, without wasting either of these precious materials.

Here the nascent science of his time came to his aid, though much of the recondite work done on plant physiology and nutrition, farriery or veterinary science, animal nutrition, and so on, was long in becoming part of the working knowledge of the ordinary farmer. It was, however, in this period that the foundations of modern agricultural science were firmly laid.

Z. W. Sneller has said that the new impulses in farming of the eighteenth century were derived from England, but, true as this may be, England herself had earlier learned much from the Low Countries, where the development of agriculture between the sixteenth and the nineteenth centuries was an example to the whole of Europe (vol III, ch 1). There were wide variations in the systems followed in the comparatively small area comprising the present-day Belgium and Holland, where differences in the soils and the level of the water-table make such variations necessary. It was the treatment of the light sandy soils that excited so much admiration in foreign visitors, and this system played a great part in the development of modern farming in Britain and in other countries.

As practised on the sandy land of the Low Countries, it was a form of what is now called mixed husbandry, but in Flanders it did not depend upon the sheep-fold. Its fundamental principles were the careful accumulation of manure, and the provision of green and root crops for animal feed. It was a sort of ley husbandry. Originally the arable rotation was the simple one practised almost everywhere on the open fields. Rye was the main winter grain, often grown for two years in succession, followed by buckwheat. For centuries, however, a part of the land was laid down with hay-seeds, occasionally sown under spring grain but also upon the fallow. The length of time the so-called 'dries' remained in grass varied in different parts of the country. It might be anything from two to six years.

During the first year the weeds and grass were cut green for feeding cattle kept in the cow-sheds, under the summer stall-feeding system. This was general all over the light-land farms throughout the Low Countries. Early in the seventeenth century clover took the place of the hay-seeds, and became one of the main crops. It is estimated that in parts of Belgium up to two-thirds of the arable area was ley. Some part of the produce was made into hay for use in winter. When the ley was broken up, and the turf turned under, it improved the soil; oats were then sown by some farmers.

Sir Richard Weston (1591–1652) observed long rotations in the mid-seventeenth century, and there was little change in the following 200 years. All the cereals had been grown from time immemorial and the ley system was very old, but this was modified before the sixteenth century, when 'the Flemish landowners allowed their tenants to grow crops besides the winter and summer corn. The tenant was free to replace the cereals by flax, weld, rape seed or hemp, at his own risk.' From this time onwards cole-seed, beans, clover, flax, and later potatoes, gradually took up the fallow land. Turnips were grown as a catch-crop and for fodder; carrots and spurrey (*Spergula arvensis*) were sown with corn or flax. Mixed grains also were grown.

Throughout the period every effort was being made to extend the area of arable, and the sandy lands were laboriously reclaimed. Broom was planted to bind the soil after it had been dug with the spade. The broom was cut, possibly after two years, and dug in, the loamy sub-soil being raised and mixed with the surface. Rye was then grown, and soon a regular rotation could be introduced.

Much the same system was followed in Holland at the end of the eighteenth century. On the light land in that country, the improved three-course rotation was generally followed; rye, rye, and buckwheat. On the unploughed stubble of the second-year rye, spurrey was sown as green fodder for cattle or to be ploughed in as green manure, and turnips also were grown. The fallow year had long since vanished. Pulse, carrots, and cole were grown in gardens where fruit trees flourished. Hemp and flax were cultivated on separate small pieces of land heavily manured, but the true Flemish husbandry was practised only in north Brabant, in the neighbourhood of Breda.

A very rough division of types of farming in the Low Countries has been made by Slicher Van Bath. Cattle-breeding was found chiefly in Groningen, Friesland, Holland, and west Utrecht, which turned over to arable farming in the nineteenth century. Commercial crops, fibre-plants, and oil- and dye-plants flourished in Flanders, west Brabant, and the islands of Zeeland and south Holland. There was an area of perpetual rye-growing without fallow in the east Netherlands, and a grain area with fallow in the south Netherlands and east Belgium, where fodder-crops were grown on the fallow after 1800. Market gardens developed near the towns, and fruit- and bulb-growing became important.

The summer stall-feeding of cattle and the housing of sheep produced accumulations of organic manure. The animals often stood upon their droppings, to which were added layers of sand and peat to absorb the liquid manure. This material was applied to arable, and especially to industrial, crops, and so much improved yields of grain and fodder that the animals were better fed and yielded more livestock-products. Turf-ashes from Holland were imported into Belgium, and town wastes—including sewage, referred to as 'beer'—were brought to the farms along the canals. This material was known to the French in the early nineteenth century as Flemish manure. Part of this system was adopted in Great Britain, where peace enabled the mixed husbandry to develop into the so-called high farming of the period 1840–80; in Flanders, however, it was on the small peasant-holdings that it was first perfected.

From the Middle Ages an important dairy industry had flourished in Holland because the country was so rich in cattle. It suffered many set-backs through floods and war in the seventeenth century. These disasters were so destructive that the original Dutch red cow, very similar to the German one, almost disappeared. Black and white Jutland cows were imported from Denmark for use as a cross, but on the lighter land of the south and east the farmers, who had less capital, imported cheap, small Munster cows. From these crosses the present breeds of Dutch cattle have developed, mainly distinguished by their markings: the black and white Friesian breed now seen on many British farms, the red and white breed, and the black-and-white-faced Groningen breed. In spite of outbreaks of disease there was a large export of butter and cheese, which continued throughout the century under consideration. Both were sent, not only to the countries that had long obtained them—France, Germany, south Netherlands, Spain, and Portugal— but in increasing quantities to England, where the growth of population and the progress of the industrial revolution created a larger demand for all sorts of agricultural produce.

By the end of the eighteenth century the flourishing business of cattle-breeding and dairying was begining to change. Improved drainage made more land dry enough to plough, and cattle disease had reduced the number of beasts. Both factors persuaded the Netherlands farmers to turn to arable, but the dairy industry nevertheless remained the main source of income. Fat cattle for slaughter were also exported. The potato became important and madder was extensively grown.

It was the ley farming which he saw between Antwerp and Ghent that so greatly impressed Sir Richard Weston. He tried it out in St Leonard's Forest and at Worplesdon, Surrey, in the seventeenth century. This rotation was flax, turnips, and oats with clover bush-harrowed in and grazed until the following Christmas, mowed three times the following year, and left as ley for four or five years. Though quite different from the four-course system eventually evolved in Britain, that system owes its origin to Weston perhaps more than to any other individual. There had, however, been commercial contact between eastern

England and the Low Countries for centuries. There is some similarity too, between the light lands of Norfolk and Suffolk and the sandy lands across the sea. Merchants and traders must have discussed farming, and it is not unlikely that the English light-land farmers learned something of the Flemish methods in this way as well. A good deal of clover was grown on the light lands of Norfolk and Suffolk by the late seventeenth century, as well as in Kent and elsewhere; turnips were grown and used as a fodder crop in several counties before the end of the century.

Then, too, Jethro Tull at Howberry designed a seed-drill that worked (p 5); this was not the first but was the one that gained most reputation. He also developed his horse-hoeing husbandry (p 6), though his book on the subject was not published until the 1730s. Clearly the stage was set by this time for the new crops and the new system of alternate husbandry, but in a large part of Britain, as in other countries, there was one insuperable obstacle to the cultivation of green crops. Where the intermixed farming of the ancient open fields was carried on, as in the midlands, all the village farmers had the right to graze the fallow and the stubble field after the grain-harvest. Consequently no one could grow fodder crops on his scattered acres in the fallow field, for they would merely be eaten by other people's animals as well as his own (plate 3). It was possible to grow clover on the fallow if all the farmers agreed to do so, and in one or two places this was certainly done, but in the majority of open-field villages there were too many objectors.

The enclosure and rearrangement of the open fields in enclosed farms was undoubtedly stimulated, in part at least, by this factor, as well as by the desire to keep good livestock apart from the common herds and flocks that grazed the waste in summer, bred promiscuously, and contracted each other's diseases. Some less admirable human traits, too, helped to urge the movement on. After 1760, enclosure both of open arable fields and of the wild grass pasture of the waste proceeded rapidly. Between that date and 1840 about 6 million acres were dealt with by private Acts, and a substantial acreage without that formality. On these enclosed farms the occupier could use what rotation of crops he wished, subject to climate, elevation, and soil. He could also choose the better of his animals to breed from in the certainty that his plans would not be ruined by haphazard mating.

During the second half of the eighteenth century the alternate husbandry spread over large areas of Britain. Some of the open arable fields that were enclosed had soils suitable for it, though a good deal of heavy clay went down to grass. It was used as a means of improving the light lands of East Anglia, already in individual occupation, and then spread to the Lowlands of Scotland, the wastes of Northumberland, and the Yorkshire and Lincolnshire wolds. Much of this was new land that had never before been ploughed.

The alternate husbandry, which came to be known as the Norfolk four-course, became standard practice by 1850, although naturally there were local variations. Some farmers preferred to leave the seed-leys down for two years, and in the south-west it was adapted to sheep-husbandry by growing two grain-crops in succession, followed by a series of catch-crops to feed the sheep.

The advantages of the system are obvious. Instead of having one-third of the arable, as in the open fields, without a crop of any kind, all the fields carried something useful. The former system of winter corn, spring corn, fallow gave place to the wheat–turnips–barley–clover rotation. Not only was the land thus continually cropped, but conditions for growth were improved. If cereals are cultivated in unbroken succession a very heavy crop of weeds appears. The grain-crops do not stifle them, especially when the land is not well worked, and eventually would be completely overpowered. For this reason the triennial fallow was necessary on the open fields, and an occasional bare fallow long remained essential on the heavier soils which were too much for implements drawn by animal traction. When seeded grass and roots were grown in alternation with the cereals there were two advantages. The roots had to be hoed to cut out competing weeds until the crop had developed enough leaf to smother them. This destroyed unwanted natural growth and kept the top soil in a fine state of comminution. Again, the clover crop fed the soil, as the farmers knew without being able to explain: only comparatively recently has science discovered that bacteria in the nodules on the roots of leguminous crops fix atmospheric nitrogen.

The natural fertility of the soil was supplemented by the larger quantities of organic manure produced by the more numerous and superior livestock that could be maintained on the new fodder crops. If sheep were folded on the roots their urine and droppings manured the land, or if part of the crop were drawn and fed to cattle in yards large stocks of rich dung were accumulated. Sheep could also be folded on the clover, or it could be cut for hay and the aftermath grazed, again an extra source of winter feed and of larger supplies of manure. The system promised an indefinite continuance of fertility and improved livestock. It was a simplified form of the Flemish seven-course rotation, but omitted the industrial crops and long ley of that system. Concentration was on the production of grain for human needs and of forage for animal needs, so that there would be continual production of meat, milk, and other livestock products. Another advantage of the system was that it enabled wheat to be grown where formerly only rye was a possible crop.

The Norfolk four-course rotation exercised great influence on continental farming in the latter part of the eighteenth century and during the nineteenth century. An analogous system, though not so highly organized, had also developed elsewhere. Tarelli, a Venetian, recommended the cultivation of fodder crops in the sixteenth century, and in the eighteenth a four-course rotation was said to be already old-established in part of Italy. This was winter grain–clover–fodder grass–fallow. Though including two years of animal-feed production it did not eliminate the break for fallow, so that here a quarter of the arable remained bare every year. Turnips were included in some rotations in Italy. Again, von der Goltz (1765–1832), on the authority of Johann Nepomick von Schwerz (b 1759), believed an alternate husbandry to have been practised in scattered places along the Moselle for many years. von Schwerz travelled widely over Germany in search of agricultural information, and visited Brabant and Flanders as well. The four-course system may have developed here because the holdings were distributed between two or four fields, and in the earlier days the rotation may have been grain-crop and fallow alternately, or possibly three grain-crops and fallow. The fallow in time began to be cultivated partly with clover and partly with roots, and eventually these alternated in the series between the two cereal crops. It is quite possible that the grasses and roots could have reached the area, because there the rivers formed an ancient and important means of communication between southern and northern Europe, and the forage crops could have been introduced from either Italy or Flanders.

The preoccupation of all farmers with winter feed had led in Britain to the introduction, between 1650 and 1700, of sainfoin as a long ley on the chalk downs that stretch from East Anglia to Wiltshire. The making of water-meadows, which began in the seventeenth century, was directed to the same end. They spread from Hampshire and Wiltshire into Berkshire, Gloucestershire, and Devon, and even into Nottinghamshire and Norfolk, where suitable streams and rivers could be stopped and their waters diverted on to the riparian meadows. Such works continued to be constructed until well into the nineteenth century. Concurrently the search for new fertilizing materials went on.

The practice of marling was revived in Norfolk in the early eighteenth century. This was in effect the same sort of soil-mixing which characterized Flemish husbandry, and was extremely ancient, having been known to the Romans. It may have fallen into desuetude in Britain and have been revived after the sixteenth century, but there is reason to believe that it was uninterrupted in Cheshire, where it replaced some of the soil-elements removed by the dairy industry, and in Kent. The clay under the peat of the fens was laboriously excavated and spread on the surface. Old turf and even clayey soil were burned to form a fertilizer. Both these last processes remained popular until 1850.

Soap-boilers' waste and tailors' shreds were two industrial by-products pressed into service. Peat-ashes were burned near Newbury and sent to other districts. Stable and cow-shed manure was collected in towns and carried by barge or cart to farms within reach. Towards the end of the eighteenth century cutlers' waste from Sheffield began to be used in the neighbouring countryside: this consisted of scraps of horn and bone resulting from the manufacture of knife-handles and so on. The good effects of this material on pasture were readily observable, and a large demand for crushed bones arose. Some farmers installed grinding machinery; others bought the material ready crushed. Later, bones were dissolved in sulphuric acid, and demand for the product became so great that the battlefields of Europe are said to have been searched for material. Late in the 1820s the first cargo of Peruvian guano arrived, to be followed not much later by shipments of Chilean nitrate. These were extensively used by the British farmers during the following decades. When Sir John Bennet Lawes (1814–1900) began to manufacture calcium superphosphate in 1842 the artificial fertilizer industry may be said to have been established.

The general preoccupation with fodder crops led agricultural writers of the eighteenth century to recommend lucerne, sainfoin, and burnet (*Poterium polygamum*), as well as clover. Ray- or rye-grass seed was collected on the Chilterns and sown in Oxfordshire about 1700. It was thereafter very usually sown with red clover. Lucerne has never come into general use, though sainfoin was accepted by the chalk-land farmers, and Jethro Tull tested his seed-drill with this crop. Burnet was tried by experimental farmers and found good for sheep, but never became general. It was a natural constituent of downland pastures. One of the greatest difficulties in grassland improvement was the want of pure seeds. Thomas Coke (1752–1842), who did so much to introduce the new husbandry, organized bands of school children to go out into the fields to collect grass seeds in their several sorts. The Royal Society of Arts supported the scheme, but it is doubtful whether anything much came of it, though some pure strains may have been developed. Besides the grasses, root-crops and brassicas of several kinds came into use. Three sorts of turnips were recognized. The mangold was discussed in the 1780s, but did not gain acceptance by practical farmers until the 1830s. The Swedish turnip or swede (*Brassica napus* var. *napobrassica*) was introduced towards the end of the eighteenth century. Rape (*Brassica napus* var. *arvensis*) had come to the Fenland with the Dutch drainers in the seventeenth century, and spread thence to other districts. Cabbage became a field crop, possibly first in Yorkshire, and kohlrabi was grown in the nineteenth century. Carrots were recommended as a forage crop in the 1780s, though they had long been grown in one part of Suffolk.

By the end of the eighteenth century very considerable improvements had been made in the management of both arable and grassland. This had been assisted by the design of new and improved implements, not the least of which was the Rotherham plough (p 2), innumerable horse-hoes and seed-drills, and the threshing machine (p 9), which was slowly coming into use.

The new wealth of feed enabled farmers all over the country to maintain their flocks and herds in good condition through the winter, and encouraged breeders to devise methods of selective breeding to create better types. Great breeders were numerous, but little is known of their methods. Robert Bakewell (1725–95) of Dishley, Leicestershire—who produced improved Longhorn cattle, created the New Leicester sheep, and bred fine horses—is possibly the most famous. The Colling brothers and Bates of Kirklevington are associated with Shorthorn development. Coke at Holkham experimented with Devon cattle and Shorthorn sheep. The Quartleys bred fine Devons in their own county. Ellman of Glynde produced the improved Southdown sheep. Other names are associated with Hereford cattle; the Ayrshire owes its place to the efforts of Dunlop, who is said to have imported Dutch cattle to improve the breed. Similar work was done on pigs, often with an admixture of Chinese blood. Horses for the plough, the wagon, and the coach, for riding, racing, and the cavalry, were essential in that age. Of these the plough- and cart-horse had the least attention, but the Shire horse, Suffolk Punch, Cleveland Bay, and Clydesdale all received careful attention during the century.

In the main the technical progress in British farming made in the late eighteenth century was achieved by practical landowners and farmers, but it could not have been made without propaganda. Arthur Young (1741–1820) was the untiring advocate of new methods through nearly sixty years. William Marshall (1745–1818) undertook a one-man survey of English farming. The Board of Agriculture, established in 1793, did the same on a more elaborate scale. Great landowners, like Coke of Norfolk and the Duke of Bedford, held annual sheep-shearings where fine animals, new implements, and improved varieties were to be seen, as well as the most modern methods of farming. Visitors came to such gatherings from all over the country, and even from many continental countries. Foreign princes and potentates visited Bakewell and other leading farmers. British farming had become the pattern for Europe, though similar developments were taking place elsewhere.

The French wars were a great stimulant, and the arable area was increased, often to an uneconomic extent; consequently there was a great set-back when the wars ended and prices fell. For twenty years farming was in the throes of despair, but in the late 1830s conditions began to improve. The Board of Agriculture had ceased to exist in 1821, though private agricultural associations, great and small, had survived. Prominent amongst them were the Bath and West of England Society, the Highland and Agricultural Society, and the Smithfield Club. Then in 1839 the English (later Royal) Agricultural Society was formed with very influential support.

The eighteenth century saw the improvement of light land, the nineteenth that of heavy land. Light land does not need a great deal of drainage; heavy land does, and this was one of the problems not finally solved until the invention of the tubular drain-pipe, about 1800, and of the method of making it mechanically, in the 1840s. This work was largely done with the assistance of government and private loans after 1850. By that date, too, the portable steam-engine had been adapted for farm purposes.

It was the English system of alternate husbandry, combined with selective animal-breeding, that made so great an impression on the European continent after about 1800, though there were other influences, internal as well as external, that stimulated its adoption, especially in eighteenth-century Germany. There, as in the Low Countries, usually only grain was grown in the open fields. Hemp, flax, cole, and other industrial crops were cultivated on special pieces of land outside the three fields. In western Germany the crops grown were wheat or rye or winter spelt, with stubble-grazing after harvest. The following spring, oats and barley were grown, with stubble-grazing after 24 June. Peas and field-beans were also grown as spring crops. The land was ploughed only twice to make a seed-bed for winter corn. Implements were simple and hauled by weak cattle. The land was heavily infested with weeds and what little manure it received was of poor quality. As elsewhere, this system provided inadequate forage. The livestock grazed on the waste in summer and in winter were fed on straw, chaff, and leaves, and—in the vine-growing areas— on vines and on grapes too poor to use. They were half starved in winter and in spring were often too feeble to stand up. Milk yields were very low. Conditions were almost exactly those of Britain under the open-field system.

Much of Germany was completely devastated in the Thirty Years War (1618–48), when the population was greatly reduced. From this and subsequent wars a recovery did not take place until the nineteenth century. The land reverted to grass and forest. Migration had to be arranged to colonize the waste areas anew.

Nevertheless, the three-field system prevailed, but by the beginning of the nineteenth century it had been subjected to some modifications.

Perhaps the most important change was the adoption of three important crops introduced from America: tobacco, maize, and potatoes (vol III, ch 1). By 1730 potatoes were grown in many parts of Germany, where the crop was encouraged by Frederick the Great. At about the same time red clover, and later lucerne and sainfoin, began to be grown in the fields as fodder crops. These formed part of an improved three-field system in which part of the fallow field—a half or three-quarters—was devoted to fodder crops, red clover, potatoes, roots, and pulse, though a part was preserved as fallow because people could not convince themselves that fallow could be completely dispensed with. This change took place alike on village farms, peasant-owned lands, and great estates. Out of it developed long rotations of six, nine, and twelve courses, including an occasional fallow, which continued until the beginning of the present century on peasant farms where the holding was in scattered pieces. The advantages of this system were more feed for livestock, of which the numbers and quality could be improved, and, when combined with summer stall-feeding as it frequently was, much larger supplies of organic manure for the arable.

Besides the improved three-field system, two other systems of cultivation were followed in Germany at the end of the eighteenth century. One was the true alternate husbandry of straw crop–green crop regularly, or nearly regularly. The other was a type of convertible husbandry: some years of cropping with cereals followed by some years under grass. On the larger Mecklenburg farms there were often two rotations. The fields nearer the house were under a system whereby cereals were more frequent and were grown on a larger area than the fodder crops, including clover and peas, which were grown after a summer half-fallow. These fodder crops were used for the stall-feeding of cattle, and often included rape. The more distant fields were under a 'sheep' rotation, in which grain-crops were less frequently cultivated than green crops.

The regular alternate husbandry was not adopted in north-east Germany because it did not include enough pasture for sheep and cattle. On the large estates the convertible husbandry (*Koppelwirtschaft*) in some form spread all over this part of Germany between 1800 and 1850. The peasants here followed the three-field or alternate husbandry. Very long rotations were found in Pomerania in 1850, including lupins for green manure, and oil-plants, as well as all the cereals, pulses, roots, clover for hay, and a two-year clover ley. Potatoes were frequently included in such rotations.

By 1850 a revolution had taken place in German agriculture. The ancient three-field system had completely disappeared. In its place farmers were practising the improved three-course, which included some fodder crops on the fallow, or the alternate husbandry combined with several years of ley. In the deeper soils and better climate of western Germany the three-field system had given place to the alternate husbandry. On the poorer soils the change had been to the improved three-field system or to the system of a few years of judicious cropping and a long ley. In the east, near the towns and on good soils, the alternate husbandry

FIGURE 10—*Seed-drill in use, 1846. This machine required three horses and three men. Another man harrows in the seed in the distance.*

had frequently been adopted, but more on small and medium holdings than on large. The last adopted the combined alternate husbandry and long ley system, while the peasant proprietors preferred the improved three-field system. Cattle were seldom grazed where the farmers practised the alternate husbandry or long ley system. Where there was grassland that could not be cultivated, as subject to common rights, open-air grazing continued.

New and better implements were adopted during the same time. The great landowners led the way, the peasants being slower to follow, but drills (figure 10), harrows, horse-hoes, extirpators, various rollers, subsoil ploughs, feed-preparing machines, steam-ploughs (figure 11), and threshers (figures 12 and 13) formed the equipment of many German farms by 1850, as they did in England.

In Britain, the change from the old three-course system to the new husbandry in all its variations was made on the initiative of individuals. The government played no part, except in so far as the great landowners who led the movement were members of the governing class. In many of the German states it was at least partly imposed by statute. For example, clover was introduced to the Palatinate by Walloon immigrants, and was first known as Brabant or Spanish clover. It did not spread far, and was not widely cultivated until after 1750, when

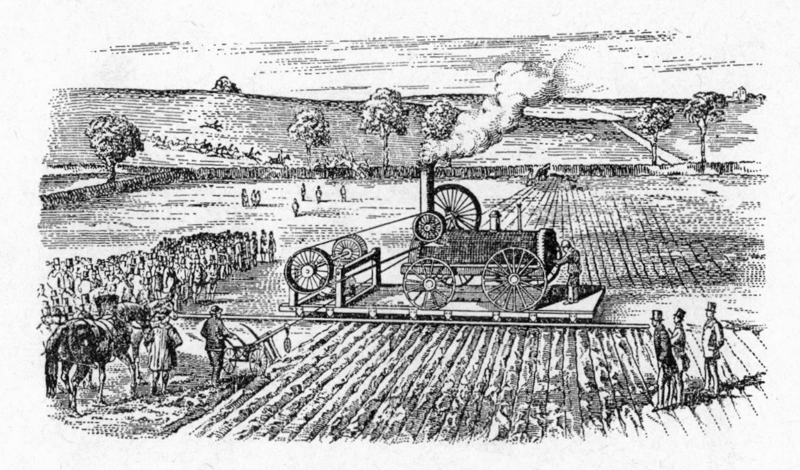

FIGURE 11—*Steam-ploughing demonstration.* c *1851.*

it was carried to other west-German districts. In 1771 Prince Karl Theodore ordered it to be grown on the summer fallow; other princes did the same. Frederick the Great promoted it in central and east Germany, together with flax, woad, hops, madder, caraway, and, especially, potatoes. He ordered orchards to be established in 1740, and brought from the Palatinate instructors in the art of growing fruit-trees. He was also interested in forestry, and the sand and heath of east Germany were planted with Scots pine. This and other soft woods were also grown in various elevated and rather sterile districts of west and south Germany. Viticulture was continued along the Moselle and Rhine.

In spite of the increased supplies of feeding-stuffs, animal breeding did not make the same progress as arable farming, with which it was so intimately bound up. Frederick the Great, under whose régime much of east Germany had been recolonized, had cows bought in Holland and sold to the settlers at low prices. Selected bulls had to be used for mating. Frederick also brought instructors in dairy husbandry from Holland, and bought cattle in Friesland, Holstein, and Holland. These efforts had some effect, and the herds of east Germany based on this new stock achieved some reputation. Cavalry horses, too, were supplied to the peasants for breeding, and stud-farms were set up, for no great state could then afford to be without adequate supplies of horses for military purposes.

Frederick the Great made another effort to improve livestock. In 1747 he imported Spanish merino rams, whose fine wool was widely famous. In their native country there were two classes of merino. One spent its life on the same farm, or in the same district, wherever there was sufficient feed; this was the breed kept

FIGURE 12—*Manual threshing-machine. England, early nineteenth century.*

in Segovia and the neighbouring mountains. Merinos of the other class were migratory, and travelled for wintering from the mountains of northern Spain, where they passed the summer, to the plains of the south. There was a further breed of sheep in Spain, larger and bearing coarser wool. This is supposed to have resulted from crossing the merino with some English sheep in the Middle Ages. It was the true merino that Frederick imported, though how he did so in face of the strict Spanish prohibition of export is not known.

Some years previously a small flock of these sheep had been imported into Sweden by an 'improver' named Alstroemer. The government supported him after some sixteen years, and offered premiums to breeders of the Spanish sheep. By 1765 there were some 65 000 pure merinos in Sweden, and 23 000 of a cross between merinos and the native breed. In this year Frederick, who had imported more flocks in 1751–2, sent 230 of his best merino sheep to the Elector of Saxony. The Elector became enthusiastic and made a further import of 300 in 1778. Though he encountered some opposition, he was able to establish the merino firmly on Saxon farms, and by the end of the century the Saxon merino was famous. The Empress Maria Theresa of Austria imported some in 1775; Frederick did the same in 1778; and by the beginning of the nineteenth century sheep-breeding had become the most important branch of animal husbandry on many large farms in northern Germany. It declined only with the growth of foreign competition from the Antipodes.

FIGURE 13—*Portable steam-engine driving a threshing-machine. c 1840.*

France showed a similar interest in merinos. A few were brought in in the early years of the eighteenth century, but owing to the stubborn opposition of the farmers this enterprise came to nothing. L. J. M. Daubenton (1716–1800), the famous French naturalist and agriculturist, favoured the production of Spanish wool, and by Turgot's orders a few rams were imported secretly in 1776. The results were so good that Louis XVI secured Spanish agreement to the importation of 334 ewes and 42 rams in 1786. Kept as a pure breed at Rambouillet these sheep had a great influence on the national flock. Fresh merino blood was again introduced in 1801 by Napoleon, under a secret clause of the Treaty of Basle. From that time onwards French flocks in Provence, Champagne, and other districts took much of their character from merino crosses, but here again interest in the breed faded away when faced with the competition of Antipodean wool in and after the 1840s.

England, too, had her enthusiasts. Some merinos were imported for George III through Sir Joseph Banks, and a Merino Society was formed, but proved a failure. The sheep was not suited to the requirements of English breeders, having little capacity for putting on flesh. The home market was for mutton as well as wool, and the native breeds suited it best. By the 1840s there were few flocks of pure merino in this country, and those declining. However, there was probably some effect on our breeds from the large amount of crossing that was done.

The sudden interest in merino sheep (figure 14) all over western Europe is an example of how economic considerations affect farming. Most of the importing countries wanted to produce fine Spanish wool themselves rather than buy it from Spain. They also wanted to improve their own breeds of sheep by crossing, but, owing to the production of large quantities of fine merino wool in Australia in the nineteenth century, the economic advantage disappeared within a century or so. Other kinds of livestock were sent from one country to another for similar purposes, but not perhaps to the same extent as the merino sheep.

FIGURE 14—*Merino sheep.*

Many crops travelled in the same way, as has already been shown; among them the sugar-beet, now cultivated in almost all countries, is a remarkable example. In 1747 Marggraf discovered that sugar could be extracted from beet, and half a century later (1799) Franz Achard told Frederick William III that he could produce from beet all the sugar necessary in his kingdom. Achard built the first sugar-beet factory in the world at Gut Gunern, in Silesia, in 1801–2, but seems to have extracted only 2–3 per cent sugar. He published the results of his work in 1809. Another factory was built by Freiherr von Koppy in Krain bei Strahlen in 1805. In Britain, Sir Humphry Davy was antagonistic; his opinion was that it was impossible to found such a sugar industry.

Napoleon, however, was very much alive to the importance of the new industry and supported it in Germany. He ordered a certain acreage of beet to be grown in the Low Countries, and factories to be built for sugar-manufacture, but after his fall both the cultivation of beet and the industry declined. Napoleon had also ordered beet-cultivation and the erection of factories in France, where the business continued to develop without interruption. By 1840 there were 58 factories there.

A marked fall in prices in the 1820s led the Germans to seek new crops. A commission went to France to investigate the sugar-beet industry and their report led to the re-establishment of the industry in Germany. It made rapid progress—in beet-growing, in weight handled in the factories, and in the percentage of sugar extracted. The sugar-beet also became important in Italy in the nineteenth century.

In France under Louis XV, farming methods (figure 15) still remained the same as in the Middle Ages, all the emphasis being upon cereals, wheat, rye, maslin (mixed grain), oats, barley, sarrasin (*blé noir*, buckwheat), beans and peas, and a little hemp and flax. The same difficulties as in other countries confronted the open-field farmer, whose holdings comprised scattered strips intermixed with those of his neighbours, where all had the right to graze their live-stock on the stubble after harvest and on the fallow field.

Except occasionally in French Flanders, in Alsace, and in Normandy, the bare fallow year was general, and in a large proportion of the country the ancient system of crop, fallow, crop, fallow was followed. It was general from the south, on the central massif, in Poitou, and even farther to the north, from Strasbourg to Wissembourg, in Franche-Comté, and in Brittany. More to the north the three-course system—winter corn, spring corn, fallow—was usual. In the Vosges and Ardennes the convertible husbandry flourished, namely a few years of arable followed by several years of grass. A large area of the country was agriculturally useless, being covered with oak forest, broom, bramble, and gorse.

France possesses widely varying soil-conditions, elevation, and climate. By 1760 maize had taken the place of the fallow in the crop-and-fallow rotation of the Mediterranean littoral. In 1789 Young was very enthusiastic about this innovation, though some French authorities think he was over-impressed. Maize may also have been grown in Burgundy. The crop had been introduced to Béarn in the seventeenth century, as it had to Spain and Italy. Growing maize on the fallow modified the old rotations used as a staple by the peasants, and paved the way for other fodder crops, the area of which expanded a little in the second half of the eighteenth century. The olive and the vine flourished on the southern slopes of the Alps. Water-meadows had been constructed in the foot-hills of the Pyrenees, as they had in Germany and in the foothills of northern Italy.

The central massif and Armorica were still medieval, although some wheat was exported. Relatively little was produced in the valleys of the Loire and the Orne, where oaks and chestnuts flourished. In parts of Brittany, Maine, and Anjou briars, bracken, and gorse covered very large areas. The grassland was

FIGURE 15—*Farming in France, 1755. Ploughing, hand broadcast-sowing, and harrowing-in the seed.*

neglected, and only cereals—oats, barley, and wheat—were cultivated. Normandy was more advanced. Fodder crops were introduced about 1750, and there was good pasture in the valley of the Auge. Here cider was beginning to take the place of wine as the common drink. Picardy had absorbed some of the Flemish husbandry and grew successful crops of flax on its heavily manured soil. Haricot beans were grown, and carrots for cattle. In Artois, spring wheat was sown after mustard. Cole was grown near Lille in 1758–9, and the haulm used as straw. The crop was fertilized with sewage and liquid manure from the cowshed. Hops were grown. The Île de France and the Paris basin grew rape and turnips for cattle-feed and for pigs. Carrots were grown here for human consumption, as well as asparagus and other market-garden crops. Vines were cultivated on the Mediterranean, in Alsace, between Orleans and the sea, and particularly in Burgundy. Anjou peasants grew vines when they could obtain chestnut poles to support them. The vine requires a dry soil, deeply dug; not much manure is necessary, but porous stones, or bits of broken pots, were placed in the soil to allow air to circulate among the roots. The vines themselves had to be carefully tended and pruned.

In general, agricultural progress was slow in France, though successive governments tried to stimulate it in the last decades of the old régime. Bertin in 1759 organized what was, in effect, a ministry of agriculture and created local agricultural societies for educational purposes. Some great landowners undertook the direction of their own estates, made experiments, tried to overcome the peasants' suspicion of any departure from traditional routines, introduced new crops and breeds of livestock, and undertook the reclamation of waste land and the improvement of soils. The exchange of scattered strips in order to make compact holdings was speeded, as well as the abolition of common grazing. All feudal remnants disappeared with the Revolution in 1789, as they did with the French annexation of the Low Countries and Germany. There was, however, no pressure of population in France—as there was in Flanders and in England—to enforce progress by an insistent demand for a more intensive system of agriculture.

Conditions in France at the end of the century are described by J. Meuvert. The large farms often had a big proportion of uncultivated land. The limit was imposed by the power of animal-draught and the distance to the fields from the buildings. If not true meadow, the waste grassland was nevertheless useful land more often in individual use than is commonly thought. Small pieces near the buildings could be well worked and manured. A variety of crops, in addition to the cereals, were grown, including vines, hemp, flax, saffron, tobacco, and perfumery plants. Sainfoin and lucerne were often grown, and the fallow in some places was cultivated with legumes and roots. Progress was delayed by the weight of tradition and by the wars. French farming, in which livestock were secondary to corn-growing, advanced more slowly in the eighteenth century than did that of the Low Countries and England.

The Normandy oxen were powerful, and the Norman and Breton cows had much in common with those of the Channel Islands. All over the country the cattle were normally grazed on pasture during the summer. Winter feed was the problem here as elsewhere. To add to the stores of hay and straw, leaves of trees were collected and dried. The beasts ate the leaves and the branches fed the fire. Vine-foliage was often mixed with small and waste grapes. As the century advanced potatoes were fed to stock, but were found unsuitable for cows.

Both flocks and herds were ravaged by disease. Between 1740 and 1750 a 'putrid' disease carried off the horned cattle. A contagious sickness destroyed many sheep in 1746, 1754, 1761, and 1762. In the following year a 'mouth' disease affected sheep, pigs, horses, and poultry, and there was another disastrous outbreak in 1773. These diseases affected all Europe, including England. The French government intervened; it had the buildings disinfected and the bodies buried, the owners being partly indemnified by the state. Perhaps it was this long series of disasters that encouraged C. Bourgelat (1712–99) to establish the first veterinary school at Lyons in 1762, an example followed by d'Alfort in 1765–6.

Particular attention was naturally paid to horse-breeding for saddle-horses, cavalry chargers, and army transport, but there were heavy breeds of strong farm-horses, especially the Normans. Limousin produced fine hackneys. Serviceable horses were bred in Auvergne, in Burgundy, and in Poitou. Pigs, as in most countries, were abundant, and supplied much of the peasant's food.

During this period much land was reclaimed by drainage. In England, the drainage of the Fens was a great enterprise. Large-scale drainage in the Low Countries was a centuries-old undertaking (vol III, ch 12). In France, Gascony was a vast marsh with scrub gradually being overwhelmed by drifting sand from the coast. The area was grazed by a few small sheep, over which impoverished shepherds mounted on stilts kept guard while industriously pursuing a handicraft of some kind. When they grew a patch of grain it had to be covered with branches to prevent the seed from being blown away. The invasion of the sand was comparatively recent, apparently dating only from the fourteenth century, but nothing was done about it until the latter part of the eighteenth century, when some slight attempts were made to stem the torrent. Under Napoleon the government decided in 1800 to afforest the area. Following the theories of

Charlevoix, tested practically by Bremontier from 1788 to 1793, the coast dunes were planted with reeds, gorse, broom, and pine trees (*Pinus maritima*). The reeds were necessary near the coast to fix the sand, and the leguminous plants, as was recognized only in recent times, supplied the trees with nitrogenous nutriment, indispensable in those very poor soils. The subsoil was impermeable, and it was only some fifty years later that the necessity for breaking it up, in order to drain the land properly, was realized by Chambrelent, a civil engineer; he worked out a general scheme of drainage for the area. The afforestation was considered complete in 1873, when some 800 000 hectares had been planted. The whole district had been made healthy and productive: where trees were not planted, good sheep-pasture had been made.

Napoleon also encouraged the cultivation of chicory, from the dried and ground roots of which a substitute for, or an addition to, coffee could be made. It flourished on sandy soils, like those between Dunkirk and Calais, where sugar-beet would not grow. Tobacco, too, came to be widely grown. Cole, linseed, poppy, and the oil-plants covered no fewer than 300 000 hectares in 1860.

Progress in French livestock husbandry did not keep pace with the arable. Much more progress had been made in the United Kingdom, but after the restoration of the monarchy it became the fashion in France to purchase expensive cattle, sheep, and pigs from famous British flocks to improve the native breeds. To what extent this was done is not clear: some royal cattle-farms were set up in unsuitable places, where beasts rapidly developed tuberculosis.

A measure of success was achieved in 1850. The good qualities of the Durham Shorthorn were added to those of the native cattle in parts of Brittany, Armorica, Maine-Anjou, and other places. The New Leicester sheep was crossed with the merino by Yvart to produce the Île de France breed. The Yorkshire pig was introduced.

In Spain the feudal system prevailed until the end of the eighteenth century. No measures had been taken—as they had in Germany, in the Low Countries, and even in France—to modify the pressure of this kind of tenure upon the peasants. The English had the advantage of being finally free from these burdens a century or more earlier. The result was general stagnation in Spain, and there was no progress in farming, though a wide variety of crops was grown. The peasants neglected manure and their methods were often irrational, but some research in irrigation was made. The rotations were often lengthy, such as wheat, rice, chick-peas (vetches), haricots and beans, potatoes. Other crops grown were flax, hemp, saffron, and vines, the latter yielding excellent wines. Cotton was grown in Andalusia, olives and sugar-canes flourished in the south and east; sunflowers were grown; figs, oranges, lemons, and almonds had a place.

The merino sheep was the source of wealth best known outside the country; it was estimated that there were some 5 m of them in 1796. The Spanish horses had a great reputation, and the stud-farms were carefully managed. The mules, too, were often fine animals. Many goats were kept, as well as cattle and pigs, but nothing outstanding was done in Spain to develop livestock or tillage.

Though a great deal of agricultural technique had necessarily been learned in Italy from classical times onwards, and progress there compared favourably with that in Spain, Italian farming-methods did not advance so rapidly as those in some other countries. An estimate that the total output rose by 75 per cent during the eighteenth century is probably over-optimistic. Tarelli had preached the need for forage crops in the sixteenth century, by which time rice-growing was practised. Maize and potatoes were relatively early introduced. There were fine water-meadows around Milan, and irrigation-works were constructed in Piedmont and elsewhere. Five cuts of hay every year were made from the Milanese water-meadows and at Lodi; those of Parma yielded a little less. Between Bologna and Tortona two hay-harvests a year were obtained, but Istria remained dry and arid and the Campagna consisted of little but unhealthy marshes. The lowlands about Siena were also marshy, though some wheat was grown.

Rotations varied. A species of four-course was already ancient in the eighteenth century, but there were others. Tuscany cultivated wheat in two successive years, next rye or maize, then beans, millet, or haricots—or rye if the second crop was maize—and finally a fallow before wheat. A wheat–beans–fallow rotation was favoured on heavy soils, as in England. Sometimes a wheat or turnip crop was followed by beans or fallow, or there were different combinations of wheat, turnips, and beans. Maize and a fallow were introduced occasionally. Citrus fruits and bergamots were grown in the warmer south, and vines flourished everywhere. The wine was naturally good, but the viticulturists did nothing to improve it. Some flax, hemp, and oats were grown all over the country. Buckwheat was important in Italy, as in France, the Low Countries, and Germany.

Legumes and maize grew well, but despite the culture of clover, rye grass, and turnips the shortage of winter fodder apparently limited livestock husbandry. The oxen in the Roman Campagna were fed on turnips, roots, and leaves in winter; the leaves of trees and vines, with the small sour fruit, were collected and preserved as fodder in pit silos. Furze was cut for both cattle and sheep. However, in spite of the difficulties of forage-supply, it had always been possible to maintain cattle more or less successfully through the winter in Lombardy,

Tuscany, and the valley of the Po. The milch kine here compared favourably with those of other countries.

A new agricultural literature appeared in Italy during the eighteenth century, but it is very doubtful whether it was read by the peasants. They had their ideas, but did not derive them from books. In Piedmont they began to grow such things as buckwheat on the fallow because they did not like to see land not bearing a crop, but the practice was not widely adopted. Maize began to take the place of rye in the food of the poor in the early eighteenth century. Rape, too, began to be cultivated then, but was not extensively grown until after 1800. Other crops were kidney- and broad-beans, chick-peas, spelt, barley, lupins, hemp, and oats. The potato, though introduced early, did not become a staple of diet until the nineteenth century.

The plains of Piedmont and Lombardy were famous for their farming in the mid-nineteenth century, but were not self-supporting in grain. Supplies were imported from the Black Sea and the Danube through Venice. The south produced silk, oil, madder, liquorice, and cotton, as well as cereals and wine. The coastal belt on the Adriatic produced a surplus of wheat that was carried over the mountains on mule-back, but in spite of the interest of capitalists in the late eighteenth century wide areas of unreclaimed land remained.

Denmark and Schleswig-Holstein were handicapped in the eighteenth century by the heavy incidence of feudal rights and dues, though some reforms took place towards its end. It was not, indeed, till well on in the nineteenth century that these countries, with the final abolition of serfdom and the rise of the co-operative movement, began to win their modern reputation for outstanding farming. A Danish agricultural society was founded in 1769, and a veterinary school at Copenhagen in 1773, both marks of liberalism in ruling circles, possibly due to the influence of the French physiocrats.

Swedish society, too, was influenced by the physiocrats. The importation and breeding of the merino sheep showed that there was an interest in improving breeds, but farming in general remained rather primitive. The implements were crude and rather inefficient, but cereals and pulse were cultivated: rye, oats, beans, peas, and, in the south, a little barley. The potato was introduced in 1738, but remained unfamilar for a century. Only with great difficulty could a second cut of hay be mown on the natural pastures. Leaves helped to eke out winter feed for the cattle, as in other countries.

As has been shown, progress in farming technique was very remarkable during the century 1750–1850, and it took a similar form in many countries. The great need was to increase supplies of winter feed, thus enabling livestock to be maintained in good condition the whole year round, and consequently to supply larger quantities of organic manure. Coupled with this there was a need for better implements, with which a finer seed-bed could be prepared. These things were achieved over wide areas, mainly by the example of Flemish husbandry. The improvement was not effected, however, without changes in social organization and land tenure, which on the continent took the form of the gradual extinction of feudalism. This system had already vanished from the English scene by the

FIGURE 16—*Manure conservation on an advanced farm in England, c 1756. The dung is carted from stable and cow-shed and deposited in the pit, and drains from these buildings carry the liquid into it.*

eighteenth century, and during that century serfdom was gradually wiped out elsewhere, being finally extinguished during the course of the French wars and the annexation of most of western Europe by France. In England the land was redistributed in separate holdings under the Enclosure Acts, and much of the waste was brought into cultivation by the same method, so that the introduction of the new crops and new methods was made easy. In the Low Countries, the peasants were encouraged to exchange their scattered strips and to enclose and distribute the common waste. Common grazing was done away with by a Prussian order of 1811, but the old arrangements of strips remained in much of the west, as it still does. France made little change in this way, in spite of the abolition of feudal rights. The serious problem there was the repeated reduction of the size of holdings by reason of the co-heir system of inheritance.

New plenty raised new questions for agricultural science to answer, in addition to those it was already attempting. How much of the new kind of fodder-crops ought the different kinds of animals to eat daily? What was the most effective quantity that ought to be given to a cow in calf? How should a working horse or ox be fed? Again, we have seen that feeding and fattening store-cattle in yards during the winter in England, and summer stall-feeding in the Low Countries and later in Germany, provided more ample supplies of manure (figure 16). This was supplemented by organic waste, by marl, chalk, lime, and so forth. Which of these things, and in what quantity, ought to be used on the land prepared for the different crops? How much seed of each plant should be sown per acre to secure the optimum yield?

Aristotle was responsible for the system of thought that ruled scientific ideas of plant-nutrition until the sixteenth century. It was that plants obtained their food through their roots from the soil already elaborated or ready to be assimilated. In 1563 Bernard Palissy (1510–88) published careful observations of the importance of salts in plant-nutrition, and formulated for the first time the idea that the minerals removed from the soil ought to be replaced if fertility was to be maintained. His work was overlooked for centuries, and, like most of the early scientific work, had no influence on practical farming.

Van Helmont (1577–1644), whose work was first published by his son in 1652, made a famous and protracted experiment from which he concluded that 'all vegetables do immediately and materially proceed out of water alone'. J. Woodward (1665–1728), who made similar experiments, believed in 1699 that the water absorbed by the plants he used carried the necessary soil-matter, presumably in solution. Marcello Malpighi (1628–94) learned experimentally in 1671 that the leaves played a part in nutrition, and thought that the action of sunlight on the leaves caused a fermentation of the nutrient sap. Nehemiah Grew (1641–1712), at about the same time, believed that the leaves played a part, as the roots and trunk had done earlier, in purifying the sap for absorption by the fruit, flower, and seed.

Edmé Mariotte (1620–84) observed the result of various grafts, and studied the composition and circulation of sap; he thought that the leaves absorbed and expelled gases and that different plants found, in the same soil, substances from which they could form the wide variety of materials of which they were composed. Early in the eighteenth century Stephen Hales (1677–1761), by his experiments, explained the movement of the sap and transpiration through the leaves, and demonstrated that air, as well as water and substances in solution, was taken in by the plant and used to build its structure. The science of his time regarded light as a substance, and he carried Malpighi's theories a step farther by suggesting that the absorption of light by the leaves was an important function in plant nutrition.

Duhamel du Monceau made experiments with the Tullian drill-husbandry and on the growth of trees, but he was influenced a good deal by Tull's theory that the more the soil is comminuted the more it becomes available as plant food; in other respects his ideas about the effect of fertilizers upon the growth of plants were those common to practical men of the time.

No further progress was made until the composition of air was known. In 1754 Joseph Black discovered 'fixed' air, which Lavoisier (1743–94) renamed carbonic acid in 1781. Joseph Priestley (1733–1804) discovered oxygen in 1774, and Lavoisier demonstrated the composition of water and of atmospheric air. He carried out experiments on his estate at Freschines, where in ten years he doubled the yield of wheat and increased by fivefold the number of livestock carried.

Priestley noticed that plants confined in an atmosphere rich in carbon dioxide produced large quantities of oxygen, and thought that this was caused by the growth of the plant. Jan Ingenhousz (1730–99), a Dutch physician who emigrated to London, was stimulated by Priestley's discoveries and studied the relation between air and plant; he was finally able to demonstrate that green shoots give off oxygen in sunlight and carbon dioxide in darkness, while non-green parts always give off carbon dioxide. This, with Priestley's work, was critically examined by Senebier (1742–1809), a Swiss, who made careful and exhaustive experiments. He proved that light, not heat, is the effective agent in the fixation of carbon dioxide, and that oxygen is liberated only when carbon dioxide is present. A decade or so later de Saussure demonstrated that green plants cannot live without some carbon dioxide. This they obtain from the small amount of carbon dioxide normally present in the atmosphere. He also showed that plants fix water coincidentally with carbon, and that oxygen is freed only as an accompaniment of the fixation of carbon dioxide. Perhaps his most important finding was that plants are dependent upon the nitrogen in the soil, which was confirmed by Boussingault almost fifty years later.

In view of these results, how did the humus theory of nutrition come to the fore? It was chiefly advocated by Albrecht Daniel Thaer (p 41) and Mathieu de Dombasle, whose opinions carried great weight with practical men. In their belief, plants, like animals, utilized carbon in the organic form, obtaining it from partially decomposed animal and vegetable matter in the soil. The inorganic salts, the significance of which could not be absolutely denied, were said to act merely as stimulants.

In 1840 Liebig proved this view false by showing that the insolubility of humic acid made it impossible, under the most favourable conditions, for more than a small fraction of the carbon found in the growing plant to have been obtained from this source. He asserted that plants were nourished by carbonic acid, ammonia, water, phosphoric, sulphuric, and silicic acids, lime, magnesia, potash, and iron. He further demonstrated that nitrogen was absorbed through the roots as ammonium salts or nitrates.

Little of this early work can have reached the ordinary farmer, who would have found it remote from his daily practice even had he been acquainted with it. Agriculture was indeed, as Francis Home said in the introduction to his book 'Principles of Agriculture and Vegetation' (1757), hardly sensible of its dependence upon chemistry.

Home made the first attempt to give practical application to the principles discovered up to his time. He adopted the nutrition of plants through their roots as basic, and divided his subject into five parts: (1) the nature and qualities of different soils, (2) the nature and qualities of different composts, (3) the action of composts on vegetation, (4) tillage and cultivation, (5) weeds and other impediments to the growth of crops.

Wallerius, a Swedish physician, under whom Gustavus Adolphus Gyllenborg produced his *Agriculturae fundamenta chemica* in 1761 (English translation 1771), pronounced that 'manuring is that operation by which land receives substances that nourish plants', and discussed the effects of using chalk, lime, marl, and clay, and of mixing soils, all matters of immediate practical value to farmers. He subscribed to the humus theory and declared that plant nutrients, to be absorbed, must be exceedingly fine, liquid, or gaseous. Making the soil 'fat' was for him the basis of nearly all agriculture. It is worth while noting that these and other agricultural chemists, before the nineteenth century, confined their inquiries to the composition of the soil, to its preparation and manuring, and to plant nutrition; they took little interest in the problems of animal nutrition.

But it was the great landowners and farmers—who carried out field-scale experiments, who tested the often peculiar, and occasionally fantastic, recommendations of the innumerable 'book farmers' of the time, and who made demonstration-farms of their land—rather than the scientists who influenced the development of farming in western Europe in the second half of the eighteenth century. Arthur Young enthusiastically described the work of many of these men. 'Turnip' Townshend and Robert Walpole were exponents of the new husbandry in the early eighteenth century; Coke of Norfolk and the Duke of Bedford in the later years. There were many others who won less fame but whose influence on their own estates and the surrounding districts was no less marked. The normal farming of various districts and the improvements which might be of service to others were described by William Marshall in his 'Rural Economy' series, and in the county reports undertaken by surveyors appointed by the Board of Agriculture after 1793. Much was written about marling, chalking, and liming, about drainage and new implements. Animal breeding and feeding were developed by practical farmers like Fowler of Rollright, Bakewell of Dishley, Ellman of Glynde, and many others, but few details of their methods remain to us. These pioneers were secretive, realizing the advantages to be gained from a monopoly of their own methods.

The Society of Arts, founded in 1754, offered prizes for agricultural experiments and inventions. Voluntary organizations of landowners and farmers did the same sort of thing and usefully published results. Innumerable smaller groups formed societies to conduct local competitions in growing both unfamiliar and familiar crops, in manuring, and in animal breeding, and served for the exchange of ideas. In France, many of the nobility set up model farms similar to those in England (figure 17), to demonstrate the economic value of the new methods.

The enthusiasm for progress was very great, though the new methods spread very slowly, at a rate of not more than a mile a year from their place of origin. Many farmers declared that they were only for gentlemen who had money to burn, and that ordinary farmers must keep to the old ways. Marked advances were made nevertheless, and this was vitally important because even by 1770 Britain had become a grain-importing country. A tentative measure of these advances is given by the rise in the yield of wheat from an average of 16 bushels an acre in the late sixteenth century to about 20–22 bushels an acre 200 years later. There was an increase, too, in the average size of livestock and their productivity, but exact figures of the increase are difficult to compute.

Examples of the new farming were not wanting in late eighteenth-century Germany. C. Reichart (1685–1775) cropped a plot of land for eighteen years in succession, applying dung only once at the rate of 24 three-horse loads because he thought different crops took different food from the soil. A change of crops therefore allowed better plant nutrition. He made personal observations and experiments, and concluded that three kinds of 'artificial grasses' were valuable —lucerne, sainfoin, and Spanish or red clover—but he did not consider the connexion of animal husbandry with tillage. Johann Christian Schubert (1734–86) grew as much clover and beet as possible upon his own estate, as well as madder and tobacco, and the cultivation of these crops involved a new rotation.

Albrecht Daniel Thaer (1752–1828) was physician in ordinary to George III, King of England and Hanover. In 1784 he joined the Royal Agricultural Society at Celle and bought an estate which in 1802 he turned into an agricultural institute. Thaer's published work had very great influence on the practical side. The management of farmyard manure, composting, and the use of lime, marl, and gypsum are well described. In the field of animal nutrition he tried to assess the value of different feeding-stuffs by reference to a 'hay unit'; this was an unfortunate choice because 'hay' is so extremely variable in composition. This was, however, the first attempt to express animal feeding-requirements quantitatively.

FIGURE 17—*Model farm, England, 1859. Note the elaborate and extensive range of buildings.*

In England, Humphry Davy's lectures on 'Agricultural Chemistry' for the Board of Agriculture were published in book form (1813). But the Board was at that time already in a decline, and was dissolved in 1821. A beginning had, however, been made towards formal agricultural education by the establishment of a chair of agriculture at Edinburgh in 1790, and of a chair of rural economy at Oxford in 1796, though both were very inadequately endowed. Much more was done on the continent. Besides Thaer's institute, a school had been founded by von Voght in Holstein in 1803; the famous Hohenheim institute was established through the efforts of von Schwerz in 1818; and schools for peasants were opened in Bavaria a little later. In France, de Dombasle formed a school of agriculture at Roville, near Nancy, in 1819, and ten years later Bella, with funds provided by large landowners, founded a similar school at Grignon. In 1836

Boussingault built in Alsace an agronomic institute devoted to the study of plants and of animal nutrition. Two years previously, Lawes had entered into occupation of Rothamsted, where he was joined by Gilbert in 1835. They did work of immense importance during their long collaboration, and the Rothamsted Experimental Station soon became famous. Altogether, the first half of the nineteenth century was a time of enormous activity in the theory and systematic practice of agriculture all over western Europe. In every country the foundations of centres of agricultural research and education were being laid—many by voluntary effort, some with government assistance—and the way lay open to the astonishing achievements that now supply the world's vast population with its daily bread.

BIBLIOGRAPHY

BATH, B. H. S. VAN. 'Agriculture in the Low Countries (*c* 1600–1800).' Relazione del X Congresso Internazionale delle Scienze Storiche. Sansoni, Florence. 1953.

BOURDE, A. J. 'The Influence of England on the French Agronomes 1750–1789.' University Press, Cambridge. 1953.

BROWNE, C. A. 'A Source Book of Agricultural Chemistry.' Chronica Botanica, Waltham, Mass. 1944.

DEMOLON, A. 'L'Évolution scientifique et l'agriculture française.' Flammarion, Paris. 1946.

FUSSELL, G. E. "The Size of English Cattle in the Eighteenth Century." *Agric. Hist.*, **3**, 160–81, 1929.

Idem. "Eighteenth Century Estimates of British Sheep and Wool Production." *Ibid.*, **4**, 131–51, 1930.

Idem. "The Technique of Early Field Experiments." *J. R. agric. Soc.*, **96**, 78–88, 1935.

Idem "Animal Husbandry in Eighteenth Century England." *Agric. Hist.*, **11**, 96–116, 189–214, 1937.

FUSSELL, G. E. and COMPTON, M. "Agricultural Adjustments after the Napoleonic Wars." *Econ. Hist.*, **4**, 184–204, 1939.

FUSSELL, G. E. and GOODMAN, CONSTANCE. "Crop Husbandry in Eighteenth Century England." *Agric. Hist.*, **15**, 202–16, 1941; **16**, 41–63, 1942.

GOLTZ, T. VON DER. 'Geschichte der deutschen Landwirtschaft' (2 vols). Cotta, Stuttgart. 1903.

GROMAS, R. 'Histoire agricole de la France dès origines à 1939.' Published by the author, Mende. 1947.

KRZYMOWSKI, R. 'Geschichte der deutschen Landwirtschaft.' Ulmer, Stuttgart. 1939.

LARGE, E. C. 'The Advance of the Fungi.' Cape, London. 1940.

LINDEMANS, P. 'Geschiedenis van de landbouw in België' (2 vols). De Sikkel, Antwerp. 1952.

MEUVRET, J. "L'agriculture en Europe au XVIIe et XVIIIe siècles." Relazione del X Congresso Internazionale delle Scienze Storiche. Sansoni, Florence. 1953.

ORWIN, C. S. "Agriculture and Rural Life", in TURBERVILLE, A. S. (Ed.), 'Johnson's England', Vol. 1, p. 261. Clarendon Press, Oxford. 1933.

PRATO, G. 'L'evoluzione agricola nel secolo XVIII.' Accademia delle Scienze, Turin. 1910.

PROTHERO, R. E. (LORD ERNLE). 'English Farming Past and Present.' Longmans, London, 1932.

PUGLIESE, S. 'Due secoli di vita agricola: produzione e valore dei terreni, contratti agrarî e prezzi nel Vercellese nei secoli XVIII e XIX.' Bocca, Torino. 1908.
REED, H. S. 'A Short History of the Plant Sciences.' Chronica Botanica, Waltham, Mass. 1943.
SALAMAN, R. N. 'The History and Social Influence of the Potato.' University Press, Cambridge. 1949.
SHERMAN, CAROLINE C. "Theories on the nutrition of plants from Aristotle to Liebig." *Yale J. Biol. Med.*, **6**, i, 43–60, 1933.
SNELLER, Z. W. 'Geschiedenis van de Nederlandse landbouw 1795–1940.' Wolters, Groningen. 1951.
SOREAU, E. 'L'agriculture du XVIIe siècle à la fin du XVIIIe'. Vol. 4 in the collection: 'L'agriculture à travers les âges.' Boccard, Paris. 1952.
WATSON, J. A. S. and HOBBS, MAY E. 'Great Farmers.' Faber, London. 1937.
YOUNG, A. 'Arthur Young's Travels in France during the Years 1787, 1788, 1789' ed. by Miss BETHAM-EDWARDS. Bell, London. 1905.

Agricultural labourer, eighteenth century.

2

FISH PRESERVATION

C. L. CUTTING

FISHING, with its offspring whaling (p 55), is the last survivor of the food-gathering stage (vol I, ch 8) of any economic importance. The flesh of fish is rapidly affected by microbial spoilage and is therefore more perishable than other fresh animal protein foods. Thus at all times it has needed special treatment to preserve the surpluses (vol I, pp 264–5, vol II, pp 120, 123), and until the days of rapid transport most fish could be eaten only in a preserved state (figure 18). Effective preservation was the condition of its usefulness. Though the principal methods of preserving adopted in Bronze Age and classical civilizations were based on salting, drying in the sun, smoking over fires, or a combination of some of these processes, there were notable minor developments in technique in the fourteenth century or thereabouts. These maintained edibility sufficiently long to permit widespread distribution of products, thus bringing the new foods within reach of the majority. The rules of the Church concerning fasts added religious emphasis to the economic dependence on fish. It may be here interpolated that though fishing has been world-wide since early times, the North Sea was by far the most important fishing-ground in the western world until the twentieth century, and that an account of the treatment of its products affords something more than a mere sample of the European fish-industry.

During the Middle Ages and for long after, fresh fish was mostly of fresh-water origin and very expensive. Every river-species was eaten; ponds were kept artificially stocked for the rich; and coarse fish were transported alive by road, notably to London. Sea-fish were also brought to port alive in boat bottoms whenever possible. Most of the population, however, ate only hard-dried, salted, and smoked products, and though at coastal villages mildly cured varieties were consumed the slowness of transport by land and sea confined trade to products that could be kept for several months without going bad. Practically all species of sea-fish and shell-fish were preserved for eating, but the main catches were (*a*) of white fish, such as cod and related species, which are plentiful in the North Sea and adjacent waters and can be taken all the year round, and (*b*) of the herring family, the capture of which is seasonal. Of the two, the herring catches were the more important.

Herring, as also salmon, are rich in oil and prone to oxidation, with resulting rancid flavour. They could not therefore be preserved for long by simple drying, even with salt, such as was suitable for the leaner, white fishes. As the Egyptians had long before discovered, an oily fish could be better preserved in a jar by covering with a salt brine, which, as we know, impedes the access of atmospheric oxygen. Rancidity could also be greatly retarded by the anti-oxidant effects of wood-smoking.

Salt herring were first prepared on a large scale at the western end of the Baltic during the twelfth century. This trade was organized by merchants from the ports of the Hanseatic League. The quality was strictly regulated by their

FIGURE 18—*Preparation of fish for preservation. Sixteenth century.*

supervision of the process of salting and packing. After landing, the fish were gutted, washed in sea-water, mixed with salt, and finally packed in barrels made of wooden staves and hoops (figures 18, 19). When full, these stood closed for ten days, during which the herring sank a little owing to osmotic shrinkage. The barrels were then reopened, filled, and closed again. Hanseatic laws forbade placing small or inferior fish in the middle of the barrel, and the fish had all to be salted alike and packed in regular layers. 'Full' herring, containing roes and in prime condition, were distinguished from spawned fish, which are meagre and deficient in oil.

This trade was, in fact, basic for the League, which did not long survive the decline in the Baltic fishery about 1400. The Netherlands then assumed supremacy in the trade and retained it until nearly 1700. Their process, which derived much from the Hanseatics, also depended on adherence to a precise specification formulated over the years and enforced by inspection and penalties.

Herring, mostly caught off the British coast, were salted at sea aboard the herring-busses (figure 20), which accommodated empty barrels and carried provisions for about 15 men, including skilled salters and coopers. These busses were sturdy broad-beamed two- or three-masted decked ships, mostly of 80 to 100 tons, capable of prolonged sojourn at sea. Large drift-nets (figure 26), 50 to 60 fathoms in length, which trapped the herring by the gills, appeared about 1416. Immediately the herring were shaken out of the net their gills and viscera were

FIGURE 19—*Packing salted herring into wooden barrels. The Dutch laws were very strict and the packing had to be done on the street or quayside.*

removed and they were first sprinkled with salt, then turned over and over, and finally sorted and packed head to tail in barrels with salt sprinkled between the layers, which were arranged alternately across each other (figure 21). Finally, the barrels were topped up with brine, made air-tight, and branded with the date of catch. Packing bad herring with good was severely punished. An ordinance issued in 1651 forbade putting old fish under new, or laying the sickly, or those bitten by dogfish, next the good, or mixing those caught on one night with those of another taking. There were also minute regulations governing mesh-size, the quantity and type of salt used, the time and place of fishing, and the making and branding of barrels—including even the number and size of staves and the nature and quality of the wood. The use of old barrels was strictly prohibited. The proportion of salt specified, about one of salt to three of fish, would result in roughly a saturated solution in the flesh, which is essential for proper keeping. A brine-tight barrel was necessary to prevent rancidity.

The fishing started off the Shetland Islands at the end of June, though the date varied from year to year, probably on account of natural variations in the

FIGURE 20—*A fleet of herring-busses returning to harbour. These were larger than the hoys and had two or three masts.*

movements and condition, particularly the oiliness, of the fish. It continued off north-east Scotland until September. In the autumn it reached to near East Anglia and ended in the Thames estuary about Christmas. After that, ships returned home to refit. The barrels were taken to Holland for branding, and could not be sold at sea or shipped direct to foreign markets. Fresh-caught herring had to be in pickle for at least ten days before sale. At sea, herring already barrelled were moistened with sea-water every fortnight. Repacking on shore had to be completed within three weeks of landing. No herring could be 'heightened' by fresh pickle, or repacked except in the public street or on the quays (figure 19). This carefully controlled technique resulted in a keeping-quality of 12 months in any climate. The Dutch could distribute fish up all the principal rivers of Europe. Thus pickled herring was one of the first foodstuffs to become a major item of international commerce, and helped to revolutionize the economic conditions of the time.

Smoked herring. Herring had been widely preserved by smoking as early as the thirteenth century, from the Baltic to France. The special type of *red herring* cured at Yarmouth had acquired a reputation by about 1350. Ungutted herring

FIGURE 21—*A hulk or great hoy at the fishing-grounds. The drift-net is being pulled in, and the men on the deck are gutting and packing the fish.*

were first hard-salted for a week, then washed to remove surface salt and hung up in a tall kiln over smouldering fires of sawdust for several weeks (figure 22). In this process they became very hard and dry and thoroughly impregnated with smoke. After being taken down from the kiln they were packed in barrels and distributed.

Stockfish is a word used for fish that are dried but not salted or smoked. Cod and members of the cod family were being dried in northern Norway as early as the thirteenth century, merely by hanging up the eviscerated fish in the open air for several weeks until it was quite hard (figures 23 and 24). The Hanseatic merchants monopolized this trade from about 1350 until 1550 by their control of Bergen.

Salt cod was prepared at sea early in the fifteenth century by English fishermen from Scarborough, Cromer, and Bristol, fishing off Iceland in two-masted ketches holding 5 to 10 men. They salted their catch in the summer months and

FIGURE 22—*A kiln showing the preparation and smoking of red herring. The salted ungutted herring were hung over smouldering sawdust fires for several weeks. When smoked hard they were packed into barrels.*

returned with cargoes of about 30 tons in the autumn. These operations are sometimes confusingly described as the 'Iceland stockfishery', despite the facts that the salted product was kept in the wet state on the ship and that the Icelanders produced true stockfish, which they exported to England.

The discovery in 1497 of Newfoundland and its prolific cod-fishery led to intense rivalry between France and England. The French had access to plenty of salt formed by solar evaporation on the Biscay coast. They split their cod and wet-salted it in barrels for sale either in that condition if the fish were large, or, if smaller, after drying in the open. British salt was for many centuries too impure to be suitable for fish curing. Bay salt, so called from La Baie (now Bourgneuf) at the mouth of the Loire, was therefore imported into Britain but used sparingly there. To ensure adequate preservation, drying-grounds were essential, and English fishermen from south-west ports occupied suitable sites in Newfoundland, New England, and Nova Scotia, while the French took over the Gaspé Peninsula.

The cod were caught on baited hooks cast from small boats. Stony beaches were preferred for drying, otherwise hurdles had to be erected to keep the fish off the damp sand or grass. French practice at Cape Breton, as described in the

FIGURE 23—*The preparation of stockfish. The fish, with their heads still on, were split open and spread out to dry on the rocks.*

second half of the seventeenth century, was typical. The fish were first dressed by slitting the throat, heading, and splitting open. They were then piled in layers, flesh-side uppermost, with salt in between, and left for five or six days, after which they were washed in the sea to remove surplus salt and piled again to drain. After this they were spread out on the beach, flesh up during the day, flesh down at night, for some weeks. Finally they were stacked in piles to 'sweat', that is, to even out moisture-gradients (figure 25). A typical ship for a salting-expedition was of 200 to 300 tons burthen, and carried a crew of 70 and 14 small boats as catchers. There were numerous variants of this process over the North Atlantic seaboard, depending on local conditions and circumstances. As a result of observation, various refinements were introduced and passed on by tradition. Thus, certain impurities in the salt produced what was termed salt-burn; if the fish had too much sun, the skin lifted off; fish bled immediately they were caught produced a whiter product. At the end of the nineteenth century various types of artificial dryer, using fans and heating, were introduced.

Fresh fish. The products described above are tough, salty, and highly flavoured. In the industrial era successful attempts to transport and market fish in the fresh state had converted it by 1850 from a luxury article into one within reach of the bulk of the population.[1] The chief factors responsible for this dietary revolution were: (*a*) improvement in communications, culminating in railways (vol V); (*b*) use of ice to preserve fish by chilling; and (*c*) vast increase in production,

FIGURE 24—*Smaller fish were headed and hung by their tails. Slatted huts gave shelter whilst permitting free ventilation.*

resulting from more efficient ways of fishing, particularly trawling, finally combined with steam-propulsion.

All these factors reacted on one another as population and the demand for food rose rapidly in the nineteenth century. The use of ice to delay spoilage permitted voyages farther from port, and resulted in the discovery of new and more prolific fishing-grounds, thus leading to increased supplies and cheaper fish. Although the following account relates to western Europe, and Britain in particular, the same general pattern of development was followed in North America.

Live fish. Keeping sea-fish alive developed into a large industry at North Sea ports, particularly Harwich and Grimsby, in the eighteenth and nineteenth centuries. The fish were caught on lines by special tackle with a gorge, to prevent injury from the hook. Well-vessels of some 50 tons carried a tank about 20 ft

[1] Canning (vol V, ch 2) was the result of another attempt to vary the diet. The traditional products of the old methods continued to be exported to less industrialized countries.

long amidships, into which the fish were thrown tail first so that they did not break their necks. The well was perforated for continuous replenishment of the sea-water. Flat-fish, which would lie on the bottom and block the holes, were stowed in boxes. Large predatory fish such as skate and halibut were tethered by a cord at the nose and tail respectively. Fish normally arrived at the surface with their swim-bladders inflated by the rapid change in pressure, so that these had to be punctured before they could swim in a natural position. Cod and haddock could normally be kept alive at sea for a week or two, the dead being removed

FIGURE 25—*In preparing salt cod, the fish were split open and laid in piles with dry salt between each layer. After five to six days they were washed, spread out to dry, and then again stacked to allow them to 'sweat'.*

daily. At port, the fish were transferred to large floating crates which were anchored in the dock until the fish were required for sale.

Trawling, or fishing by dragging a net over the sea-bottom, was reported from time to time between the fourteenth and seventeenth centuries, chiefly in sheltered waters such as the Thames estuary and the Zuider Zee. By the end of the eighteenth century the fishermen of Barking and Brixham were having success in coastal waters with a much larger net of this type, kept open by a beam of wood. They extended their operations to the North Sea and, by the middle of the century, settled at Hull and Grimsby for proximity to the prolific Dogger Bank area. Trawling was a more productive method of fishing than lining. The fish, however, were mostly dead when landed on deck and could be distributed to consuming centres in sound condition only if handled expeditiously, as by fleeting (p 53), or if chilled by means of ice.

Fleeting. The use of specially swift ships to carry the catches from the busses to the harbour was practised by the Dutch from at least 1600. In Britain, the firm of Samuel Hewett (1797–1871) of Barking, which owned a number of North Sea sailing trawlers, first organized the system of fishing as a fleet, under an 'admiral'; the catch from every ship was collected daily and sent to Billingsgate market in London by special, swift, cutter-rigged carrier-vessels which, after 1864, were steam-powered. The trawlers themselves continued for some time to be sail-driven, despite a number of attempts to apply steam-power to them from 1860 onwards. About 1877 converted paddle-tugs began to be used for

FIGURE 26—*Small boat preparing to take in drift-net.*

trawling, and steam-powered capstans and winches for hauling the nets. The first successful steam-trawlers were built about 1883 and steam-drifters for herring soon after.

Refrigeration. The first use of ice to preserve fish during transport in Britain was in 1786, following a report that it was common practice in China. Salmon from the north of Scotland were thereafter sent to London packed in ice in boxes. The ice was collected from lochs during the winter and stored in earth houses. Such ice is also reported to have been used for herring just before 1800, and it was becoming common in the normal fresh-fish trade by about 1820. About the middle of the century it began to be used systematically by Hewett's for the preservation of fish at sea. Ice from the Thames marshes was collected as a crop by the farmers and brought in carts to a large store at Barking. Ice-lugs then took it out to the cutters in the river. The supplies of ice were scarcely adequate for requirements; it had to be used sparingly, and only on the most valuable species. 'Offal fish', including plaice and haddock, often had to be thrown overboard. Hull and Grimsby trawlers first started using ice about 1860, relying on imports from Norway. More ample supplies made it possible for trawlers to go farther afield in search of fish, thus developing new trawling grounds off Iceland (1891) and later farther away still. Larger steam-trawlers with improved fishing-gear, such as the otter-trawl and steel warps, brought back ever-increasing quantities. By 1900 factories were erected for making ice artificially for the trade. The limited preservative properties of ice, however, set a corresponding limit to the distance ventured from port, and this is still a major problem in the twentieth century.

Mildly smoked fish. The advent of railways made possible the distribution of less heavily cured products. Red herring gave way to Yarmouth bloaters (1835) and Newcastle kippers (1843). Finnon haddocks, originally a local product cured on a domestic scale at Findon, near Aberdeen, provided an outlet for surplus trawled haddock landed at London, Hull (1847), and Grimsby (1856). On the continent a preference developed for hot-smoked products, such as the *Bückling*, which was probably a descendant of a much earlier Baltic product. In all these products the chief purpose of smoking is to impart an attractive flavour. The degree of preservation is inadequate for a delay of more than a few days between production and consumption.

BIBLIOGRAPHY

ALWARD, G. L. 'The Sea Fisheries of Great Britain and Ireland.' Gait, Grimsby. 1932.
BEAUJON, A. "The History of the Dutch Sea Fisheries" in 'International Fisheries Exhibition Literature', Vol. 9, Pt II: 'Prize Essays.' London. 1884.
CUTTING, C. L. 'Fish Saving.' Hill, London. 1955.
HERBERT, D. (Ed.). 'Fish and Fisheries. A Selection from the Prize Essays of the International Fisheries Exhibition, Edinburgh, 1882.' Edinburgh. 1883.
HOLDSWORTH, E. W. H. 'Deep Sea Fishing and Fishing Boats.' London. 1884.
INNIS, H. A. 'The Cod Fisheries.' Yale University Press, Newhaven. 1940.
JENKINS, J. T. 'The Herring and the Herring Fisheries.' King, London. 1927.
POWER, E. and POSTAN, M. M. (Eds). 'Studies in English Trade in the Fifteenth Century.' Routledge, London. 1933.
SAMUEL, A. M. 'The Herring; its Effect on the History of Britain.' Murray, London. 1918.

A NOTE ON WHALING

L. HARRISON MATTHEWS

UNTIL recent times, whales have been valued for their oil and certain other products for industrial and domestic use rather than for their meat as food. Their immense size and the rapidity with which their flesh undergoes decomposition have made it necessary to cut them up and carry out the preliminary processing 'in the field' immediately after capture, thus combining in a single enterprise the techniques of fishing, processing, and preserving.

Whales are mammals, not fish, though they have no legs and their arms are modified to fin-like flippers. They are warm-blooded, breathe air, and bear living young which they suckle. The larger sorts are the largest animals that have ever existed—a large blue whale is nearly 100 ft long and weighs about 150 tons. No animal of such size whose body was not supported by immersion in water could exist. But not all members of the whale tribe are of gigantic size, and the porpoises and dolphins are comparatively small.

There are many species of whale, but they fall naturally into two main groups, the whalebone whales (Mystacoceti) and the toothed whales (Odontoceti). The latter have uniform peg-like teeth for seizing their prey, which consists of fish and, probably even more important, squids and cuttlefish.

The feeding-mechanism of the whalebone whales is quite different. They do not catch individual animals for food, but filter the sea-water to extract in bulk the vast numbers of minute organisms that are collectively termed plankton. This consists of small plants and animals, many of microscopic size, which float in vast numbers in the upper layers of the sea. The largest whales feed on little else. The apparatus of the whalebone whales for filtering plankton out of the sea is most peculiar. These creatures have no teeth, but hanging from the upper jaw is a series of many fibrous horny plates set crosswise on each side, where the upper teeth are placed in ordinary mammals. These plates are known as baleen, or, incorrectly, 'whalebone'. The inner edges of the plates are frayed out into separate fibres, so that a sort of hairy mat, supported by the inner edges of the plates, is formed in the mouth. When the whale is feeding it takes in a mouthful of sea-water together with its contained plankton, shuts the mouth, and raises the tongue so that the water is driven through the mat, between the plates of whalebone, and out between the lips at the side. The plankton thus left stranded on the mat of whalebone fibres is then swallowed.

Even primitive man appreciated the value of whales, as is shown by the bones sometimes found in ancient kitchen-middens and hut-sites. A stranded whale (figure 27) must have been a godsend to dwellers near the coast—a position now curiously reversed when the responsibility for removing a malodorous dead whale as a serious public nuisance devolves on the owners of foreshore-rights. In far-off days the meat provided by a whale was doubtless a great attraction, but for many centuries the main value of whales has been their yield of oil.

The oil was used for illumination and for lubrication up to the middle of the last century, and it was not until about the beginning of the twentieth century that the process of hydrogenation was applied on a large scale to it. Chemically, whale-oil is a mixture of the esters of unsaturated fatty acids with the trihydric alcohol glycerol, and is liquid at ordinary temperatures; after hydrogenation it is a solid fat extensively used in the manufacture of margarine and soap. The oil is extracted partly from the thick heat-insulating coating of blubber that envelops the whale's body beneath the skin, partly from the bones, and partly from the meat. After the oil has been extracted by boiling (nowadays in steam-heated open boilers for blubber, and superheated steam-digesters for meat and bones), the meat and bones are kiln-dried and reduced to meal, the better

FIGURE 27—*An old woodcut showing a stranded whale being cut up on the beach. The pieces were then carried away in carts, 200–300 journeys often being needed. Olaus Magnus, 1555.*

grades being compounded in food for pigs and poultry, and the poorer used as fertilizers. The horny plates of baleen find a limited use in the manufacture of brushes and sieves. Whalebone was formerly used extensively for making umbrella-ribs, corset 'bones', hoops for crinolines, and the handles of punch-ladles; for springs in light mechanical devices; and, when frayed out into its component fibres, for the plumes on soldiers' helmets. Occasionally whale bones were used for building (figure 28).

The oil of the sperm whale and some of the smaller toothed whales differs from that of the whalebone whales, as does a second substance, spermaceti, that separates from the oil as a solid when it cools. Chemically, both are esters produced by combination of fatty acids with monohydric alcohols, and are liquid waxes that cannot be hydrogenated into edible fats. Both are liquid at the temperature of the sperm whale's body, but, on cooling, the spermaceti solidifies whereas the sperm oil remains fluid. They are mixed together in the tissues of the whale, but the proportion of spermaceti greatly preponderates in the head, where, in front of the brain-case, there is a series of spaces filled with it and surrounded by a network of fibres and tendinous tissue. From this hollow part, the 'case', spermaceti can be baled out or poured off. Spermaceti sets to a white wax on cooling and was formerly the base of the best quality of candles. It is still used for candles for religious ceremonial purposes, and in making cosmetics. The unit candle-power was originally defined as the light emitted by a standardized spermaceti candle burning at a specified rate.

Ambergris is a substance obtained from the intestines of some sperm whales, but its physiological origin is unknown; it is said to be a pathological concretion found only in whales that are sickly. It is a black greasy substance with a horrible smell when found in the whale, but when exposed to the air it becomes harder, and lighter in colour, and exchanges its bad odour for a characteristic faintly aromatic, earthy smell. The best sort is found floating in the sea or washed ashore; it has then had ample time to undergo its natural refining-process, probably an oxidation. Ambergris is used in cosmetics to fix and intensify perfumes, and commands a very high price.

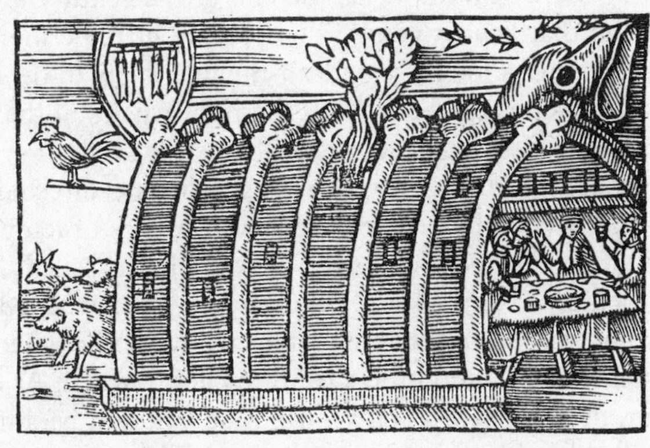

FIGURE 28—*Whale bones were sometimes used in the north, where timber was scarce, for building such things as gates and seats. Whale ribs are not large enough to make a house like that illustrated, but jaw bones would be suitable. Olaus Magnus, 1555.*

It was discovered at some early date that fortuitous strandings of whales could be improved upon by deliberately driving the animals ashore. This primitive way of hunting was practised in Scandinavia in the Middle Ages and still survives in the Faeroe Islands, where schools of a rather small species are annually driven ashore by the hundred and slaughtered, cut up, and boiled down for their oil. A similar fishery lasted into the present century in Orkney and Shetland.

During the Middle Ages the Basques carried on a profitable fishery by attacking in small boats the rather slow-moving and coast-frequenting Atlantic 'right' whales, which they exterminated locally. They evolved the technique of harpooning them with barbed spears attached to the boat by a line, and playing them until they could be approached and killed by stabbing with a lance. The dead whales were towed ashore to be cut up. When the number of whales declined through over-fishing these enterprising men fitted out ships to go farther afield in search of their quarry. The base of operations was thus merely transferred from shore to ship, for the actual hunting was done as before in small boats which were now lowered from the larger vessel. As the right whales became rare in temperate European waters, lengthy voyages into high latitudes became the practice.

Here the whalers found a further reward for their boldness, for within the Arctic circle they discovered another sort of whale, the Greenland right whale, which yielded a greater quantity of oil than any other (plate 4 A). Throughout the seventeenth and eighteenth centuries a large fleet of whalers—French, Dutch, English, and Scandinavian—was regularly engaged in voyages to the north. Some ships boiled out their oil at such places as Spitzbergen, Jan Mayen Island, or Bear Island, but others merely casked the blubber after cutting it into small pieces and brought it back to be boiled out at home. The chief British ports concerned were Whitby, Hull, Peterhead, and Dundee. The 'Greenland' fishery was for long carried on almost entirely at Spitzbergen, but later it was extended also to Davis Strait and Labrador.

After the mid-nineteenth century, northern whaling steadily declined, for Greenland whales were becoming scarce, and towards the end of the century it was only the high value of the whalebone that kept it going. The passing of the crinoline, together with the introduction of steel busks for corsets, dealt the final blow to the industry. With the twentieth century sailing-ships ceased to hunt the right whales of the Arctic.

On the New England and Connecticut coasts of America a similar evolution of whaling took place during the eighteenth century, but the pursuit was directed not only towards the right whales of the Arctic but towards the sperm whales of temperate and tropical seas. In the first half of the nineteenth century Yankee whalers sailed the seven seas from such ports as New Bedford, Nantucket, New London, Fairhaven, Mattapoisett, Stonington, and Sag Harbor, but during the American civil war (1861–5) many of the whale-ships were sunk as block-ships, and others captured and burned. At the same time the rise of the petroleum industry (vol V, ch 5), which substituted paraffin for whale-oil as an illuminant, started the ruin of American whaling. The first decade of the present century saw its end.

During the second and third quarters of the nineteenth century whaling-voyages got longer and longer. They ultimately extended up to five years, during which there would be visits to the Arctic and Antarctic, as well as months of cruising after sperm whales in the tropics. If the ship filled her holds before the end of the voyage she forwarded her full barrels home by freighter from some convenient port and then continued her hunting. The crews were paid by shares in the profits of the voyage, but few of a crew lasted out a five-year voyage. Unscrupulous skippers and mates sometimes gave their crew such a rough time that sooner or later practically every hand would have deserted the ship at intermediate ports, thus forfeiting their shares. Even those that returned home as crew often found themselves so much in debt to the ship for advances of pay and credit from the slop-chest that they received only a few dollars at paying-off.

On these long voyages the Americans developed the practice, adopted by whalers of other nations, of stripping the blubber from the dead whales in the water alongside the ship and extracting the oil by boiling the finely minced blubber in a series of cauldrons set in brickwork (plate 4 B). The fuel used was the oil-soaked fibrous scrap remaining after the oil had been boiled out of the blubber. Despite the danger of such operations on a wooden ship there was no unduly high loss from fire.

This industry was carried on by spearing the whales with harpoons hurled from small

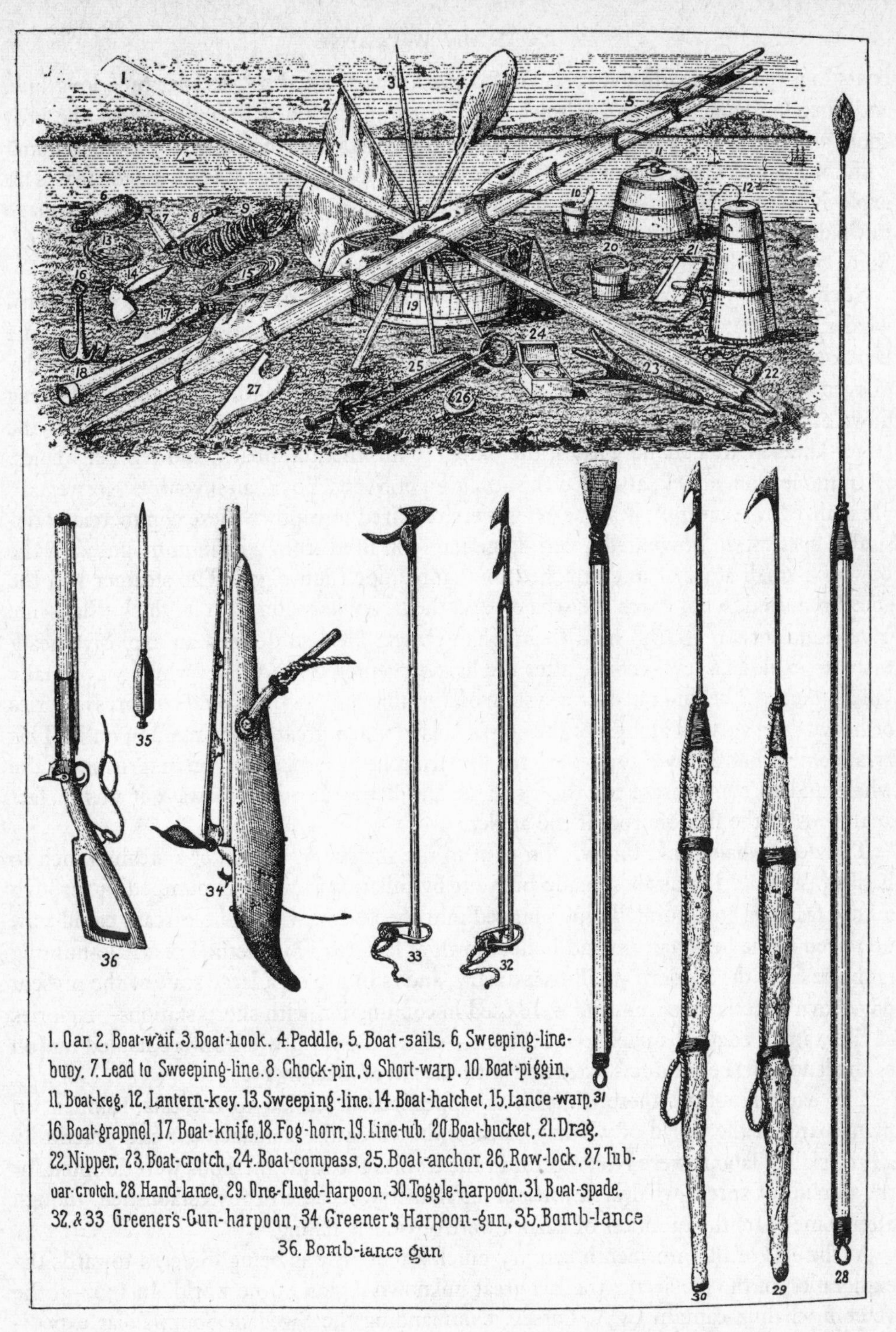

FIGURE 29—*Some of the gear provided for each boat lowered from a nineteenth-century sailing whale-ship.*

boats lowered from sailing-ships. The harpoon was secured to the boat by a long line, and once harpooned the whale towed the boat until it was so exhausted that the boat could approach closely by hauling in the line. The whale was then dispatched by stabbing with long lances mounted on poles. About 1850 the bomb-lance was invented. It was an explosive dart fired from a heavy shoulder- or swivel-gun. This saved time and damage to whale-boats and their crews, but met with little success and was not extensively used. Some nineteenth-century whaling gear is shown in figure 29.

Such whaling was restricted to the few species of whale, mainly right and sperm whales, that float when dead. Other and larger species were inaccessible to this technique because they are so large and active that the danger of attacking them, and the difficulty of even approaching them, were too great. Further, when dead they sink and would drag down any boat made fast to them. But about 1860 the existence of large numbers of the larger kinds of whalebone whales, the blue, the fin, the humpback, and the Sei whales, all immune from attack, attracted the attention of Svend Foyn, an inventive Norwegian. He realized that entirely new methods were required to capture these commercially desirable species, and invented a very large harpoon fired from a cannon mounted in the bow of a small steamer and attached to a stout rope (figure 30). The steamer had the speed required to approach the whales, and the heavy harpoon with its thick whale-line gave sufficient strength to hold them when struck. He also devised an explosive head, fused to explode a few seconds after the harpoon entered the whale, which was usually killed at once. The line ran over a system of movable pulleys that could compress a series of heavy steel springs alongside the ship's kelson when great strain came upon it. This arrangement had a 'give' to prevent the line from being broken by the first rushes of the whale and to compensate for the rise and fall of the ship in a seaway; it was in fact analogous to the flexible rod of the angler.

The dead whale sank, but was brought to the surface by means of a steam-winch to haul in the line. It was then made buoyant by inflating it with air pumped in through a hose fastened to a pointed pipe plunged into the body-cavity. The carcass could now be towed home to be cut up and boiled down at leisure. This method of whale-hunting is the basis of the modern whaling-industry, and is in use on a large scale at the present day. Foyn's methods of hunting were used in conjunction with shore-stations—factories at the water's edge in a sheltered harbour—where the dead whales were hauled out on to the land and the products extracted with the aid of machinery.

The exploitation of these hitherto untapped resources led to the establishment in many parts of the world of whaling-stations, in which the management and practically all the skilled labour were Norwegian; in the tropics the same methods were adopted for the pursuit of sperm whales. A prosperous industry became firmly established, though after some years the numbers of whales were obviously falling.

At the end of the nineteenth century much attention was being directed towards the exploration of the Antarctic, the last great unknown region of the world. In 1902–3, the veteran whaling-captain C. A. Larsen, commanding the Swedish South Polar expedition's ship the *Antarctic*, noted the abundance of whales and the suitability of many of the islands of that region for whaling-stations. His ship was lost, but after his rescue and return he found financial backing in South America to organize a whaling expedition on modern lines.

In 1904 he started the first Antarctic whaling-station in a sheltered cove on South Georgia. Whales were abundant and the enterprise was a great success; it paid a dividend of 70 per cent in its first year. The then recent invention of the hydrogenation process for converting oils into fats (p 56) had created a demand for animal oils in the margarine and soap trades. A rush for the new El Dorado started, and within a few years many whaling companies were working on this island and on the South Orkneys and South Shetlands farther south. A quarter of a century later, the introduction of pelagic floating

FIGURE 30—*Modern version of Svend Foyn's harpoon cannon, which is mounted in the bow of the whale-catcher. The shank of the harpoon is pushed into the barrel of the cannon, and the head, which has arms that open like an umbrella, projects. The rope runs over pulleys in the bow.*

factories freed the industry from dependence upon land-bases and from the attentions of the colonial tax-gatherer. These great self-contained ship-borne factories—which can haul the carcass of the largest whale on deck for processing—with their attendant fleets of whale-catchers seek out whales wherever they are most abundant. Many of the ships now carry aircraft to locate the whales. In recent years the world catch has varied from 24 000 to 44 000 whales annually, producing from about 400 000 tons to over 540 000 tons of oil. To prevent the destruction of the basic stock of whales the catch is now limited by international agreement.

Europeans and Americans are not the only peoples that have developed highly specialized techniques for the capture of whales. The Japanese were carrying on a prosperous whaling industry before the end of the eighteenth century. Several species of whalebone whales regularly come close inshore among the Japanese islands on their annual migrations, and the fishery for them was efficiently organized. Barbed harpoons were used in the hunt, and lances for the death blow, but the method differed fundamentally in that the initial stages of the capture were made by nets. As soon as whales were sighted from the look-out stations, a fleet of boats put out to sea across the path of the approaching whales and laid a series of nets, somewhat like the drift-nets of the North Sea herring-fishermen on a gigantic scale. Once the whale was entangled, other boats attacked with harpoons and lances, and naked men plunged into the sea and mounted on the back of the wounded whale to make fast ropes passed through incisions cut in the blubber with cutlasses carried in the mouth. The most usual quarry was the humpback whale, which generally sinks when dead; the hunters therefore brought two barges alongside and secured them to the animal before death to support it and carry it to the shore-station.

When the dead whale was brought to the factory it was dismembered, and the oil was boiled out of the blubber. The meat was cut up for human consumption, and many by-products were manufactured from the bones, sinews, intestines, and other parts. The industry was the monopoly of certain feudal landowners, and was carried on by great numbers of serfs.

A more primitive technique of whaling was in use until recently off the coasts of the Malayan islands. Whales such as humpbacks were harpooned from canoes, but the line instead of running was made fast to the boat. On striking a whale the crew jumped into the sea and swam about until picked up by their companion boats. The whale took the canoe down with it and dragged it about as a sort of sea-anchor until it was so exhausted that it could be killed with lances. The main object of this fishery was to obtain the meat for human consumption.

When the American whalers set off on their lengthy voyages they obtained the basic elements of their crews by 'shanghai'-ing the dockside scum of the New England ports and the 'hick hayseeds' from the Middle West who had come to the coast to seek their fortunes. The first part of the cruise, in search of the comparatively small blackfish or pilot whales, took them across the Atlantic, and they then put into the Azores or the Cape Verde Islands to complete their crews and engage skilled harpooners for the main voyage. The hand-harpoon technique of whaling from sailing-ships still lingers in the Azores, where it is carried on from shore-stations. A sperm-whaling industry of some importance is even yet preserved there. Look-out stations, like those formerly maintained by the Japanese, keep watch for the whales and signal the waiting boats when the quarry is sighted. The boats, and all the whaling-gear, are exactly as those used by the Yankee whalers of a century ago, and even the old American-English technical terms are in vogue, modified into the Portuguese speech of these hardy islanders. Their only concession to modernity is that the boats are towed out to the whaling-grounds by motor-launches, which also tow in the dead whales. But the boats are propelled by oar and sail, and all the ancient technique is retained.

The demand for fresh meat led to the development of a minor branch of whaling immediately after the 1939–45 war. Whale-meat is coarse, though palatable enough if removed from the whale soon after death, and it quickly becomes tainted by the incipient decomposition of the oil if it is not quite fresh. Whale-meat has always been used by whalers to supplement preserved foods, and has long been marketed in Scandinavia. Before the Reformation the flesh of the small kinds of whale, the porpoises and dolphins, was considerably esteemed because it was regarded as fish, and so could be eaten during Lent and on fast-days.

BIBLIOGRAPHY

AAGAARD, B. 'Den gamle Hvalfangst. Kapitler av dens Historie.' Hvalfangstmuseet, Publ. no. 13. Sandefjord. 1933.

JENKINS, J. T. "Bibliography of Whaling." *J. Soc. Bibl. nat. Hist.*, **2**, 71–166, 1948.

RISTING, S. 'Av Hvalfangstens Historie.' Christensens Hvalfangstmuseet, Publ. no. 2. Sandefjord. 1922.

SCAMMON, C. M. 'The Marine Mammals of the North-western Coast of North America together with an Account of the American Whale-fishery.' San Francisco. 1874.

STARBUCK, A. 'History of the American Whale Fishery from its Earliest Inception to the Year 1876.' Waltham, Mass. 1878.

Hand-harpooning from open boats, nineteenth century.

3

METAL AND COAL MINING, 1750–1875

J. A. S. RITSON

ALTHOUGH the mining of metalliferous ores and of coal have many features in common, they differ in two major respects. First, deposits of coal commonly have a great horizontal extension, whereas mineral deposits tend to follow a near-vertical course. Secondly, coal-mining practice has to pay great attention to the possibility of the presence of explosive or poisonous gases and of explosive dust, which are not normally encountered in metal mines. Like most generalizations both these have exceptions—some of which will be noted later—but they are of sufficient force to make it appropriate to discuss the two subjects separately.

METAL-MINING

I. LOCATION OF MINERAL DEPOSITS

In the middle of the eighteenth century mining was confined mostly to western Europe. Small mining enterprises were developed in other regions, but these were mostly concerned with the working of surface deposits. It is true that great quantities of precious metals came to Europe from Central and South America, but much, indeed most, of this supply had been laboriously won from the earth by the natives before their conquest. After the decline of the Roman Empire, when much mining was done by slave labour, mining languished in Europe. There was slight activity in the ninth and tenth centuries, but it was not until the fifteenth century that the Germans, Saxons, and Bohemians staged a full revival (vol II, ch 1). This is clearly shown in central Europe and in the near East, where there is evidence of mining (said to be by Saxon miners) up to the time of the Turkish conquest. After this, the operating mines show evidence of having been abandoned until they were rediscovered and reopened in the twentieth century.

An example of the vicissitudes a mine can pass through is well illustrated by Parys Mountain in Anglesea. This is said to have been exploited originally by the Romans, then for 1700 years it lay idle until the 1780s, when it became for a few years, in the hands of Thomas Williams, the largest copper mine in the world, 1000 tons of copper being smelted annually at the mine's own works in Lancashire. After Williams's death in 1802 it languished, but came to life for a time in 1850 and again languished. In 1956 it underwent still another reopening.

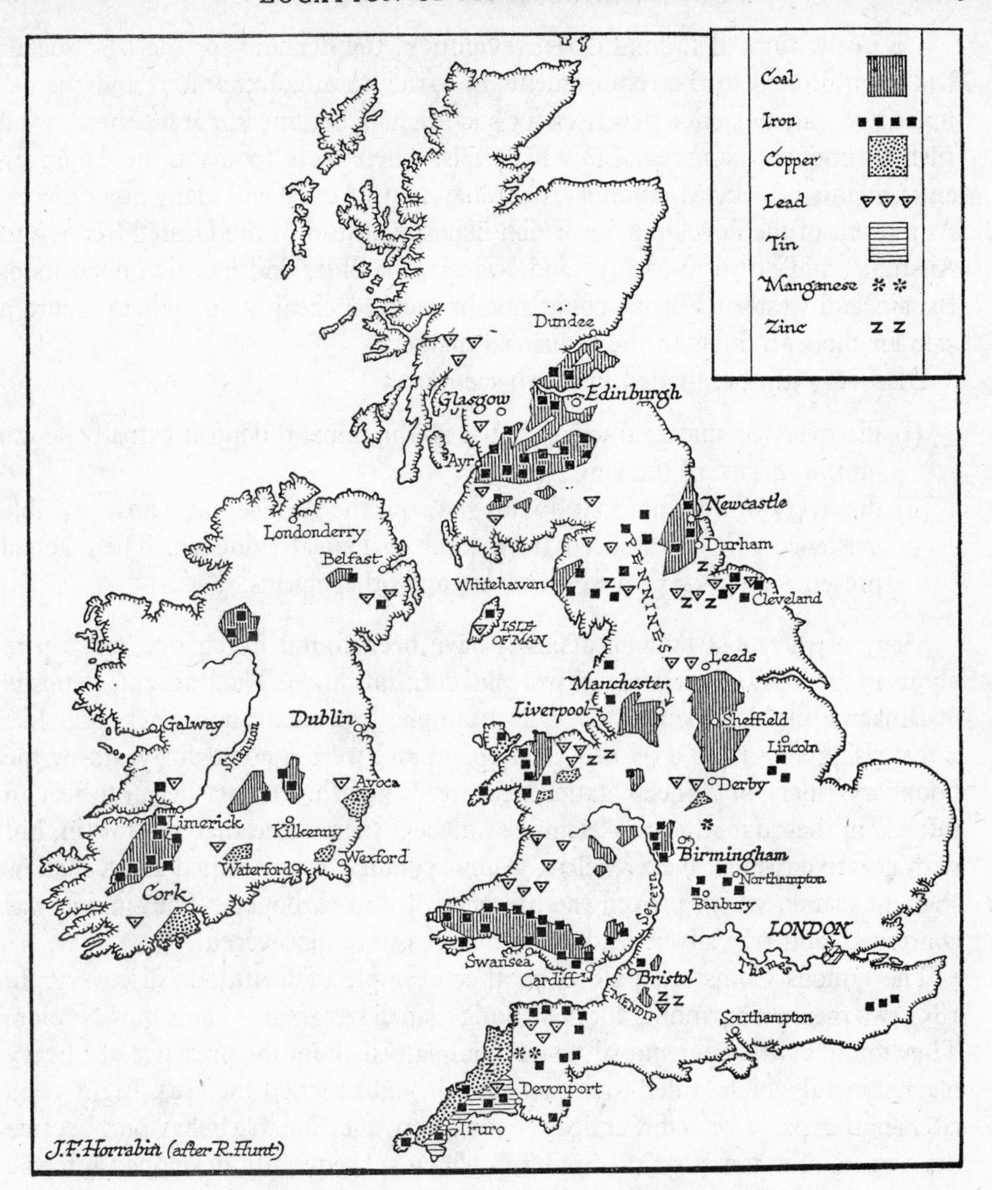

FIGURE 31—*Mineral map of the United Kingdom, 1851.*

During the late eighteenth and early nineteenth centuries there was great metal-mining activity in Britain (figure 31), Sweden, Bohemia, and Spain. In the middle of the nineteenth century, after the discovery of gold in California, American prospectors began to uncover the mineral riches of the western States; they were followed by British and American engineers, who developed the finds.

Up to the time of the industrial revolution, the demand for the base metals had been limited to the requirements of agricultural communities and the demands of war, but once new uses for such metals became apparent there was a rush to find new sources of raw materials. These were found in the American and Canadian Rocky Mountains, Australia, South Africa, and many other places. As a result of the development of rich deposits of lead in the United States and Australia, and of tin in Malaya and Nigeria, the older and less rich deposits of Britain and western Europe could not be worked cheaply enough to secure a sale for their products in the industrial markets.

Discovery can be divided into two sections:

(i) discovery of surface outcrops; that is, the mineral deposit actually shows on the surface of the land;

(ii) discovery of deposits that do not show on the surface but whose possible existence can be deduced from local geological evidence. Their actual presence must be proved by boring and other means.

Many of the most famous deposits have been found by chance, and up to about 1750 most known deposits were adventitious finds. The lead-zinc deposits of Broken Hill, New South Wales, for example, formed a rough black ridge like a reef rising above the level of a dusty plain and were ignored for years by the boundary riders of a sheep station near by. When they at last began to feel an interest in the ridge, they took samples and sent them to be analysed for tin, but with negative results. Nevertheless, a small syndicate was formed and a shallow shaft was sunk, which proved the presence of lead carbonate. The sinking was continued, and rich silver, lead, and zinc ores were discovered.

The famous Comstock lode is another example of fortuitous discovery. In 1851 two men were panning for gold along a small stream in what is now Nevada. They found a little gold and silver but complained about the presence of a heavy black mineral which fouled their pan, and they abandoned the area. Eight years later another party visited it and, after some very questionable behaviour, became the owners of a 500-ft strip of outcrop which subsequently developed into the fabulously rich Comstock mine: the heavy black mineral was silver sulphide.

During the period 1750–1850 there does not appear to have been any remarkable discovery of further mineral deposits. After 1850, discoveries of many kinds were made in various parts of the world; for example, gold in California and Australia, nickel in Canada, lead in Missouri, and diamonds in South Africa, and most of these again were found by pure chance.

Chance has done much, but properly directed efforts can do more. The indications that guide a prospector are natural features such as form of the ground, colour, nature of decomposed outcrop, mineral springs, special plants, altered flora, burrows of animals, old workings, slag heaps, bygone records, and the chemical contents of vegetation. If the mineral deposit is harder or softer than the surrounding ground, the process of geological weathering will leave either a projecting wall or a hollow. The reefs of Western Australia, the Mother lode of California, and the quartz reefs of Wales are examples of hard rock left exposed.

Until about 1875, the ancient methods of prospecting for a deposit whose presence was suspected from evidence such as the above were still in common use. They included shoading, trenching, and hushing. Shoading involves walking up a stream and examining the pebbles by hand and eye, and also washing samples of the finer sands on a prospector's pan. As the seeker travels up the stream the 'show' pieces become more and more numerous and more and more angular until at last they cease altogether. Somewhere nearby is the outcrop. Cross-trenches a yard or so wide are dug to bed-rock across the supposed line of outcrop, and then, with luck, the vein will be laid bare. Hushing, no longer practised in civilized countries, consists of damming a stream near the top of a hill or valley to form a small reservoir. When a sufficient volume of water has been collected, the dam is breached and the water rushing downhill removes the top soil and lays bare the rock below. Search is then made for a mineral vein.

II. PROSPECTING BY BORING

Surface boring tools are used for many reasons, such as to ascertain the nature of a mineral deposit, its depth from the surface, thickness, angle of dip, and direction of strike, or to obtain liquid minerals such as oil and brine. During the period now under discussion three principal methods of boring were in use. They were, respectively, (*a*) by rotation, (*b*) by percussion with rods, and (*c*) by percussion with ropes.

Soft rocks such as clay, soft shale, sandy clay, and sand were bored by an open auger, resembling the familiar carpenter's tool. The auger was attached to a wooden or iron rod and was fitted with a capstan head, which was rotated by hand. As the hole became deeper, more and more rods were added until the required depth, or the limit of human strength, was reached. Such hand-bored holes rarely exceeded 200 ft in depth. For deeper boring, horses were used to rotate the drill, and these in turn were superseded by machines. A wooden tripod was erected over the hole and a small hand-operated winch was used to raise and lower the rods.

In the middle of the nineteenth century a great improvement in rotary drilling for prospecting purposes was effected, namely the application of industrial diamonds, or bort, as the cutting agent. This not only increased the speed and reduced the cost of drilling but provided a solid sample of all rocks passed through. The drill rods consist of a string of hollow tubes, to the lower end of which is attached a soft metal ring into which diamonds are fixed. The ring is rotated and cuts out a cylinder of the rock through which it passes. This cylinder is gripped within another hollow tube, called the core-barrel, and at suitable intervals is drawn to the surface and removed for examination. Hence a complete visual record is obtained of all rocks passed through, which can be retained for further examination. In the early days a small number of diamonds of several carats each were used, but owing to their cost and the difficulty of finding stones without too pronounced cleavage planes, the more modern diamond 'crowns' were introduced. These consist of a multitude of small stones or chips embedded in a matrix of cast metal. Alternatively, and particularly where no accurate record is required, three conical serrated wheels of very tough steel are used to grind the rock to powder. This powder is washed out of the hole by a continuous stream of water which flows down the inside of the hollow rods, round the cutting or pulverizing wheels, and up the outside of the rods, carrying the dust and sand with it.

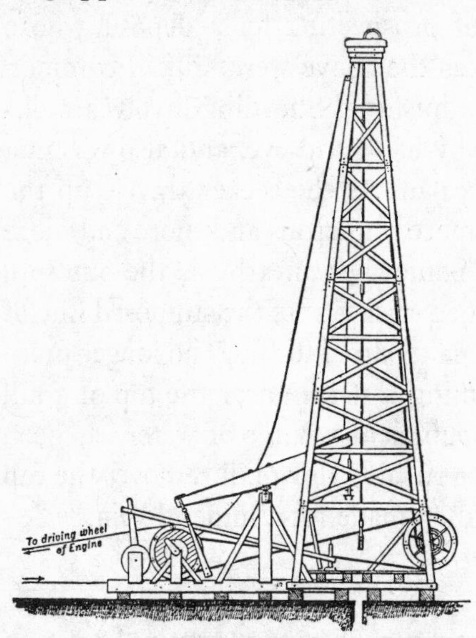

FIGURE 32—*'American rig' for boring by percussion with rope. The high derrick enables the whole string of boring tools to be extracted from the hole without disjointing. The power for this rig was provided by a 15-hp steam-engine.*

In the eighteenth century, drill-holes for proving minerals were also made by means of chisels attached to iron or wooden rods. The latter were raised and then allowed to drop vertically, the rods being slightly rotated between successive blows so as to ensure symmetrical working. The bore-hole was kept full of water and the soft paste of debris was removed from time to time. This method was very slow.

Percussion with ropes is one of the earliest forms of boring and was practised more than a thousand years ago in China, when putting down bore-holes for the purpose of dissolving rock-salt into brine. It resembles percussion boring with rods, save that the chisel is raised and lowered by means of a rope. It was not practised much in Europe and America, however, until the nineteenth century, when it was brought to great perfection in the United States for tapping oil and gas, hence its common name, the 'American rig' (figure 32).

III. APPROACH OR METHOD OF ENTRY

In the early days the limiting factor to successful working at any depth below the surface was water; adequate pumps were not then available. Luckily, many of the mineral deposits of the world are found in or close to hard rock such as igneous rock or limestone, and the surrounding country is hill and dale. Consequently it was possible to drive level or slightly rising roads into the hillside, thus allowing any water encountered to run away. Then all useful minerals above this level could be mined.

When the more easily accessible deposits of minerals showed signs of exhaustion, the possibility of direct extraction diminished and shaft-sinking was begun. At first the shafts were close together and regularly spaced along the outcrop of the vein. As there is rarely any poisonous or inflammable gas in a metal-mine, only a single shaft was sunk in each unit area, fresh air for ventilation being allowed to find its own way to the workers. Usually a stream of fresh cold air crept along the floor of the levels and the warmer vitiated air flowed out close to the roof. It is said that a road could be driven 400 yds from a shaft, but the conditions at the far end must have been unpleasant. To improve conditions the custom grew up of sinking rectangular shafts divided into two sections by a wooden partition. The underground road also was divided into two sections by wooden or canvas partitions, and thus fresh air had a way in and foul air a way out. As the workings became deeper, two levels were utilized, one above the other, either in or parallel to the vein. The fresh air then entered by the lower level and returned by the upper.

It became the practice to sink rectangular shafts almost exclusively; the sides were supported by local timber, since the metal-miners, usually being pioneers in opening up a country, often had no other material for lining the shaft. The space within a rectangular shaft could all be put to a directly useful purpose. In a three-compartment rectangular shaft, for example, one compartment could contain the ladderways, and the other two be used for hoisting. The rectangular shaft is still in common use, but where the mine has been worked to a great depth, say 6000 ft, the rock pressure on the long sides of such a shaft becomes excessive and circular shafts are sunk. At great depths the need for cooling air becomes increasingly important, and unused space in a circular shaft serves for ventilation.

IV. BREAKING GROUND

Most of the rock underground was won manually with the aid of a pick, crowbar, and wedge (plate 5 A). Many of the mines were shallow and above the level of the water-table: consequently the rocks were weathered and fissured. Hand tools could therefore make some impression upon them. The form of these tools

FIGURE 33—*Splitting rocks by fire.*

has not altered very much with the passage of time, except that hardened steel has now superseded cast iron in the picks, and plate iron has replaced wood in the shovels.

Where the ground was too hard to bore, so that explosives could not be used profitably, fire-setting was practised. It was in use in Saxony, Hungary, and the Harz during the latter half of the eighteenth century. In this process horizontal layers of billets of firewood, disposed crosswise one above the other, were piled up in a nearly vertical position so as to present four free vertical faces (figure 33). They were then set on fire. The flame played on the face of the ore, which became shattered; when cooled it was easily broken up with a pick or bar. The splitting of the rock was increased by pouring cold water on to it while still hot. At

Goslar, in the Harz, the fires were lighted on Saturday night and kept burning until Monday morning. Early on Monday water was poured on the rock so that it was cooled and broken up before the miners arrived for their fresh week's work.

At this time ordinary black gunpowder, in granulated form, was in common use, for high explosive was available only at the extreme end of the period now under consideration. Holes 3 to 4 ft in depth and 1 to 3 inches in diameter were bored by hand. A quantity of loose powder was poured or pushed to the back of the holes, and a thin copper bar or pricker was then inserted. The remainder of the hole was filled with plastic clay, hammered well home, and the pricker was withdrawn. Straws, preferably wheaten, were filled with powder and pushed into the hole so that a continuous train of powder reached to the back. A piece of touch paper or a slow match was fastened to the outer end and ignited from the miner's lamp.

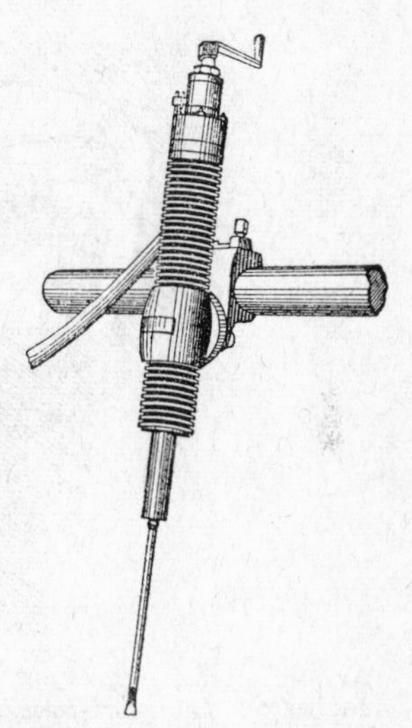

FIGURE 34—*Single-acting pneumatic drill mounted for quarry work.*

All this was very laborious work and many attempts were made to ease it. Rotary rock drills were tried, but being manually operated and constructed of indifferent steel they were unsuccessful. The inventor of the first mechanical rock-boring machine (1813) is said to have been the Cornish engineer Richard Trevithick (1771–1833), but it was forty years before the boring of shot-holes by machinery became practicable, with the invention by Bartlett of a steam rock-boring machine which was used in the Mont Cenis tunnel. Later, Sommelier showed how a similar machine could be worked by compressed air; a single-acting pneumatic drill is shown in figure 34. In the United States, Fowle produced a similar steam-operated drill, but the modern prototype, the Ingersoll drill, was not made until 1871. The principle upon which the earlier machines were based was the boring of a hole either by the continuous motion of a rotating drill or by intermittent blows delivered by a pointed tool striking the rock.

Low's machine, made by the Turner firm at Ipswich (figure 35), attempted a combination of these operations. It consisted of a cylinder into which the tool, similar to the hand-held chisel, was inserted. This cylinder was housed within another cylinder in which it was made to rotate slightly but continuously between each blow of the drill, the latter striking between 300 to 500 blows per minute. The whole machine was carried on a trolley and driven by compressed air.

Later, a light drill which could be held by one man was produced. This consisted of a cylinder in which a piston travelled backwards and forwards at a high speed, up to 1500 times a minute, and delivered a series of blows on a chisel inserted in the bore-holes. After each blow the chisel or 'steel' automatically turned through a small arc, allowing the succeeding blow to strike new ground. To clean the hole the chisel had a small tubular passage down its centre through which water or air was forced in order to remove the cuttings.

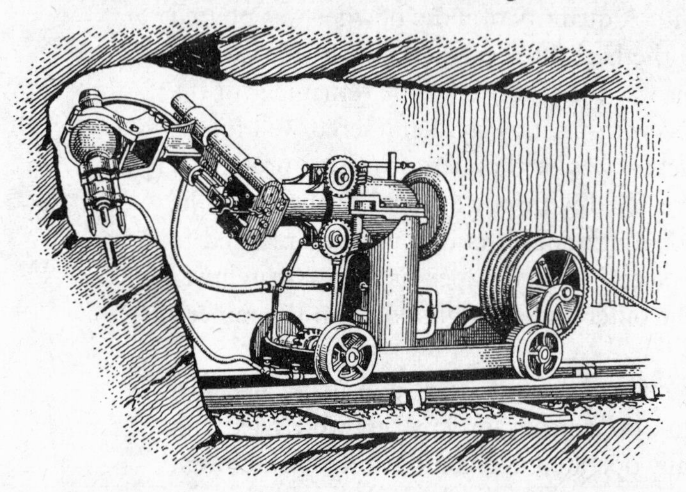

FIGURE 35—*Low's rock-boring machine. This was driven by compressed air at a pressure of 70–90 lb per sq in. It was capable of working at a distance of more than a mile from the compressor.*

V. METHODS OF MINING

Extraction of ore was effected in two operations. First, the mine was divided up into large square or rectangular blocks: secondly, the blocks were removed. The first operation consisted of driving levels in the deposit at a definite vertical distance apart, say 300 ft, and constructing small connecting shafts, raises or winzes (figure 36), at intervals of 300 to 600 ft. The object of these roads was twofold: (*a*) to probe the deposit and prove whether it continued to be valuable, and (*b*) to provide routes for subsequent extraction of ore. Although the fissures, into which seeped the mineral-bearing solutions from which the ore derives, may persist for long distances both horizontally and vertically, it does not follow that the entire area will be equally mineralized. It is common experience to find some sections much richer than others, and hence thorough exploration is necessary.

When sufficient exploratory roads had been driven to make certain that an adequate tonnage of valuable ore was available, extraction was put in hand. What is considered an adequate tonnage varies with each mine, and depends, among other factors, upon the capacity of the ancillary plant available and how much ore it is considered should be in reserve to enable the mine to continue operation even if further exploration runs into barren ground. It was, and still is, good practice to have three years' work blocked out in advance whenever possible. Exploratory work is expensive and unremunerative; many mining companies at

FIGURE 36—*Winze-shaft in a Cornish mine.*

this time could not afford it and consequently often worked from hand to mouth. Profits therefore fluctuated widely and failures were common. This was particularly so where the so-called cost-book system was prevalent. Under this system, mines were opened by a small group of adventurers with limited capital. At the end of a given period, say one month, the accounts were made up. So much was then paid to the mineral owner, say one-tenth to one-seventh; the tributers or bargain men were paid their share; and what was left over was divided amongst the adventurers. As a rule little or nothing was put to reserve. Consequently the amount of development possible was limited; if the mine ran into a poor stretch of ground there was no money available to carry it on except by a fresh call on the adventurers. In time this system gave way to the institution of limited liability companies, which resulted in a more cautious and stable method of working.

The cost-book system was adopted in Cornwall during the period when the

FIGURE 37—*Working by descending levels, as practised in Saxony, Hungary, and Rhenish Prussia in the early nineteenth century.*

upper portions of the veins were being worked. These contained copper which persisted down to about 1000 ft; below this there came a poorly mineralized zone, below which again was tinstone. The cost-book mines made a regular profit while in the region of copper ore, but with no reserves could not weather the unprofitable barren zone.

The method of extraction of the ore pillars was overhand or underhand stoping, that is, working in steps. To open a new underhand stope a pillar of solid ground was, or was not, left below an upper level carrying the road for haulage and the travelling road. If no pillar of solid ground was left, an artificial floor of wooden planks was laid and work started beneath this. A slice of the pillar the width of the lode and roughly 6 ft high was taken right and left from one of the connecting winzes. Bore-holes were made either vertically downwards or horizontally, charged with gunpowder, and fired. The broken ground was then shovelled to the winze, where it fell to the level below and was thence transported to the shaft. When the first levels had travelled a few yards, two more were started below them, so that in time there was a series of descending levels travelling in echelon outward from the winze (figure 37). If barren or poor ground was encountered, the valueless material was piled on scaffolds carried by timbers fixed between the walls of the lode, or else was left *in situ* as a support. In overhand stoping (figure 38) the procedure was reversed, except that driving was almost always horizontal and rarely vertically upwards. The coming of mechanical drills, with the consequently easier work, allowed of variations in these basic methods—such as rill-stoping to reduce the labour involved, or flat-back stoping to enable mechanized haulage devices such as scrapers to be used—but there was no fundamental change.

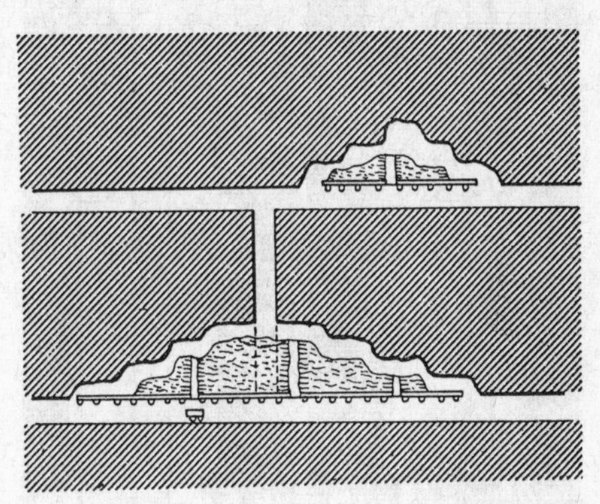

FIGURE 38—*Overhand stope, with ascending levels.*

When the walls of the lode or vein were strong, little or no support was needed, but in thicker veins, or in those with soft and slabby walls, precautions had to be taken. Where timber was plentiful and cheap, or the vein of material very rich, the open space left after the removal of the mineral was sometimes filled with frames of timber cut and fitted together into hollow cubes on the surface and then fitted into the open space underground. These were known as square sets. A simpler, and possibly more satisfactory system, used whenever possible, was to run down—through old workings from the surface or some other convenient spot—barren material from which all valuable ore had been extracted. When in place underground, any water in this rubble drained out and the material set hard. It was kept so close up to the face of the stopes that the men could stand on it to work. Another variation, developed towards the end of this period for working very thick deposits, was the removal of pillars by taking thick slices and allowing the worked space to cave in. The area above what had already been worked usually caved in also, but the descent of the caved-in material was regulated by placing thick layers of timber on the floor of the section being extracted. These timber mattes fell with the rest but had a restraining influence on the broken rock.

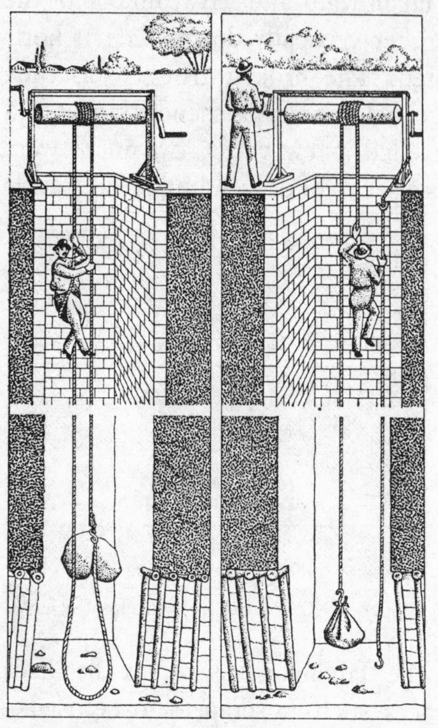

FIGURE 39—*Apparatus for descent into mines, developed in Australia about 1870. This method is based on the counterbalance principle and, as shown on the left, can be used by one man alone; in this case he grasps the ascending rope to govern his speed. At the right is shown the way in which the method is used when a second man is available at the surface.*

VI. RAISING AND LOWERING OF MEN AND MATERIALS

Before the days of the steam-engine workmen went underground by ladders—a method that continued long after the introduction of steam hoisting-engines. As long as the mines were shallow, this was no great hardship, but to climb 600 ft or more up ladders at the end of a hard day's work was very wearisome. Sometimes counterpoise methods were used when no power was available (figure 39). From very shallow mines mineral was raised in baskets by hand-worked windlasses or even cast by shovel from stage to stage. For deeper mines the horse-whim (figure 49) was common if no water-power was available.

An interesting device for bringing miners up and down was the man-engine (figure 40 and plate 5B), which persisted into the twentieth century. To understand the working of this engine it must be remembered that nearly every mine had trouble with water, a problem that was dealt with by a surface pumping-engine which transmitted vertical motion by rods down the shaft to a stationary pump at or near the bottom. These rods had a stroke of 6 to 12 ft, with a pause at the end of the stroke while the valve-gear reversed at the pumping-engine.

At the side of the shaft, exactly opposite the point of the end of the stroke of each rod, and spaced the distance of the stroke apart, were fixed strong platforms to hold a man, or possibly two men in an emergency. At corresponding points on the pump-rods smaller platforms were fixed. Suppose that a man wanted to go to the surface. At the bottom of the shaft, when the pump-rod momentarily halted between strokes, he stepped on to the attached platform. As the rod ascended the man was carried up and when it stopped at the end of its stroke he stepped on to the convenient platform fixed to the shaft. The rods descended again, stopped, and the man stepped on to the next platform on the rods and so was carried up another stage when the rods ascended. At the end of the shift in a deep mine there might be a hundred men side-stepping between rods and shaft platforms at each stroke of the pumping-engine. This device was known as the man-engine; its use is particularly associated with Cornwall, but it was used all over the world until more efficient hoisting-systems came into general use.

FIGURE 40—*Form of Cornish man-engine.*

VII. HAULAGE

Haulage in metal-mines has never been so important as in coal-mines, because veins of metal ore tend to be more or less vertical and do not extend horizontally for great distances. Exceptions are the sedimentary gold-mines of the Transvaal, the bedded copper-mines of Northern Rhodesia, and a few others. The little haulage normally necessary was provided during this period by men or animals, who either carried the load on their backs, or pushed or pulled a wheeled tram. In the early days wheelbarrows with a low centre of gravity were often used. The sequence in a new mine was first, human porters, then wheelbarrows, and, finally, tracked vehicles pulled by horse or mule.

VIII. REMOVAL OF WATER

Nearly all mines, and metalliferous mines in particular, have a water problem, and in many instances this represents a major item in the cost of operation.

Before the development of efficient steam-power many mines could not cope with the problem at all and had to close down. This was particularly, but not exclusively, true of the mines in Central and South America, which were extensively worked before and after the Spanish conquest; it was true also of the Cornish copper-mines. Many remained idle until after Boulton and Watt developed their steam-powered pump and engine.

The oldest way, and still the best way when practicable, to drain a mine is by means of an adit; this is a tunnel driven from the lowest possible point in a valley at a slightly rising gradient, say 1 in 300, into a hillside so as to penetrate a mineralized area. There are adits today in Cornwall, the Harz Mountains, and many other places, which with their side-shoots extend to a total of 40 to 50 miles each. Some are 200 years old and are still being extended. Naturally, adits can drain only the workings above them, but they are invaluable even in deeper mines because they reduce the head against which the water has to be pumped.

In 1778 W. Pryce wrote in his *Mineralogia Cornubiensis*, 'with all the skill and adroitness of our miners they cannot go to any considerable distance below the adits before they must recourse to some contrivance for clearing the water from their workings'. During this period the rag-and-chain pump was not wholly discontinued, although it was falling into disfavour on account of the great expense and heavy labour involved. According to Pryce, the rag-and-chain consisted of 'an iron chain with knobs of cloth stiffened and fenced with iron, seldom more than 9 ft asunder. The chain is turned round by a wheel 2 to 3 ft in diameter furnished with iron spikes to enclose and keep steady the chain so that it may rise through a wooden pump 3, 4, or 5 inches bore and from 12 to 22 ft long and by means of the knobs bring up with it a stream of water.' These pumps, mounted on timbers set across the shaft, were placed in series down it, each lifting water from and to a wooden box or sump also fixed to the side of the shaft. The pumps were worked by manual labour and the work was so hard that it was the cause of many deaths (cf vol II, figure 21).

When water-power was available, water-driven whims were used to draw water in barrels to the surface. Water-wheels were also used where circumstances allowed. These water-wheels were fitted with cranks, attached by a straight balk of wood to heavy 'bobs' pivoted at the centre. As the cranks revolved the ends of the bobs rose and fell. One end of the bob was over the shaft and was fitted with a heavy iron chain which passed over an arc to give it a vertical motion. This chain was attached to a vertical piece of timber hanging in the shaft; at the lower end was a piston fitting into a cylinder on the shaft. For example, the water-wheel at the Cook's Kitchen mine in Cornwall was 48 ft in diameter and worked tiers of pumps of 9-in bore. There were four lifts, enabling water to be raised from 480 ft and delivered into an adit (cf vol II, figure 20).

When water-power was not available, steam-engines (plate 7 A) were extensively used. In 1778 more than 70 Newcomen engines were working in Cornwall, but by 1790 all but one of them had disappeared, having been replaced by the much more economical Boulton and Watt engine. As an example of the kind of economy thus effected, it may be mentioned that when seven Newcomen engines were replaced by five of Boulton and Watt's at the Consolidated mines, Cornwall, in 1781, the consumption of coal was reduced from 19 000 tons a year to 6100 tons. This represented a yearly saving of £10 830, at the price of coal then ruling. By 1798 there were forty-five Boulton and Watt pumping-engines in use in Cornwall alone. Such engines, commonly known in mining as Cornish engines, continued in use well after electricity became common in mines. The popularity they achieved in their day is easily recognized by the great number of gaunt, tall buildings which housed the engines and which still dot the landscape of any old metal-mining district.

However, the size of these machines, the amount of room the rods took in the shaft, the great engine-houses, and the cost of new parts all spelt their doom. Their place was taken by smaller reciprocating or centrifugal pumps electrically driven.

COAL-MINING

By 1750 coal-mining had become a well established industry in Britain and western Europe, and had reached its highest development on the north-east coast of England. In Britain during this period coal output rose from 7 m to 150 m tons annually. This was before the days of the general use of steam, but the stage of manual labour was nearing its end and the mechanical age was looming ahead. Little power except water-, animal-, and man-power was used in coal-mines at the beginning of this period, but during the century 1750–1850 manual labour gave way to steam-power and mechanization began in earnest. Shallow mines were becoming exhausted, but the availability of power enabled larger and deeper mines to be developed to meet the growing demand for coal as the industrial revolution progressed (figure 41).

The early years of the eighteenth century saw the introduction into mining of Savery's 'fire' engine and Newcomen's 'atmospheric' engine. Newcomen's invention not only solved the water-problem of many collieries and metal-mines but marked a new and great demand for coal as a source of power. The use of this engine in the north brought into production large areas that were previously considered unworkable because of the difficulties with water. In 1769, 120 Newcomen engines were in use in coal-mines. The introduction of surface-railways, at first horse-drawn on wooden rails, and underground wagon-ways added a further impetus to the development of mining. Where practicable, tracks were so laid that the full wagons gravitated to staithes on the river, whence the empty ones were pulled back by horses. Watt's double-acting steam-engine began to replace water-wheels for driving the hoisting-engines, and trams came into use underground in place of sleds.

I. COAL-GETTING: TOOLS AND MACHINES

The usual methods of coal-getting during this period were by hand-pick (figure 42) and crowbar, and by blasting with gunpowder. The miner cut a groove under the coal close to the floor to a depth of 2 to 4 ft and broke the coal down

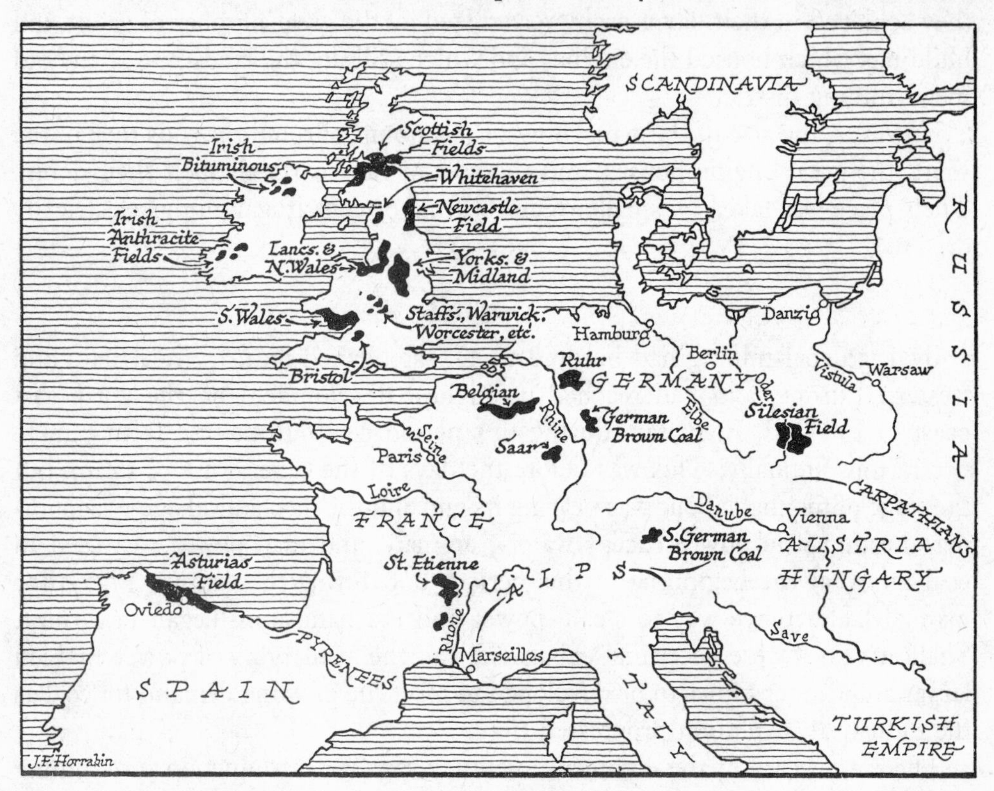

FIGURE 41—*Coalfields of the United Kingdom and western Europe, 1851.*

either with a pick, a crowbar, or a wedge. In the harder coals a hand-worked rotary drill was used to bore a hole 1–1½ inches in diameter, into which was put a charge of loose black powder. The method of firing the charge has been described already in connexion with metal-mining (p 71).

Towards the end of the period William Bickford, of Tuckingmill, Cornwall, invented a form of safety-fuse that made the operation of blasting much less hazardous, but black powder was still used. Undercutting the coal by hand was very hard and slow work, and early attempts to mechanize this operation were made. Even today, however, no coal-mine is completely mechanized. Coal is undercut by machines, broken down by explosives or other means, and loaded at the coal-face on to conveyors of various kinds, which deliver it into trams on the haulage-roads or at the shaft itself; but the actual loading of the broken-down coal on to the conveyor is still done by manual shovelling.

Many attempts have been made to produce an economical and mechanically satisfactory combined cutter-loader, but so far complete success has not been attained. Up to about 1850 all coal was cut by hand and loaded by means of shovels or forks (to eliminate small coal) into small trams taken right up to the coal-face. In thin, hard seams this was very laborious work. In the early nineteenth

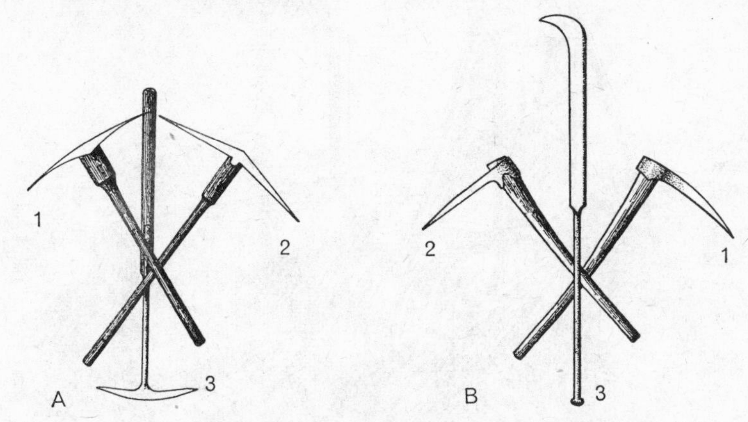

FIGURE 42—*Tools used in coal-mining about 1880.* (A) (1) *Holing pick, north Staffordshire,* (2) *anchored pick, Durham,* (3) *pick from Rivelaine, Belgium.* (B) (1) *Pembrokeshire coal-pick,* (2) *Westphalian pick,* (3) *Liége pick.*

century a machine with an arc-like motion, imitating the swing of a pick by man, was made. This 'iron man' cut as much coal as a single efficient miner, but several men were needed to work it, so the invention was dropped.

A later device, the disk-machine, was based on a circular saw, but nothing of any value materialized until improved metallurgy gave a steel pick that would not wear away after a few hours' work and, equally important, until a form or forms of power had been developed that could be used both safely and economically underground. The later growth of mechanism in the mines ran parallel with the development of compressed air and electricity, particularly the latter, as sources of motive-power.

The invention of the steam-engine, which did so much to mechanize other branches of industry, had little effect on coal-mining, except for machinery on the surface, where it was rapidly and skilfully applied, especially for pumping, hauling, and hoisting (figure 43). Attempts to use steam underground, except close to the bottom of the shaft, were not successful. If power had to be used in the working, it could be applied only through the medium of rigid iron rods running on small rollers alongside the main roads, or by endless ropes, chains, or bands. None of these methods proved satisfactory.

Thomas Harrison made the first practical coal-cutter in 1863. It consisted of a toothed wheel fitted to the spindle of a compressed-air turbine, driving, through gearing, 'a circular revolving cutter or disk having a serrated edge like

FIGURE 43—*Steam winding-gear for mines*, c *1880*.

a circular saw but stronger, or, alternatively, a hollow circular box or frame' into which were fitted any required number of cutting-tools. This machine exemplified the transition from reciprocating motion to the rotary motion which characterized the development of all subsequent coal-cutting machinery.

The introduction of the principle of rotary or continuously moving cutters opened the way to an enormous increase in capacity for cutting, and by multiplying the number of cutting picks made it possible with a single machine to apply greatly increased power to the operation. Development was slow but there emerged three well defined types of machine (figure 44):

(A) The disk, whose cutting-member consists of a disk or wheel armed at its periphery with cutters.

(B) The chain, whose cutting-member consists of a projecting arm or jib carrying an endless chain, the links of which are armed with cutters.

(C, D) The bar, whose cutting-member consists of a projecting, rotating bar armed with cutters throughout its length.

These machines were at first driven by reciprocating compressed-air motors, and later by compressed-air turbines. Unfortunately, while compressed air is a

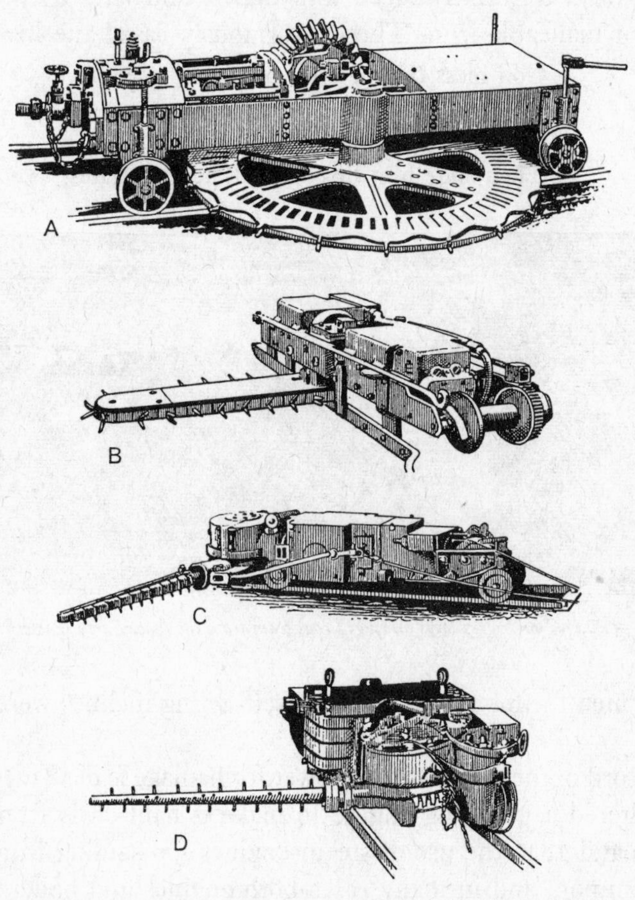

FIGURE 44—*Three types of coal-cutter:* (A) *disk,* (B) *chain,* (C) *and* (D) *bar.*

very safe form of power to use underground, where precautions have to be taken against the danger of gas or coal-dust explosions, it is uneconomical, mainly because of transmission-losses from the compressor to the machine. With the coming into general use of electricity, first as direct and then as alternating current, smaller, more powerful, and more economical machines were constructed. Except for the addition of more safety-devices, electrical coal-cutters have not altered materially in design during the last fifty years.

II. HAULAGE

In the eighteenth century haulage of coal underground was effected by wooden sleds on which were placed wicker baskets. These were at first pulled along the roads by men or women, but by 1763 ponies began to be used underground. By 1789 wheeled trams were introduced into mines, and later they were adapted to light rails of malleable iron. These enormously eased the heavy toil:

> God bless the man wi' peace and plenty
> That first invented metal plates.
> Draw out his years to five times twenty
> Then slide him through the hevenly gates.[1]

FIGURE 45—*'Putters' or trolley-boys moving a coal tram from the face. Early nineteenth century.*

Ponies still formed the motive-power, but self-acting inclines were coming into use.

The first record of the use of steam-power for haulage is in 1812, when George Stephenson altered a pumping-engine to make it haul coals from a dip-road. Between 1820 and 1840 the use of steam-engines for hauling from the dip became more common, and in many cases both engines and boilers were placed underground. The use of mechanical haulage on the level roads came later. An early record states that in 1841 'at Peacock Mine, Hyde, a stationary engine is used to draw the wagon along the main level'. In 1844 John Buddle introduced the slow-moving continuous or 'endless' rope haulage at Wallsend, and in the same year the 'main and tail' system[2] was installed at Haswell, Co. Durham.

These forms of haulage were employed only on the main roads. On subsidiary roads and face-roads, animal or manual labour still served (figure 45).

[1] 'The Pitman's Pay', by Thomas Wilson, *c* 1799.

[2] Full wagons were drawn by the main rope and empty ones returned by the tail rope.

At the end of the nineteenth century all coal was loaded on to wheeled trams (figure 46), except in a few isolated cases where it was still first loaded on sleds and dragged along the coal-face. This meant either that tram-rails had to be laid along the coal-face, which could be done only in seams 3 ft or more in thickness; or that roads had to be made partly in the coal and partly in the roof at intervals of 12 to 15 yds, so that the hewer could fill the tubs without having to cast his coal along the face more than once, or occasionally twice. In highly inclined seams the coal was induced to slide along the floor to the road, where it was loaded.

FIGURE 46—*Coal in baskets being loaded underground on to a tram.*

The first satisfactory coal-face conveyor was invented by W. C. Blackett at Durham in 1902. In the specification of his patent Blackett set out the advantages of face conveyors. These are, *inter alia*, the avoidance of the necessity of forming, and maintaining at comparatively short distances apart, gate-roads for the transport of coal from the working-face, thus avoiding the heavy cost of such ancillary work in thin seams; reduction of the physical labour of filling tubs by hand; and the avoidance of breakage.

Blackett's conveyors consisted of a steel trough laid alongside a longwall face (p 87), usually extending for *c* 100 yds. In this trough moved an endless scraper-chain, driven by a machine at one end, which carried the coal to the waiting tub. After each cut by the machine, the coal was stripped and loaded into the conveyor; when all was cleared, the conveyor was advanced the distance of a cut ready for the next stripping. Since that time several types of conveyors have been produced, such as the shaking-conveyor, which jerks the coal along a trough, and the endless belt. The latter, of which there are several varieties, is in common use today.

III. METHODS OF WORKING

As the majority of the mines were shallow, the workings were entered by drifts or tunnels from the surface wherever possible. When this could not be done, shallow shafts were sunk from the surface and as much of the coal as possible was worked away from the sides of the shaft. It had been found that if all the coal was worked, the roof collapsed, and so the practice was developed of leaving pillars of coal *in situ* to hold it up. These pillars were irregular in pattern and shape and resulted in much coal being lost.

The next stage was the recognition that it was both practicable and economical to divide the seams of coal up into large pillars from 22 to 60 yds square by roads driven at or near right-angles (the 'whole' workings), and subsequently to 'follow up' by extracting the pillars or 'broken' workings. At first the whole area was worked into pillars, but the ventilation was then difficult to control; later, the practice of dividing the area into small areas or panels by leaving solid ribs of coal was found very advantageous. This system divided the mine into separate compartments, each self-contained, with the result that any misadventure in one panel did not necessarily affect any other area. It was found to be more economical, and much safer, to extract the pillars shortly after they were formed.

The extraction of each individual pillar is done by taking slices about 6 yds wide off one side. One slice is extracted, the roof meanwhile being supported by vertical timber props which are set under horizontal planks and bars, usually made of round props sawn into halves longitudinally down the centre. When the slice has been removed, the timber supports are withdrawn and the roof is allowed to collapse. After complete collapse another parallel slice is started, and so on until the whole pillar is extracted. With good management, and a certain amount of luck, at least 90 per cent of the pillar is removed. One important point, which was early noted, is that the line of the removed pillars or fallen roof should make an angle of about 45° with the main natural 'slips' or breaks in the roof. By this means the danger of an unexpected collapse is minimized and usually averted.

This method, which is technically known as bord-and-pillar working (bord is a Saxon word meaning road), is, in effect, extraction in two operations. It has been found to be an excellent system where the workings do not lie under too great a thickness of overlying rocks. The maximum permissible depth is of the order of 900 ft, but the figure is very variable. Where the depth is greater, the weight of the overlying rocks tends to crush the pillars as, or sometimes before, they are removed. As a consequence some coal is lost or, alternatively, crushed into small pieces or slack. To overcome the drawback, extraction in one operation was developed; this is technically known as the longwall method (figure 47). When the mines were shallow, or where the coal was thick, clean, and strong, this system was not used, and it did not come into common use elsewhere until after 1850. Longwall working has many advantages where it is practicable. It is an excellent system for mechanical coal cutting in dirty seams, that is, seams with a layer of stone or shale within them; or where the seam is hard, because, if properly worked, the weight of the overhanging roof will assist in breaking down the coal. In this system a wall of coal about 100 yds long is won out and removed bodily in line. As the coal is removed any stone available is built into dry stone walls or packs some 6 to 21 ft wide, arranged in parallel lines at right-angles to the advancing wall or face. The purpose of these walls is to cushion the lowering of the roof after its supporting coal is removed and thus preserve as far as possible its unbroken state, especially at the face itself.

FIGURE 47—*Longwall mining, as practised in Shropshire in the late seventeenth century.* Above, *plan;* below, *elevation.*

Naturally these two methods—bord-and-pillar and longwall—do not cover every eventuality encountered in practice, and hybrids were developed to cover varying conditions. The most common was the Welsh stall system, in which a short longwall face of some 10 to 20 yds was driven in one direction, after which the miners turned round and removed a similar and parallel slice back to the main road.

IV. WINDING OR HOISTING

When shafts had to be sunk to reach the deeper coals, some form of machinery had to be developed to replace the women and boys who carried coals on their

backs in wicker-work baskets up ladders round the edges of the shafts (figure 48). The hand-windlass was first used, but was replaced by the horse-whim or -gin (figure 49 and plate 6B). This consisted of a horizontal rope drum, 12 to 16 ft in diameter, built round a vertical axis, the foot of which turned on a stone or an iron casting and the head pivot of which was supported by a long span-beam resting at its end upon inclined legs. The horses were attached at one or both ends of a strong horizontal beam, generally 30 to 36 ft long, which embraced the vertical axis close to the drum. The ropes passing off the opposite sides of the drum were conducted over small pulleys overhanging the shafts.

With the introduction of the steam-engine, the modern horizontal drum was developed, but this was originally driven by a large low-pressure single-cylinder vertical engine with hand-operated valves. The winding was slow and very wasteful of steam. One of the difficulties experienced arose from the necessity of overcoming the unbalanced weight of the rope hanging in the shaft. Various forms of counterbalance were tried, but no satisfactory solution was developed in this period.

The ropes originally used were round and made of hemp. They consisted of several strands wrapped to form a composite rope. Instead of forming the strands into a round rope, many preferred to lay

FIGURE 48—*Women coal-bearers, Scotland, early nineteenth century. Coal was often carried in this way from depths exceeding 100 ft.*

them side by side and stitch each strand to its neighbour to form a flat rope. This had the advantage that during winding the rope could be wrapped layer upon layer on a narrow drum or pirn, thus varying the leverage. The heavy load at the bottom of the shaft corresponded to the smallest radius of the drum and the empty cage or basket at the top to the largest.

At first the wicker baskets were lifted from the trams, hitched to the rope, and raised up the shaft. Owing to the twist in the rope, however, they spun round and round and also swayed from side to side. Consequently the speed of winding

FIGURE 49—*Horse-whim, c 1820.*

was slow and accidents in the shaft were frequent. Iron-wire ropes were first tried in 1829 and came into general use about 1840.

To overcome the oscillation, shaft-guides were introduced in 1787. The baskets were suspended from cross-bars which were fixed to wooden guides attached to the sides of the shafts. Later, tubs or corves with wheels securely attached were made, and at the same time cages or open boxes running on guides were introduced into the shafts. By this means a load of coal could be hauled on wheels from where it was filled at the face, run into the cage, safely hauled to the surface, and there emptied before the cage was returned underground (figure 50).

V. MINE-GASES AND EXPLOSIONS

In the earlier part of the eighteenth century, most of the coal-mines were shallow, and the only mysterious gas or vapour with which the miners had to contend was 'stythe', now known to mining engineers as black-damp. It consists essentially of air deficient in oxygen, and is a variable mixture of carbon dioxide, nitrogen, and some oxygen. Another name is choke-damp, because its presence in large quantities may choke or suffocate all coming in contact with it. In most coalfields, however, the term choke-damp denotes the products of incomplete combustion more commonly known as after-damp; this contains varying percentages of the most poisonous gas met with in mining, namely carbon mon-

FIGURE 50—*Bottom of pit shaft, showing loaded trams waiting to be hauled to the surface.*

oxide. The word damp in this context derives from the German *Dampf*, meaning fog or vapour.

No flame will burn when the percentage of oxygen in the air falls below a certain limit. The miner therefore had ample warning of the presence of black-damp because his light gradually became dimmer and dimmer before finally dying out; this gave him time to retire to fresher air and safety.

Choke- or after-damp was understandably feared, but because carbon monoxide has neither smell nor taste, and is a cumulative poison, the concentration in the blood gradually rising without warning until the victim becomes unconscious, little was known about it.

Later, as the mines became deeper and more extensive, fire-damp—a mixture of methane and air—began to be encountered, and the era of serious mine explosions began. Though the explosiveness of fine coal dust was suspected, it had not been proved, and all explosions were attributed to fire-damp.

Fire-damp is produced during the decay of vegetable matter. During the conversion of vegetation into coal, the gas given off is occluded in the cleavage-planes of the coal and also in the rocks of the roof and floor. When the coal is worked the gas is driven out into the air, with which in certain proportions it forms an explosive mixture. The explosive limits of the mixture are between 5·4 and 13·5 per cent of methane under normal atmospheric conditions.

At this time mines had little or no artificial ventilation and the light gas tended to collect in stagnant ends and disused parts of the mine, particularly in old workings. When the atmospheric pressure began to fall, the gaseous contents of these old workings expanded and flowed into the active areas, where the fire-damp could ignite at the flame of an open lamp.

At times practically pure methane flows out of the rocks in the form of a concentrated jet or blower. Thus the miner may suddenly, almost without warning, become surrounded by an explosive mixture, and an explosion may follow. Towards the end of the eighteenth century and in the early years of the nineteenth, explosions—in some cases of great violence—became common, especially in the north of England (p 94), and gave rise to national concern.

The general use of a safety-lamp (p 95), though the lamp was not at that stage truly safe, reduced the incidence of explosions, but every few years the world was shocked by a catastrophe involving the death of a hundred or more miners. Towards the middle of the nineteenth century explosions became less frequent, but their magnitude and violence increased. Thus in 1860 145 men were killed in the Risca mine at Newport; in 1867 178 lives were lost at the Ferndale colliery in the Rhondda Valley. Such explosions have since been proved to be due to the ignition of fine coal-dust, and today steps are taken to combat this risk.

An interesting side-light on the daily life of the coal-miner in those days is shown by the origin of the term 'fireman'. Today, a fireman in a mine is a junior official in charge of a section of a mine, where he is responsible essentially for the safety of the workmen under his charge. In the days of small mines, and before the invention of the early safety-lamps, it was the custom for one of the more resolute of the miners to wrap himself from head to foot in damp sackcloth and to arm himself with a pole some 10 ft long on the end of which he stuck a lighted candle (figure 51). With this in his hand he travelled the underground workings. When he came to a working face he crawled on his hands and knees into the face with the candle close to the ground. When he arrived at the face itself he buried his face in the wet sacks, raised the end of his stick, and ignited any gas present. The place was then considered safe for the ordinary miner to come to his work.

VI. VENTILATION

No attempts were at first made to induce a flow of fresh air round the mine to dilute and render harmless any noxious or inflammable gas. As mines became

FIGURE 51—*Fireman, swathed in damp sacking, igniting fire-damp to clear workings.*

more extensive, however, something had to be done to ward off the possibility of disastrous explosions.

The first step in more up-to-date practice was to make two roads into the mine, one by which the air went in and the other by which it came out. This provision did not become compulsory until after a disaster at Hartley, Northumberland, when a large pump on the surface broke, fell down, and blocked the only shaft, with the result that many men lost their lives.

If there are two roads into a mine, and if in one of them the temperature is higher than in the other, a flow of air will take place from the region of lower to that of the higher temperature, because the density of air decreases as the temperature rises. In shallow mines this variation in temperature is slight and the flow of air small. Further, the temperature differential is apt to reverse between night and day, and between summer and winter, so that the rate of flow of air is also variable and may often be negligible. To overcome this unsatisfactory circumstance and produce a steady flow, fire-buckets were lowered into one entrance-shaft, thus producing an artificial temperature difference. As the mines became larger, something better than fire-buckets became necessary, and furnaces were constructed at the foot of the rising or up-cast shaft. If the mine gave off dangerous quantities of inflammable gas, the furnace was fed with fresh air from the down-cast shaft and the products of combustion were admitted into the up-cast shaft at a temperature below the ignition point of a mixture of fire-damp and air. Steam-jets were also tried but were not satisfactory. Extracted fire-damp was often burned at the surface (plate 6A).

The first known mechanical ventilator was an air-pump used by Buddle at Hebburn colliery in 1807. It was a suction-pump consisting of a wooden piston 5 ft sq with a stroke of 8 ft, working in a wooden-lined chamber. At 20 strokes a minute it exhausted 6000 cu ft of air in that time; this figure may be compared with 600 000 to 1 000 000 cu ft a minute in today's mines. The air-pump principle was extensively adopted at the same time both in Belgian coal-mines and in the lead-mines of the Harz. At first, all efforts were devoted to the improvement of the air-pump; Struvé's ventilator was an example largely adopted in south Wales. The piston of this device was a wrought iron bell, closed at the top, of 12 to 22 ft diameter, working up and down in water. By means of ranges of valves above and below, placed in the walls of the piston-chamber, it drew in and forced out air at each up and each down stroke respectively. When worked in pairs these pumps could displace as much as 100 000 cu ft of air a minute.

Another pump was Nixon's ventilator. This had a horizontal piston, in some cases as large as 30 ft by 22 ft, supported on wheels. The chambers were fitted with flap-valves, as in Struvé's machine. When doing nine 7-ft strokes a minute it was reputed to displace 160 000 cu ft of air in that time.

About 1830, successful attempts were made to develop fans. The idea was not new, for Agricola had discussed their use nearly three centuries earlier. Typical early types were designed by Waddell, Guibal (Belgium), and Fabry; these were all centrifugal fans. The general idea was a drum made to rotate horizontally by a steam-engine. Air from the mine was drawn into the centre of the drum, and then expelled to the outer air from its circumference. It reached the outer air through a widening chimney, which diminished the velocity at which the expelled air regained the open. This was the *évasé* chimney of later years.

In addition to the production of a ventilating current, changes occurred in the method of conducting the air round the workings. In the beginning, when mines were small, no attempt appears to have been made to guide the air. It went where it listed and probably in most cases it went nowhere very useful. Then parallel, instead of single, roads were driven, with connecting roads between them. As a new connexion was completed, the previous one was blocked up, thus forcing the air to travel up one road and down the parallel one. Where connexions had lagged behind the working faces, a temporary circuit was made by dividing the road into two, either by a wooden partition or by tarred canvas (brattice cloth).

FIGURE 52—*Flint-and-steel mill*, c *1813*.

When connecting-roads were required for traffic and could not be permanently blocked up, temporary blocks (doors or stoppings) made of canvas sheets were hung from the roofs of the roads; for permanent working hinged wooden doors were used. These were opened and closed by small children (trappers) as traffic required.

At first the air travelled round the mine in one circuit, but this was found to have many disadvantages, such as excessive friction, contamination, and leakage. Later, the main current of air was divided so that each section of the mine received a separate fresh supply. The air was split, but the separate streams all reunited at or near the up-cast shaft. In order to control the quantity of air entering each district of the mine, artificial resistances or regulators were inserted into the low-friction areas. Further, in order to make sure that no accumulation of gas lurked in an unused portion of the mine, the air was coursed through all the open workings.

VII. LIGHTING: DEVELOPMENT OF THE SAFETY-LAMP

Owing to the exhaustion of the best seams close to the surface in the vicinity of the rivers Tyne and Wear, mining engineers in this district had to sink shafts as deep as 600 ft to reach unworked areas. The increase in depth brought in its train an increasing volume of methane. Consequently, the number of underground explosions began to assume very serious dimensions. As these explosions all originated at the unprotected flame of a candle or oil-lamp, some alternative system of underground lighting had to be found. One of the earliest expedients used was the phosphorescent glow from decaying fish, but this was unsatisfactory as a luminant and also, with the limited ventilation then prevalent, decidedly unpleasant.

Between the years 1740 and 1750 a flint-and-steel mill (figure 52) for miners was invented by Charles Spedding of Whitehaven, Cumberland; the first allusion to this instrument was made in a poem by John Dallin, published in 1750. The machine was strapped to a man's chest; by rotating the handle he produced a steady stream of sparks which could, however, have given only a poor light. The sparks gave indications of the presence of inflammable air by an increase in their size and luminosity; on approaching the explosive points they assumed a liquid appearance and adhered closely to the periphery of the wheel, giving off a bluish light. This device was also known and used on the continent of Europe. However, it could and did cause explosions, so the problem was not fully solved.

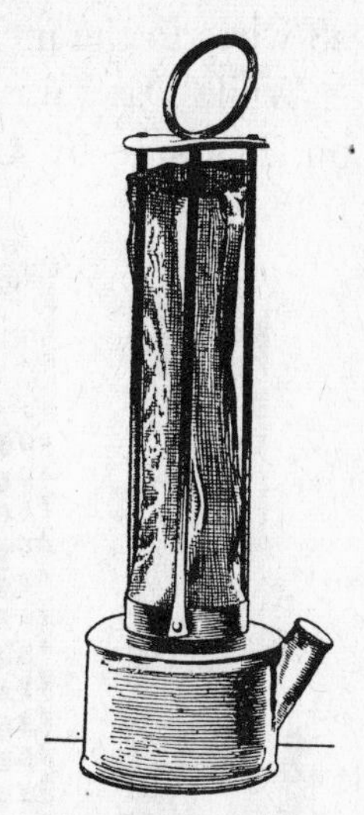

FIGURE 53—*One of the first Davy lamps to be taken underground, 1816.*

Reflection of light from the surface by mirrors was tried, but abandoned as unsatisfactory, except in sinking shafts in which blowers, or continuous evolutions of gas in the form of jets, were encountered.

About 1812 explosions became so frequent and, with the increasing size of mines, so disastrous to life, that the Sunderland society for preventing accidents in coal-mines was formed in 1813, largely through the efforts of the Rev. John Hodgson, rector of Jarrow-on-Tyne. The Sunderland society determined to interest the leading scientists in the country in the problem, and decided first to approach Sir Humphry Davy. Davy was at that particular time (August 1815) shooting in Scotland, but he was intercepted at Newcastle on his way south and steps were taken to interest him. After visiting several mines, and discussing the problem with people on the spot, he had some specimens of the gas sent to him at the Royal Institution in London. By November in the same year he had discovered the conditions under which fire-damp explodes, its degree of inflammability, and its behaviour when mixed with certain quantities of air. He also studied the passage of flames through tubes of varying diameter, and observed that metal was more effective than glass in retarding it. He found wire gauze to be an effective barrier. On 9 November 1815 he published his results and showed three lamps incorporating his findings (figure 53). The third lamp included the principle upon which modern safety-lamps depend. On 1 January 1816 he wrote to Newcastle announcing his discovery of the 'absolute safety' of a wire-gauze cylinder surrounding a naked or unprotected flame. The gauze was made from iron wire ranging from 1/40th to 1/60th of an inch in diameter, and containing 28 wires to the inch, or 784 apertures to the square inch.

While Davy was busy in London, other experiments were being carried out on Tyneside by George Stephenson and by W. R. Clanny (1776–1850), an Irishman from County Down who was practising medicine in Sunderland. Stephenson's first lamp was based on the principle that if a number of candles were held to the windward side of burning blowers of gas, the blowers were extinguished by 'the burnt air which was carried towards them'. He also noticed that when fire-damp was ignited an appreciable time was necessary for the flame to travel from one point to another, and he concluded that 'if a current of air could be produced in the opposite direction at a greater velocity than that at which the burning fire-damp travelled it would be possible to arrest it and prevent the flame from passing at all'. Hence he conceived the idea that if a lamp could be made to contain the burnt air above the flame and to permit the fire-damp to come in from below and to be burnt as it came in, 'the burnt air would prevent the passing of the explosions upwards and the velocity of the current from below would prevent it passing downwards'. The result was his first lamp, the 'tube and slider'. After further experiments underground, in which no accident occurred, Stephenson arranged the admission of air through small circular holes in the side, not the bottom, of the oil-vessel and then through more small holes, 2/25ths to 1/22nd inch in diameter, into a space between two plates, and finally to the flame through a further series of holes 1/12th to 1/18th inch in diameter (figure 54).

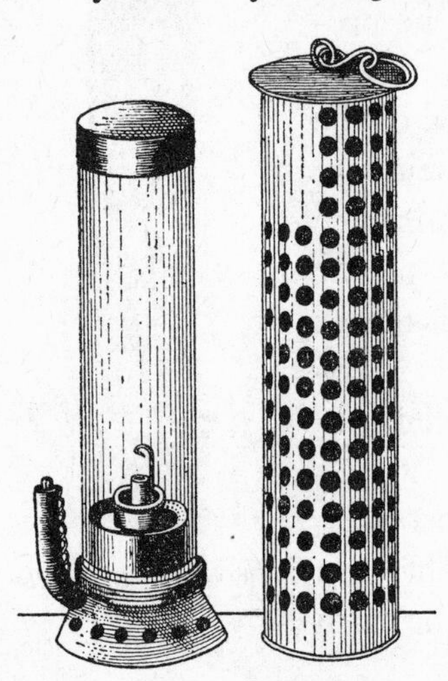

FIGURE 54—*George Stephenson's third safety lamp, 1816.*

Clanny's first lamp was the 'blast' lamp; this preceded Davy's idea by two years, but was never developed (figure 55). Later, Clanny surrounded the flame with a glass cylinder surmounted by a Davy gauze. The first lamp had a cistern of water above and below the flame, through which the outer air was forced by a hand-bellows. The South Shields committee for investigating the cause of accidents in mines expressed the opinion in 1843 that 'Dr Clanny, in this country, appears to have been the first man of science that conceived it possible to enter into a contest with the destructive element [fire-damp] and has never ceased for 35 years to devote his talents and exertions to mitigate the horrors consequent upon the explosions'.

The first real proof that a safety-lamp had been produced was made at Hebburn colliery in January 1816, with the Davy lamp, when Buddle reported: 'to my astonishment and delight, it is impossible for me to express my feelings when I first suspended the lamp in the mine and saw it red hot. If it had been a monster destroyed I could not have felt more exultation than I did. I said to those around me "we have at last subdued this monster".'

FIGURE 55—*Clanny's blast-lamp, second form, 1816. The lamp was carried on a belt worn by a boy, who also worked the bellows.*

In point of fact Buddle was too optimistic, because the early lamps were not wholly safe and the volume of light they gave was meagre. The chief defect of the Davy gauze was that when it became red hot flames could pass through it, as heat could not be carried away quickly enough. This was overcome by the use of two gauzes, one inside the other. The quantity of light given out was improved by surrounding the flame with a glass cylinder, allowing the air to enter through gauzes either below or above the flame. It was later noticed that increased safety was obtained if the circular gauzes were surrounded by a bonnet to shield them from the current of the ventilating air, which in unprotected lamps tended to blow the flame against the gauze, causing it to become red hot and thus allow the passage of flame.

During the next thirty years many alterations and improvements were made, notably by Meuseler in Belgium in 1840. His lamp was about 10 in high, including the oil-vessel. Round the flame was a very strong glass. Above the glass, and forming a continuation of it, was a wire-gauze cylinder 4½ in high and 1¾ inches in internal diameter, having a brass top full of minute perforations. The glass and the wire gauze, closely united, made a continuous cylinder about 8 in high, having a piece of wire gauze stretched across the junction of the two materials, above the top of the glass. Through the centre of this piece of horizontal gauze was a small metal chimney to convey the smoke and 'de-oxygenated air' away from the flame. The chimney passed down to within an inch of the wick; it was

4 in high, about 0·7 inches in diameter at the bottom, and tapered to 0·4 in at the top. Subsequently, further improvements were made by Marsaut, in France, and others, but no fundamental change was made.

BIBLIOGRAPHY

FORDYCE, D. W. 'A History of Coal, Coke, Coalfields.' London. 1860.

HAIR, T. H. 'Views of the Collieries in Northumberland and Durham.' Madden. 1860.

HUNT, R. 'British Mining.' London. 1884–7.

MINING ASSOCIATION OF GREAT BRITAIN. 'Historical Review of Coal Mining.' Fleetway Press, London. 1928.

PRYCE, W. *Mineralogia Cornubiensis.* London. 1778.

SIMONIN, L. 'Mines and Miners; or Underground Life' (trans. from the French and ed. by H. W. BRISTOW). London. [1869.]

SMYTH, W. 'A Rudimentary Treatise on Coal and Coal-Mining' (5th ed., rev. and enl.) London. 1880.

Transactions of the Institution of Mining Engineers.

Female coal-bearer. Seventeenth century.

4

PART I

EXTRACTION AND PRODUCTION OF METALS: IRON AND STEEL

H. R. SCHUBERT

THE period from 1750 to 1850 was marked by fundamental changes in the iron industry. Coke and coal were substituted for charcoal as a fuel. Water was replaced by steam as a motive-power. Cast iron, which hitherto had constituted less than 5 per cent of furnace-production, was produced in increasing quantities for machinery and constructional purposes. Production of wrought or bar iron also increased considerably after Henry Cort's invention of puddling and of the grooved rollers which made it possible to produce wrought iron more cheaply and in larger masses than with the hearths and hammers of the older forges. A more homogeneous steel was produced by the crucible process invented by Benjamin Huntsman.

Until about 1800, however, all these changes and improvements were only in the initial stage of development and were confined mainly to Britain. Thus the whole period may be subdivided into two consecutive phases, roughly corresponding to the last half of the eighteenth and the first half of the nineteenth centuries respectively.

In the first of these two phases development proceeded very slowly, even in Britain. Attempts to smelt iron ore with coke or coal instead of charcoal had been made long before. Best known in this respect is Dud Dudley (1599–1684), who claimed that as early as 1619 he had with coal successfully produced cast iron in the blast-furnace as well as wrought or bar iron in the forge. His claims to have succeeded where all others before him had failed were, and still are, generally rejected. The only way of utilizing coal for smelting was to produce coke first, since coking eliminates the sulphur content of raw coal, which tends to weaken the metal. The first successfully to smelt iron ore with coke was Abraham Darby (1677–1717) in 1709, at his Coalbrookdale works in Shropshire.

Darby's success was in part based on the nature of the clod coal found near the surface at Coalbrookdale. It contains a very low proportion of sulphur, the presence of which had been the principal obstacle in all the previous attempts.

As a fuel, coke had distinct advantages over charcoal, first because it was obtained from mineral coal, of which there were abundant resources; this was in marked contrast to charcoal, the demand for which was rapidly depleting the woodlands. Thus coke was available at a very much lower price than charcoal. Secondly, coke was less friable, so that a greater burden could be charged into the furnace without the danger of the fuel being crushed and the draught blocked. As a result, it was possible to use larger furnaces, by which production was increased (plate 7 B). The greater height of the furnace made the ore remain longer in contact with the incandescent fuel. The stronger blast that coke could stand without destruction caused a greater reduction, so that the iron became more liquid in the smelting process than did charcoal-produced iron. On account of its increased liquidity the metal was able to run into smaller channels in the moulds, so that castings of a lighter and more delicate design could be produced. The sphere of the operations conducted by the founder was thus enlarged. At the start of the coke-smelting at Coalbrookdale, Darby's main production was cast ware of a fine type, such as his bellied pots and other utensils. Since they were much superior to the heavy products hitherto produced by casting in iron derived from the charcoal-fired blast-furnace, an open market was secured to him.

On the other hand, the use of coke had distinct disadvantages. Coke contains more impurities than charcoal, which, being made from vegetable matter, contains only traces of minerals. The quantity of ash is smaller (0·011 per cent) than in coke (about 0·029 per cent) and, in consequence, very much less phosphorus is present. Phosphorus contributes to the fluidity of iron, but it adversely affects the strength. In England the presence of phosphorus was an additional disadvantage, since many of the iron-ore deposits exploited in the eighteenth century were themselves of a phosphoric kind. Moreover, not all the mineral coal used for coking had the low sulphur-content characteristic of the clod coal of Coalbrookdale.

It is, therefore, not surprising that in the early years smelting with coke was confined to Coalbrookdale and a very limited number of furnaces outside the area, and that in all these furnaces coke was used only intermittently, alternating with charcoal. The main product consisted of small cast iron ware. Pig iron made by smelting with coke was defective on account of the brittleness caused by impurities; it could be sold only because of its cheapness, and it served mainly for the manufacture of nails. Coke-produced pig iron did not rival charcoal iron until at least 1750, but after that date the forge-masters in Worcestershire began to accept it.

About that time several innovations were introduced, and smelting with coke was improved considerably. Closed coking-ovens of brick, in shape resembling a beehive, began to be used in place of open piles similar to those in which charcoal was made (figure 56). Of greater importance was wider adoption of foundry furnaces for the remelting of coke-produced iron. Remelting for foundry purposes was already no novelty; small movable furnaces used to remelt cast iron for making bullets were described by the French scientist R. A. F. de Réaumur in 1722. In the English iron industry the use of remelting furnaces began about 1702. The furnace was an improved form of a reverberatory furnace, in which the iron did not come into immediate contact with the coal used as fuel, so that impurities in the latter could not exert any detrimental effect upon the metal. The invention of an improved furnace of this type is ascribed to Edward Wright, a physician and chemist in London. From 1696 he carried out experiments on the smelting and refining of lead in north Wales. The successful outcome of these, in 1701, led to the erection of a lead-smelting works equipped with a furnace of Wright's improved type to which the name 'cupola' was given. It was the first time that the term was used and Wright was subsequently regarded as the inventor, but the exact nature of his improvements is not known. It is supposed that Abraham Darby used such a cupola furnace when he started the casting of iron wares at Bristol before he settled at Coalbrookdale. An English foundry furnace was depicted and described by the French engineer Gabriel Jars (1732–69), who visited England in 1764–5 (figure 57).

FIGURE 56—*Brick-built 'beehive' coking oven.*

By remelting, the coke-smelted iron obtained from the blast-furnace was greatly improved in respect of both homogeneity and purity. This improvement was of national importance, since the casting of better-quality cannon, in particular for the Royal Navy, was made possible. The advantage of the process for naval purposes was greatly appreciated by a French brigadier, M. de la Houlière, who in 1773 had made some moderately successful experiments in smelting iron ore with coke and came to England two years later to study the English methods. On a visit to works at Bersham, in Denbighshire, managed by William Wilkinson, he was greatly impressed by the product of the foundry furnaces, and particularly by the casting of cannon. In his report to the French government he summarized his experiences and pointed out that during the twenty years that had elapsed since the adoption of the foundry furnace not one English naval cannon had burst, while in the French navy such accidents were so common that the sailors 'fear the guns they are serving more than those of the enemy' [1]. William Wilkinson subsequently went to France and was manager of the state ironworks and cannon-foundry on the island of Indret, near Nantes, from 1777 to 1780. There he installed two small cupola furnaces.

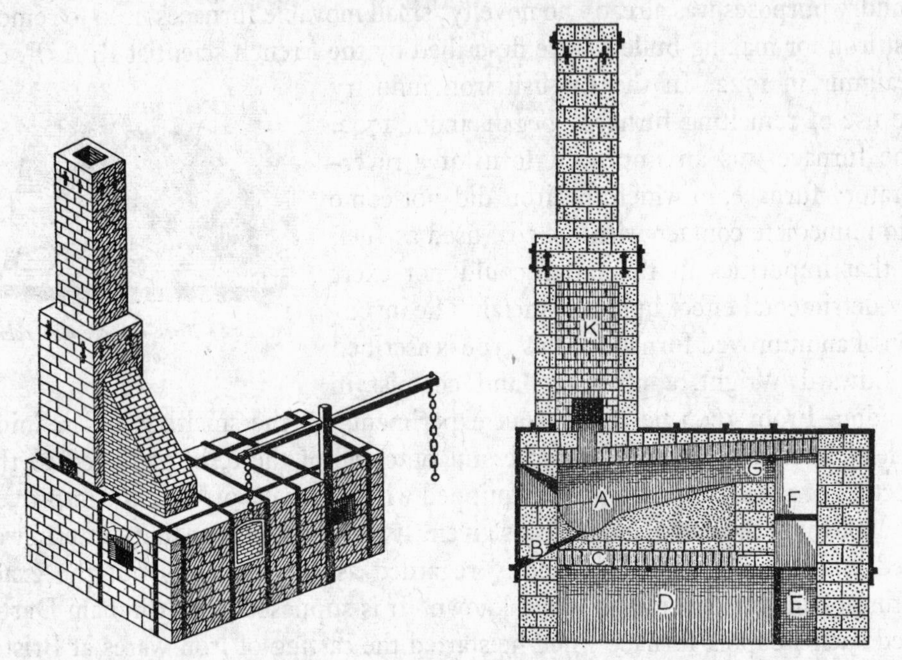

FIGURE 57—*Foundry furnaces (external view and elevation) near Newcastle upon Tyne, 1765. In these the ignited fuel was on a grate* (F) *above the ash-pit* (E). *The flame passed (through* G) *into the main basin* (A) *of the furnace, the bottom of which was filled with sand laid upon the brick roof* (C) *of a vault* (D). *The molten metal was let out into the moulds for casting through a channel* (B). *The smoke escaped through a chimney* (K).

Despite the increasing use of cupola furnaces, castings continued also to be produced directly from the blast-furnace. The old furnace at Coalbrookdale was rebuilt in 1777 for casting the 378½ tons of bridge-members for the local bridge over the Severn (p 455). In contrast to the older pattern, the shaft was made very wide and short and the hearth or crucible very deep, so as to accumulate a larger mass of liquid metal for casting.

The desire to lower the high cost of production resulting from this double process, conducted first in the blast-furnace and afterwards in the cupola, led Wilkinson to construct a new type of cupola resembling a small blast-furnace. The new cupola, larger than the old one, was not a success, but is historically noteworthy as a precursor of the modern cupola furnace.

The use of coke, which was less easily burned than charcoal, made it necessary to apply a stronger air-blast. For the charcoal-furnace, motive-power was produced by a water-wheel which operated a pair of wood and leather bellows supplying an intermittent blast into one *tuyère* and thence into the furnace. The diameter of the water-wheels did not exceed 22 ft even in the early seventeenth century, but the desire to obtain a stronger blast when coke was introduced led to the wheel at some ironworks being of a diameter of 30 to 40 ft. The blast

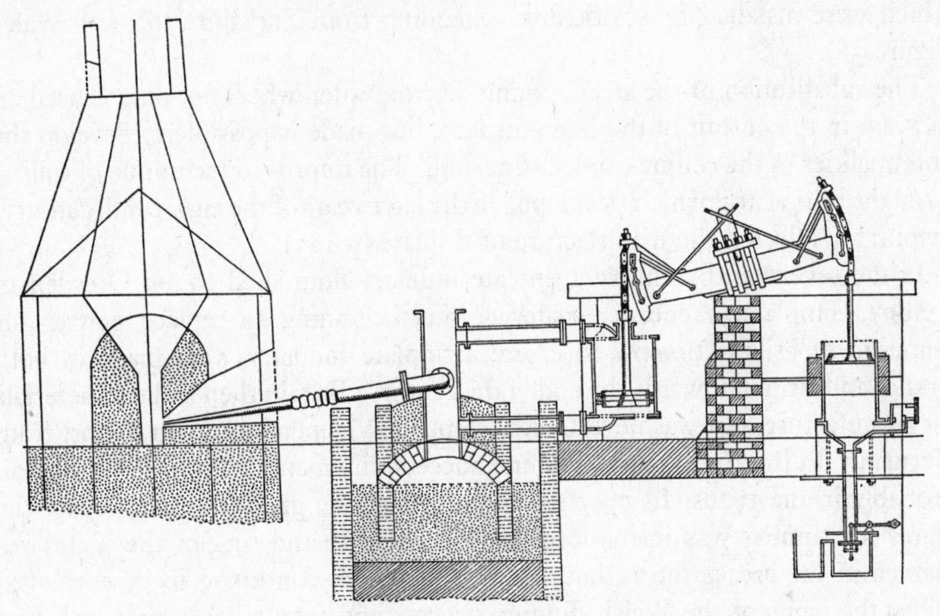

FIGURE 58—*Arrangement of blowing-engine, water-blast regulator,* tuyères, *and furnace.*

obtainable from water-driven bellows, however, was insufficient to obtain the full benefit of Darby's invention.

In 1762 a new type of blowing-apparatus began to appear. Shortly after this date John Smeaton (1724–92) introduced his blowing-cylinders, the use of which ensured a more complete combustion. Water-power, however, still remained the motive-force. It was not until James Watt's steam-engine was applied to blowing-cylinders that the final victory of coke over charcoal was won.

The early cylinders delivered to Watt for his steam-engines were not satisfactory, since they were not sufficiently accurate in bore to prevent leakage of steam. It was John Wilkinson (1728–1808) who produced the first completely satisfactory cast iron cylinders for steam-engines by a new method he had invented for boring cannon and had patented in 1774 (p 421). The improvement in the steam-engine was tremendous.

In 1776 a steam-engine was used for the first time for purposes other than pumping water. This engine, which had a 38-in cylinder, was used to blow Wilkinson's furnace at Willey in Shropshire. Four years later, Wilkinson had four engines employed in producing blast for iron-smelting. The success of Watt's invention soon led other ironmasters to order furnace engines, which were installed in a wide area extending from Yorkshire to south Wales (figure 58).

The substitution of the steam-engine for the water-wheel not only caused an increase in the output of the blast-furnace, but made it possible to develop the potentialities of the rolling- and slitting-mill. The improved technique of rolling wrought iron plates, which developed in the later years of the eighteenth century, favourably affected the manufacture of tinplate (p 125).

In the seventeenth century a tinplate industry flourished round Dresden in Saxony. Tinplate, a cheaper material, was beginning to replace pewter for domestic utensils. Attempts to create a tinplate industry were made in both France and Britain towards the end of the century; Britain then had the materials for manufacture, but was nevertheless completely dependent upon import from Germany. In Britain, tinplate was first successfully manufactured at Pontypool, probably in the 1720s. In 1745 the use of a separate grease-pot to prepare the plates for tinning was introduced. Before going to the tin-pot the plates remained in the grease for an hour, a method which continued to be employed under the name of the Welsh dipping-process and is to some extent still used for the tinning of prefabricated articles of steel. In 1800 eleven tinplate works are recorded as working in Britain; they were located in south Wales, Monmouthshire, and Gloucestershire, and their products had begun to be exported [2].

The next important step was the application of steam-power to forging. Water-driven hammers were in use (p 116), but the first forge-hammer driven by a steam-engine was erected only in 1782, for John Wilkinson at his forge at Bradley in Shropshire; this hammer could strike 300 blows a minute. Its head weighed 7½ cwt and was raised 2 ft 3 in before each blow. A hammer of this type used in Yorkshire in the 1820s is shown in the accompanying illustration (figure 59).

The effect of all these various improvements is reflected in the increased number of coke-fired furnaces. In Britain the rate of increase was slow at first, but from 1775 onwards became rapid. In 1760 not more than 17 coke-furnaces were in operation, and only 14 more were established in the following 15 years; but, by 1790, 81 out of 106 blast-furnaces in Britain were operated with coke, almost half of them in the Midlands (Shropshire 24, Staffordshire 11).

Outside Britain the adoption of coke-furnaces proceeded very slowly. The first continental one for iron-smelting was erected at the French state ironworks at Le Creusot built by William Wilkinson in association with de Wendel and Toufaire in 1781–5. The next country was Prussia, where, at the invitation of the Prussian government, William Wilkinson unsuccessfully tried to smelt iron with coke at Friedrichshütte, in Silesia, in 1789. In 1791–2 a German engineer, T. F. Wedding, successfully used coke for smelting at Malapane, and in 1794–6 another coke-furnace was erected at Gleiwitz; both these places are in Upper Silesia. In the coal-basin of the German Ruhr smelting with coke did not start earlier than about 1850. In Belgium the coke-furnace was introduced by John Cockerill at Seraing, near Liége,[1] in 1823. Five years later a coke-furnace was established at Wilkowitz, now in Czechoslovakia. It was the first in the whole of the former Austrian Empire.

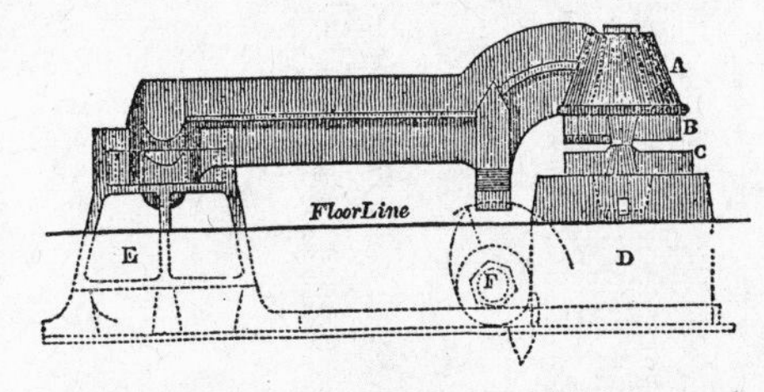

FIGURE 59—*Helve-hammer used at Milton ironworks, Yorkshire. The helve was of cast iron weighing about 6 tons.* A *is the hammer head and* B *the hammer. The anvil* (C) *was fitted into a cast iron block* (D), *which weighed upwards of 4 tons. The hammer was lifted by a cam or lifter* (F). *The helve worked in a frame* (E) *which was of iron, so that the cumbersome wooden frame of the old forge hammer was disposed of.*

As late as 1813, however, the use of coke for smelting and of the steam-driven blowing-cylinders instead of water-driven bellows was still almost completely confined to England. According to a statement made in 1813 by Thomas Cooper, professor of chemistry and mineralogy at Carlisle in Pennsylvania, nine-tenths of all the iron then produced in England was made with coke. In the United States, as well as on the continent of Europe, charcoal was still almost exclusively used [3].

The increase in the production of cast iron does not alone explain the rapid rise of the British iron industry in the last quarter of the eighteenth century, although cast iron was more in demand than at any time previously. An extensive replacement of other metals and of wood by cast iron took place in building (ch 15) as well as in the construction of machinery (ch 14). In 1760 the Carron Ironworks in Scotland began to cast iron cog-wheels. The first all-iron plant was designed by John Rennie for the Albion Mill in London in 1784. It had, as has been indicated, become possible to make quite large castings, such as those for the Severn bridge at Coalbrookdale (plate 30 A) and the steam-hammers.

[1] Since 1945 Liège, although its inhabitants are still Liégeois.

Despite all these remarkable achievements, however, the demand for cast iron was still smaller than that for wrought or bar iron. Wrought iron, although now an unimportant commodity, was still the principal metal in use about 1800, and remained so for at least half a century (plate 9).

Pig iron made by smelting with coke was found unsuitable for conversion into wrought iron because of the impurities introduced into the iron by the coke; these made wrought iron so brittle that it crumbled under the hammer. The problem of producing a pig iron suitable for conversion into wrought iron seems to have been solved about 1749–50 by Abraham Darby II (1711–63), but unfortunately nothing is known about the technique he applied. After him, the brothers Cranage, skilled iron-workers at Coalbrookdale, made iron in a reverberatory furnace using raw coal alone. The credit for final success is generally given to Henry Cort (1740–1800) of Gosport, who in 1784 obtained a patent for the conversion of pig iron into malleable, that is wrought, iron by puddling. Peter Onions, however, used a process which was essentially that of puddling and had been patented a year earlier.

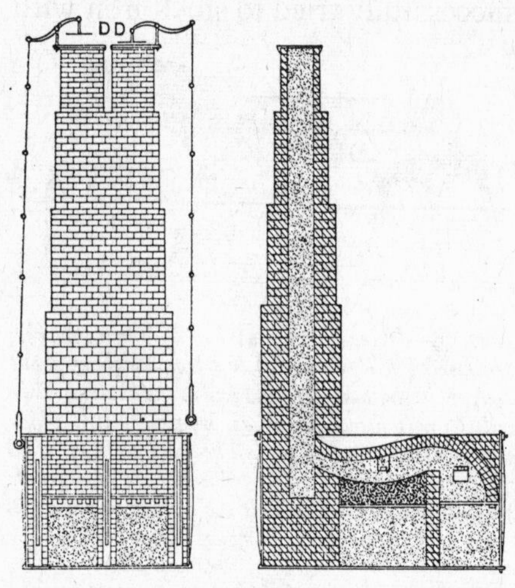

FIGURE 60—*Puddling-furnace;* (left) *external view;* (right) *vertical section.*

The process of puddling used by Cort consisted essentially of stirring molten pig iron on the bed of a reverberatory furnace. The puddler turned and stirred the molten mass until, through the decarburizing action of air which circulated through the furnace, it became converted into malleable iron. In this process contact between the metal and the raw coal that served as fuel was avoided, and the need for blowing-machinery was dispensed with. How Cort's method was superior to those of his predecessors, in particular that of Onions, is not known. Perhaps it was the use of dampers on top of the furnace (D, D in the accompanying illustration) for regulating the heat (figure 60).

Cort is also credited with the invention of grooved rollers (figure 61), patented in 1783. There too, however, he had predecessors; Christopher Polhem, in Sweden, apparently constructed a rolling-mill equipped with similar rolls in 1745. Previously, bars had to be made either by hammering, or by cutting hot strips from a rolled plate with a slitting-mill. With grooved rollers 15 tons of

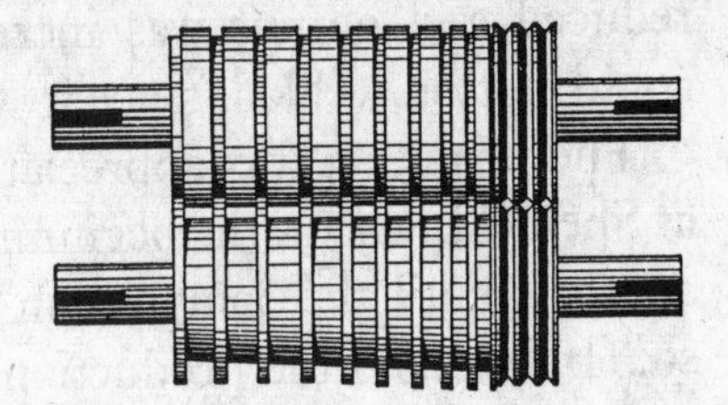

FIGURE 61—*Grooved rollers for bar-making.*

iron could be dealt with in 12 hours, whereas it was difficult to produce one ton in the same time with the forge-hammer.

Cort's success was immediate, owing to the combination of the two processes he introduced. He achieved a simplification that resulted in lower cost of production. Although puddled iron was inferior in quality to charcoal iron, it was very much cheaper. His success was reflected in a tremendous increase in the production of British pig iron required for making puddled iron. This increase is demonstrated by a graph illustrating development between 1740 and 1840 (figure 62) [4].

One branch of the industry not affected by the great increase in production in Britain was steel manufacture. The quality of steel produced mainly depended upon the ores employed, and for this reason steel produced from German manganiferous ores still enjoyed the highest reputation in the eighteenth century. Attempts to make England independent of foreign steel led to improvements in the cementation process. The greatest development in the production of steel took place shortly before 1750: it was the invention of crucible or cast steel, which was more homogeneous in composition and more free from impurities than any steel produced previously. The inventor of this process was Benjamin Huntsman (1704–76), an Englishman of Dutch descent. As an instrument-maker at Doncaster he started experiments with the object of producing a more uniform steel for the springs and pendulums of clocks. At Handsworth, near Sheffield, where he settled between 1740 and 1742, he finally found, after many failures, a method by which steel could be produced in a molten state (figure 63). He melted bars of blister steel, with the addition of fluxes, in closed clay crucibles; the intense heat necessary was generated by coke. The two crucibles were placed in a chamber lined with fire-brick. The top of the furnace was closed by a cover of fire-brick, which was level with the floor of the melting-house. A vaulted cellar gave access to the ash-pit.

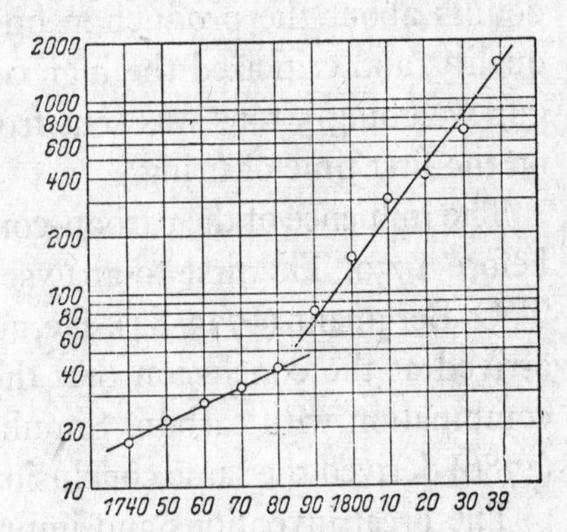

FIGURE 62—*Pig iron production (thousands of tons) in England, 1740–1839.*

Huntsman's process was less complex than those previously used for the production of steel. As a result, costs of production were reduced and output was increased. A difficulty, however, was that cast steel could not be welded, since it would not bear more than a red heat (*c* 900° C).

The invention was appreciated first in France. The manufacturers of cutlery at Sheffield, who in the beginning considered Huntsman's steel too hard, did not accept it until the competition of imported French cutlery forced them to do so. In England the production of cast steel increased very slowly before 1770, and even then some further decades elapsed before Huntsman's invention was adopted more widely.

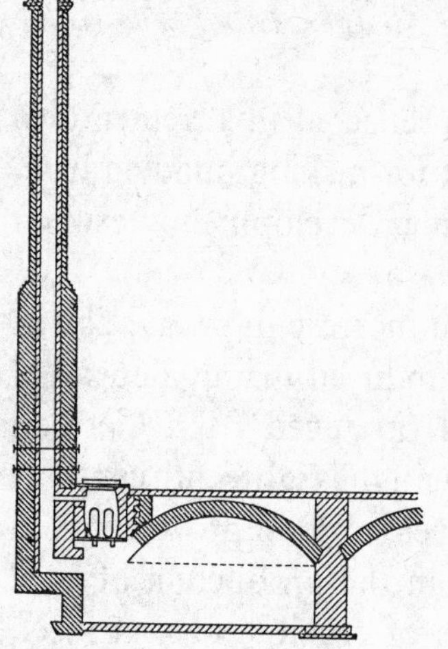

FIGURE 63—*Cross-section of Huntsman's melting-furnace, showing two crucibles in position.*

On the continent cast steel was first manufactured by Johann Conrad Fischer, one of Switzerland's leading industrialists, at Schaffhausen about 1802. Since Huntsman's process was kept secret, Fischer had to invent the method for himself. He also invented copper-steel and nickel-steel alloys, which he called 'yellow steel' and 'meteor steel' respectively. Fischer soon extended his industrial interests beyond Switzerland by setting up steel works and engineering-shops in Austria and France.

In the whole of the period with which we are now concerned cast iron remained superior to every other material for the construction of ordnance. Attempts were indeed made to substitute cast steel for cast iron in the manufacture of artillery. Thus Krupp proposed the use of cast steel, but his first gun, a three-pounder with a tube of cast steel inside an outer tube of cast iron, finally burst under the severe tests to which it was submitted in Berlin in 1849. A committee of Prussian artillery officers expressed doubts about the production on this principle of heavy ordnance of uniform quality, and criticized the high cost involved. About the same time, a cast steel gun weighing 5 tons was sent from Essen to Woolwich, but when tried it burst on the first time of firing.

The influence of the carbon-content of steel upon its hardness was not realized before 1750. The first to analyse carbon in iron was the Swedish metallurgist T. O. Bergmann (1735–84). He, and after him Guyton de Morveau (1737–1816), arrived at the conclusion that the conversion of iron into steel was due to its combination with carbon. Simultaneously with Guyton de Morveau, Priestley (1786) derived the same conclusion from experiments on nails at Birmingham.

The great inventions and improvements that caused a revolution in the iron industry, and a completely new orientation, had almost all been made by the close of the eighteenth century. After the end of the Napoleonic wars in 1815, when the demand for war material ceased, a temporary depression affected the iron trade, but after 1830 a tremendous growth occurred in every branch of British manufacture, including iron-making. There was a period of unusual prosperity, which culminated in 1835. Production of iron increased rapidly as a result of improvements in the processes conducted in both the furnace and the forge.

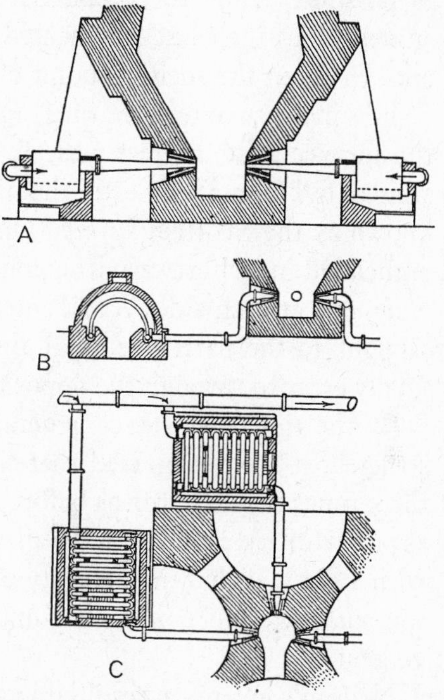

FIGURE 64—*Elevation* (A) *of Neilson's hot-blast stove erected at the Clyde works, Glasgow, in 1832. It consisted of a wrought iron chamber 4 ft long, 3 ft high, and 2 ft wide, similar to the wagon-head steam-boiler, and set in brickwork over a grate. A cold blast entered at one end and passed out to the* tuyère *at the other end, the temperature being raised to c 200° F. Below is the elevation* (B) *and plan* (C) *of an improved device in which the iron chambers were replaced by cast iron retort-shaped vessels enclosed in brick. Subsequently, water-cooled* tuyères *were introduced by John Condie (not illustrated).*

Perhaps the greatest of the improvements was the application of a hot instead of a cold blast in the smelting of iron. The first idea that a higher temperature in the furnace could be achieved by heating the blast before its entrance through the *tuyères* was due to James Beaumont Neilson (1792–1865), manager of the Glasgow gas-works. He obtained a patent in 1828, and early in the following year his invention was applied in the Clyde Ironworks at Glasgow.

The apparatus first used by Neilson consisted of a small chamber of wrought iron set in brickwork, with a grate below. The cold blast entered at one end, above the grate, and passed out into the *tuyère* at the other end after having attained a temperature of about 200° F. Each *tuyère* had one heating chamber. It was found that iron chambers of this kind soon succumbed to heat and oxidation, so Neilson replaced them by cast iron retort-shaped vessels completely enclosed within a brick casing. By this means waste of heat was prevented, and the temperature could be increased to 280° F. After several further improvements an oven was erected at the Clyde works in 1832 which represents the first practical realization of the cast iron tubular stoves (figure 64).

Here, the cold blast was supplied to each oven by a pipe branching off the large main from the blast-engine. The blast entered the oven at the end remote from the *tuyère* and passed through the arched tubes over the fire into the pipe on the other side of the grate, whence it passed into the *tuyère*. The whole apparatus was enclosed in an arched oven, so as to retain and reflect as much heat as possible. While traversing the two longtitudinal pipes and the connecting arched pipes the blast was heated directly and was raised to a temperature of 600° F, about the melting-point of lead.

This increase in temperature required protection of the *tuyères*, which entered the furnace at its hottest part. It was achieved by the water-cooled *tuyère* invented by John Condie of the Blair ironworks in Scotland, and commonly known as the Scottish *tuyère*. This consisted of a coil of wrought iron tubing embedded in a short cast iron cone. Both ends protruded from the base of the cone, one at each side. Water entered at one end of the protruding pipe, passed straight to the narrow end of the *tuyère*, circled back through the coil, and finally escaped through the opposite protruding pipe.

By the time that stoves generating a temperature of 600° F had been constructed, it was recognized that with them the same amount of fuel produced three times as much iron as before, and that the same amount of blast acted twice as powerfully as a cold blast. Realization of the enormous potentialities of smelting with a hot blast led the majority of the ironmasters to accept it, although there was some resistance in the beginning. By 1835 the use of a hot blast had become general.

Neilson's invention resulted in a great increase in the output of iron. Application of hot blast not only made it possible to smelt a greater quantity of ore with the same amount of fuel but to build larger furnaces. A further advantage was that with the higher temperature generated by a hot blast not only coke but raw coal could be used as a fuel. This was of great importance in Scotland, since very few of the Scottish coals made good metallurgical coke. It also rendered it possible to make use of the black-band ironstone which had been discovered in Scotland at the beginning of the century but was almost useless for iron-smelting until the hot blast was introduced.

By the invention of the hot blast yet another important source of fuel was made available for smelting, namely the anthracite coal of south Wales and Pennsylvania. The idea of using anthracite with hot blast first occurred to an American of German descent, W. Geissenheimer. He was a Lutheran pastor in New York, where he used a small experimental furnace in the winter of 1830–1. After obtaining a patent in 1833, he erected the Valley furnace on Silver Creek, Pennsylvania, and then successfully smelted iron ore with anthracite and hot blast. Unfortunately, working ceased after two months because of an accident.

Independently of Geissenheimer, George Crane and his employee David Thomas put the same idea into practice in Britain in 1837; his works was at Ynyscedwin in the anthracite-bearing region of south Wales. After Geissenheimer's death his American patent was bought by Crane in 1838; in the summer of that year Thomas settled in the United States and began to erect an anthracite furnace at Catasauqua in Pennsylvania. It initiated a new era, in which the large deposits of anthracite—already well known but of little use—were made available for the American iron industry. Thomas's activity had far-reaching consequences in another respect, for he was the first in America completely to realize the immense value of powerful blowing-engines. About 1852 he introduced engines by which the pressure of blast was increased to double that customary in England at the time.

In the United States the flourishing state of the iron industry based on anthracite retarded the development of smelting with coke. Since anthracite and hard coal were available in large quantities they were naturally preferred to coke. Although attempts to smelt with coke were made as early as 1819, it was not until after 1850 that coke was used on a large scale in the United States.

The use of blowing-cylinders for supplying air to the furnace made bellows unnecessary. As a result, the large aperture in the outer casing of the furnace through which the nozzles of the bellows were inserted could be replaced by smaller apertures for the pipes that conducted the blast from the cylinders. Consequently there was sufficient room for two or three *tuyères*. More *tuyères* could not be employed as long as the old quadrangular shape of the furnace-shell was retained. The desire to employ a greater number of *tuyères*, stimulated by the necessity of generating more blast in order to increase production, led to important alterations in the exterior form of the furnace. The outer casing was given a round shape and was placed on five strong brickwork pillars. This innovation, which started in the 1820s, did not, however, allow more than four *tuyère* openings. Since a greater number became desirable to obtain the full benefit of hot blast after its introduction about 1830, the hearth was laid completely free. By placing the outer casing of the furnace upon cast iron pillars, the hearth was made accessible from all directions, so that the number of *tuyères* could easily be increased. The stone walls of the shell were made considerably thinner and were bound by wrought iron hoops, later replaced by a casing of boiler-plates. Furnaces of this type were known as Scottish furnaces, because the first was erected at Dundyvan, in Scotland, in the early 1830s (figure 65). Not long afterwards the new type was introduced on the continent, first at Hayange in France, where a furnace of this type was operated from 1838. The

Dundyvan type represented a considerable step forward in development towards the modern form of the blast-furnace, but the change did not affect the interior of the furnace.

The internal cavity was circular in section as far down as the hearth; this shape was first introduced about 1650 and gradually extended to the vast majority of furnaces. Despite this, the ironmasters clung to rectangular hearths

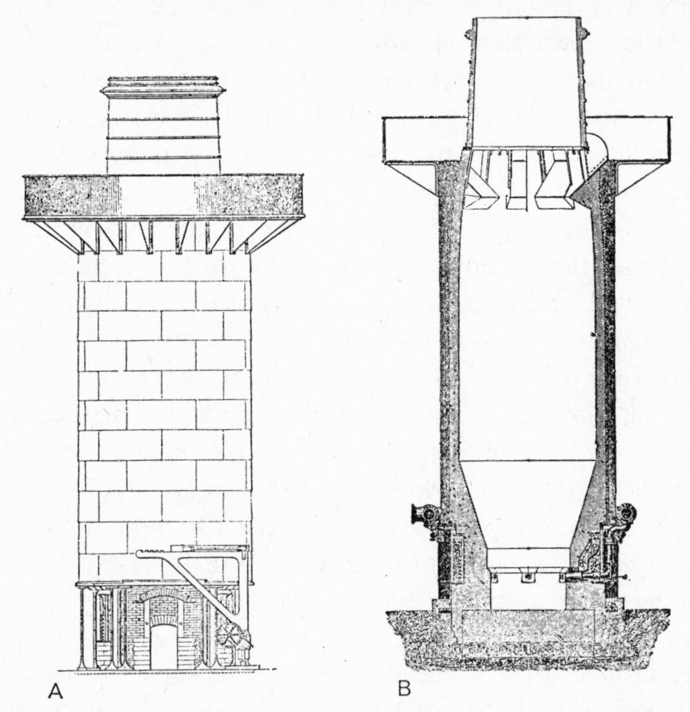

FIGURE 65—*Blast furnace of the Dundyvan type at Russel's Hall near Dudley, Worcestershire.* (A) *Front elevation,* (B) *vertical section. The crane shown in* (A) *was used to remove the large cake of slag that formed.*

or crucibles for the collection of the molten metal. In the late eighteenth century French literature on iron-making was beginning to recommend a circular shape; for example, this suggestion was made by the French ironmaster P. C. Grignon in 1775. The suggestion was no more than the fruit of practical experience, for the hearth gradually became round in the course of smelting on account of the destructive effect of the fire. It was, however, not until 1832 that such a shape was accepted and deliberately put into practice. The change took place in south Staffordshire in a new furnace built by T. Oakes at Corbyn's Hall, Brierley Hill, for the ironmaster John Gibbons (figure 66).

The immediate effects of Gibbons's alterations were a distinct acceleration of the smelting process, a considerable saving of fuel, and, in consequence, an increased output of metal. Gibbons's furnace set the pattern for the further development of the blast-furnace. It was first taken up by the ironmasters of the Black Country. The furnaces, which before 1832 had an average height of 35 to 40 ft, increased to a height of 50 to 60 ft.

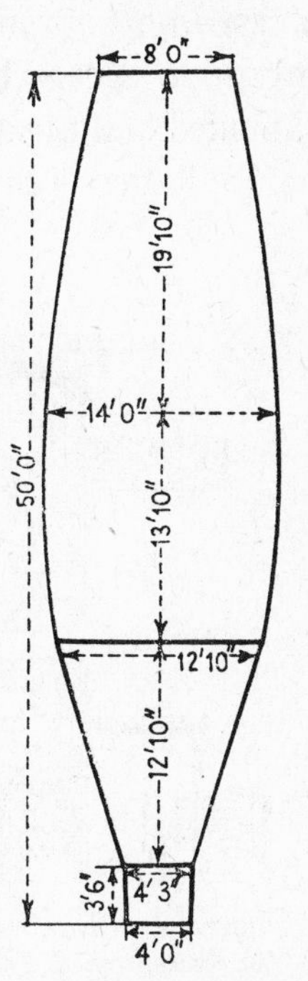

FIGURE 66—*Diagram of Gibbons's furnace at Corbyn's Hall. Gibbons modified the internal measurements of the furnace so that its life was longer.*

Further innovations affected the top aperture or 'mouth' of the blast-furnace. For several centuries this aperture had been left open, so that the gases escaped. The burning gases rising high into the air presented a spectacular sight, especially at night, but their free escape represented a waste. Attempts to utilize the waste gases were made in Württemberg, Germany, by A. C. W. F. Faber du Faur in 1831. The first practical success was achieved in 1832 at the ironworks of Schopfheim, in Baden. The gases were taken off the top of the furnace and conveyed through pipes to the hot-blast stoves (cf. figure 67). In England the first attempt to utilize the furnace-gas for heating the hot-blast stoves was made by Lloyds, Fosters and Company of the Old Park ironworks at Wednesbury, Staffordshire, in 1834. The heat produced, however, was so small that a supplementary oven near the *tuyère* was required for raising the temperature of the blast still further before it entered the furnace. Utilization of furnace-gas spread rapidly, and the method was improved on the continent, but in England it did not come into general use until the device introduced by James Palmer Budd, of the Ystalyfera ironworks near Swansea, and patented in 1845, became more widely known. This cup-and-cone device for feeding the blast-furnace was first used by George Parry at the Ebbw Vale ironworks in Monmouthshire in 1850 (figure 67). The simplest form had a fixed cup and a movable cone which could be raised or lowered. The device guaranteed a more even distribution of the charge than that attainable in furnaces in which the top was open.

Improvements in the early nineteenth century extended also to the forge and to the practice of making malleable or bar iron. A drawback in the process of puddling resulted from the use of sand for the bottom of the puddling-furnace. Combination between the silica of the sand and oxidized iron was liable to form a slag too acid to take up the phosphorus contained in pig iron made from ordinary phosphoric ores. The resulting corrosion of the bed of sand caused considerable loss through repairs and made the furnace less productive. A remedy was found by Samuel Rogers of Nant-y-Glo, Monmouthshire, who substituted a cast iron bottom plate. During the years 1816–18 he tried hard to make his invention acceptable to the ironmasters in south Wales, but his efforts were ridiculed and earned him the nickname of 'Mr Iron Bottom'; it was some years before Rogers's cast iron bottom plate was universally adopted.

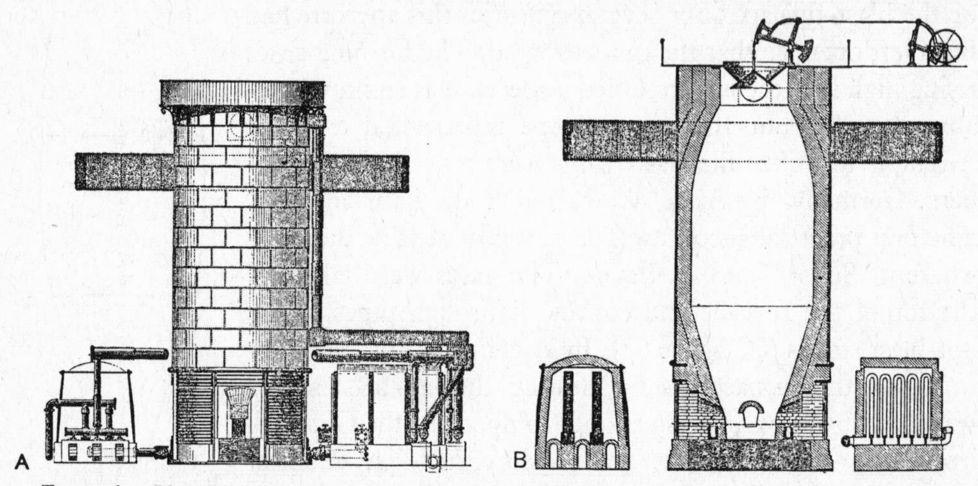

FIGURE 67—*Blast-furnaces at Ebbw Vale, Monmouthshire.* (A) *Front elevation showing hot-blast stoves;* (B) *vertical section. The mouth of the furnace is fitted with a 'cup-and-cone'. There is a circular opening for taking off the hot gases, which are then conveyed by pipes to the hot-blast stoves.*

Not only the furnace but the process of puddling itself was materially altered. Since Cort's invention almost all wrought iron had been produced by 'dry' puddling; this was slow, because it necessitated stirring the metal with iron bars in order to expose it to atmospheric action. An acceleration of the process was achieved by Joseph Hall of the Bloomfield ironworks at Tipton, in Staffordshire. In 1839 he obtained a patent for calcining 'top cinder' or 'bull dog'—the slag from puddling-furnaces—in kilns. After calcination the 'bull dog' was allowed to cool, broken into small pieces, and used for coating the floor of the furnace. The oxide of iron contained in 'bull dog' combined with the carbon in the charge and produced carbon monoxide below the surface of the molten metal; in escaping, this gas created the appearance of boiling, which gave the process the name of pig boiling. From the liquid nature of the slag, which was absent in the old method of puddling on sand bottoms, the name of 'wet' puddling is derived. By the new method, in which the iron was melted in a single stage, the process was greatly accelerated and was quickly adopted.

In the second quarter of the nineteenth century British puddlers migrated to the continent and went from factory to factory in Belgium and Germany instructing foreigners in their craft. They came mostly from south Wales, then the centre of puddling and rolling. The first puddling- and rolling-plants in France were installed in 1818–19, at Hayange (near Thionville) and St-Étienne (Loire). In Germany, Cort's puddling-process (p 106) was first introduced in 1824–5 at Rasselstein, near Neuwied, and at the Hoesch ironworks at Lendersdorf-Krauthausen, near Düren. At both these works British puddlers were employed,

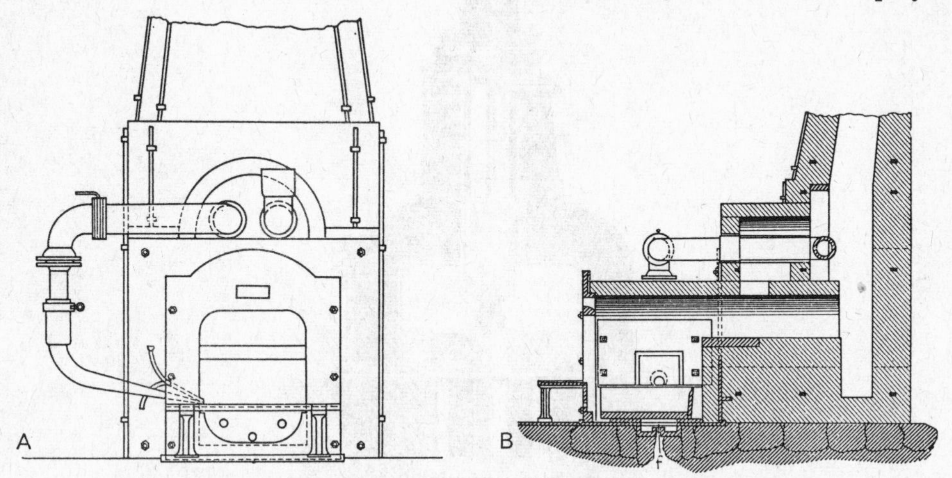

FIGURE 68—*Swedish Lancashire hearth.* (A) *Front elevation,* (B) *longitudinal section.*

and nearly all of them came from south Wales or Monmouthshire. Skilled workers from south Wales were also engaged in 1829 for the manufacture of charcoal-plate in Sweden. They introduced into Sweden a refining-hearth which developed into the so-called Swedish Lancashire hearth (figure 68). These workers evidently came from Pontypool, Monmouthshire, which at that time was the only place in the south-west of Britain where the old method of refining iron was still employed. The forges at Pontypool obtained their pig iron from Lancashire, which may have given rise to the name 'Lancashire' hearth. There is no evidence that such a hearth was used in Lancashire. There were three main characteristics in which the Lancashire hearth differed from the usual hearth employed for the refining of pig iron. Firstly, the chimney was not above the hearth, but set right at the rear. Secondly, and in consequence, the hearth itself was covered with an arched roof that reflected the heat and thus caused a notable economy in fuel. Thirdly, a shallow cast iron box (f in figure 68 B) was placed beneath the hearth. During the process of refining, water continually flowed through the box so that the bottom of the hearth was cooled. From Sweden the Lancashire hearth was reintroduced into England; it was also adopted in Germany.

The invention of a practical steam-hammer by Nasmyth was of immense importance. His hammer was a simple, direct-working machine which dispensed

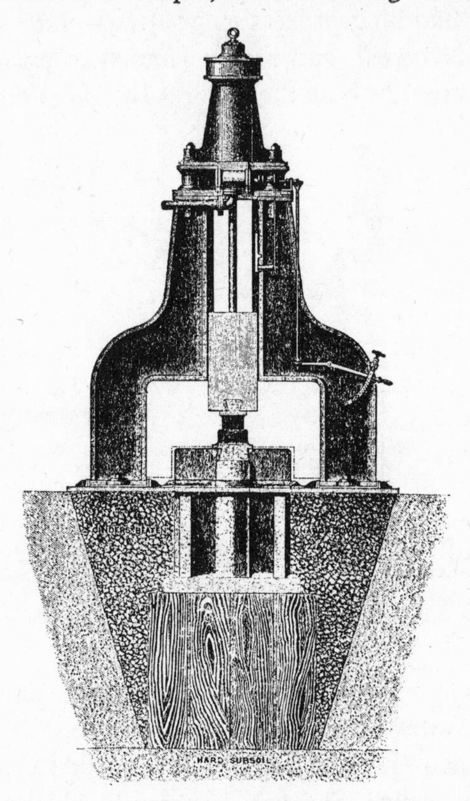

FIGURE 69—*Double-acting steam-hammer erected at the Atlas works, Sheffield. The steam-hammer was originally suggested by Watt in 1784 and afterwards planned by Deveral in 1806, but it was Nasmyth who developed it for practical use. Originally steam was used only to lift hammers, but by using it on both the up and down strokes the power of the hammer was increased.*

with much of the cumbrous wheel-work required with the old-fashioned trip-hammer (p 431) (figure 69 and plate 24 A). A further advantage was the ease with which the strokes could be regulated according to the size of the object and the force of the blow required. This was of particular importance in small works (plate 8 B), in which it was not practicable to have a number of different sizes of hammer according to the sort of work in hand. A modification of Nasmyth's hammer was the steam-hammer invented by John Condie and patented in 1846.

REFERENCES

[1] LA HOULIÈRE, M. DE. "Report to the French Government (1775)", ed. by W. H. CHALONER in *Edgar Allen News*, December 1948 and January 1949.
[2] HOARE, W. E. *Bull. Instn Metall.*, **8**, 1–23, 1951.
[3] COOPER, T. 'The Emporium of Arts and Sciences', p. 19. Philadelphia. 1813.
[4] SCHULZ, E. H. *Arch. Eisenhüttenw.*, **26**, no. 7, 370, 1955.

BIBLIOGRAPHY

ASHTON, T. S. 'Iron and Steel in the Industrial Revolution' (2nd ed.). University Press, Manchester. 1951.
GILLE, B. 'Les origines de la grande industrie métallurgique en France.' Collection d'histoire sociale, no. 2. Domat Montchrestien, Paris. 1948.
HENDERSON, W. O. 'Britain and Industrial Europe, 1750–1870.' University Press, Liverpool. 1954.
JOHANNSEN, O. 'Geschichte des Eisens' (3rd ed.). Stahleisen, Düsseldorf. 1953.
KARSTEN, C. J. B. 'Handbuch der Eisenhüttenkunde' (3rd ed.). Berlin. 1841.
PERCY, J. 'Metallurgy', Vol.: 'Iron and Steel.' London. 1864.
SCHUBERT, H. R. 'History of the British Iron and Steel Industry, *c* 450 B.C.–A.D. 1775.' Routledge & Kegan Paul, London. In the press.
SWANK, J. M. 'History of the Manufacture of Iron in all Ages.' Philadelphia. 1892.

The 'Old Furnace' at Coalbrookdale, rebuilt by Abraham Darby III in 1777. One of the iron beams seen above the tapping-hole is dated 1658. From this furnace the metal for the iron bridge was cast.

4

PART II

EXTRACTION AND PRODUCTION OF METALS: NON-FERROUS METALS

F. W. GIBBS

A GREAT change of outlook occurred in the whole field of metals during the century or so with which this chapter deals. Developments in engineering—the introduction of railed ways for haulage, and of steam-driven machinery for pumping water from mines and for blowing air into blast-furnaces—made possible deeper and larger workings and helped to increase greatly the whole scale of operations throughout the metal industries. A great change, too, had been brought about by advances in physics and chemistry (ch 8) which improved beyond measure the understanding of the traditional processes by which metals were won from their ores. The new field of electrometallurgy had acquired considerable industrial importance by 1850–70. Above all, the remarkably rapid development of analytical chemistry (p 221) in the later eighteenth century led to the discovery of a large number of metals that had not previously been characterized. Many of them were mixed with the commoner metals in their ores, and this made improvements possible in methods of separation and purification. Work on the new metals was also made easier by the invention of the oxy-hydrogen blowpipe, with which small quantities of materials could be heated to much higher temperatures than ever before.

Manufacturers, however, at first showed little inclination to test these new methods and materials, and the metal industries were not greatly affected by them for a considerable time. A writer in 1828 said that a number of the new metals were little better than hypothetical assumptions; some of them, such as potassium and sodium, were so different from the popular conception of a metal that 'nothing but the rage of the day for the invention of new metals could have prompted their insertion in the list'.

In the main, the methods used for the extraction of the non-ferrous metals in the early nineteenth century were the same as had been found satisfactory in the early eighteenth. Thus the extraction of copper, one of the most difficult processes, still remained somewhat haphazard, and the product was often brittle.

If a reliable grade of the metal was required for some purpose, copper coins were sometimes used; for example, the silver-platers of Birmingham are said to have sought for copper coins issued during and since the reign of Queen Anne, as these were easier to work than much commercial copper made in the later eighteenth and early nineteenth centuries.

In the principal mining-centres of Germany, however, improvements in analysis were put to good account, and operations were often carried out with exceptional skill and care, particularly when local ores contained several elements for each of which a good market could be found. In many other parts of the continent, and in Britain, older and often wasteful methods at first prevailed, and this sometimes meant that only the richest ores could be successfully worked on the commercial scale.

Among the new metals of the period, special mention must be made of zinc and the platinum metals. Zinc was by this time being extracted direct from its ores by a method apparently brought to this country from China and first used in Europe on the commercial scale at Bristol. Among other metallic products of the Far East, Malacca tin and Chinese sheet lead became well known. Platinum, iridium, and rhodium were obtained from the *platina* brought to Europe from Spanish America. Platinum was especially prized; it was much used for laboratory vessels and for stills with a capacity of 35 gallons or more. Little use was found for many of the other new metals; yet by 1830 it was known, or claimed, that cadmium, iridium, nickel, osmium, and palladium could be worked into plates or drawn into wire, and that tellurium could be cast. The furnaces then available could not produce temperatures high enough to permit the easy working of cerium, chromium, cobalt, columbium (now known as niobium, but then sometimes confused with tantalum), manganese, molybdenum, rhodium, tungsten, titanium, and uranium, and only a few of these metals found occasional use in alloys.

Thus, apart from iron and steel and the useful half-metals arsenic, antimony, and bismuth, the commercially important metals of the period were lead and tin; copper and zinc; mercury, silver, and gold; the platinum metals; and cobalt, nickel, and manganese. Their extraction, production, and chief alloys will be described in that order. Lead and tin were among the easiest to smelt, whereas copper and silver offered some of the most difficult metallurgical problems. The use of mercury for the extraction of silver and gold makes it convenient to treat them together; they and the platinum metals played an important role in the history of Spain and of the Spanish possessions in South America. Cobalt, nickel, and manganese had not yet assumed the importance they were later to have in the steel industry.

I. BISMUTH, ANTIMONY, AND ARSENIC

No outline of the technology of the non-ferrous metals would be complete without some mention of these important elements, which, unlike most metals, lack true permanence in air and are easily calcined, melted, and vaporized. They were used in numerous alloys and in many arts, as well as for the manufacture of several compounds widely needed in industry. They all occur native to some extent, and were often found together in German and Scandinavian ores used for the extraction of other metals.

Bismuth was the easiest to obtain. This was done by liquation; that is, by heating the ore and allowing the liquid metal to run off into a receiver. Normally, cast iron retorts placed obliquely in a furnace were charged with about ½ cwt of ore and heated, when the liquid bismuth ran down the retorts and out into iron pans. As the pans filled, the bismuth was ladled out and cast into bars of 20 to 50 lb each. In the middle of the nineteenth century, about 10 000 tons were prepared annually by this method at Schneeberg, wood still being used as fuel.

Pure bismuth for medicinal purposes was prepared chemically on a laboratory scale, the bismuth of commerce being largely used for the production of alloys. With tin it gave bell metal; two parts of bismuth with one of tin and one of lead gave 'fusible metal', so called by Sir Isaac Newton; one part of bismuth, two of tin, and one of lead gave soft solder for use with pewter. The oxide and nitrate were also made on a large scale.

Antimony occurs naturally as the sulphide, stibnite, European deposits of which are found in Czechoslovakia and Yugoslavia. Antimony sulphide is also often present in ores of other metals. It is easily fusible, and was therefore separated from such ores, or from gangue in the case of stibnite, by liquation. The metal was then extracted by a two-stage process, in which the sulphide was first heated with free access of air to give the oxide, and this was then reduced to metal by heating with crude tartar. In Germany, antimony was sometimes obtained in one operation by heating the sulphide with scrap iron, which combined with sulphur, and an alkali carbonate: later this became the chief method. The impure antimony thus obtained was purified by fusion with a little antimony sulphide and sodium carbonate. On partial cooling the metal separated from the slag, and the process was repeated if necessary.

Antimony was used chiefly in alloys, such as the two common type-metals (70 or 75 per cent tea-lead,[1] 25 or 20 per cent antimony, 5 per cent tin) and

[1] As the name suggests, this was sheet lead used to line tea-chests. It was made in China by hand, molten lead being pressed between flat stones, and was used for some purposes in preference to European lead as it was relatively hard and stiff.

stereotype metal (112 lb tea-lead, 18 lb antimony, and 3 lb tin). Britannia metal, used for table-ware, was 90 per cent tin and 10 per cent antimony. Antimony was also used for concave mirrors required to take a high polish; in bell metal to

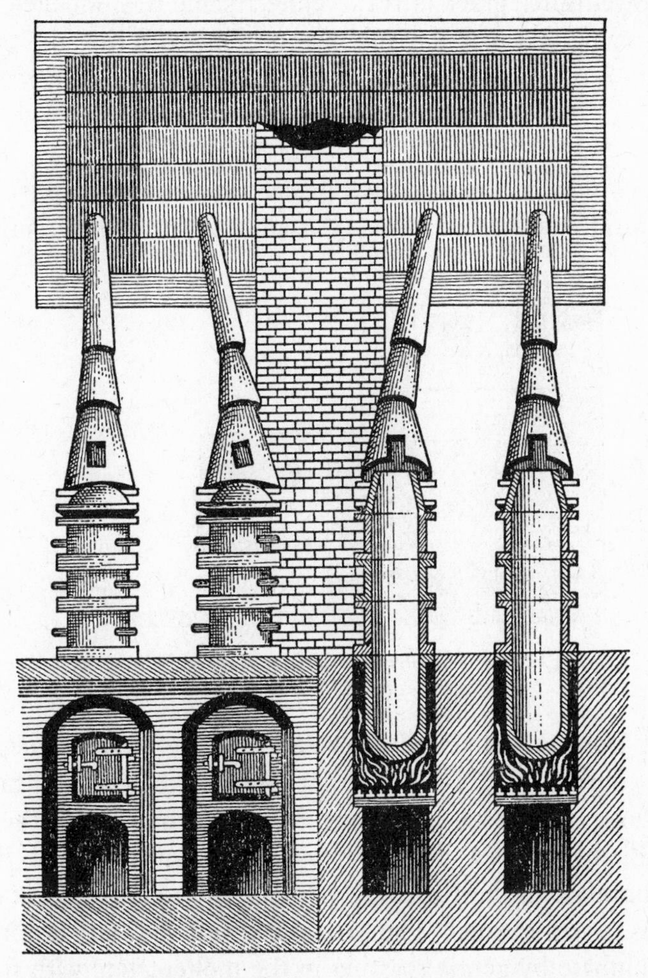

FIGURE 70—*Purification of white arsenic by sublimation, at Reichenstein.* (Left) *Front elevation;* (right) *vertical section.*

give a stronger and clearer sound; and to improve the fusibility of metals used for casting, such as that for cannon-balls.

Arsenic, unlike bismuth and antimony, was obtained chiefly from native arsenic or the ores containing it, particularly mispickel (arsenical pyrites), by sublimation in earthenware retorts and collection of the solid in large receivers, in which it was allowed to settle on pieces of sheet iron. Again unlike bismuth, arsenic was widely used in the arts, chiefly in the form of compounds. These included the oxide (white arsenic); the sulphides (orpiment and realgar, or red orpiment); and salts, such as the copper compounds known as Scheele's green (1778) and Schweinfurth green (1814). White arsenic was obtained from arsenical ores by carrying out a similar sublimation, but with the admission of air to effect oxidation. A typical sublimation furnace of the period is shown in figure 70.

II. LEAD

Lead occurs widely as the sulphide, galena, but also as sulphate, carbonate, phosphate, chloride, and other forms. Throughout this period, however, it was

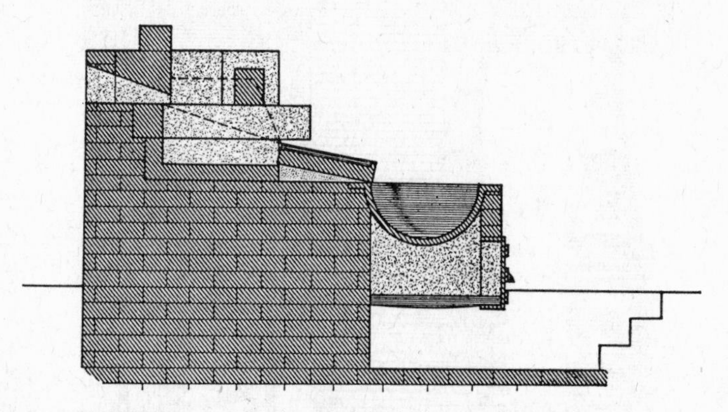

FIGURE 71—*Smelting lead in the ore-hearth (section).*

smelted chiefly from galena. In the nineteenth century several methods, traditional and new, were in use, in which either reverberatory or blast furnaces were employed. Among the most important of the former were the Flintshire, Spanish, and Bleiberg types. The first two were similar in that the lead was allowed to accumulate in the furnaces, whereas the metal ran out of the Bleiberg furnace as it was formed. The ore, after grinding and washing, was first converted to sulphate by gentle roasting in the molten state with free access of air. It was then mixed with a roughly equal amount of sulphide and reduced by strong heating without air, the furnace gases passing directly over the hearth on their way to the flue.

Blast-furnaces were used mainly with very rich ores. The most important types were the ore-hearth (figure 71), or Scotch furnace, and the American blast-furnace, the latter introducing the important innovation of pre-heating the air used in the blast by leading the pipes round the back of the hearth (figure 72). In the Scotch furnace the ore was placed on a cast iron hearth, and heated sufficiently to effect a partial oxidation without melting the galena. When the ore began to soften it was rabbled to produce a fresh surface. After about half the ore had been oxidized it was all drawn out into water and then dried. It was then returned to the hearth, mixed with coal and peat, and heated, the blast being forced in by a condensing-engine or by a fan worked by steam. At frequent intervals the slag was separated, the lead was run off into the vessel seen on the right of figure 71, and fresh fuel and ore were added. The process was continued without interruption for about 15 hours, when the hearth was emptied.

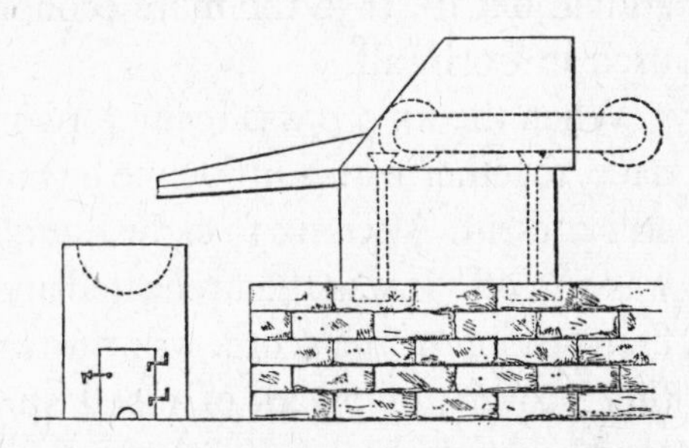

FIGURE 72—*Smelting lead in the American ore-hearth (side elevation).*

By these methods very large quantities of lead were produced in England and Wales, Spain, Germany, Sardinia, France, Belgium, Greece, and Austria-Hungary—in that order of importance. In the early part of the period some lead was used as sheets for sheathing the bottoms of ships, but copper was preferred in the eighteenth century. Sheet lead was also required for roofing and other purposes. At first such sheets were made by pouring molten lead on to a large stone and pressing another over it, but later grain rolls were employed, the former method being retained only for a few special purposes, such as making plates of metal. Much lead was required in the nineteenth century for water- and gas-pipes, but for the so-called composition pipes the tea-lead from China was sometimes used. At Birmingham, antimony was added to lead to impart hardness. Considerable quantities of the purest lead were also used in sulphuric acid chambers and for the manufacture of white lead and red lead.

III. TIN

In the eighteenth and nineteenth centuries nearly the whole of the tin of commerce was smelted from tinstone (tin oxide), with which sulphide ores containing copper and iron pyrites were often associated, as for example in Cornwall (plate 6B). The ore was first broken up and sorted into heaps of various qualities and then reduced to powder in a stamping-mill, driven by a water-wheel or by steam. After further sorting and purification by washing, any arsenic and sulphur compounds were removed by roasting in a reverberatory furnace. Later a special furnace was used, called Brunton's calciner after its inventor. This was provided with a hopper fitted in the arch over the bed, which consisted of a revolving cast iron table kept turning throughout the calcination. Oxides of sulphur passed out through the wide flue, in which the arsenic was retained in a number of chambers. The tin oxide was allowed to fall off the table into a lower compartment.

After about 1840, acids also were used for the purification of the ore—hydrochloric acid when the chief impurities were iron compounds and sulphuric acid for the separation of copper. Tungsten, too, was being removed at this time, the ore being first fused with alkaline salts: in Oxland's process crude soda was added, but by 1850 the more economical saltcake (sodium sulphate) was being used in Cornwall.

When the tin ore was ready for smelting, it was placed in a reverberatory furnace, together with a little lime or powdered fluorspar to combine with any silica still present. After six to eight hours, it was well rabbled and any metal formed was run off. It was then reheated and the floating scoria removed in stages. The first portion of the scoria was thrown away; the second was stamped to permit the recovery of pieces of metal spread through it; and the final skimmings, together with the recovered pieces, were kept for smelting with the next charge. The clean metal was then run out through a gutter into a cast iron pot, the slag and other impurities rising to the surface were skimmed off, and the tin was poured into moulds holding up to 3 cwt each.

Metallic impurities, usually iron and lead, but sometimes also copper, tungsten, and cobalt, had now to be removed. This was done in a number of ways. In 'boiling', a bundle of green-wood billets was lowered by a crane into a pot of molten tin. A great deal of seething took place, and the impurities were oxidized by the steam generated. In 'tossing', melted tin was lifted in ladles and allowed to fall again; this led to the formation of a small amount of oxide, which on mixing with the mass lost its oxygen to the more easily oxidized metals, thus causing them to rise as a slag. A further method was liquation. In this operation the blocks of metal were heated slowly in a reverberatory furnace until the tin began to melt, and the temperature was then kept constant until no more tin would run off. The impurities remained in a solid alloy of higher melting-point.

In Germany, and particularly at Altenberg, small blast-furnaces (figure 73) were preferred to reverberatories, and with them very good metal was produced, though the loss of tin was estimated at 15 per cent and the fuel consumed was nearly twice as much as in a reverberatory furnace.

Tin was used in large quantities for the production of alloys, such as bronze, bell metal, and solder, and for the manufacture of tinplate, tin-foil, and a number of compounds for use in pottery, glazes, and colours and as mordants in cloth-printing. Tin-foil, like lead-foil, was made by passing a thin slab backwards and forwards between rollers.

The manufacture of tinplate grew to large proportions during the final half-century of the period; for this purpose iron was required in sheets. The iron for 'charcoal' plates was prepared in a charcoal-fired refinery, whereas a light spongy coke was used for preparing 'coke' plates. During the nineteenth century these terms lost their significance and 'coke' plates were made from puddled iron. The prepared iron was heated and worked into blooms, which were cut and rolled into bars; the bars were sheared into lengths suitable for rolling into sheets.

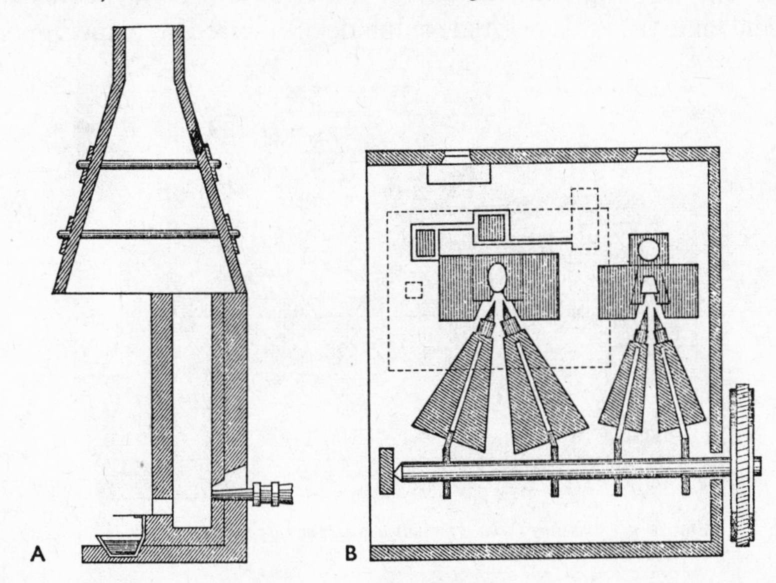

FIGURE 73—*Smelting tin by bellows-blown blast-furnace, at Altenberg.* (A) *Vertical section,* (B) *plan: (the right-hand furnace was for re-smelting slags).*

Scale was removed by pickling in an acid liquor and rubbing with sand and water, and the plates were then annealed and again pickled before tinning in a stow. This consisted of a row of baths of molten tin and of grease with fires below. The plates were first dipped in grease and then in tin. In a divided compartment the plates received a longer immersion to complete the tinning, and then, after brushing with hemp to remove any surplus, a short immersion in the purest tin. They were immediately placed in a grease pot to prevent the tin cooling more quickly than the iron and so cracking the surface of the plate. They were next immersed in melted tallow at a lower temperature. In the final bath, the list-pot, the plates were dipped in about a quarter of an inch of molten tin to remove the 'wire' of tin formed on the edges.

IV. COPPER

Copper occurs widely as sulphide, but considerable amounts of oxide and carbonate ores were also used in this period, particularly in Germany. Traditional methods of extraction were followed with little change until the nineteenth century, when the scale of the industry greatly increased.

In Britain the chief extraction centres were Neath and Swansea, with Bristol and parts of Lancashire important in the eighteenth century. The ores were obtained mainly from Cornwall and Ireland, but some came from Anglesey. By 1830–50 ores were being obtained mainly from South America, Canada, Cornwall, Ireland, and Wales. Low-grade sulphide ores were also being imported by

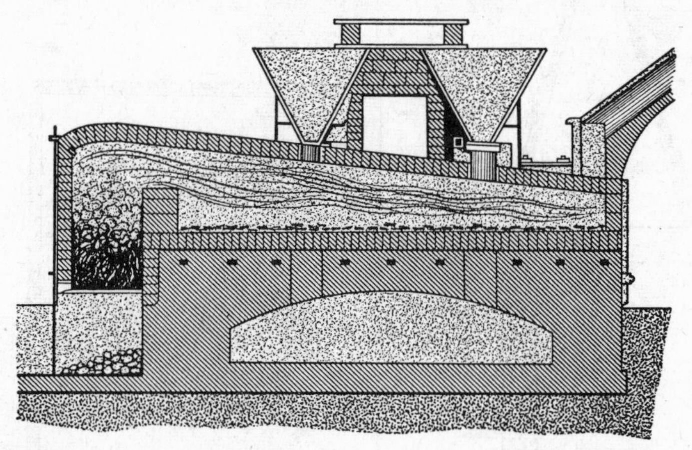

FIGURE 74—*Roasting furnace for sulphide ores of copper (vertical section).*

chemical manufacturers for the sake of the sulphur, and these were afterwards sold to the copper-smelters. Normally, reverberatory furnaces were used, though in other parts of Europe blast-furnaces were preferred. The methods of extraction, particularly from sulphide ores, were somewhat complicated; they derived from methods that in the sixteenth century took as long as eighteen months for their completion. Some makers recognized fourteen stages, but during the nineteenth century the work was considerably simplified, and the Welsh process, with its six major operations, will be described here.

(i) The ore was first roasted, in quantities of about three tons, and after 12 to 24 hours was raked into holes at the side of the bed and cooled with water (figure 74).

(ii) The brownish-black material was melted in the ore-furnace with 'metal slag' from process (iv). This gave 'coarse metal' containing about 35 per cent copper, which was separated from the slag. When the bed was full the coarse metal was granulated by running it into a pit filled with water (figure 75).

(iii) The granulated coarse metal was then calcined for 24 hours with frequent stirring, the temperature being gradually raised towards the end.

(iv) The calcined coarse metal was melted with the slag from (v) and (vi) or with ores rich in copper oxide. This gave metal containing about 75 per cent copper, and 'metal slag'.

(v) The metal was run out of the furnace and made into pigs (figure 76),

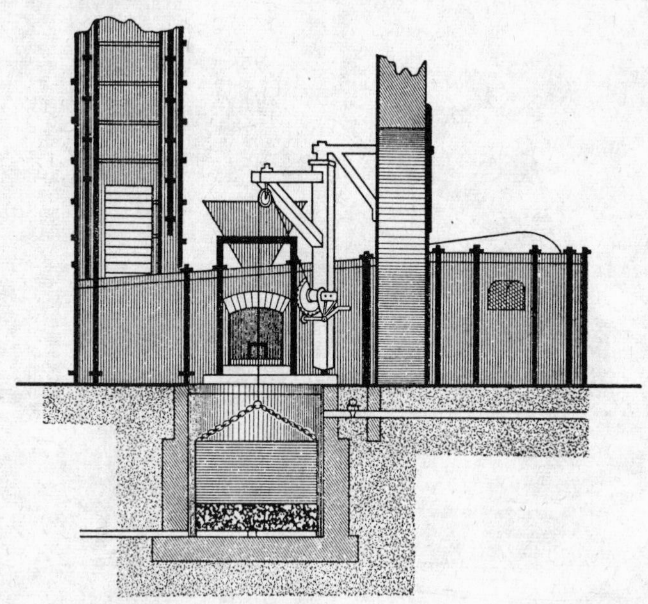

FIGURE 75—*Side view of melting furnace for sulphide ores of copper, showing water tank. The fused matte flowed into the tank from the furnace, and was thus granulated.*

which were transferred to a melting-furnace and heated, with air passing freely over the fire-bridge. The products were 'blister copper', containing 95 per cent copper, and 'roaster slag'. During this process the melt appeared to boil owing to the liberation of gases in the reaction. After removal of the slag the copper was tapped into sand-moulds.

(vi) The product was then further refined to give marketable copper and 'refinery slag'. This was done in a melting-furnace having an inclined bottom. About 6 to 8 tons of blister copper were melted and allowed to oxidize for about 15 hours in the air entering the furnace; the slag was then skimmed off. The copper was next toughened by throwing charcoal or anthracite on the surface and poling with green wood. In poling, the thick end of a long birch or oak pole was pushed into the melt and kept depressed by means of a prop. Much gas and vapour were evolved, and the metal was splashed about and exposed to the reducing action of the charcoal or anthracite. The copper, now in the state of 'tough pitch', was ladled out and quickly cast into moulds (figure 77), poured

FIGURE 76—*Copper furnaces at St Helens, Lancashire, in the nineteenth century. Tapping copper to make into pigs.*

into hot water to give 'bean shot', granulated for 'feather shot', or mixed with lead if intended for rolling into sheets.

Two enterprising methods of further simplifying the process of extraction may be mentioned. In 1846 James Napier patented a process, used near Swansea, that followed the four stages in the Cornish method of assay. It involved adding saltcake in the melting-furnace (stage ii) and afterwards breaking up the mix in water to separate impurities such as tin and antimony. The separation was not, however, complete, and the method was later abandoned. In 1859 Henry Hussey Vivian (1821–94) took the calcination direct to stage iv to obtain metal with 70 per cent copper. As a result large quantities of copper-rich slag were formed, which was the reason why this part of the process was normally stopped at about 35 per cent copper. Vivian smelted the slag separately in a blast-furnace, thus following the method customary on the continent.

All these processes were used with fairly rich sulphide ores. The Swedish ores, such as those smelted at Åtvidaberg, the chief centre of the industry there, were

FIGURE 77—*Casting purified copper in moulds. St Helens, Lancashire.*

in comparison very poor. As in France and Germany, blast-furnaces were used, and by 1861 the blast was being pre-heated by the waste gases. The ore was first roasted in kilns or in heaps. It was then fused, after mixing with slag rich in iron oxide, to give 20 to 30 per cent copper and a slag of iron silicate, the lower half of which contained sufficient copper to make it worth while using again. The furnace was tapped every two or three days. The coarse metal or regulus was then roasted and afterwards fused to give 'black copper' (95 per cent), which was refined in the blast-furnace to give 99·5 per cent copper.

Apart from its use for a great variety of vessels and utensils, copper was sold in very large quantities to the brass-makers, while a high proportion of the copper sheet made was used for sheathing the bottoms of ships. It was first used on warships about 1761, all ships being so sheathed by about 1780. Though later superseded in the merchant service by Muntz's metal (a brass containing about 3 parts of copper to 2 of zinc patented in 1832 by G. F. Muntz of Birmingham), copper sheet was still used in the Royal Navy long after this time. Both kinds of sheet often corroded rapidly and had to be replaced at frequent intervals.

Copper, together with silver, was also used in the eighteenth century for 'Sheffield plate', introduced about 1742 by Thomas Bolsover, a Sheffield cutler. Bolsover discovered that a billet made by fusing or soldering a thick sheet of copper to a thin one of silver could be rolled or flattened without unequal spreading of the metals. He applied this process to button-making and was thus able to supply the market at much below the usual prices. About 1758 Joseph Hancock used the new material to make household goods, such as coffee-pots and candlesticks, and soon afterwards the method spread elsewhere. Matthew Boulton of Birmingham entered the field about 1762, and after 1770 there were several firms of platers in Birmingham. One of the difficulties with Sheffield plate was the adequate protection of exposed edges, and Boulton was one of the first to use sterling silver thread, soldered on, for this purpose.

V. ZINC

In 1702 Nehemiah Champion and a number of merchants formed the British Brass Battery and Copper Company to exploit the calamine (zinc carbonate) deposits on Mendip, and by 1730 there were several works at Bristol and to the east of the city. Champion's sons William (1709–89) and John (1705–94) are credited with being the first in Europe to manufacture zinc from calamine and zinc blende (zinc sulphide) respectively. William is said to have learned of the Chinese method of obtaining zinc from calamine (vol III, p 691), possibly by way of the Dutch trading-posts in the Far East and Holland. By 1737 he had worked out a commercial process on these lines and he patented it in the following year. Later he had 31 furnaces producing copper, zinc, and brass, with associated rolling-mills and wire-mills. The machinery was run by water-power, a steam-engine being used to return the water to the pond. His interest in these ventures was eventually sold to the Bristol Brass Wire Company.

John Champion also built a works to produce zinc, and introduced a method for using blende instead of calamine, the ore being roasted to oxide before reduction. Other patents acquired by the brothers covered the removal of arsenic from copper and the production of alloys containing antimony and bismuth.

In the middle of the nineteenth century the extraction was carried out in a similar manner by the 'English' process, for example at Swansea. The ore was

FIGURE 78—*Zinc reduction house; English process,* c *1850, showing two vertical sections at right angles.*

crushed between iron rollers and then, after washing, roasted on a flat-bedded calciner. Sometimes double-bedded calciners, heated by the waste gases from the reduction furnace, were used. The reduction house (figure 78) had two storeys; in the upper the roasted ore and coke were heated, and in the 'cave' below the zinc vapour was condensed. Barrel-shaped pots, with holes at the top and bottom, were made from Stourbridge clay, glasshouse potsherds, and old spelter-pots. Over the bottom hole were placed plugs of old wood, then coke, then quantities of calcined blende and coke alternately. A short tube was fitted below the hole. On heating, the flame issuing beneath was watched until it

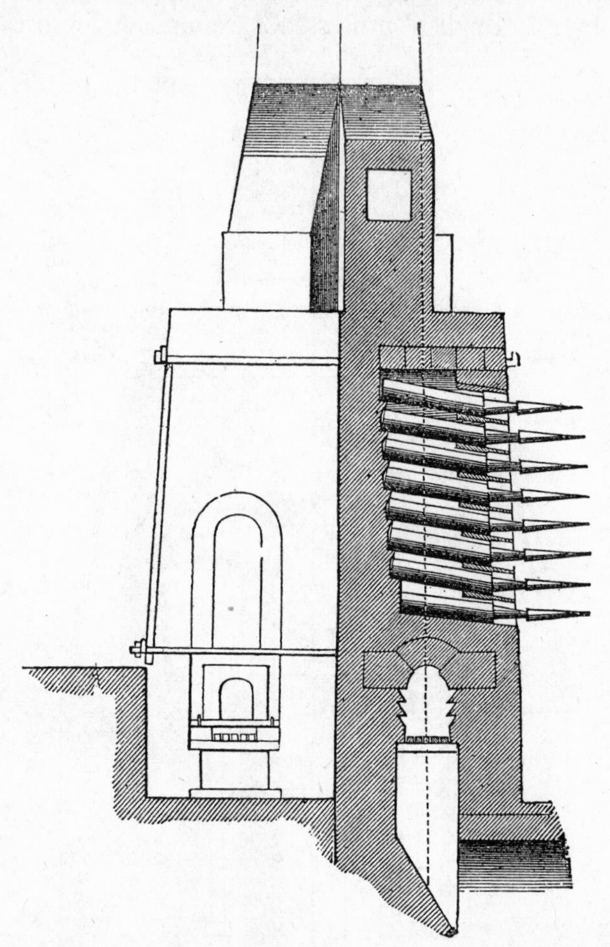

FIGURE 79—*Belgian process for zinc extraction at Vieille Montagne.* (Left) *Side view, showing position of furnace.* (Right) *Side section showing retorts.*

changed from brown to light blue. At this point a long tube or pipe was attached, and the metal condensed in trays as 'rough zinc'. This was melted in cast iron pots, skimmed, and ladled into flat open moulds. The skimmings or 'sweeps' were worked again.

Other processes employed on the continent differed from the English one mainly in the design of the reduction plant. In the Silesian process the vapour was taken off from the upper part of the retort and condensed in tubes. In the

Belgian process, introduced in the region of Liège in the early nineteenth century, parallel rows of retorts were placed over a fire in a narrow arched chamber (figure 79). The retorts were cylindrical vessels of refractory clay fitted with clay nozzles or condensers.

VI. BRASS

In the early eighteenth century Bristol was an important centre of the brass industry, but Birmingham later held pride of place, 1000 tons being put to use there in 1795. Brass, an alloy of copper and zinc, was much prized for its resemblance to gold when polished. A number of alloys were distinguished, with colours varying from yellow to burnished gold. In the range of 70 to 85 per cent copper were Prince's metal, Mannheim gold, and Dutch metal. In the lower range came Muntz's metal (p 130), containing 50 to 63 per cent copper.

Two methods of production were employed. Either the two metals were alloyed in the required proportions, or 'calamine' brass was prepared without melting the copper. In the direct method the metals were melted in crucibles or reverberatory furnaces, skimmed, and poured into sand-moulds or rolled into sheets. If rolled, the sheets were afterwards pickled in sulphuric acid to remove scale and then washed in water. Considerable quantities of wire were also made.

For calamine brass, copper was heated in pots with calamine and charcoal. The product was not homogeneous, but it had a characteristic appearance when polished and was much in demand in the eighteenth century for 'gilt' objects, such as the buttons for which Birmingham became famous. By the end of the period we are now considering, however, the manufacture had ceased.

The consumption of brass was further increased by reason of the variety of surface effects that could be produced by chemical and other means. For example, dead-dipping or etching the surface of finished goods with nitric acid to give a pale yellow subdued appearance was for some time a very popular treatment. In other brass-work the colour was heightened by lacquering with shellac dissolved in proof spirit and coloured with the resin known as dragon's blood, obtained from a species of *Dracaena*. Sometimes the brass was 'bronzed' by dipping into a solution of arsenious acid in hydrochloric acid, by dilute platinum chloride solution, by a solution of mercuric chloride mixed with vinegar, or by rubbing with plumbago. The bronze-like tint was made permanent with lacquer.

VII. MERCURY

The principal ore of mercury, cinnabar (mercury sulphide), has been known from very early times. The liquid metal is readily separated from several of its compounds and often occurs dispersed through the ore. Mercury was also found in parts of South America as an amalgam with silver, as in the rich mines of Arqueros, or with gold, as mixed with some platinum ore in Colombia. On the large scale, however, mercury was prepared from cinnabar.

In the nineteenth century the most important mercury mine was that at Almaden in Spain, where the traditional method of extraction was still carried out in aludel furnaces (figure 80). The ore was heated with admission of air, which was sufficient to oxidize the sulphur and liberate the mercury as vapour;

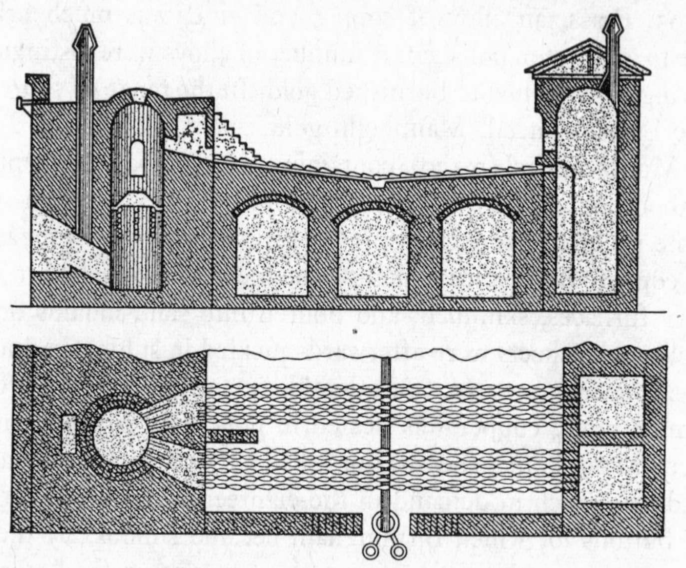

FIGURE 80—*Aludel furnace for extraction of mercury at Almaden.* (Above) *Vertical section.* (Below) *Plan. Note long files of aludels to condense the mercury.*

this was led away with the other gases through long files of earthenware condensers (aludels). The aludels were detached and emptied after two weeks.

Another mine that became famous was that worked at Idria in Italy, where the Almaden system was adopted in 1750 as an improvement on the crude method previously followed. However, towards the close of the century a large distillation furnace of a new pattern was erected (figure 81). Here the vapours emerging from the furnace were led alternately downwards and upwards through communicating compartments on either side. In the last compartment water was made to fall on a series of inclined boards fitted from one wall almost to the opposite one, so as to condense the last traces of mercury. The metal flowed out from each chamber into a receiver and thence to the main tank. After filtering through ticking it was put into cast iron bottles for sale and export.

At works in the duchy of Deux-Ponts the ore was heated with quicklime to avoid using extensive condensing equipment. Up to 52 earthenware retorts (cucurbits) were arranged in double row sin a gallery over a coal fire, and the metal was collected in earthenware receivers.

A new method used at Lansberg in Bavaria was designed by Andrew Ure (1778–1857) on a principle resembling that employed for coal-gas manufacture (figure 82). The plant was erected in 1847 and consisted of a series of cast iron retorts arranged in threes under arches of masonry. A pipe from each retort led

FIGURE 81—*Mercury distillation furnace at Idria*, c *1800*. (Above) *Vertical section*. (Below) *Plan*.

down to a wide condenser-pipe cooled with water. In this way a charge of 6 to 7 cwt of coarsely powdered ore and quicklime was worked off in a few hours.

About 1844 some Mexicans attempted to obtain gold from the red earth of a cave in California. This led to the discovery of another important source of mercury and to the opening up of the mine at New Almaden by Barrow, Forbes & Company. By 1853 nearly 20 000 bottles, each containing 75 lb of mercury, had been exported from New Almaden through the port of San Francisco, some 20 miles away. In 1856 there were 14 smelting-furnaces with condensing chambers; these were very similar in principle to the furnaces introduced at Idria some fifty years earlier.

VIII. SILVER

The metallurgy of silver, according to Percy, was 'the most extensive, the most varied, and the most complicated of all'. Although silver could be obtained fairly readily from its compounds, the high value of the metal meant that it was profitable to extract it from other metals, such as copper and lead, with which it was often mixed in relatively small amounts. Though in the earlier part of this period silver occurring in copper was in part removed by liquation, the

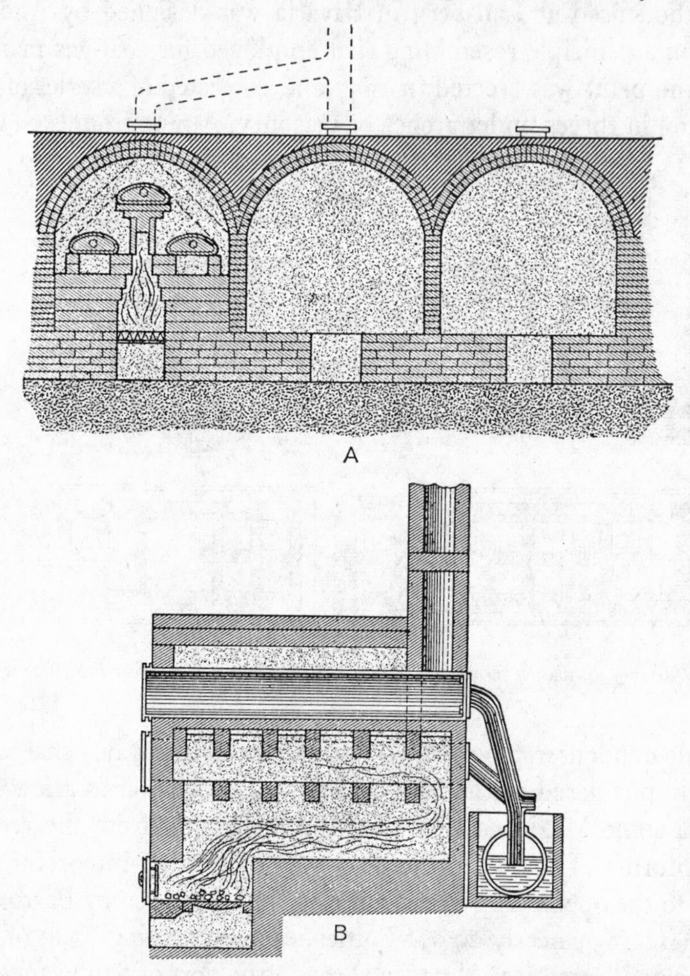

FIGURE 82—*Mercury extraction at Lansberg, Bavaria, in 1847.* (A) *Vertical section;* (B) *section through a retort. The mercury liberated in the triple stills in* (A) *is condensed in the condenser seen in the bottom right of* (B).

later method was to remove it at the reguline stage. It was fused with a large excess of lead at a temperature below the melting-point of copper; the lead flowed off, carrying with it most of the silver. The lead was then removed by cupellation (p 137). The copper that remained was impure, being always contaminated with lead and retaining some of the silver.

The most important developments in the extraction of silver, however, were two processes introduced by H. L. Pattinson (1796–1858) and Alexander Parkes (1813–90) respectively for the removal of the metal from lead. Until 1833 this was done by cupellation, in which under the action of an air-blast the lead was converted to litharge and blown out in the molten state. This was continued until the lead–silver alloy contained about 8 per cent of silver, when it was tapped out. It was then refined again in a similar way, the fire being increased towards the

FIGURE 83—*Pattinson's process, 1833.* (Above) *Section and plan of cast iron pots and fires.* (Below) *Removal of lead crystals with perforated ladles. The small pot on the right was for melting poor lead.*

end of the operation and the silver kept molten until all the lead had been removed.

A much greater recovery of the silver became possible after 1829. In that year Pattinson, of Newcastle upon Tyne, discovered that when molten argentiferous lead is cooled until it begins to crystallize, the first crystals to separate are of pure lead. From this observation a new process of separation was worked out and patented in 1833 (figure 83). A row of eight or ten cast iron pots, each large enough to contain 5 tons of molten lead, was arranged in a brickwork gallery with a fire under each pot. The lead was put into the middle pot, melted, skimmed, and allowed to cool with constant stirring. The crystals were removed in a perforated ladle, from which any molten metal was shaken off, and this was continued until about three-quarters to four-fifths of the original lead had been removed. The enriched lead that remained was then transferred to the next pot on the one side and the crystals to the next on the other side. The middle pot was recharged and the process was repeated until the pot of enriched lead was nearly full. This enriched charge was heated, and the process was repeated until 'lead riches', with 300 oz silver per ton, were obtained. They were then purified by cupellation in a reverberatory furnace. The new method was soon in use throughout the United Kingdom, and about 1850 was adopted in the lead foundries of France, Spain, and Prussia.

A further process, patented by Alexander Parkes of Birmingham in 1850, was based on the observation that when zinc and lead are melted together and

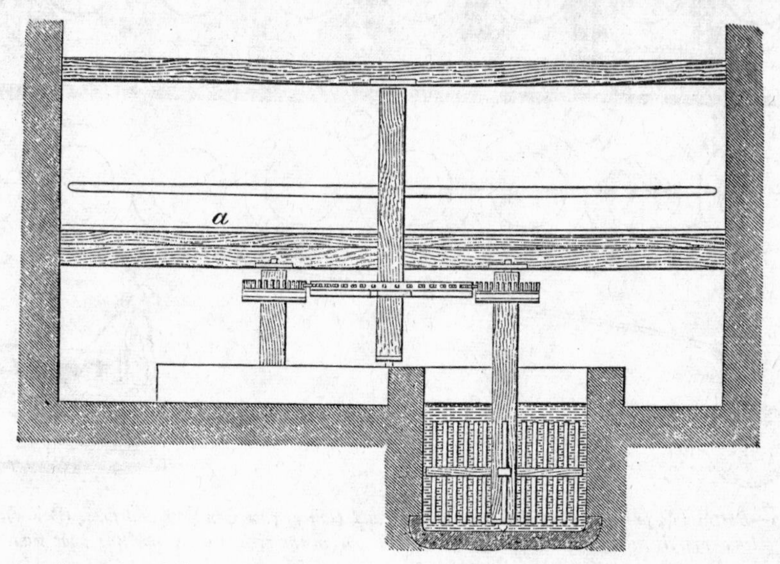

FIGURE 84—*Extraction of silver amalgam by washing*, c *1840. The stirring apparatus is worked by mules, walking on platform* (a). *The amalgam is taken out from the bottom of the vat* (bottom right).

allowed to cool, any silver present becomes concentrated in the zinc. The method used in 1851 was to add 22·4 lb zinc for every 14 oz silver in each ton of lead to be treated. On cooling the melt, the zinc–silver crystals that rose to the surface were drawn out in a perforated ladle. Lead and zinc were removed by heating to dull redness in air, skimming, and then removing the remaining zinc by means of acid or by distillation. The zinc in the impoverished lead left in the pot was separated by poling with green wood. By Parkes's method almost complete separation of the silver was effected, and it eventually superseded Pattinson's process. The method was not successfully operated in Germany until 1866.

Poor ores, worked for their silver content only, were often extracted by the amalgamation process, introduced in Mexico by Bartolomeo Medina, a miner of Pachuca, in 1557. This was a considerable achievement, for it was an intricate process, but the only one possible in a country deficient in both fuel and water-power. The method was taken to Peru in 1570, when the Spaniards were beginning to exploit the mercury in the area of Huancavelica. The amalgamation method was introduced into Hungary in 1786, and thence carried to Saxony,

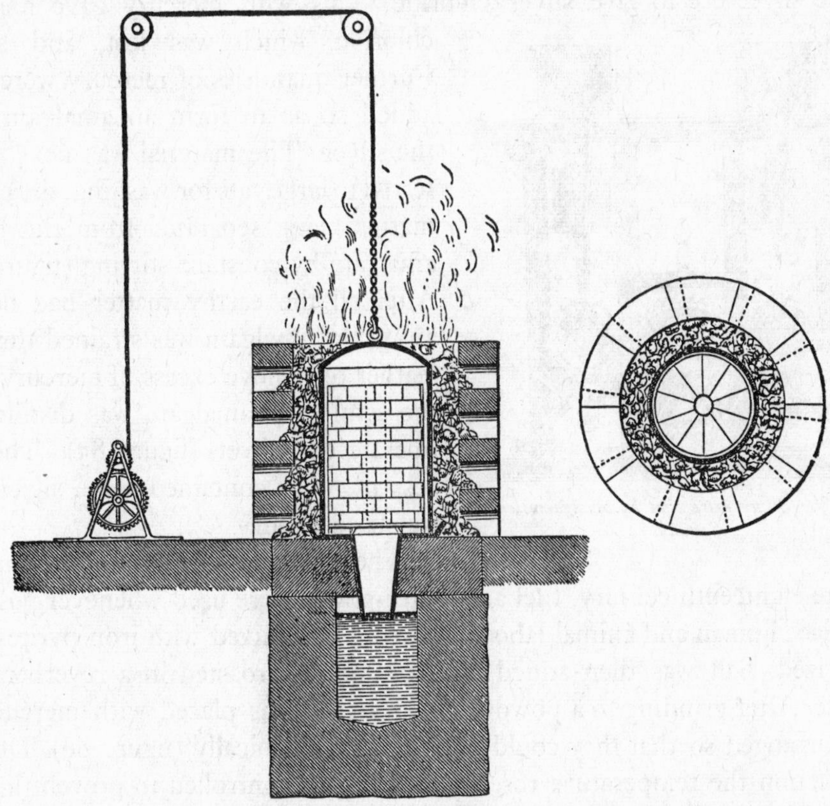

FIGURE 85—*Furnace for the pressed amalgam distilling, seen in section and plan. The amalgam was stacked in the centre of the apparatus and the mercury collected in the reservoir beneath it.*

when it was found that some Freiberg ores could be treated similarly to those of Oaxaca and other parts of Central America.

In America the ore was first stamped, and then pulverized with the addition of water until a mud or soft paste was formed. The fine state of division so obtained was essential to avoid great loss of mercury during the amalgamation. The paste was then placed in pits to dry. The amalgamation-floor was a flat, open space on which several heaps of crude sea-salt were arranged and covered with quantities of the paste. The materials were thoroughly mixed by turning over with shovels and prolonged treading by mules. Roasted and pulverized copper ore, such as copper pyrites, was then added and intimately mixed. Mercury was afterwards sprinkled over the heap by straining it through coarse cloth. Turning over and treading were repeated for several days until all the mercury had been incorporated.

The salt and copper ore reacted to give copper chloride, which in turn acted on the silver ore to give silver chloride. This with mercury gave mercury chloride, which was lost, and silver. Further quantities of mercury were then added so as to form an amalgam with the silver. The material was next transferred to large vats for washing, the earthy matter being separated from the heavy amalgam by constant stirring (figure 84). After all the earthy matter had flowed away, the amalgam was strained through leather to remove excess of mercury, and the semi-solid amalgam was distilled to liberate the silver (figure 85). The excess mercury contained some silver and was used again.

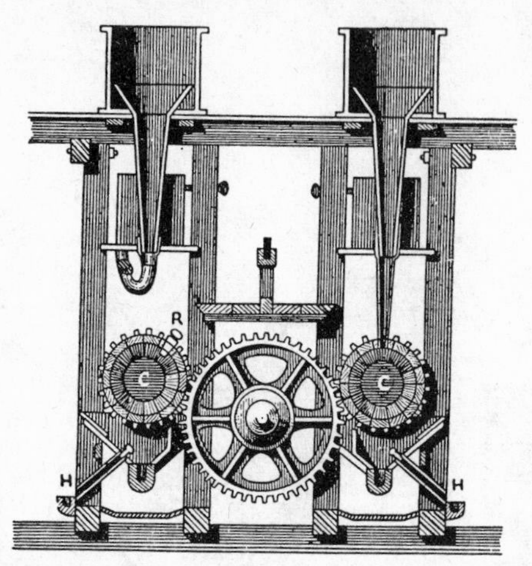

FIGURE 86—*Silver extraction by amalgamation in Saxony.*

When the method came to Europe in the late eighteenth century, fuel and water-power were used whenever possible to replace human and animal labour. The ore was mixed with iron pyrites and pulverized. Salt was then added and the mixture roasted in a reverberatory furnace. After grinding to a powder, the material was placed with mercury in casks arranged so that they could be rotated mechanically (figure 86). During the reaction the temperature rose and had to be controlled to prevent loss of mercury in a fine state during washing. After the amalgamation was complete, the casks (C) were filled with water and turned for two hours. The bungs (R) were then removed, stop-cocks were inserted, and the amalgam was run out into gutters (H) leading to a reservoir. The mercury was next distilled off by placing the amalgam in flat iron dishes and heating under a bell-shaped apparatus. The remaining silver was melted in open crucibles and cast into ingots containing about 80 per cent of silver, the remainder being mainly copper.

The chief methods of refining are mentioned later (p 142).

IX. GOLD

The only gold of commercial importance was the native metal, most commonly obtained by washing sand and gravel from the beds of streams and rivers and alluvial deposits in general. Plentiful supplies of water were necessary for this purpose, but not much equipment. The discovery of rich new sources of gold in California (1847) and eastern Australia (1851) caused world-wide excitement. In 1860 it was considered that a sand containing 1 part of gold in 36 000 was

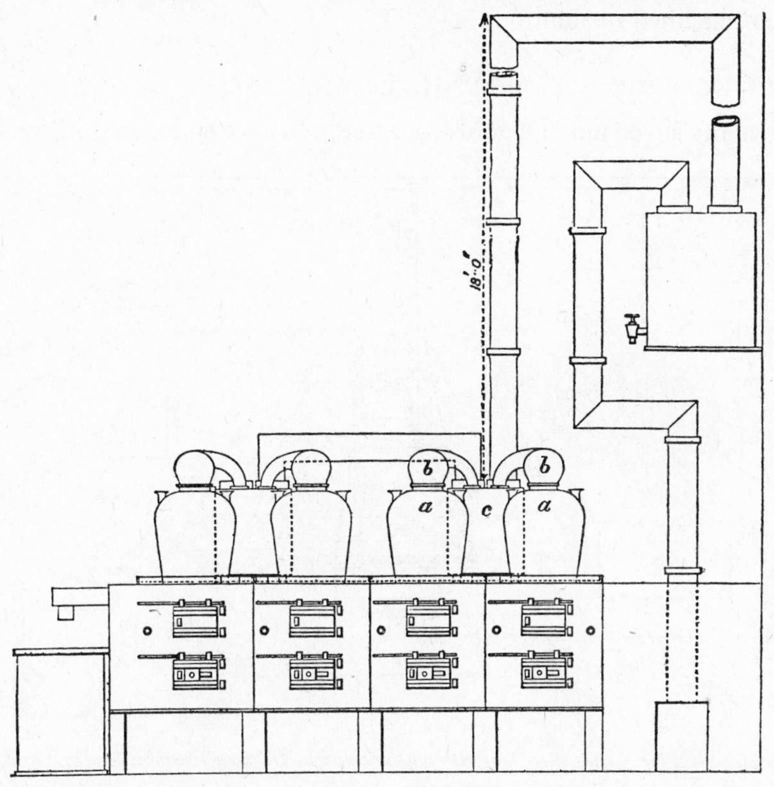

FIGURE 87—*Parting with nitric acid in platinum vessels, with arrangements for carrying off nitrous fumes: Johnson Matthey & Company,* c *1850. Each platinum vessel* (aa) *is set over a separate furnace;* bb, *still-heads. The receivers* (c) *are of earthenware.*

worth working; with modern chemical methods it later became profitable to extract gold occurring to the extent of only 1 part in 100 000 of quartz and 1 part in 3 000 000 of sand.

The process of amalgamation was introduced primarily to extract the fine particles of gold from the quartz in which it was often found dispersed, and by 1850 it was becoming generally realized that amalgamation was advantageous also in working alluvial sands.

Not much gold was obtained in Europe, the most important sources there being Hungary and Russia. For a time a novel method was used to extract gold from the arsenical pyrites at Reichenstein in Silesia: it was suggested by the analyst C. F. Plattner and earned a medal at the Great Exhibition of 1851. After roasting to remove arsenic, a current of chlorine was passed through the ore and the chlorides of iron and gold were removed with water. Hydrochloric acid was then added and hydrogen sulphide was passed through to precipitate the gold. The iron remained in solution.

X. REFINING PROCESSES FOR SILVER AND GOLD

Neither the silver nor the gold from the processes so far described was pure.

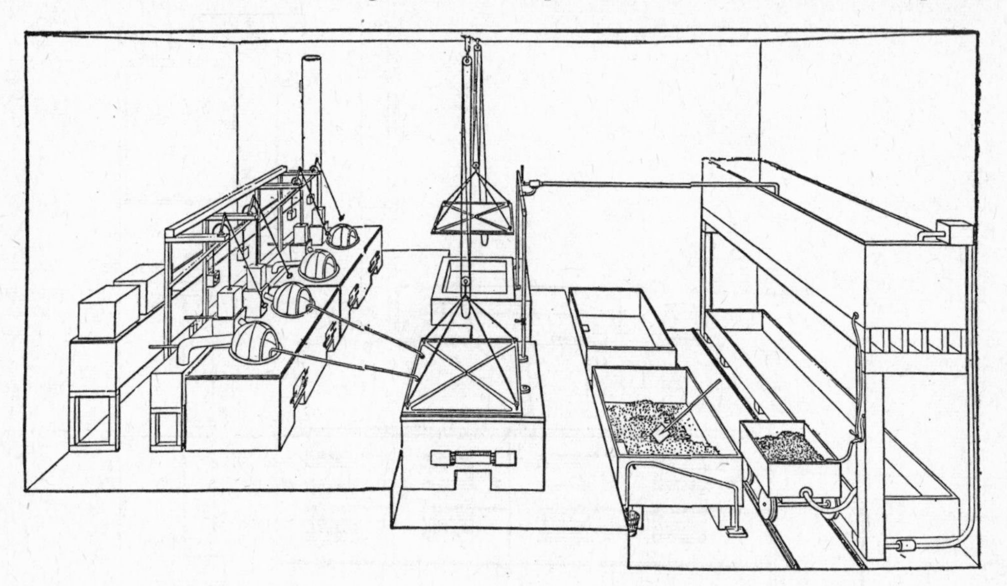

FIGURE 88—*Plant for parting silver bars with sulphuric acid by Gutzkow's method. San Francisco, c 1867.*

Silver often contained copper and some gold, while gold was frequently admixed with copper, silver, and the platinum metals. For some purposes the presence of copper in silver was not a serious disadvantage, but if necessary the silver could be melted with excess lead; the lead was removed by cupellation, carrying the copper with it. Similarly, although a number of chemical methods for detecting and separating platinum, which was sometimes used to debase gold, were worked out in the eighteenth century, they were not often conducted on a large scale. The most important operations were those used to separate silver and gold.

Several such methods were in use before 1700: for example, 'parting' with nitric acid, and with sulphur, sulphur and iron, sulphur and litharge, and antimony sulphide, in addition to the 'cementation' process. Parting with nitric acid was commonly carried out in platinum vessels (figure 87) when that metal became available, all the metals other than gold and platinum dissolving. When required free from copper, the silver was sometimes precipitated from the solution with salt.

A cheaper but nevertheless efficient method of parting, with sulphuric acid, was introduced about 1840 and was soon in use at the Royal Mint and in some refineries on the continent. By 1870 it was widely practised in Europe and

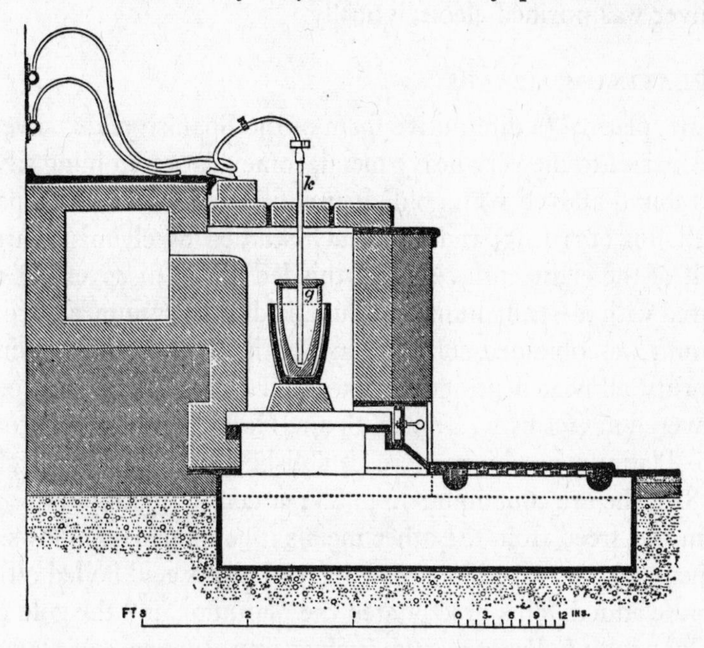

FIGURE 89—*Purification of gold by chlorine at Sydney,* c *1867. The gold is melted in the crucible* (g) *and chlorine is admitted through the pipe* (k).

America (figure 88). Vessels of cast iron were employed at first; after a time a change was made to platinum, but later there was a return to cast iron. The silver was dissolved in strong boiling sulphuric acid (figure 88, left), when the gold and any platinum formed a sediment. Copper, lead, and tin also dissolved but they could be largely removed by throwing the mass into water. Before 1830 the limit to parting by any of the methods then available was 0·08 per cent of gold; with the sulphuric acid method it was 0·03 to 0·05 per cent, a considerable advantage with such a valuable metal.

By the end of our period two other methods had been developed. In the first, which was adopted at the Sydney mint, gold was refined by chlorine in special crucibles (figure 89) made by Payen of Paris and Morgan of Battersea. The gold was melted and borax added. On passing chlorine through, fumes consisting of the volatile chlorides of the baser metals were emitted. After a time these fumes ceased and chlorine was then absorbed until all the silver had been acted upon: the operation was known to be complete when free chlorine passed through. The melt was then cooled until the gold solidified, when the liquid silver chloride was poured off. The chloride was made into slabs and arranged alternately with slabs of iron or zinc in a vessel containing acidulated water. This was fitted up as a cell, and the silver was purified electrolytically.

XI. THE PLATINUM METALS

The name 'platina' (a diminutive form of the Spanish *plata*, silver) was given in South America to the very heavy metal, somewhat resembling silver, that was sometimes found alloyed with gold. It was first reported in Europe in 1736 by Antonio d'Ulloa (1716–95) and was much studied by chemists throughout the second half of the eighteenth century; this led to the discovery of other metals that occurred with it—palladium, rhodium, iridium, osmium, and ruthenium. At first platinum was obtained solely from South America, but during the nineteenth century alluvial deposits were worked in the Urals, and other sources were discovered in Germany, France, Spain, Hungary, and the Ratoo mountains in Borneo. Platinum washings were established on the western slopes of the Urals in 1824, the ore containing 70 to 88 per cent of platinum.

Platinum was freed from the other metals it contained as follows. To remove gold the metal was dissolved in *aqua regia*, the excess acid boiled off, and ammonium chloride added. This precipitated the platinum, and the gold chloride was separated by washing. Baser metals, such as iron, copper, and manganese, were removed by treating the metal grains with strong nitric and hydrochloric acids alternately until the base impurities were removed. The platinum was then redissolved in *aqua regia*, precipitated with ammonium chloride, and reduced, the latter merely by gradually raising the temperature to red heat. To prevent precipitation of the other metals of the platinum group, the solution in *aqua regia* was freed as much as possible from excess acid, and nitric acid was added before precipitation with ammonium chloride. The platinum black, or powder, obtained in this way, was pressed and beaten into sheets.

At St Petersburg (Leningrad) ore from the Urals was treated in a number of open platinum basins ranged on a sand-bath and covered with a glazed dome surmounted with a ventilator-pipe. It was heated for 8 to 10 hours with *aqua regia* and subsequently decanted, the platinum salt then being precipitated with aqueous ammonia. After settling, it was again decanted and cooled, when the iridium salt crystallized out. The precipitates were evaporated in porcelain vessels and heated to redness. The platinum powder was placed in a mould and pressed with a rammer; it was then baked in a porcelain kiln for 36 hours, after which it could easily be forged as required. This was a modification of the process known as Wollaston's method, which was also arrived at independently by L. N. Vauquelin (1763–1829).

Crucibles and other laboratory wares were manufactured by means of special moulds into which the powder was rammed. It was afterwards heated in an air-furnace, then in a very hot blast, and finally finished off on the anvil. In addition, the metal was employed for the equipment used in sulphuric acid rectifiers, in the construction of electric batteries, and in dentistry. It was not, however, used at this time for jewelry.

XII. COBALT AND NICKEL

The metal cobalt was obtained by the Swedish chemist Brandt in 1733 from the mineral cobalt or zaffre, long used to give a blue colour to glass. Until the second half of the nineteenth century the metal was scarcely more than a laboratory curiosity and was not extracted on the large scale. Some of its compounds, however, were in frequent use. The chloride, nitrate, and sulphate were sometimes employed as sympathetic inks, while the phosphate was used as the pigment known as Thenard's blue. Cobalt oxide and cobalt silicate (smalt) were in large demand and were prepared on the commercial scale in the following way. The ore was smelted and the regulus calcined, and the product was then dissolved in concentrated hydrochloric acid. After removing iron with milk of lime, copper and some other impurities were precipitated by means of a stream of hydrogen sulphide. The cobalt was then precipitated with bleaching-powder and the solid was dried and heated to red or white heat, giving blue oxide or 'prepared' oxide respectively. In England these oxides were made chiefly at Birmingham by the nickel refiners.

Smalt was obtained, mainly in Germany, by a method not greatly different from that practised in earlier times (vol III, p 703), by roasting the ore to impure oxide and then vitrifying it with pulverized quartz and calcined potash in an oven resembling a glass-furnace.

Nickel was recognized as a distinct metal by Axel Cronstedt (1722–65) in 1751. He obtained it from *Kupfernickel*, or false copper, an ore resembling one of copper but from which copper could not be obtained. It was chiefly extracted from this ore, mined in Germany and Norway, or from ores containing nickel and cobalt. *Kupfernickel* was first roasted to remove arsenic, and was then mixed with sulphur and potash and fused in a large earthenware crucible. After this treatment warm water was added, when arsenic and sulphur, which had reacted with the potash, were removed. The nickel sulphides, usually contaminated with iron, were then dissolved in sulphuric acid and a little nitric acid. The nickel and iron were precipitated from the solution as carbonates and treated with oxalic acid. The nickel oxalate was separated by dissolving it in ammonia, and on evaporating the solution to dryness and strongly heating the residue in a luted crucible a globule of nickel was obtained.

In the nineteenth century a different method was used at Birmingham. The ore or speiss was fused with chalk and fluorspar, powdered, and then roasted to expel arsenic. The residue was dissolved in hydrochloric acid, and the iron was oxidized with bleaching-powder and precipitated with milk of lime. The liquid was next treated with hydrogen sulphide to remove impurities such as copper, bismuth, and lead. This left cobalt and nickel in solution. On adding bleaching-powder, the cobalt was precipitated. Milk of lime was then added to the remaining solution until no more precipitate was given.

Nickel was used mainly in alloys, the chief of which was German silver, sometimes used as a substitute for silver or for cheaper plated articles. The normal composition was 1 part nickel, 1 part zinc, and 2 parts copper, but if the alloy were intended for rolling the proportions of nickel and copper were raised somewhat, a common formula being 5 parts of nickel to 4 of zinc and 12 of copper. For casting, a small amount of lead was added to the latter. By 1860 a number of alloys were distinguished in the English midlands, having the following approximate compositions:

	Copper per cent	*Nickel per cent*	*Zinc per cent*	*Use and chief characteristics*
Common German silver .	60	15	25	Cheap wares. Minimum nickel feasible to avoid tarnishing.
Good German silver . .	55	20	25	Better wares, near silver in appearance.
Electrum (normal) . .	51·5	26	22·5	Slight blue shade, like polished silver. Better wares.
Electrum (richest) . .	46	34	20	Highest proportion of nickel feasible. Best wares only.
Tutenag (Chinese alloy) .	46	17	37	For casting; very hard and fusible.

At this time nickel-plated articles were coming into favour, the metal being deposited electrolytically with a nickel slab as anode and nickel chloride as electrolyte.

XIII. MANGANESE

Though the character of manganese compounds was known in the eighteenth century through the work of C. W. Scheele (1742–86) and J. G. Gahn (1745–1818), the extraction of the metal was difficult and it remained a laboratory process until late in the nineteenth century. Some manganese compounds were, however, widely used, particularly the common black oxide. This and other oxides were required in large quanitites for making glass and pottery and for preparing chlorine for the manufacture of bleaching-powder. Manganese sulphate was used in dyeing and calico-printing.

BIBLIOGRAPHY

Much information for this period is collected in the following works, among others:

DUPORT, H. ST CLAIR. 'De la production des métaux précieux au Mexique.' Paris. 1843.

GRAY, S. F. 'The Operative Chemist.' London. 1828.

MUSPRATT, J. S. 'Chemistry, Theoretical, Practical, and Analytical as applied and relating to the Arts and Manufactures' (2 vols). Glasgow. 1853, 1861.

PERCY, J. 'Metallurgy', Vols 1, 3, 5. London. 1861–80.

URE, A. 'A Dictionary of Arts, Manufactures and Mines.' London. 1837–9.

The following illustrate various aspects of the subject:

'Copper through the Ages.' Copper Development Association, London. 1934.

DICKINSON, H. W. 'Matthew Boulton.' University Press, Cambridge. 1937.

GUILLET, L. 'L'Évolution de la métallurgie.' Alcan, Paris. 1928.

HAMILTON, H. 'The English Brass and Copper Industries to 1800.' Longmans, London. 1926.

'History of Henry Wiggin & Company, Ltd., 1835–1935.' Henry Wiggin & Co., Birmingham. 1935.

LIPPMANN, E. O. VON. 'Die Geschichte des Wismuts zwischen 1400 und 1800.' Springer, Berlin. 1930.

McDONALD, D. 'Percival Norton Johnson: The Biography of a Pioneer Metallurgist.' Johnson Matthey, London. 1951.

PAIRPOINT, F. 'Antique Plated Ware' (4th ed.). Pairpoint Brothers, London. 1925.

PURSEY, L. N. W. "The Champions of Bristol." *Discus*, 11, 1955.

'The Platinum Metals Exhibition.' Institution of Metallurgists, London. 1953.

Chilian mill for crushing silver ores.

5

POWER TO 1850

R. J. FORBES

I. THE INDUSTRIAL REVOLUTION

DURING the last 250 years five great new prime movers have produced what is often called the Machine Age. The eighteenth century brought the steam-engine; the nineteenth the water-turbine, the internal combustion engine, and the steam-turbine; and the twentieth the gas-turbine. Historians have often coined catch-phrases to denote movements or currents in history. Such is 'The Industrial Revolution', the title for a development often described as starting in the early eighteenth century and extending through much of the nineteenth [1]. It was a slow movement, but wrought changes so profound in their combination of material progress and social dislocation that collectively they may well be described as revolutionary if we consider these extreme dates.

The roots of this revolution stretch back into the sixteenth century, when important technological changes slowly began to take place. These had gained momentum by the middle of the eighteenth century. Outside Britain the revolution was far from complete even by 1880; thus Germany cannot be said even to have entered the industrial stage before the 1870s. In the United States, though it began early in the 1860s, it did not obtain a firm grip until the turn of the century. Economically the basic factor in the industrial revolution was the remarkable expansion of overseas trade in the seventeenth and eighteenth centuries. The new markets came first, the inventions followed. Unconsciously, the successful inventors worked within the limits laid down for them by the changing society in which they dwelt and the new materials that were becoming available.

That the industrial revolution first gained momentum in the British Isles and that its results first began to become most clearly visible in Scotland and the midland counties of England may be ascribed to many fortuitous factors. Britain, by conquering the seas, established the largest foreign markets; she had the necessary capital for industrial experiments, a currency firmly based on gold, an efficient banking system, political and social stability, abundance of iron ore and coal, a humid climate suitable for textile manufacture, and social circles interested in scientific knowledge. The economic demands were met by scientific and technological advances of an increasingly high standard. Much of the new science of the seventeenth century had from the beginning stressed the importance of practical aims.

From the days of Stevin (1548–1620) and Galileo (1564–1642) the science of mechanics yielded fresh understanding of machines, particularly when, in the eighteenth century, mathematics came to be constantly applied to the theory and practice of their construction. That century also saw the start of experiment on the strength of materials, and thus notably contributed to practical mechanics

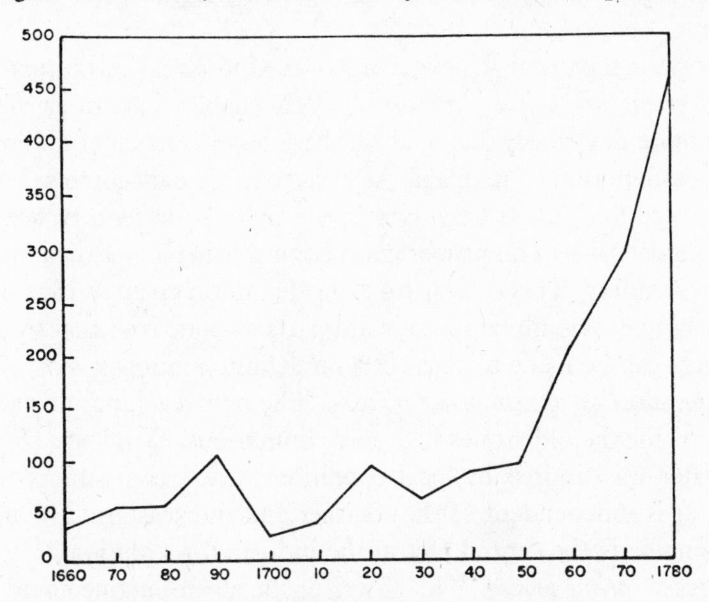

FIGURE 90—*Numbers of patents of inventions, 1660–1780.*

and the design of well built engines. Exact measurement, the very basis of science, was becoming ever more important for the design and maintenance of all complex mechanisms. Moreover, practical engineering itself had gained momentum [2]. The classical world had been seriously concerned with the study and control of motion, though several factors, notably slave labour, had kept power resources at a low level (vol II, ch 17). Subsequent developments had involved changes in scale rather than in principle. In the words of Usher, 'these developments may seem to be little more than a diffusion of knowledge already attained. For a long time, no additional theoretical knowledge would have been of much practical use. It would be an error, however, to minimize the magnitude of the technological changes that opened up the first extensive applications of power. It was the beginning of an essentially new stage in mechanical technique' [3].

By the mid-seventeenth century there were many who saw clearly that co-operation between science and practical engineering formed the essential basis of technical improvements. In this century and the following one there was a notable rise in the number of patents (figure 90). Adam Smith (1723–90) realized that these improvements were not only the work of practical engineers but that 'some came to be by the ingenuity of those men of speculation, whose trade it is not to do anything, but to observe everything; and who, upon that account, are often capable of combining together the powers of the most distant and dissimilar objects'.

The four basic technical achievements of the industrial revolution were:

1. *Replacement of tools by machines.* Both enable man to perform certain operations more dextrously than with the bare hand. The chief difference is that the tool is set in motion by man's physical strength, the machine by some natural force. The word machine is here used in the eighteenth-century sense, for both then and long afterwards no proper distinction was made between prime movers and other machinery. This is clear from the definition given in 1875 by Reuleaux [4]: 'A machine is a combination of solid parts so contrived that by means of it natural forces can be made to cause certain definite motions.'

2. *The introduction of new prime movers.* The new machines demanded a new prime mover, for the older ones had grave limitations. Wind was cheap but unreliable, water was limited by local conditions, but steam suffers neither disadvantage. It is independent of the weather and the seasons. The invention of the steam-engine is the central fact in the industrial revolution.

3. *The mobile prime mover.* The power of the steam-engine could be created where needed and to the extent desired. This mobility is the most characteristic feature of the Machine Age, and made possible the industrialization of many countries that had no great resources of water-power. Moreover, the steam-engine proved capable of producing much more power than the older prime movers, and thus in time it raised energy-output to a significantly higher level.

4. *The factory as a new form of organization of production.* Factories were built long before the advent of the steam-engine. Thus the early textile mills and ironworks were of this type, rather than of the workshop type so characteristic of medieval and earlier technology. In the eighteenth century, however, the word factory was not used in its present sense. A factory then was merely a shop, a warehouse, or a depot, and only by the end of the century was the word used for mills or machine-factories. The word mill was much more common, for the machine that first caught the eye was usually the great water-wheel. Not only the flour mills but the ironworks and foundries with their hammers and bellows

were worked by water-wheels in sixteenth-century England, and so were the first cotton mills. The first legal use of the word factory is in the Textile Factory Act of 1844. The concentration of machines driven by steam-engines had become a characteristic feature of the industrial revolution by 1800, but certainly not the only one; much of the manufacturing still took place in workshops, and the part of factories in the industrial revolution has been overstressed.

II. THE EARLIER COMPETITORS OF THE STEAM-ENGINE

The steam-engine did not rapidly displace the earlier prime movers. It was some time before it had been sufficiently developed as a prime mover with an appreciably higher average energy-output. Mobility alone was not enough to displace the treadmill, the water-wheel, and the windmill. In fact, the earlier phase of the industrial revolution was certainly not characterized by the steam-engine. Windmills still dotted many a landscape. Water was the main source of power in eighteenth-century England, driving fulling-stocks, millstones, saws, bellows, and ore-crushers. The new textile inventions came in an area of hills, valleys, and streams, and the early mills were built on river-banks. The pioneers of the industrial revolution hardly thought in terms of steam-engines. Wyatt pictured the mechanized textile industry as a kind of mill with wheels turned either by horses, by water, or by wind. Lewis Paul (d 1759) and he used two donkeys for their first machines; Cartwright drove his invention with a cow; Arkwright speaks of a 'water-frame'; and the first two power-looms in Scotland (1793) were worked by a Newfoundland dog.

For many industries in the sixteenth and seventeenth centuries, the obstacles to the use of power were cost and physical availability rather than the mechanical difficulty of application. The capital involved was large relative to the amount of power generated, so that power-using devices were not generally preferred to mechanisms actuated by the workman. Much early machinery was concerned with exchanging low intensities exerted through long distances for high intensities exerted through short distances. Many machines were designed so as to make it a simple matter to arrange for them to be driven by any prime mover capable of producing rotary motion. But until power became cheap, reliable, and generally available, there was no purpose in attempting to run them from a specialized power-plant.

In the eighteenth century no factory could be established far from a stream powerful and swift enough to work its machines. Mill-owners therefore crowded in narrow valleys, where an artificial fall could be secured by using dams. Hence the importance of the valleys of the Pennine range for eighteenth-century British industry. This continued as long as water was the driving-power of machinery, but the introduction of steam gradually brought industrial ruin to those districts where no coal was available locally.

In many other parts of England the water was mostly slow-flowing. Even the

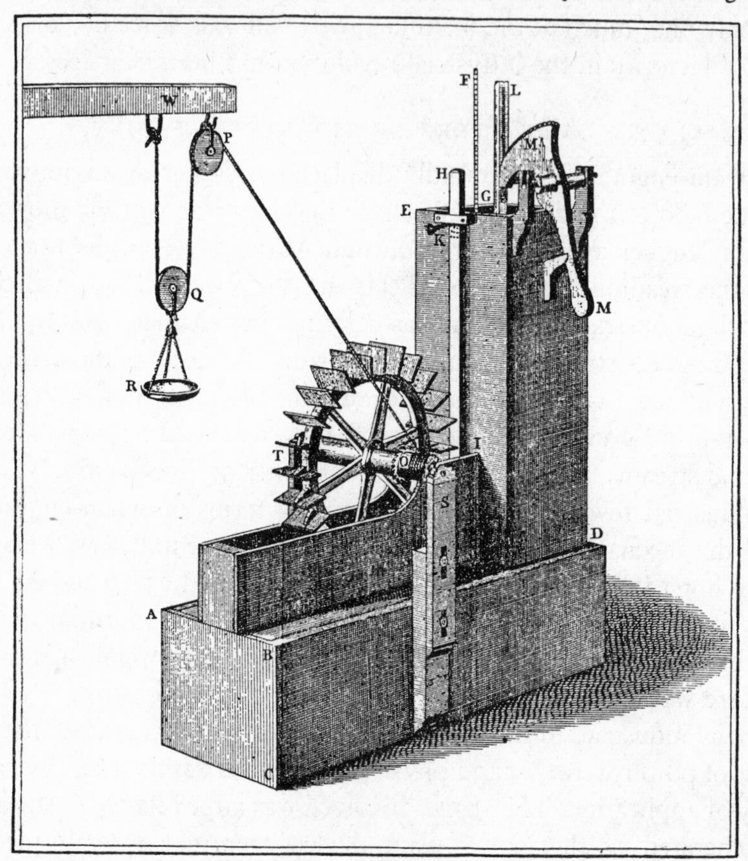

FIGURE 91—*Smeaton's model for measuring the power of undershot water-wheels.* ABCD, *cistern to receive water;* DE, *cistern to receive water raised by pump;* FG, *float marked in inches;* HI, *rod to open sluice;* K, *peg to hold* HI; GL, *upper part and pump;* MM, *handle for pump;* N, *catch to check* MM; O, *cylinder with cord that goes over pulleys* P *and* Q *to raise* R, *the pan with weights;* W, *beam;* S *and* T, *devices to adjust level of wheel.*

little water-power that was available was wasted by the clumsy systems of wheels and troughs used to collect and transmit it. The only practicable method was to create artificial waterfalls. The water had then to be raised to the level of a reservoir by a pump. It was for raising water that the first steam-engines came into use.

In the eighteenth century, competition for available water-supplies became very keen, notably in the midlands. In the seventeenth century the rolling-mills, paper-works, and similar enterprises began to congregate about the Tame and Stour. Arthur Young (1741–1820) commented at the end of the eighteenth century on the small use of water at Birmingham and other metallurgical centres in the midlands. He was surprised at the amount of work done by hand without

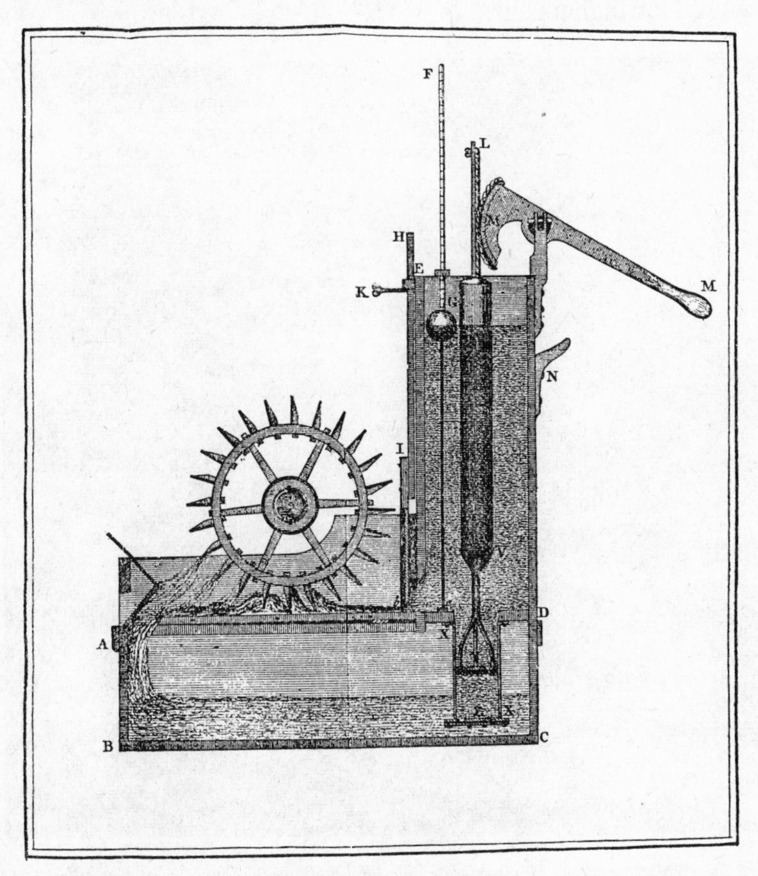

FIGURE 92—*Cross-section of Smeaton's model for measuring the power of undershot water-wheels, cf figure 91.* XX, *pump-barrel 5 inches in diameter and 11 in long;* V, *piston;* Z, *valve. By a modification of the model the power developed by an overshot wheel could be calculated.*

the aid of machinery. The midlands were badly in need of water-power, and this need, combined with the needs of the collieries, stimulated the search for a new source of power.

About the middle of the eighteenth century the combined use of Newcomen engines and water-wheels was found everywhere. Early Watt engines were similarly used. Indeed, the steam-engine would have remained an accessory to the water-mill, pumping up the water that worked the wheel, had not Watt by his invention of the 'sun-and-planet motion' and his 'parallel motion' (ch 6) solved the problem of converting the oscillation of the beam into rotary motion. About 1780 Richard Arkwright used a Newcomen pump as an accessory to his 'hydraulick machine', and the first steam spinning-mill was set up for Robinson at Papplewick, Nottinghamshire, in 1785.

FIGURE 93—*Water-wheels at Marly-la-Machine for supplying the fountains at Versailles, 1725.*

It would be interesting to establish the energy-output from the water-wheels with which the steam-engine had to compete in its early stages, but unfortunately the data are very meagre. No theoretical calculations or considerations entered into the construction of the first water-wheels. With experience in the construction of gears and transmission of power during the sixteenth and seventeenth centuries, water-wheels became more efficient and attempts were made to calculate their capacities. Most of them in the sixteenth century were undershot; Olaus Magnus (1555) is among the few who illustrate overshot wheels. The first to make serious attempts at measuring the power-output of water-wheels was John Smeaton [5] (figures 91, 92). In 1759 he laid down certain rules for the determination of the theoretical energy-output and the amount of energy consumed in overcoming the friction of the wheel's parts (p 203). He showed on theoretical grounds that 'the effect therefore of overshot wheels, under the same circumstances of quantity and fall, is at medium double that of the undershot.

FIGURE 94—*Inside the wheel-house at Marly-la-Machine as reconstructed in the mid-nineteenth century.*

The higher the wheel is in proportion to the whole descent, the greater will be its effect.'

From the figures available for eighteenth-century water-wheels we can conclude that their energy-output was seldom better than 10 hp, and on the average only 5 hp. This poor record was mainly due to the limitation of water-power in Britain and to the primitive gearing and consequent loss of power in transmission. The largest series of water-wheels was the colossal 'machine of Marly' built for Louis XIV by the Liège carpenter Rennequin in 1682 (figures 93, 94). It had a potential capacity of 124 hp and delivered at least 75 hp in actual work, but owing to faulty maintenance it had less than one-fortieth of its original capacity by 1796. Nevertheless, even when the output of the steam-engine rose above the average of 10 hp, it did not quickly displace the water-wheel. Water-wheels continued to play an important part in the mechanized industries of England till at least 1850. Cotton, the steam industry *par excellence*, still drew a quarter of its power from water in 1830 and one-seventh in 1850. The other textile industries drew even more of their energy from water. Only where there was no water-power was the steam-engine rapidly adopted.

The windmill was not a popular prime mover in eighteenth-century England, but it played an important part on the coasts of the North Sea and the Baltic. Since the windmill came to western Europe many improvements had been made in it [6] (vol III, ch 4). It was used not only for grinding corn but in mining, especially in central Europe. This was not something novel, for a fifteenth-century manuscript from Bohemia shows a hoist in a mine moved by a windmill. The sixteenth century saw many new applications of the windmill. Cornelis Dircksz Muys invented (1589) a marsh-mill with an inclined shaft rising from a low point, where it drove an Archimedean screw, to the necessary height. The *tjasker* still popular in Friesland is probably derived from this invention (vol III, figure 204).

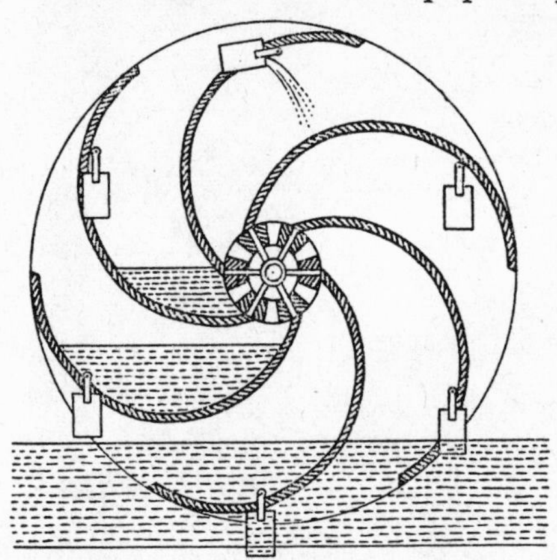

FIGURE 95—*Scoop-wheel for raising water. Early nineteenth century.*

Certain districts were favoured by nature. The banks of the river Zaan, west of Amsterdam, were flat, windy, and easily approached by water. This became the main industrial district of Holland. By the end of the seventeenth century it had 900 windmills (marsh-mills included). Wind-driven mills were built in the Zaan district after the French war of 1672, when paper-making in the eastern provinces became too dangerous. Other industrial districts deriving their power from windmills were around the towns of Leiden, Rotterdam, and Dordrecht [7]. Many towns had windmills on their city-walls and fortifications, to raise water in war-time. Altogether the United Provinces had some 8000 windmills, 2000 of which survived in the year 1900. 1306 were still in existence in 1950, but many in a damaged state.

The introduction of the windmill as a prime mover did not proceed smoothly. The craftsmen's guilds of Holland protested against them in 1581, claiming that they would throw many craftsmen out of work. A mechanical saw worked by a windmill was built in 1766 at Limehouse, east of London, but was destroyed by a riotous mob two years later.

We have very few data on the energy-output of these windmills. The capacity of a mill depends on the velocity of the wind and the span of the sails. Taking a windmill with a span of 100 ft and modernized sails, we estimate the following figures for the power at the windshaft:

	Energy-output in	
Velocity of wind (m/sec)	*hp*	*kwh*
3	10	7
4	22	16
5	42	31
6	68	50
7	108	79
8	159	117
9 and over	227	167

Whereas modern windmills respond to a wind of 3 m/sec, the eighteenth-century form required one of at least twice this.

The standard works of the Dutch millwrights of that century [8] contain only constructional detail. The only early attempts at the calculation of windmill capacities concern marsh-mills. Simon Stevin wrote on them about 1590, when he was at work on improving the gearing and scoop-wheels of such mills. He not only obtained patents, but actually engaged in certain experiments with mills built according to his plans. In his account of this work, which was not printed until nearly 300 years later, he tried to calculate the amount of water thrown out by the scoop-wheel and the pressure on the sails needed to raise this water, but he omitted many factors. About 1600 Jan Adriaanszoon Leeghwater (1575–1650) measured the output of two marsh-mills, expressed as the fall of the level of the lake they pumped. Similar measurements, comparing a marsh-mill turning a scoop-wheel with one turning an Archimedean screw, were made near Leiden in 1763 [9]; the output in cubic feet of four marsh-mills near Rotterdam was measured in 1774–6 [10]; and a comparison of the efficiency of scoop-wheels (figure 95) and Archimedean screws was carried out in 1821–4 [11]. None contains accurate measurements of wind-velocities.

In 1759 John Smeaton reported [12] on his experiments on windmills and different forms of sails. He used windmill-models having a span of about 3½ ft, acted on by an artificial wind (figure 96). He thus avoided consideration of the turbulence of the wind, though he published a table giving a rough scale of winds expressed in feet per second. His experiments certainly established the changes with wind-velocity of the capacity of a known mill; but they told little of the actual capacity of windmills, for he lacked the proper instruments, and even units, with which to evaluate and express this energy.

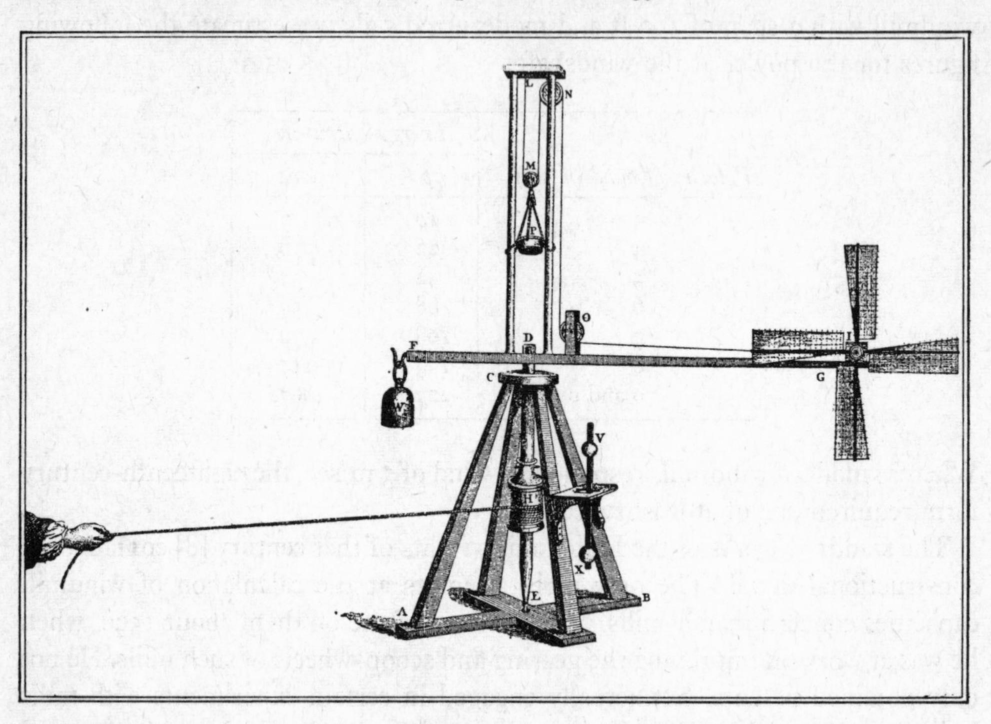

FIGURE 96—*Smeaton's model to measure the power of windmills.* ABC, *frame to support moving parts;* DE, *upright axis on which is* FG, *an arm to carry sails;* H, *barrel with cord round it to give circular motion to* FG, *allowing the sails to be directed to the wind.* L *fixes the line that goes over pulleys* MNO *and ends at barrel* I. *When the sails turn, the cord is wound up and raises* P, *a scale in which weights are placed;* VX, *adjustable pendulum for time measurement.*

Smeaton wrote:

Desaguliers makes the utmost power of a man, when working so as to be able to hold it for some hours, to be equal to that of raising a hogshead (63 ale gallons) of water ten feet high in a minute. When working at a mean rate, the 30 ft sail will be equal to the power of 18·3 men, or of 3·66 horses, reckoning 5 men to a horse; whereas the effect of the common Dutch sails, of the same length, will be scarce equal to the power of 10 men, or of 2 horses.

That these computations are not merely speculative, but will hold good when applied to works in large, I have had an opportunity of verifying; for in a mill with the enlarged sails of 30 ft, applied to the crushing of rape seed, by means of two runners upon the edge, for making oil, I observed, that when the sails made 11 turns in a minute, in which case the velocity of the wind was about 13 feet in a second, the runners then made 7 turns in a minute; whereas 2 horses, applied to the same two runners, scarcely worked at the rate of 3½ turns in the same time.

The common Dutch windmill of the eighteenth century had a span of 100 ft and a windshaft some 45 to 50 ft above the ground. According to Smeaton's calculations it should have had an energy-output of some 10 hp, and this agrees quite well with modern measurements. The smaller Dutch windmills with 24-ft sails were found to give 4·5 brake-hp in a 20-mile wind. Interesting estimates were obtained with an old marsh-mill of the large type, built about 1648 [13]. When pumping 35 cu m of water per minute against a head of 2 m and with an average wind-velocity of 8 to 9 m/sec it produced 40 hp on the windshaft, the actual output being only 15·6 hp (39 per cent). Therefore 61 per cent of the energy derived from the wind was lost in transmission. Further experiments with modern sails and improved gear showed that the eighteenth-century mill would produce an average of 10 hp. This could be improved to 13 to 14 hp by increasing the moment of inertia of the sails, and to 18 to 20 hp by using more modern sails. Changing the gearing-system and using modern sails might raise the output to some 30 hp, but this represents the maximum attainable without changes in construction such as are to be seen in the modern wind-motor. Similar results have been obtained with other eighteenth-century Dutch marsh-mills. They needed a wind-velocity of 8 to 9 m/sec to work efficiently and they produced 10 to 12 hp, or 15 hp at the utmost, in an average wind. All this agrees well with the ratings of the various prime movers as given by Rankine and d'Aubuisson:

Man working a pump	0·036	hp
Man turning a crank	0·04–0·078	„
Man pushing a capstan bar	0·047	„
Horse turning a gin at a walk	0·367–0·578	„
Various 18-foot overshot wheels	2–5	„
Post windmill	2–8	„
Turret windmill	6–14	„

Smeaton used cast iron to strengthen parts of the windmill, but this practice spread slowly and the windmill remained essentially a wooden construction. Its maximum was about 50 hp on the windshaft, but it lost much of this in transmission through the use of wooden cog-wheels and pinions—though these had the advantage of damping down vibrations better than cast iron parts do. The windmill reached the upper limits of its evolution in the eighteenth century, then inevitably gave way to the steam-engine when this prime mover developed more energy more cheaply.

In the east, the windmill had the form of a circle of sails acting on a vertical axle (vol II, p 615). Wind-turbines were occasionally tried there, which is interesting in view of the later development of the turbine [14]. They are not mentioned in the Dutch handbooks on windmills of the eighteenth century, but

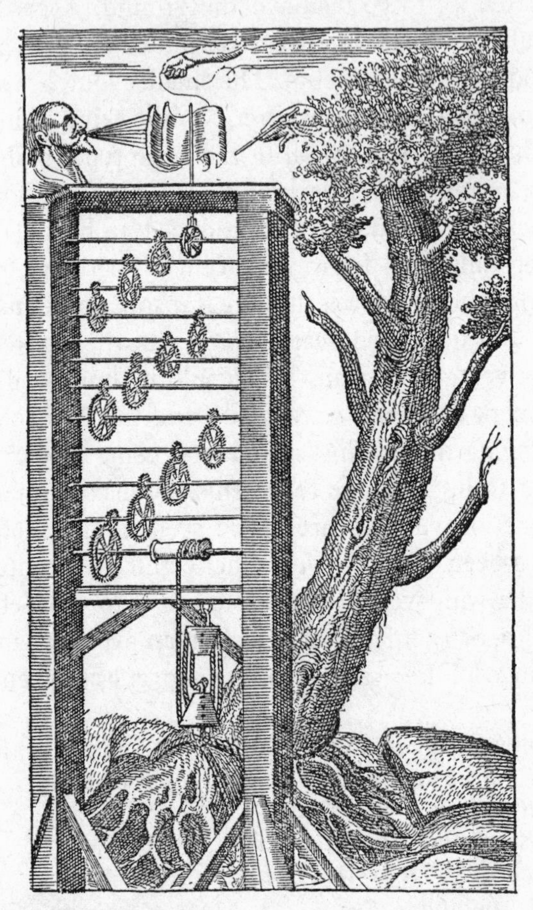

FIGURE 97—*Wind-turbine. The roots of the oak are supposed to extend over about ½ sq mile and the weight of soil on them is taken to be 4000 m lb. By means of two double pulleys and 12 wheels it was calculated that a small windmill could uproot the tree.*

Dutch patents for mills worked by wind-turbines go back to the seventeenth century (cf figure 97). The hot-air turbine, though never developing into a prime mover, occupied the attention of many a famous engineer. In the period we are discussing it took the form of the blades of a fan moved by the hot air rising in a chimney, the fan in its turn moving gears that turned a spit on which meat was roasted. Early designs are found in manuscripts of the sixteenth century from

Leonardo da Vinci onwards. It became known as the chimney-wheel, draft-mill, and smoke-jack, and is illustrated by Branca (p 168) and others (figure 98). Some even contemplated making it move a roller-mill for iron bars.

III. THE STEAM-ENGINE AS A PRIME MOVER

The coal-mines and the iron industry proved the best promoters of the steam-engine [15]. Scarcity of charcoal and limitation of water-power were economic

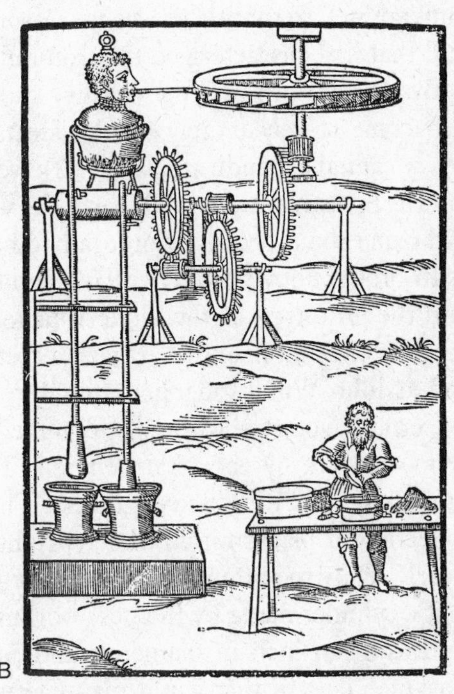

FIGURE 98—(A) *Proposed chimney-wheel by which hot air rising up a chimney was to work a rolling-mill.* (B) *Proposed stamp-mill, to be worked by hot air.*

threats to the iron industry of the eighteenth century. Many attempts were made to break this tyranny of wood and water. In 1757 Isaac Wilkinson took out a patent for a new machine or 'bellows . . . so that a furnace, forge or any other works may be blowed from any waterfall or falls . . . to several miles distant by means of a pipe'. This was never used and, until late in the century, iron-works continued to use direct water-power. Inadequacy in the fall of water caused a tendency to separate the smelting and the finishing of the metal. The adaptation of the steam-engine to crushing ores in iron-works discouraged this separation. More important still, Watt's engine freed the ironmasters from their dependence on constant supplies of running water for their bellows, hammers, and mills.

Before its introduction it was estimated that the average period of working in iron-works was about forty weeks a year, but a season of drought might curtail this considerably and bring financial loss to the masters and distress to the workers. Attempts at economy of water had been made with various devices; at Coalbrookdale the water that had passed over the wheel was raised above it again by a Newcomen engine, and at Furness hand-pumps had been used for the same purpose. Steam-power meant that the iron-works could be carried on with cheap mineral fuel, so that there was no reason for the separation of furnace, forge, and mill that had characterized the iron industry in the early years of the century.

By the end of the same century the coal-pits throughout the midlands had also come to rely largely on the steam-engine for their working. This meant heavy capital expenditure, since a Newcomen engine cost about £1500 to install, but the investment was well worth the while of the larger enterprises. The change had come about because Boulton had had the Kinneil steam-engine designed by Watt brought down from Scotland and had turned his Soho (Birmingham) works into the prototype of the modern factory. The first two steam-engines built by the firm of Boulton and Watt were erected at Bloomfield colliery in Staffordshire and at John Wilkinson's new foundry at Broseley, Salop, respectively.

Certain factors, however, prevented the rapid displacement of the earlier prime movers by the steam-engine. The early machine-builders were handicapped by want of skilled engineers. Their engines were built by a miscellaneous collection of blacksmiths, wheel-wrights, and carpenters, as their designs show clearly. Only too often the parts refused to work when put together. Watt found that a cylinder made by the best workmen available in Glasgow varied by three-eighths of an inch in diameter, and Smeaton told him 'that neither tools nor workmen existed that could manufacture so complex a machine with sufficient precision'. John Wilkinson, however, could tool metal with a limit of error not exceeding 'the thickness of a thin sixpence' in a diameter of 72 inches. No wonder that Watt avoided applying high-pressure steam in his engines (p 182), even though this was the only way to higher thermal efficiency and energy-output.

The builders of the first engines had therefore both to train the necessary specialists to build their machines, and to devise means of finishing their parts with sufficient precision. Prime movers had hitherto been of wood with few metal parts; steam demanded stronger and more durable material. The way to precision was to clamp the relevant tool and material firmly in a machine; then the tool could be adjusted and guided to do its work of grinding, boring, slotting, drilling, turning, or cutting (vol III, pp 334–6). Maudslay's slide-rest of 1794 was the first of a series of such fundamentally important machine-tools developed by the new engineers, but the co-operation of science and mechanical engineering was not yet sufficiently close to allow a rapid advance.

When Watt's patent expired in 1800 there were 496 Watt engines at work in Britain in mines, metal plants, textile factories, and breweries. Of these 308 were rotative engines and 164 pumping-engines, while 24 were for producing blast-air. One or two were rated at 40 hp, but the average capacity was only 15 to 16 hp and therefore not significantly higher than that of the windmill and the water-wheel. The steam-engine profited by its relative mobility and its dependence on coal rather than on the fickle elements, but it could have revolutionized technology only very slowly if it had stopped at this point.

The real development of the steam-engine into a new and stronger prime mover came between 1800 and 1850. In the earlier days of Watt the nascent theory of heat had had some influence on the development of the steam-engine, but it was not yet ready to assist in the proper calculation of such engines. The engineers themselves had by trial and error found the means of introducing high pressure, and they made the methods of transmission of energy from engine to machinery less cumbersome. Several branches of science provided new knowledge useful for the building of steam-engines. The science of applied mechanics was gradually extended after the testing of materials by such men as Coulomb and La Hire had yielded practical rules for calculating the proper dimensions of engine parts. The rise of the art of bridge-building (ch 15) contributed much to the calculation of the constructional details of steam-engines. Tools and methods were devised to measure elasticity and the different stresses acting on parts of the engine. The inquiry into friction and its importance in engine and transmission came rather later. Important also was the elaboration of the theory of gases by such men as Mariotte (1620–84), Gay-Lussac (1778–1850), and Regnault (1810–78).

Fundamental, too, was the further development of the theory of heat, not only in calorimetry and temperature measurement, but most of all in the rise of the new science of thermodynamics. The foundation of thermodynamics was laid by Sadi Carnot (1796–1832) in his 'Motive Power of Heat' [16]; he stated that the efficiency of an engine depended on the working substance and the temperature-drop between cylinder and condenser. In 1842 Robert Mayer (1814–78) calculated the work equivalent to a unit of heat. The law of conservation of energy —the first law of thermodynamics—was formulated in 1847 by Helmholtz (1821–94). Joule (1818–89) carefully measured the mechanical equivalent of heat (1843), and his work was later confirmed by Rankine (1820–72). Clausius (1822–88) finally reconciled Carnot's theory of heat and the discovered equivalence of heat and work, and was thus able to formulate the second law of thermodynamics, namely that heat cannot of itself pass from a colder to a hotter body. Only after the elaboration of these laws could real progress be achieved in designing steam-engines.

Earlier engineers found perplexity in expressing the power of their engines and comparing them. For the most part, figures are given expressing the engine's 'duty', the unit being one million ft-lb per bushel (84 lb) of coal. This allows us to calculate the thermal efficiency of the engine, but gives no accurate data on its power. The following data are reported [17]:

RECIPROCATING STEAM-ENGINES

Date	*Builder*	*Duty*	*Percentage thermal efficiency*
1718	Newcomen	4·3	0·5
1767	Smeaton	7·4	0·8
1774	Smeaton	12·5	1·4
1775	Watt	24·0	2·7
1792	Watt	39·0	4·5
1816	Woolf compound engine . .	68	7·5
1828	Improved Cornish engine . .	104	12·0
1834	,, ,, ,, . .	149	17·0
1878	Corliss compound engine . .	150	17·2
1906	Triple-expansion engine . .	203	23·0

The rapid rise in thermal efficiency in the early nineteenth century is remarkable.

Boulton and Watt speak of '20-horse engines', using a unit devised by Watt in 1783, each 'horse' being the power to lift 33 000 lb through one foot in a minute, but in fact the early engineers had great difficulty in finding a proper unit of work. Boulton and Watt built their engines in series of 4 to 30 horses and 36 to 100 horses, the '20-horse engine' being the most popular one. Thomas Young (1773–1829), discussing the efficiency of the steam-engine, said:

The daily work of a horse is equal to that of five or six men, the strength of a mule is equal to that of three or four men. The expense of keeping a horse is generally twice or thrice as great as the hire of a day labourer, so that the force of horses may be reckoned about half as expensive as that of men. . . . On the authority of Mr Boulton a bushel (84 lbs) of coal is equivalent to the daily labour of 8⅓ men or perhaps more; the value of this quantity of coal is seldom more than that of the work of a single labourer for a day, but the expense of machinery generally renders a steam-engine somewhat more than half as expensive as the number of horses for which it is substituted [18].

Heat-economy and thermal efficiency were of the highest importance for the future of the steam-engine. Full exploitation required the introduction of high-pressure steam. Evans and Trevithick worked with a steam-pressure of 3·5 atm in 1810, this rising to 5 to 6 atm by 1830 (p 190). Between 1840 and 1850 many older engines were converted into high-pressure engines. However, the inter-

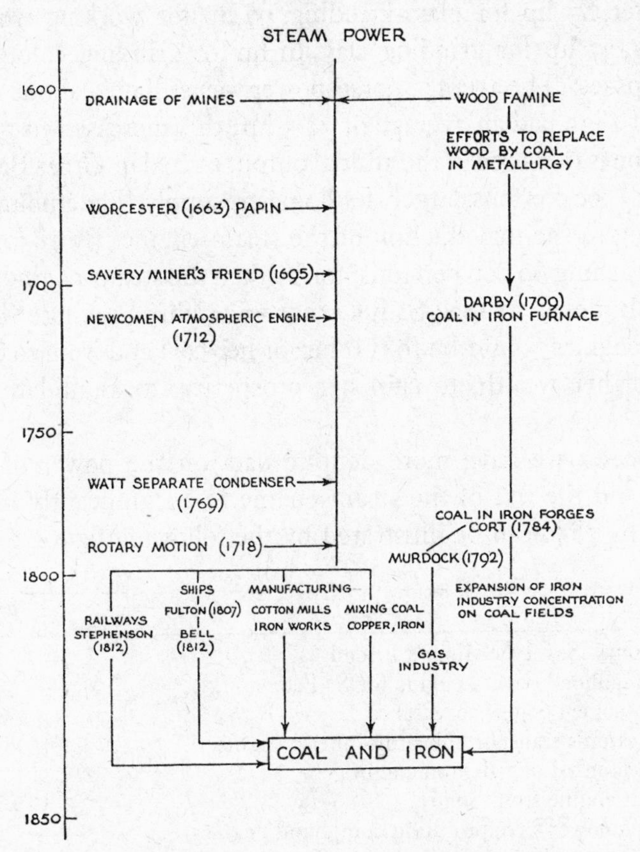

FIGURE 99—*Chronological chart of the introduction of steam.*

penetration of science and engineering proceeded slowly, and there is some truth in L. J. Henderson's statement that 'until 1850 the steam-engine did more for science than science did for the steam-engine'. The idea of energy and the recognition of its laws form the real division between the old and the new engineering, and this will be clear from the perusal of the early handbooks on the steam-engine by Farey [19] and Tredgold [20].

Hence the improvement of the steam-engine in the early nineteenth century was slow (figure 99). By 1820 Birmingham had only 60 engines with '1000 total steam-power in horses'. In 1835 Lancashire and the West Riding of Yorkshire had 1369 steam-engines and 866 water-wheels. A list of steam-engines extant in Birmingham in the same year mentions a total of 169, developing altogether 2700 hp, built between 1780 and 1835, of which 94 were ten years old or less; 275 hp was used for grinding flour, 1770 hp for working metals, 279 hp for pumping water, 87 hp for glass-grinding, 97 hp for working wood, 44 hp for paper-making, 37 hp for grinding clay, 61 hp for grinding colours, and 50 hp for other purposes. The average horse-power was still only about 15. In Prussia the engines of 1835 had an average of 31·5 hp; this increased to 55·1 by 1904.

The situation is mirrored in the annual output of coal in Great Britain. In 1700 this was about 3 000 000 tons, largely for domestic supply. The amount had doubled by 1800, owing to the introduction of the steam-engine. By 1850 it had multiplied by 20, reaching 60 000 000 tons, for by then the steam-engine was dominating industry. But even in 1824 Sadi Carnot was right in saying: 'To rob Britain of her steam-engines would be to rob her of her coal and iron, to deprive her of her sources of her wealth, to ruin her prosperity, to annihilate that colossal power.'

In certain cases we have more definite data on the power of early steam-engines [21], and the rise of the steam-engine to a significantly more powerful prime mover by 1850 can be illustrated by the following figures:

Date	*Engine*	*Power in hp*
1702	Thomas Savery's Miner's Friend	1
1717	Desaguliers' Savery engine for St Petersburg	5·5
1732	Newcomen engine for France	12
1765	Smeaton's transportable atmospheric engine	4·5
1772	Smeaton's Long Benton engine	40·5
1778	Watt engine from Soho	13·8
1790	Hornblower's reciprocating compound engine	11·5
1793	Thompson's reciprocating atmospheric engine	48
1807	Fulton's marine engine	20
1812	Evans and Trevithick's high-pressure engine	1–100
1837	Cornish engine for London Water-works	135
1846	Corliss engine (exceptional for the period)	260
1848	Cornish engines for Haarlemmermeer	40
1850	Woolf compound engine	40–50
1870	Sulzer engine	400
1876	Corliss Philadelphia Exhibition engine	2500
1881	Edison's Pearl Street power-station engine	175
1890–1900	Electric power-station engines	1000 and over

REFERENCES

[1] VOWLES, H. P. and VOWLES, M. W. 'The Quest for Power.' Chapman, London. 1931.
HARTLEY, SIR HAROLD. *Nature*, *Lond.*, **166**, 368, 1950.

[2] MCCLOY, S. T. 'French Inventions of the Eighteenth Century.' University of Kentucky Press, Lexington, Ky. 1952.
SMITH, E. C. *Phil. Mag.*, 150th anniv. no., 92, 1948.

[3] USHER, A. P. 'A History of Mechanical Inventions' (rev. ed.). Harvard University Press, Cambridge, Mass. 1954.

[4] REULEAUX, F. 'Theoretische Kinematik', p. 38. Berlin. 1875.

[5] SMEATON, J. *Phil. Trans.*, **51**, 100, 1759.

[6] WOLFF, A. R. 'The Windmill as a Prime Mover.' London. 1885.
WAILES, R. 'Windmills in England.' Architectural Press, London. 1948.

[7] BOONENBURG, K. 'De Windmolens.' De Lange, Amsterdam. 1949.

[8] LINPERCH, P. '*Architectura mechanica* of Moole-boek.' Amsterdam. 1727.
VAN ZYL, J. '*Theatrum machinarum universale* of groot algemeen molenboek.' Amsterdam. 1761.
VAN NATRUS, L., POLLY, J., and VAN VUUREN, C. 'Groot Volkomen Moolenboek' (2 vols). Amsterdam. 1734, 1736.

[9] NOPPEN, J. 'Rapport van Proeven gedaan op de werking van een vijselmolen en een Scheprad-Molen staende aan de Westvaart onder Haserswoude.' Leiden. 1765.

[10] DOUWES, B. J. 'Verhandeling over de proporties tussen de vermogens der gewone watermolens, werkende met een staand scheprad en de nieuwelings door Gebr. Eckhardt uitgevonden hellende schepradmolens.' The Hague. 1779.

[11] GRINWIS, C. H. C. *Nieuwe Verh. proefonderv. Wijsbeg.*, **9**, 1, 1844.

[12] SMEATON, J. *Phil. Trans.*, **51**, 138, 1759.

[13] 'Het Prinsenmolenboek.' Veenman, Wageningen. 1942.

[14] BATHE, G. 'Horizontal Windmills.' Published by the author, Philadelphia. 1948.

[15] ASHTON, T. W. 'Iron and Steel in the Industrial Revolution' (2nd ed.) University Press, Manchester. 1951.

[16] CARNOT, S. 'Réflexions sur la puissance motrice du feu et sur les machines propres à développer cette puissance.' Paris. 1824.
Idem. 'Reflections on the Motive Power of Heat and on Machines fitted to develop that Power' (ed. by R. H. THURSTON). London. 1890.

[17] DICKINSON, H. W. 'Short History of the Steam Engine.' University Press, Cambridge. 1938.
Idem. 'James Watt.' University Press, Cambridge. 1935.

[18] YOUNG, T. 'Lectures on Natural Philosophy', Vol. 1, pp. 132 f. London. 1807.

[19] FAREY, J. 'Treatise on the Steam Engine.' London. 1827.

[20] TREDGOLD, T. 'The Steam Engine.' London. 1838.

[21] MATSCHOSS, C. 'Die Entwicklung der Dampfmaschine' (2 vols). Springer, Berlin. 1908.

6

THE STEAM-ENGINE TO 1830

H. W. DICKINSON

I. TO DENIS PAPIN (1647–1712)

THE earliest known contrivance operated by steam-power was the 'Sphere of Aeolus' or aeolipile devised by Hero in the first century A.D. It may be described as an elementary type of reaction-turbine, but was a mere philosophical toy yielding no appreciable power. Hero invented another heat-engine, in which the expansive force of air when heated was used to drive water from a tank up through a siphon into a suspended bucket which, as it descended with increasing weight, opened the doors of a temple against the action of a counterweight (vol II, p 635, figure 575).

Not until the seventeenth century was attention again turned to the derivation of power from heat. Giovanni Battista della Porta (1538–1615) in his *Tre libri de' spiritali* (Naples, 1606) explained not only how water could be forced upwards from a tank by pressure of steam on its surface, but also how the condensation of steam could produce suction for drawing water from a lower level. In 1615 Salomon de Caus, a French gardener, described an ornamental fountain worked by steam. A boiler was fitted with an open-ended pipe extending downwards nearly to the bottom. The pipe ended externally in a nozzle provided with a cock. When the steam-pressure was high enough, the cock was opened and a jet of water projected upwards. For the next display, the boiler was refilled and the pressure again raised. Giovanni Branca (1571–1640), an Italian architect, was the first to realize that a jet of steam could turn a wheel by acting on blades around its circumference. In 1629 he described a sort of impulse-turbine working on this principle. It was connected to a pair of drop-stamps through treble-reduction gearing (figure 98). The design was far too crude to work, and the idea lay dormant until the nineteenth century.

An important step leading to the invention of the steam-engine was the discovery of the pressure of the atmosphere. The accepted explanation of the rise of water into a vacuous space created by pumping or otherwise, was that 'nature abhorred a vacuum', but this gave no reason why the rise should be limited. It is said that because of the failure of the engineers of Cosimo de' Medici II,

Grand Duke of Tuscany (1590–1620), to make a suction-pump draw water from a depth of 50 ft (although experience had shown that a lift of about 30 ft was the limit), an appeal was made to Galileo (1564–1642). Galileo began to make experiments, which were continued after his death by his pupil Evangelista Torricelli (1608–47). Torricelli announced in 1643 that the atmosphere exerted a

FIGURE 100—*Otto von Guericke showed in a demonstration how even sixteen powerful horses could not pull apart the two halves of an evacuated sphere.* c *1654.*

pressure equal to that of a vertical column of mercury of about 30 inches in length, and that it was this pressure that determined the height to which a liquid could be made to rise by suction. Torricelli predicted that the pressure would fall with increasing altitude, and this was confirmed in an experiment suggested by Blaise Pascal (1623–62), who in 1647 had a barometer carried to the top of a 4800-ft mountain in the Auvergne. The mercury fell by about 3 in during the ascent.

The discovery suggested the possibility of using atmospheric pressure to do work on a piston beneath which a vacuum could be created. It thus led to experimental work, in many countries, that culminated in the invention of the steam-engine.

A successful attempt to create a vacuum mechanically was made by Otto von Guericke (1602–86), burgomaster of Magdeburg, who applied existing knowledge of pumps to the development of one to draw air instead of water. With its help he made spectacular demonstrations (figure 100) of the effects of atmospheric pressure. In one of them, performed at Ratisbon in 1654, he used a fixed vertical cylinder with a diameter of 20 inches in which a well fitting piston was suspended from a rope passing over a pulley. Connecting an air-pump to the cylinder he created a partial vacuum below the piston, causing it to descend in spite of the joint efforts of 50 men pulling on a rope to hold it up. He used the same apparatus to lift heavy weights. Thus it was evident that, if a vacuum could be established and re-established at will, the design of a useful engine working by atmospheric pressure would be in sight.

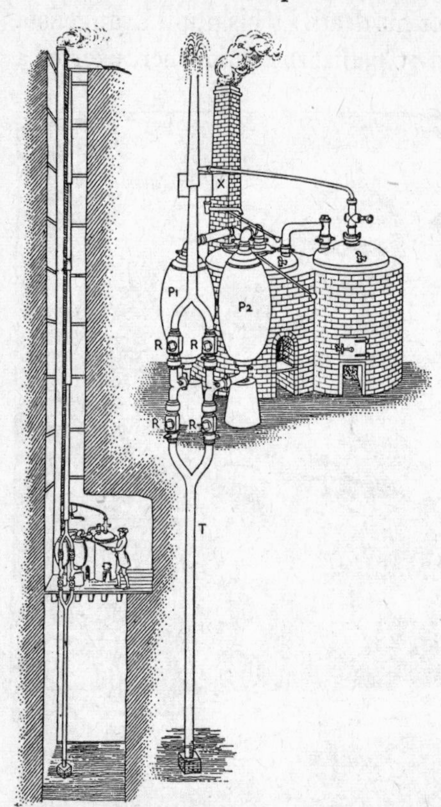

FIGURE 101—*Savery's 'Miner's Friend, or an Engine to Raise Water by Fire'. Steam is admitted to the oval vessel* P1 *and displaces the water upwards through a check-valve* R. *When* P1 *is emptied of water the supply of steam is stopped and cold water from a cistern* X *is poured on* P1 *to condense the steam there. This creates a vacuum and water is sucked through* T *and valve* R. P2 *is filled with steam while* P1 *is being cooled.*

Something of the sort was attained in 1663 by Edward Somerset (1601–67), later second Marquis of Worcester. His description is too vague for discussion here, but he certainly achieved something, and that not merely on a laboratory scale, for the French historian Samuel Sorbière (1615–70) in 1664, and Cosimo de' Medici in 1669, recorded having seen the marquis's machine at Vauxhall; it would force water to a height of 40 ft. In 1663 the marquis secured an Act of Parliament enabling him 'to receive the Benefit and Profit of a Water Commanding Engine by him invented . . . for a term of 99 years'. It failed to achieve commercial success.

Several early inventors thought of the explosive force of gunpowder as a source of power. The idea was generally to employ it to produce a vacuum and so to enable power to be derived from the pressure of the atmosphere. Thus Christiaan Huygens (1629–95) in 1680 suggested a form of gunpowder-engine in which the explosion took place in a cylinder beneath a piston held in a raised position by a counterweight, nearly all the gas of the explosion escaping through automatic relief valves. As the remaining fraction cooled, the pressure of the air forced down the piston and thus raised the weight. In his first experiments with this device, Huygens had as his assistant Denis Papin (1647–1712?), who became well known by his inventions of the 'digester' (1681) or steam pressure-cooker, and of the safety-valve which he devised as a precaution against its explosion.

Papin realized that the gas remaining in the cylinder after the explosion made it impossible to attain a satisfactory vacuum beneath the Huygens piston, and saw the necessity of using some substance that would leave no residue. In 1690 his thoughts turned to steam, and he wrote:

> Since it is a property of water that a small quantity of it turned into vapour by heat has an elastic force like that of air, but upon cold supervening is again resolved into water, so that no trace of the said elastic force remains, I concluded that machines could be constructed wherein water, by the help of no very intense heat, and at little cost, could produce that perfect vacuum which could by no means be obtained by gunpowder.

Papin's engine of 1690 consisted of a vertical tube, about 2½ inches in diameter, fitted with a piston and rod. A little water was put into the bottom of the tube and, by applying heat to the outside, the generated steam raised the piston to the top of the tube where it was held by a catch. When the steam had condensed through the cooling of the tube, the catch was released by hand and atmospheric pressure forced down the piston. The tube thus had to perform the triple duty of boiler, engine-cylinder, and condenser. Papin's engine demonstrated a principle, but was of no practical use. Nevertheless he was the first to employ steam to move a piston in a cylinder, and to indicate a cycle of operations afterwards put to practical effect by Newcomen.

II. SAVERY (1650?–1715), NEWCOMEN (1663–1729), AND SMEATON (1724–92)

In those days the need for machinery was felt most for the pumping of water. Of all patents granted during the reigns of Elizabeth I, James I, and Charles I about one in seven related to pumping. Amongst the many who devoted their attention to the subject was the military engineer Thomas Savery, a prolific inventor and the first to construct a practical steam-pump. His principle was to raise water by the condensation of steam in a closed vessel to as great a height as the atmospheric pressure would permit; to retain the water; and, by the application to it of as great a steam-pressure as could safely be employed, to force the water up to a still higher level. In practice, he used two vessels so arranged that one refilled while the other was discharging. His master patent of 1698 was taken out for a

new Invention of Raiseing of Water and occasioning Motion to all sorts of Mill Work by the Impellent Force of Fire, which will be of great Use and Advantage for Drayning Mines, Serveing Towns with Water, and for the working of all Sorts of Mills where they have not the benefit of Water nor Constant Windes.

The patent was for the usual period of 14 years, but in the following year an extension to 21 years was given by Parliament. In 1701 the rights for Scotland, to terminate at the same date as those for England, were granted to James Smith, of Whitehill in Midlothian. In his 'The Miner's Friend' (1702) Savery writes:

Though my thoughts have long been employed about waterworks, I should never have pretended to any invention of that kind had I not happily found out this new, but yet much stronger and cheaper cause of motion than any before made use of. But finding this of rarefaction by fire, the consideration of the difficulties the miners and colliers labour under by the frequent disorders, and cumbersomness in general of water engines, incouraged me to invent engines to work by the new force.

Savery made a working model of his apparatus which he demonstrated to the king at Hampton Court, and in 1699 he showed it in operation to the fellows of the Royal Society, with a drawing of his engine (figure 101) [1].

An advertisement of 1702 [2] shows that Savery was an energetic business man:

Captain Savery's engines which raise Water by the force of Fire in any reasonable quantities and to any height, being now brought to perfection and ready for publick use; These are to give notice to all Proprietors of Mines and Collieries which are incumbered with Water, that they may be furnished with Engines to drain the same, at his Workhouse in Salisbury Court, London, against the Old Playhouse, where it may be seen working on Wednesdays and Saturdays in every week from 3 to 6 in the afternoons, when they may be satisfied of the performance thereof, with less expense than any other force of Horse or Hands, and less subject to repair.

Thus Salisbury Court, between Fleet Street and St Bride's church, harboured the first workshop in the world for making steam-engines. Their employment was necessarily restricted by the pressure that boilers, piping, and displacers could withstand. Savery also had trouble with high-pressure steam, for when he used pressures up to 8 or 10 atmospheres

its heat was so great that it would melt common soft Solder; and its strength so great as to blow open several of the Joints of his Machines; so that he was forc'd to be at the Pain and Charge to have all his Joints solder'd with Spelter or Hard Solder [3].

His engines, nevertheless, achieved considerable success for comparatively low lifts, and many were adopted for the water-supply of large buildings. They were also used to pump up water for water-wheels, and thus, indirectly, to produce mechanical power. An improvement of Savery's engine was effected by Desaguliers, who arranged for the condensation of the steam inside the displacement-chamber by a jet of water.

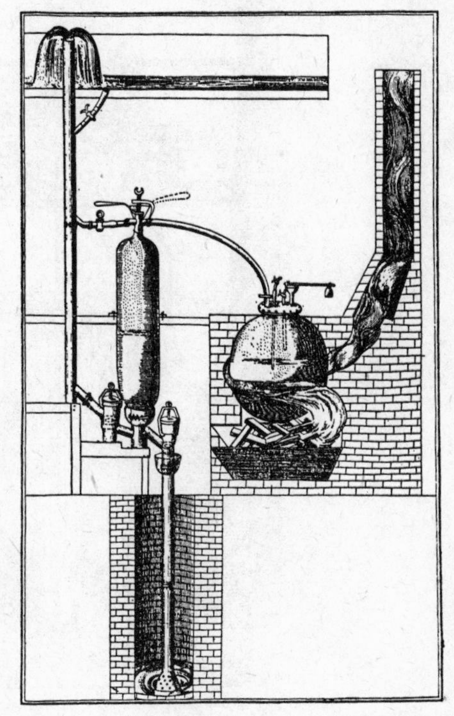

FIGURE 102—*Papin's modification of Savery's engine, 1705.*

Savery's engine fell into disuse early in the eighteenth century.[1] An attempt to improve it was made in 1705 by Papin (figure 102), but here he abandoned his earlier and promising plan of condensing steam beneath a piston in a cylinder and thus deriving power from the pressure of the atmosphere. This principle had the outstanding advantage that steam was required at only about atmospheric pressure, so that the construction of both engine and boiler was well within the capacity of the artisans of the time. The idea of proceeding along Papin's original lines was conceived independently by Thomas Newcomen, who achieved a success immeasurably greater than anything previously attained. He first established the steam-engine as a practical and reliable machine.

Newcomen left no account of the conception or the development of his invention, but the Swede, Marten Triewald (1691–1747), who came to England in 1716 and assisted Newcomen with the erection of at least one of his engines, wrote [4]:

Now it happened that a man from Dartmouth named Thomas Newcomen, without

[1] Its principle was revived in Hall's 'Pulsometer' (1876), which still provides a simple and useful means of emergency pumping.

any knowledge whatever of the speculations of Captain Savery, had, at the same time also made up his mind, in conjunction with his assistant, a plumber by the name of Calley, to invent a fire-machine for drawing water from the mines. He was induced to undertake this by considering the heavy costs of lifting water by means of horses, which Mr. Newcomen found existing in the English tin mines. These mines, Mr. Newcomen

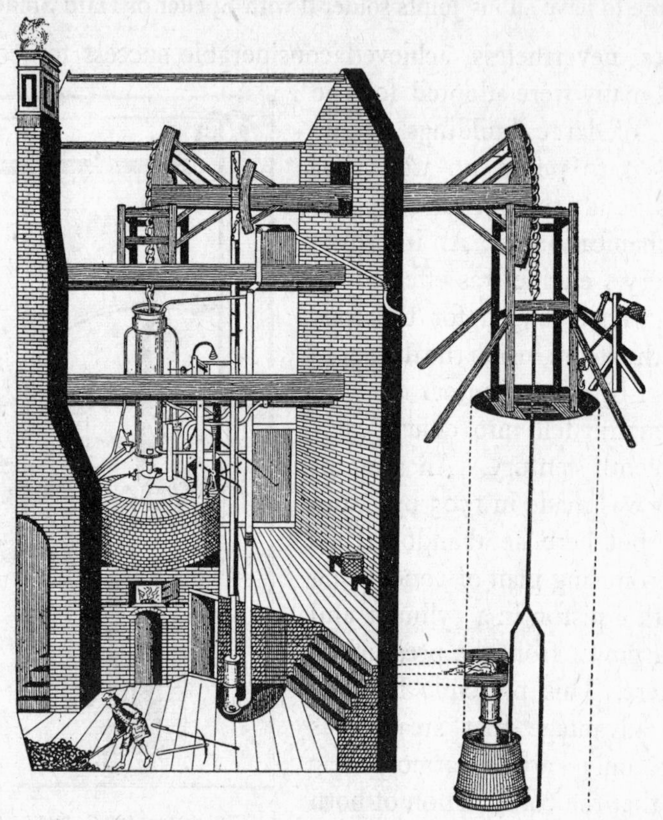

FIGURE 103—*The steam-engine erected by Savery and Newcomen at Dudley Castle in 1712.*

often visited in the capacity of a dealer in iron tools with which he used to furnish many of the tin mines.

The statement that Newcomen had no knowledge of what Savery was doing is corroborated by another writer, Stephen Switzer, who wrote in 1729 [5]:

> Mr. Newcomen was as early in his Invention as Mr. Savery was in his, only the latter being nearer the Court, had obtained the Patent before the other knew it, on which account Mr. Newcomen was glad to come in as a Partner to it.

The association of Savery and Newcomen, referred to by Switzer, is confirmed by an engraving of 1719.

Regarding the priority of this engine, we have the assurance of Triewald that 'Mr. Newcomen erected the first fire machine in England in the year 1712, which erection took place at Dudley Castle in Staffordshire' (figure 103).[1] In an engraving of the engine there is a note in a contemporary hand which tells that the beam 'vibrates 12 times in a Minute and each stroke lifts 10 galls of water 51 yds p'pendr.' This duty would require about $5\frac{1}{2}$ hp.

As regards the association of Savery's name with the Dudley Castle engine, it seems that when Newcomen, after ten years or more of experimental work, had produced a satisfactory steam-engine, he found his way blocked by Savery's master patent which covered the use of 'The Impellent Force of Fire' by any and every kind of engine. All that he could do was to come to some arrangement with Savery. By 1712 the latter must have realized that there was no future for his own engine, and that Newcomen's was vastly superior.

In Newcomen's engine, as constructed in 1712 (figure 104), the boiler with its setting was little more than a large brewer's copper, producing steam at only atmospheric pressure. When the steam was admitted to the bottom of the cylinder above the boiler, the piston rose to the top, mainly by the weight of the pump-rod hanging from the other end of the beam. The steam discharged any air or water that had got into the cylinder, through the eduction pipe and water-sealed valve, and then, after the closing of the connexion to the boiler, it was itself condensed by a jet of cold water. The resulting vacuum allowed the atmospheric pressure to force the piston back to the bottom of the cylinder, thereby raising the pump-rod. The cycle was then started again by admission of more steam. The steam-valve and the injection-cock were perhaps at first operated by hand, but, according to a story, in 1713 the boy whose duty it was to work the valves arranged for this to be done by the engine itself, by means of 'catches and strings'. There is no confirmation of this legend and since there is, on the contrary, evidence of its untruth, it may perhaps rank with the later legend of the boy Watt and the tea-kettle. There is, in fact, no reason to suppose that the method of operating the valves automatically by the motion of the rod of the injection pump, as shown on the engraving of the Dudley Castle engine, was not employed when that engine was first set to work in 1712.

The need for the water-seal was due to the impossibility, in those days, of making an accurately bored cylinder of the size required. Cannon- and pump-barrels up to about 7 inches in diameter could be bored successfully, but anything larger was beyond the capacity of the workshops. Hence at first the only way of finishing the cylinders for Newcomen's engines was to rub the inside of

[1] More precisely, Dudley Castle is in an enclave of Worcestershire.

the castings smooth with abrasives. The pistons would thus not fit very well, and the difficulty was overcome by fixing to the top of each piston a flexible leather disk and keeping it sealed with water to maintain the vacuum.

The engine at Griff colliery, near Coventry, must have been erected almost simultaneously with that at Dudley Castle. At first it was not a success, but

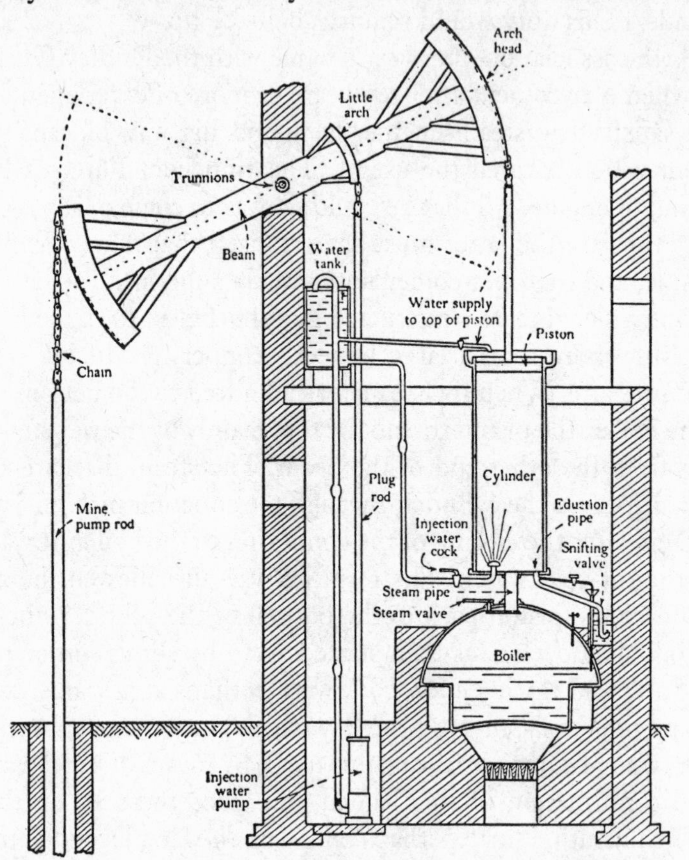

FIGURE 104—*Diagram of Newcomen's atmospheric engine, 1712.*

this was not wholly unfortunate, for thereby it aroused the interest of a local resident, Henry Beighton (1686–1754), a land-surveyor. He was the first to study the Newcomen engine scientifically and is credited with suggesting improvements to the valve-gear. It was he who provided the information about the engine which Desaguliers published in his 'Experimental Philosophy' (1744). This includes Newcomen's method of calculating the power of his engines from the diameter of the cylinder and the barometric pressure, with allowance for estimated frictional and other losses. In practice, to be on the safe side, engineers usually assumed a mean effective pressure of half an atmosphere on the piston. Beighton published a table (see below) of his recommendations for the diameters of pumps and cylinders for engines to draw water from depths of from 15 to 100 yds, in quantities from 48·51 to 304·48 hogsheads an hour.[1] In all cases the engines are assumed to have a 6-ft stroke and to make 16 double strokes per minute.

On Savery's death in 1715 his patent rights were acquired by certain 'Proprietors', who in 1716 advertised their readiness to treat for the erection of

A *Physico-Mechanical* Calculation of the Power of an *Engine*.

Diameter of the Pump inches.	Draws at a 6 Foot stroke.	at 16 St. in a Min. draws per Hour.	The Diameter of the Cylinder.												
			The Depth to be Drawn in Yards.												
Inch	Ale Gall.	Hogsh. Gall.	15	20	25	30	35	40	45	50	60	70	80	90	100
4	3. 20	48. 51	Inches				9	10	11	11½	12	13½	14	15	16
4½	4. 04	60. 60				10	11	11¾	12	13	14	15	16	17	18¼
5	5. 02	66. 61			10	11	11¾	13	13¾	14	15½	16¾	18½	19½	20¼
5½	6. 26	94. 30		10	11	12	13	14	15	15¾	17	19	20	21	22¼
6	7. 22	110. 1	9½	11	12	13	14	15½	16	17	19	20½	22	23	24½
6½	8. 46	128. 54	10	12	13	14	15½	16¼	18	19	20	22	23	24½	26¼
7	9. 82	149. 40	10¾	13	14	15½	16¾	18¾	19	20½	22	24	25½	27	28½
7½	11. 32	172. 30	11	13¾	15	16½	18	19	20	21¼	23¼	25	27	28½	30¼
7¾	12. 02	182. 13	12	14	15½	17¼	18¾	19¾	21	22	24¼	26	28	29¼	31½
8	12. 82	195. 22	12½	14½	16½	18¼	19	20¼	21½	23	25	27	29	30½	32½
8½	14. 52	221. 15	13½	15¼	17¼	19	20¼	21¾	23	24	26¾	28½	31	32½	35¼
9	16. 24	247. 7	14	16¼	18	20	21½	23	24¼	25	28	30½	33	35	36½
10	20. 04	304. 48	15½	18	20	22	23¾	25¼	27	28¾	31¼	33¾	36	38¼	40

From 'The Ladies' Diary', p 22. London, 1721.

atmospheric engines, mentioning that some had already been erected in the counties of Stafford, Warwick, Cornwall, and Flint. There were in fact others in Lancashire, Yorkshire, Northumberland, and Durham, of which the 'Proprietors' seem to have been unaware. One of their agents, John Potter, erected such an engine at Edmonston, Midlothian, in 1725. Many interesting details concerning it are known, among them that the cylinder had a diameter of 29 in and a stroke of 9 ft. This and the pumps came from London, the cylinder alone costing £250. The beam of the engine came from Yorkshire and cost £82 16*s* delivered. The annual royalty was £80. For looking after the engine the engineers were to be paid £200 per annum, together with half the profits of the colliery. The licence

[1] The hogsheads were apparently the old wine measure of 63 gallons, and the exactness of the deliveries listed is academic rather than practical. The printing of the original is poor and a few of the fractional values in the table are doubtful.

was to terminate in 1733, when the English and Scottish patents for the Savery engine were due to expire. This shows that Newcomen's invention was being exploited under these patents. The client paid separately for the materials and component parts, which were assembled and erected on the site by the appropriate craftsmen supervised by an engineer.

By 1725 the Newcomen engine was coming into general use for pumping, especially for mines, and also to raise water for operating water-wheels to drive machinery. An engraving of 1726 shows an engine with valve-gear of the tappet type; and also an arrangement for feeding the boiler with the water from the eduction-pipe of the cylinder instead of from the almost cold water on the top of the piston, as was done at first. It is not known if this improvement was Newcomen's own.

The knowledge of the new power extended to the continent. The first Newcomen engine outside Britain was erected in 1722 at Königsberg, near Chemnitz in Hungary, for J. E. T. von Erlach of Vienna. He had visited England and had taken back with him an experienced workman to do the job. This man later erected several other Newcomen engines in Hungary, where he was regarded as their inventor. In France the first engine was installed in 1726, at Passy, a suburb of Paris, to supply the city with water from the Seine. One of the erectors was a member of the committee exploiting the engine on behalf of the 'Proprietors'.

Newcomen died in 1729, having lived to see his engine in use in Hungary, France, Belgium, and possibly Germany and Spain. Whether he derived much pecuniary benefit from his important invention is doubtful. It seems most likely that he had been thrust aside by the proprietors of Savery's patent, who took the major share of the profits.

In 1733 the patent expired and the employment of the engine spread rapidly, for it met a definite want and had no competitor. The coal-mining industry, particularly, benefited from its use, for it permitted far deeper mining than did pumping by animal-power (vol III, ch 3). In the deep coalfields of the north of England, where many pits had been flooded by the end of the seventeenth century, it brought about almost a rebirth of mining. As the numbers of engines increased, so did their size, though the design remained little changed. The larger engines, however, needed increased boiler-power, and two or more boilers replaced the single one of Newcomen.

In 1765, Gabriel Jars (1732–69), a French metallurgist, visited Newcastle upon Tyne, and described the engine he saw working at the Walker colliery near by (figure 57). It had been built by William Brown, a local colliery-engineer, and was the largest in the district. It was served by three boilers with another in reserve. Jars states that the boilers were of wrought iron with lead tops, except the one immediately beneath the cylinder, which had a copper top for ease of connexion. The piston was packed with hemp rope, and three water-jets were used for condensing because of the large size of the cylinder. From another source we learn that the cylinder had a diameter of 74 in and a length of $10\frac{1}{2}$ ft. It weighed $6\frac{1}{2}$ tons and came from Coalbrookdale in Shropshire.

For long after Newcomen's death the development of his engine was due to practical men, for the 'philosophers' seem to have considered machinery beneath their notice. The first scientific engineer to devote much attention to steam power was John Smeaton, famous as the constructor of the Eddystone lighthouse (ch 15, p 468). As a youth, he became interested in a Newcomen engine at a colliery close to his family home in Yorkshire. Later, in the course of his professional work, he grew much dissatisfied with the design and performances of the engines that he had observed. In 1767 he designed an engine to take the place of horses in raising water from the New River in London to a reservoir at a higher level. The engine did not come up to expectation, so in 1769 he constructed in his private workshop an experimental engine with a cylinder 10 inches in diameter and of 38-in stroke. He also obtained from William Brown (p 178) a list of about 100 engines in the north of England, with particulars of the performances of 15 of them having cylinders ranging from 20 to 75 inches in diameter, and collected further particulars of 18 large engines in Cornwall. From the data, he found that on the average they raised the equivalent of 5·59 m lb of water one foot high for the consumption of one bushel (84 lb) of coal. This was the way that the 'duty' of an engine was then reckoned. The average effective pressure on the pistons was only 6·72 lb to the sq in [6], which was no better than Newcomen had obtained.

In 1772 Smeaton compiled a table of proportions of the parts of engines with cylinders up to 72 inches in diameter, and in the same year designed and superintended the construction of an engine for Long Benton colliery, Northumberland, with a cylinder of 52-in diameter. Owing to improvements in details and workmanship, and especially in boring the cylinder (for which he designed a special mill at Carron Iron Works), the Long Benton engine (figure 105) could do 9·45 m ft-lb of useful work per bushel. This was a very remarkable advance on current practice. In 1775 Smeaton designed an engine with a cylinder of 66-in diameter for emptying the docks at Kronstadt, Russia, and at almost the same time he built his most famous engine—that at Chacewater in Cornwall—which had a 72-in cylinder.

Smeaton, with knowledge and manufacturing facilities unavailable to Newcomen, almost doubled the efficiency of the atmospheric steam-engine, raising its performance about as high as was possible with the type. This, however, was extremely low, mainly because of the great waste of heat in using the working

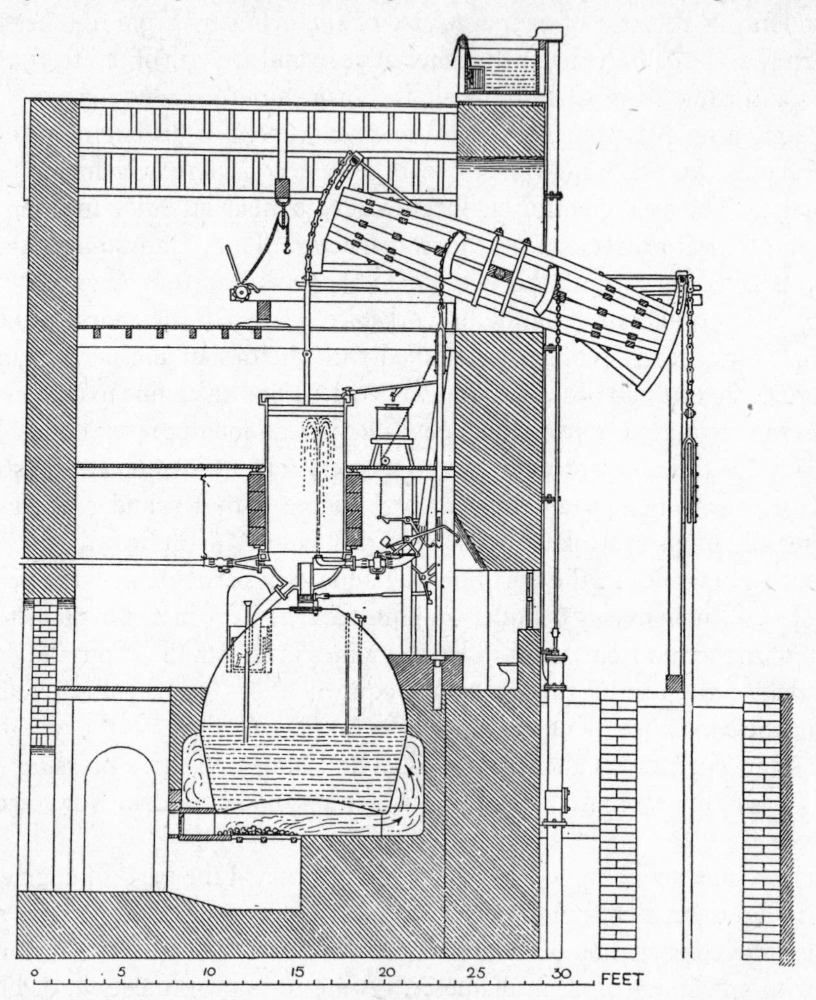

FIGURE 105—*The Newcomen engine made by Smeaton in 1772 for Long Benton colliery.*

cylinder also as a condenser. He regarded the performances of his Long Benton engine as a standard of quality; yet, if one assumes that low-grade coal of only 12 000 B.Th.U. per lb was used for raising steam, his figures show the overall thermal efficiency to have been only about 1 per cent. But, despite its enormous consumption of coal for work done, the Newcomen engine held the field unchallenged for more than 60 years. It was the main factor in the exploitation of the mineral resources of Britain, thereby laying the foundations of the industrial development of the country.

The limitations of the Newcomen engine, except for pumping, were very great. It was inherently a single-acting engine, as the chain-connexion between the piston-rod and the end of the beam precluded any thrust on the upward stroke. To obtain a rotary motion the engine could be provided with a connecting-rod driving a crankshaft and fly-wheel. In this case the beam had to be overloaded at the crankshaft end sufficiently to produce the required downward pressure on the crank-pin during the upward stroke of the piston. The arrangement, though clumsy, was often used instead of horses for winding coal from shallow pits, and survived into the nineteenth century. Alternatively, the engine could be made to pump water into an overhead tank, the water then being allowed to descend over a water-wheel that drove the machinery. This method gave the uniform motion needed in such industries as cotton-spinning. Smeaton employed it to obtain reversible drives by using a water-wheel resembling that shown by Agricola in 1556, in which one half of the width had a right-handed set of buckets, and the other half a left-handed set, the water being diverted from one set to the other as required.

III. WATT (1736–1819)

After Newcomen, the first to make any outstanding advance in developing power from steam was James Watt, who by his inventive and scientific genius made a fundamental improvement in the efficiency and mechanical design of steam-engines. Watt, the son of a master carpenter and ship-wright at Greenock, went to London as a youth to learn the craft of instrument-making. He returned to Glasgow in 1757, was appointed 'Mathematical Instrument Maker to the University', and had a workshop in the college buildings.

In 1763 he repaired a model Newcomen engine belonging to the university, and made it work, though a London instrument-maker had failed to do so. The cylinder of the model had a bore of 2 in and a stroke of 6 in, the boiler being about 9 inches in diameter. Watt found that its consumption of steam was so great that it could make only a few strokes at a time before coming to a standstill. He attributed this to the loss of heat by conduction through the cylinder-walls, the surface of which was greater in proportion to the volume than in a larger engine. To minimize this source of loss he made another working model with a wooden cylinder 6 inches in diameter with a 12-in stroke. From experiments with this model he decided that the real cause of the high steam-consumption was the cooling of the cylinder by the injection-water at every working stroke. During this research he independently discovered the phenomenon of latent heat of steam, which, unknown to him, had already been discovered by his friend Joseph Black (1728–99), then professor of chemistry in the University. In Watt's own words [7]:

> I perceived that, to make the best use of steam, it was necessary, first, that the Cylinder should be maintained always as hot as the steam which entered it; and secondly, that when the steam was condensed, the water of which it was composed, and the injection itself, should be cooled down to 100°, or lower where that was possible. The means of accomplishing these points did not immediately present themselves; but early in 1765 it occurred to me that, if a communication were opened between a Cylinder containing steam, and another vessel which was exhausted of air and other fluids, the steam, as an elastic fluid, would immediately rush into the empty vessel, and continue to do so until it had established an equilibrium; and if that vessel were kept very cool by an injection, or otherwise, more steam would continue to enter until the whole was condensed.

Watt goes on to explain that he proposed to maintain the vacuum in the 'other vessel', or condenser, either by draining it through a water-sealed vertical pipe more than 34 ft long, or, preferably, by using a pump or pumps for the purpose. As soon as possible after the idea of using a separate condenser had occurred to him, he made a rough model to test its practicability, and this 'answered his expectation'. He realized that Newcomen's method of sealing the piston with cold water would have to be abandoned, because it conflicted with the principle of keeping the cylinder as hot as possible, and that the atmosphere should not act directly on the piston for the same reason. He therefore decided to provide a cylinder-cover with a hole and stuffing-box for the piston-rod to pass through, and to use steam instead of atmospheric pressure to force the piston down. He intended that the cylinder should be kept hot by a steam-jacket, the outside of which would be lagged with wood. Watt constructed a large cylinder on these lines, and experimented with it in conjunction with a surface-condenser of his own design. However, he feared that, in service, this type of condenser would become encrusted with deposits from the water, and believed that the much simpler and smaller jet-condenser would serve the purpose better. To this view he always adhered. Watt's first notion was to connect the piston-rod directly with the pump-rod which it was desired to operate, but he finally decided that the better way would be to transmit the motion of the piston through a rocking beam, as Newcomen had done.

As Watt had neither the money nor the facilities to develop his invention on a practical scale, Black introduced him to John Roebuck, an enterprising industrialist, who was interested in the drainage of coal-mines. Roebuck suggested that a patent be applied for, and in 1769 Watt was granted his historic patent for 'A new Method of Lessening the Consumption of Steam and Fuel in Fire Engines'. The essential element in this was the use of a separate condenser. In return for taking over the expenses already incurred, Roebuck came in as a partner to the extent of two-thirds. An experimental engine of the beam type with a cylinder 18 inches in diameter and a 5-ft stroke was erected at Roebuck's residence; but the matter could not be followed up vigorously, partly because Watt had begun practising as a civil engineer, and partly because Roebuck was becoming financially embarrassed.

Watt had occasion to visit London on business, and on his return, furnished with introductions from friends, he called upon Matthew Boulton (1728–1809), a leading manufacturer whose works was at Soho, near Birmingham (plate 31 A). Boulton became interested in the engine because his own works was short of water-power and he was seeking means of pumping back the water that drove his machinery. Boulton, however, was not disposed to develop the engine unless he could exploit it on a scale sufficiently large to justify a special factory for making it, and to this Roebuck would not agree. In 1773 Roebuck became bankrupt, and his share in the patent, which the receivers valued at only about a farthing, was taken over by Boulton in discharge of the debts that Roebuck owed him. Watt then brought his experimental engine to Birmingham and gave his whole time to its development, with such success that in 1774 he wrote: 'The fire engine I have invented is now going and answers much better than any other that has yet been made.' The patent, however, had only eight more years to run, and Boulton realized that it would expire before any profit could be earned. Watt therefore petitioned Parliament for an extension, which was granted in 1775, for twenty-five years ending in 1800. The famous partnership of Boulton and Watt was entered upon for a like period.

Boulton was enthusiastic about the new engine, and persuaded Watt to proceed at once to construct one with a 50-in cylinder for Bloomfield colliery in Staffordshire, and another with a 30-in cylinder for blowing blast-furnaces belonging to John Wilkinson (1728–1808), an ironmaster at New Willey in the same county. Wilkinson had made and patented in 1774 a new type of boring-mill for making cannon (p 421). The greatly increased accuracy attainable by this machine made it invaluable for boring cylinders to the fine limits that Watt needed. Both these engines of Boulton and Watt were most successful. Their consumption of coal was less than a third of that normal at the time. Inquiries poured in from the tin- and other metal-mines in Cornwall, where coal was dear and the cost of pumping limited the depth at which mining was commercially practicable. Cornwall, indeed, provided so important a field for the engine that it became necessary for one or other of the partners to be on the spot. A royalty

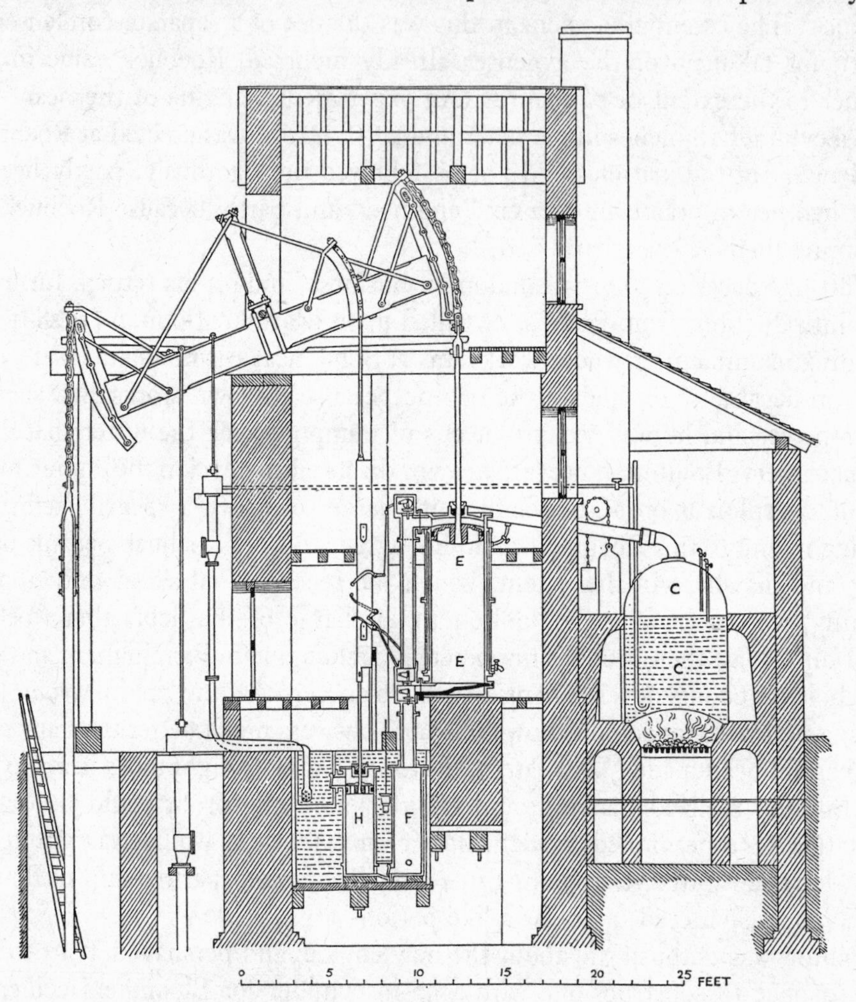

FIGURE 106—*Watt's single-acting engine for pumping water for draining mines, 1788. The boiler* C *is placed in an outhouse, and the steam passes to the cylinder* E, *which is kept hot all the time by a separate steam jacket.* F *is the separate condenser and* H *an air-pump.*

equal to one-third of the saving in the cost of fuel, as compared with that of the common engine, was charged to the users, and to determine this ratio Watt made careful tests of many existing engines both in Cornwall and elsewhere. On the basis of these trials he concluded that the effective pressure on the piston of the common engine was 7 lb per sq in, while in his own engine it was 10·5 lb.

In the final design of the single-acting engine of Watt, as used from about 1788, there were several new features (figure 106). The boiler (C) had a greater heating-surface. Noteworthy are the closed and steam-jacketed cylinder (E) and the jet-condenser (F) with air-pump (H) alongside in a hot well below floor-level. The piston was rendered steam-tight by a packing of hemp rope held in a recess around its circumference by a junk-ring fastened by studs. By the side of the cylinder was a pipe, at the head of which was the inlet valve which, when opened, admitted live steam above the piston and also to the interior of the pipe. Near the lower end of the pipe was the equilibrium valve, which allowed steam to pass from the space above the piston to that below it. A third valve, the exhaust valve, controlled the flow of steam from beneath the piston to the condenser. All the valves were of the drop type, operated by tappets.

The operation of the engine was as follows. When the piston was at the top of its stroke, the exhaust valve was opened to produce a vacuum beneath it, and the inlet valve was simultaneously opened to admit steam above it. The piston was then forced downwards by the atmospheric pressure and the pressure of the steam. When the piston reached the lower end of its stroke the inlet and exhaust valves were closed and the equilibrium valve was opened. The piston, having then an equal pressure on each side, was pulled up again to the top of the cylinder by the weight of the pump-rod.

Watt was urged by Boulton to devise some way of obtaining rotary motion from his engine, which would give it wide application in manufacturing industries. The old idea of using a crankshaft driven by a connecting-rod from the working end of the beam had occurred to Watt, but was taken up by one of his workmen and patented in another name in 1780. The patent might have been contested, but the long-headed Watt, who himself held numerous patents, was too wise to become involved in litigation of that type. He devised other expedients, which he patented in 1781. One of these, the epicyclic or sun-and-planet gear, suggested by his assistant William Murdock (p 262), came into general use. It consisted of a spur-wheel keyed to the end of the driven shaft, and geared with a similar non-rotating wheel fixed to the end of a connecting-rod hanging from the beam, the wheels being kept in gear by a link joining their centres; the shaft would thus make two revolutions for each double stroke of the engine. The sun-and-planet motion was used for all Boulton and Watt rotative engines until the expiry of the crankshaft and connecting-rod patent in 1794.

In 1782 Watt patented two very important improvements. The first made the engine double-acting, and thus able to develop twice the power from the same cylinder-volume. The second used the steam expansively, admitting it to the cylinder only during the early part of each stroke, after which it would drive the piston by its expansive force. To render the engine double-acting, the flexible chain connecting the piston-rod to the beam had to be replaced by some mechanism that would transmit a force in either direction. Watt's first notion was to extend the piston-rod by a rack which would gear with a toothed arc on the end of the beam. This was a clumsy device, and in 1784 he patented his well known three-bar straight-line motion, which he himself regarded as his masterpiece. Within a few months, he saw that he could double the length of the linear path by employing the pantograph principle. Thus he produced his elegant 'parallel motion', which characterized the rotative beam-engine throughout the century or more of its service (figure 107).

In 1787, to ensure constancy of speed with varying loads, Watt provided the engine with a conical pendulum-centrifugal governor controlling a butterfly-valve in the steam-inlet pipe (vol III, p 105, and plate 4A). Such governors were already in use for controlling the setting of the millstones in flour-mills, but Watt was the first to use them for regulating steam-engines. By this time the double-acting rotative steam-engine had become practically standardized, and remained so until the expiration of Watt's master patent for the separate condenser in 1800. Watt then retired from active work, after having not only provided industry with a prime mover of an efficiency hardly improved for the next half-century, but having also raised the performance of pumping-engines from the 9·45 m ft-lb per bushel of coal attained by Smeaton (p 179) to the 30 m ft-lb or more that Boulton and Watt could guarantee at the close of their partnership.

The further development of the beam-engine was practically confined for many years to mechanical and constructional improvements, the most outstanding of which was the control of the steam-flow into and out of the cylinder by a single sliding valve in place of the separate drop-valves employed by Watt. The slide-valve was invented and patented in 1799 by Murdock, who also devised the eccentric on the crankshaft as a means of operating it. After expiry of their master patent the first serious competitor of Boulton and Watt was Matthew Murray (1765–1826) of Leeds. He simplified and lightened Murdock's valve in 1801 by bringing the steam- and exhaust-ports of the cylinder close together in a single facing, so that they could be controlled by a comparatively small valve. About this time cast iron beams began to replace the wooden beams of Newcomen, Smeaton, and Watt, and connecting-rods of cast iron succeeded the wooden rods flitched with iron plates that had at first been used. But the beam-engine underwent no other noticeable change until 1845, when John McNaught, of Bury in Lancashire, gave it a long extension of life by his simple and effective way of converting it into a compound engine.

The persistence of the beam-type of engine is to be explained by the embryonic state of mechanical engineering in those early days. Its great size and

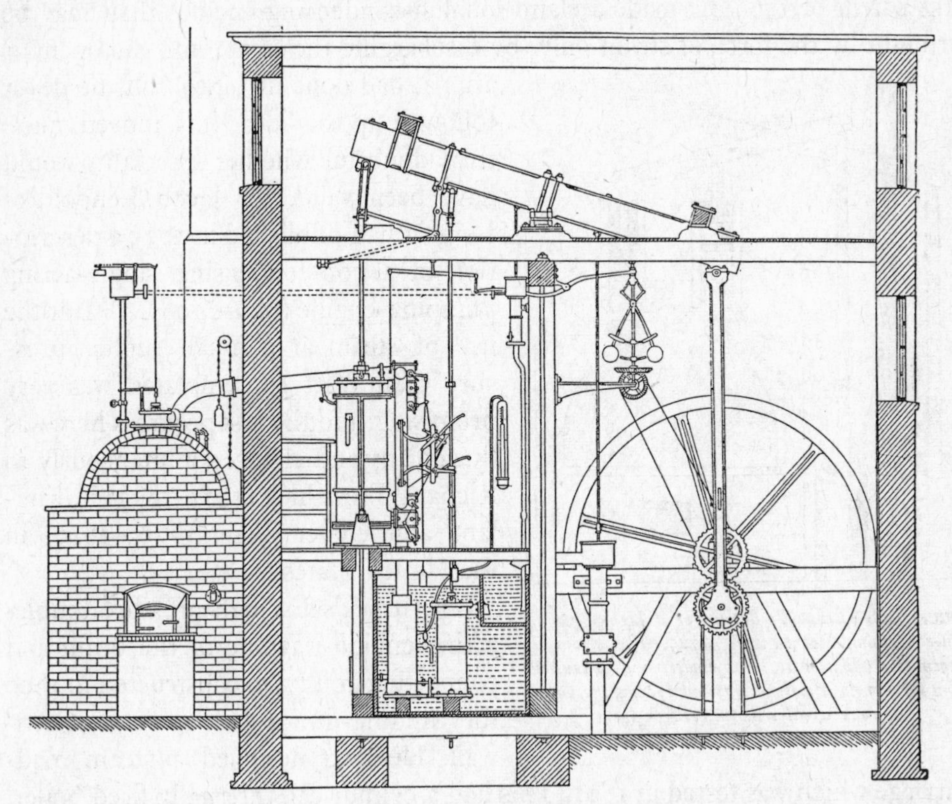

FIGURE 107—*Watt's double-acting rotative steam-engine, 1784. The parallel motion bars are seen on the raised end of the beam. Note also sun-and-planet gear.*

weight, and the height of the engine-house required, were more than offset by ease of manufacture with such appliances and tools as were available. It had very few flat surfaces to be finished by the skilled and tedious manual labour needed for such work before the planing-machine (p 433) was introduced about 1820. One of its greatest virtues was tolerance of quite appreciable misalignment, on account of the length of its beam, connecting-rod, and eccentric-rod. The cottered brasses of its numerous pin-joints also simplified any required adjustments by the operator, and the whole engine was very durable.

IV. EARLY ENGINES OF TREVITHICK

Despite the enormous improvements by Watt, the engine, as he left it, was still essentially a vacuum-engine, for he was resolutely opposed to steam-pressure higher than a few pounds above atmospheric, because of supposed danger. In his first patent of 1769, he made a claim for non-condensing engines that 'may be wrought by the force of steam only, by discharging the steam into the open air after it had done its office', but he never followed up this idea. It is, indeed, more than doubtful whether his claim would have been valid, for Jacob Leupold of Leipzig had published in 1725 a description of a non-condensing single-acting pumping-engine (figure 108) [8]. But the use of steam at a much higher pressure than Watt contemplated was very promising, and the first progress here was due chiefly and almost simultaneously to Richard Trevithick (1771–1833) in England and Oliver Evans (1755–1819) in the United States.

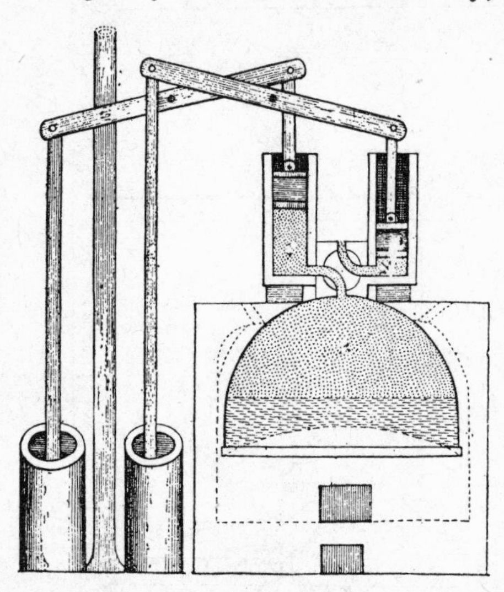

FIGURE 108—*Leupold's design for a high-pressure, non-condensing steam-engine, 1725. The steam is alternately admitted to the cylinders and exhausted from them to the atmosphere by one rocking motion of the circular valve shown between them.*

Trevithick's first high-pressure double-acting engine was one of the beam and connecting-rod type, constructed in 1800 for winding-duties at a mine in Cornwall. He next designed a steam road-carriage which was tested in 1801. This had a cylindrical, internally fired boiler, with return flue. The vertical cylinder was partly sunk into the boiler, and the piston-rod drove the rear wheels by a cross-head with slide-bars and connecting rod. The exhaust steam was turned up the chimney to increase the draught. The vehicle would carry several persons, had a loaded weight of about 30 cwt, and ran at some nine miles an hour on a level road. In 1802 Trevithick, jointly with his cousin Andrew Vivian, took out a patent for 'Improvements in the Construction and Application of Steam Engines', which covered the mechanical details of both a stationary engine and a road locomotive engine. In the former, the unit consisting of boiler and cylinder is shown oscillating on trunnions so as to avoid the need for slide-bars or connecting-rod (plate 10A).

In 1802 Trevithick built at Coalbrookdale an experimental pumping-engine of the beam type, working at the unprecedented pressure of 145 lb per sq in. The boiler was of cast iron with a diameter of 4 ft and a thickness of $1\frac{1}{2}$ in; the cylinder was 7 inches in diameter with a 3-ft stroke. It astonished everyone who saw it by reason of its small size in relation to the power developed [9]. The next year he built another steam-carriage with a single cylinder and a pair of 8-ft wheels driven by gearing. It would carry eight or ten passengers, and made several trips in London, but excited no general public interest. Trevithick then returned to Cornwall to exploit his stationary engines, which seemed to offer a better field for his energies. While there, he undertook to build a steam-locomotive to draw a load of 10 tons over the $9\frac{3}{4}$ miles of cast iron tramway connecting the Pendarren ironworks with the Glamorganshire canal. Its trial in 1804 was completely successful, though it caused the breakage of several of the tramway plates. The engine, which weighed about 5 tons without water, would easily pull much more than its specified load, and, as Trevithick said, 'was the first and only self-moving machine that ever was made to travel on a road with 25 tons at four miles per hour, and completely manageable by only one man'.

Trevithick was thus not only the originator of the locomotive, but had proved —what was then disbelieved—that there would be sufficient adhesion between smooth wheels and rails to transmit the tractive force. His device of turning the exhaust steam up the chimney to provide an adequate draught, had he patented it, would have given him as great a control over locomotive development as the invention of the separate condenser gave to Watt in the field of stationary engines. He probably influenced locomotive history by designing a locomotive, similar to his Pendarren engine, for a colliery near Newcastle upon Tyne. This was built at Gateshead in 1805 by one of Trevithick's mechanics, and there can hardly be room for doubt that a knowledge of it must have stimulated George Stephenson in 1813 to make his first locomotive for use at the Killingworth colliery in the same coalfield.

Trevithick's incursions into locomotive work did not interfere to any extent with the development of his stationary engines. In a long letter [10] of 1804 to his friend Davies Giddy (1767–1839),[1] he spoke of nearly 50 of his engines, their tasks including driving sugar-mills, corn-grinding, pumping water, and rolling iron. He constructed them with either horizontal or vertical cylinders: the former design (1803) with his original globular boiler (figure 109), and the latter, a few years later, with his internally fired return-flue boiler.

Oliver Evans inaugurated the use of high-pressure steam in the United States about the same time as Trevithick did in England. Evans was a wheel-wright, but

[1] In 1817 Giddy changed his surname to Gilbert. He was president of the Royal Society from 1827 to 1830.

in 1780 entered into partnership with his brothers, who were flour-millers. He had already shown inventive genius, and in 1797 obtained a patent for a steam-carriage. In 1803, when there were probably not more than half a dozen steam-engines in the United States, he constructed a steam dredging-machine, and the next year built a successful direct-acting vertical stationary engine with a double-acting cylinder 6 inches in diameter and a stroke of 8 in, to run at 30 rpm. The steam- and exhaust-valves were three-way cocks operated by pins on the fly-wheel. Like Trevithick, he used a cylindrical boiler with an internal fire-plate

FIGURE 109—*Side view and section of Trevithick's high-pressure engine with horizontal cylinder and dome-topped boiler, 1803.*

and flue, and in 1805 was proposing to use steam at a pressure of 120 lb to the sq in. His enterprise received no encouragement in his lifetime, but its influence was shown by the extensive use of high-pressure steam in the United States while the Watt engine was still the prevailing type in Britain.

By 1800 several inventors had attempted to make improvements on Watt's beam-engine for mine-pumping, but all had been frustrated by their inability to use a separate condenser. Thus in 1792 Edward Bull, once an erector for Boulton and Watt, and later associated with Trevithick, put up at Dalcoath mine in Cornwall an engine of his own design. In this he had eliminated the beam and further simplified the construction by inverting the cylinder and connecting the piston-rod directly to the pump-rod below, but as he was using a separate condenser Boulton and Watt took legal action and in 1794 obtained an injunction against him.

V. HIGH-PRESSURE ENGINES

With the opening of the nineteenth century, the use of a separate condenser was free to all. The lead given by Trevithick in the use of high-pressure steam brought the compound engine definitely into sight as a practical objective. Such an engine would allow a greater range of expansion of the steam to be employed without infringing Watt's principle that a working cylinder should be subjected to the least possible temperature range, and it also made possible greater uniformity of the torque on a crankshaft.

The first to exploit the compound engine under the new conditions was Arthur Woolf (1776–1837), a versatile engineer who had been employed in the Cornish mines. In 1803 he patented an engine of this type, and experimented with the principle by adding a high-pressure cylinder to an existing Watt engine at Meux's brewery in London, where he was then working. The result was not satisfactory for, thinking that steam at a pressure of *n* lb could be expanded to *n* times its original volume without reducing its pressure to less than that of the atmosphere [11], he had made his high-pressure cylinder far too small, so that the engine would not give the power required. However, to develop his ideas, he left the brewery and entered into partnership with Humphrey Edwards, a millwright who had a workshop at Lambeth, and in time they standardized a satisfactory design. This was a beam-engine with two cylinders, side by side, both piston-rods being connected to the same pin of the parallel motion. A test of one of their compound engines in 1811 showed a saving of about 50 per cent in fuel, as compared with a simple Watt engine. In the same year the partnership was dissolved, Woolf returned to Cornwall, and a few years later Edwards went to France, where he had already erected about 100 of the Lambeth-made engines. He had secured a French patent for the engine in 1815, and in partnership with a French firm built up an important engine-manufacturing business in that country, where he remained until his death. Other firms later took up the manufacture of the Woolf engine, which was being built in France until about 1870.

Woolf's return to Cornwall was influenced by reports of the decline in performance of the engines there since Boulton and Watt had ceased to have their former financial interest in them. In 1800 the duty obtained per bushel of coal had been about 30 m ft-lb, whereas in December 1811 the average duty of 12 engines was found to be only 17 m ft-lb. Woolf foresaw here an opening for his compound engines. In 1814 he erected one to work with steam at a pressure of 40 lb and using 8- or 9-fold expansion; another was set up in 1815. Both did extremely well, but he did not have the field to himself, for by 1812 Trevithick, having been bankrupted by the failure of certain enterprises in London, had returned to Cornwall determined to retrieve his fortunes. He had sold his last interest in his engine-patent, but his faith in high-pressure steam was as great as ever. One of his first feats in Cornwall was the construction in 1812 of a high-pressure 'Cornish' beam-engine for pumping, the earliest example of a type which, on account of its remarkable efficiency and negligible cost of maintenance, held its own for waterworks-pumping until the close of the nineteenth century. It was supplied with steam at a pressure of 40 lb by one of Trevithick's internal-flue 'Cornish' boilers 26 ft long. This design of boiler is still used, almost unchanged, for small industrial duties.

Except for the high steam-pressure and expansive working, the steam-cycle was similar to that of the Watt pumping-engine (p 184). The cylinder was single-acting, with a diameter of 24 in and a stroke of 6 ft. It was not steam-jacketed, but lagged with straw and plaster. With the piston at the highest point, steam was admitted above it to force it down and thereby raise the pump-rod at the other end of the beam, the underside of the piston being open to the condenser. The steam was cut off as early as one-ninth of the stroke, the remainder of the stroke being effected by its expansion. After a pause to allow the pump-barrel to become filled with water, an equilibrium valve was opened to equalize the pressure on both sides of the piston so that the latter was raised again to the head of the cylinder by the weight of the ram and pump-rod. The duration of the pause was regulated by a 'cataract' device, in which the time required for a given weight of water to escape through an adjustable orifice determined the moment at which the valve opened.

Trevithick, however, did not confine himself to pumping-engines. Among his various activities, he built a number of engines of the self-contained type for threshing corn, grinding meal, and other agricultural purposes. One of these, supplied in 1812, continued in use until 1879 and still survives (plate 10B).

Apparently not realizing that with his 'Cornish' pumping-engine he had originated a type that was soon to have no rival, Trevithick almost simultaneously designed and built what he called a plunger-pole engine for pumping-duties. The plunger-pole was simply an iron ram, in this case 16 inches in diameter and of $8\frac{1}{2}$-ft stroke, which replaced the ordinary piston. It worked through a stuffing-box at the top of the cylinder, and had the advantage of making unnecessary an accurate boring of the cylinder. The latter stood on bearers across the head of the pit-shaft. At the head of the ram was a cross-head sliding in guides, and from the cross-head side-rods descended to another cross-head below the cylinder, from which the pump-rod was hung. With this arrangement there was no need for any reciprocating beam.

This engine, of course, was of the single-acting type, the ram being raised by steam-pressure and descending by its own weight and that of the pump-rod. The air-pump for the condenser was worked by a tumbler mechanism. Steam was used at 100-lb pressure and was cut off at one-third of the stroke. Inertia of the moving parts assisted the expanding steam to complete the stroke. Trevithick wrote in 1813 that it was 'lifting 40 million pounds 1 ft high with one bushel of coal, very nearly double the duty that is done by any other engine in the County'. He took out a patent for the plunger-pole engine in 1815, and erected others on the same principle, besides compounding a number of existing Watt engines by working them with high-pressure steam which was first expanded in a plunger-pole cylinder added to the engine, thereby substantially increasing both power and efficiency.

The design of the plunger-pole engine probably reached its highest point in one erected in 1815. This worked with steam at a pressure of 120 lb, and had a plunger 33 inches in diameter making 10-ft strokes. In consequence of rumours, Trevithick had it tested in 1816 by independent engineers, who reported that its duty was 48 m ft-lb per bushel of coal, but that they had no doubt that it would do over 60 m when the bottom of the mine was reached. They found that it was operating with steam at 100 to 120 lb per sq in, and was making an average of 9¼ ten-ft working strokes a minute, with a cut-off at one-sixth of the stroke. When non-condensing the duty was 28 m.

Trevithick's patent for his plunger-pole engine had also included a claim for a high-pressure non-condensing reaction-turbine, working on the principle of Hero's aeolipile (p 168), except that he did not require the boiler to revolve. In 1815 he constructed such a machine, which he called his whirling-engine. It consisted essentially of a hollow shaft through which steam at a pressure of 100 lb was conveyed to the interior of a pair of hollow arms mounted at one end of the shaft. Each arm was 7 ft 6 in long, and had an orifice near its tip through which the steam escaped to the atmosphere in a tangential direction and thus drove the machine by its reaction. Power was taken off by a belt from a pulley on the shaft. As the shaft could not be run at much more than 250 rpm, giving a nozzle-velocity of about 200 ft per sec, the efficiency was low. Trevithick was, nevertheless, enthusiastic about the machine, mainly because of its light weight, but he did not develop it further.

A matter that aided Trevithick and Woolf in improving Watt's engines was that the mine-owners of Cornwall began from 1811 to publish regular reports on the performances of their engines, to encourage rivalry and so to promote efficiency. In the first report, the average duty of the 12 engines tested was no more than 17 m ft-lb per bushel of coal. By 1816 the average of 35 engines had risen to 23 m, and by 1826 the average of 51 engines reached 30·5 m, the increase being ascribed to new and improved engines, as well as to the spirit of emulation that developed. By 1844 the average duty of engines in Cornwall was said to be 68 m [12], though much higher figures were reported in individual cases. The best record is said to have been obtained by an engine having a cylinder 80 inches in diameter and a 10-ft stroke, erected at Fowey Consols mine, for which a duty of 125 m ft-lb per 95-lb bushel of coal was claimed in 1835. Since this would be equivalent to almost exactly $1\frac{1}{2}$ lb of coal per hp-hour, it is hard to believe.

Neither the plunger-pole engine of Trevithick nor the compound beam-

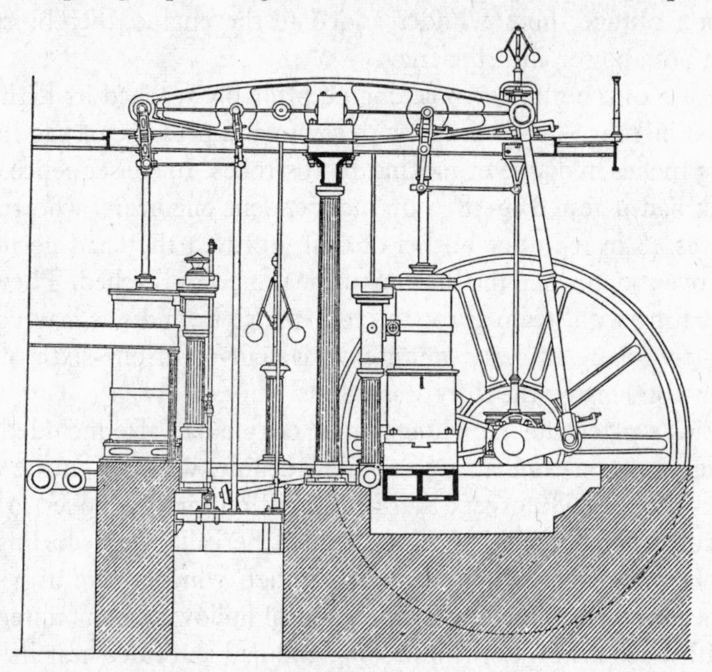

FIGURE 110—*Elevation of McNaught's 60 hp compound beam-engine, 1848. McNaught compounded many existing engines by adding a high-pressure cylinder midway along the beam.*

engine of Woolf long survived. The ram of the former was difficult to keep steam-tight, and its cooling by repeated exposures to the atmosphere was a further disadvantage. Woolf built no more of his compound engines after 1824 because, in spite of their efficiency, their greater cost and complexity made them unable to compete with the high-pressure Cornish engine of Trevithick, which held the field for heavy pumping-work without serious rivalry until nearly the end of the century.

For the heavier industrial duties, such as driving the machinery in factories and mills, the design of the rotative beam-engine held its own for many years, almost as it had been left by Watt. The only important improvement was in 1845 by John McNaught, of Bury, Lancashire, who compounded it by adding a small short-stroke high-pressure cylinder, having its own parallel motion, to act on the beam about half-way between the centre of the latter and the end driving the connecting-rod (figure 110). Many existing Watt engines were thus compounded to be operated with high-pressure steam, while for new engines the inclusion of a 'McNaught' cylinder taking steam at a pressure of 120 to 150 lb was adopted as standard.

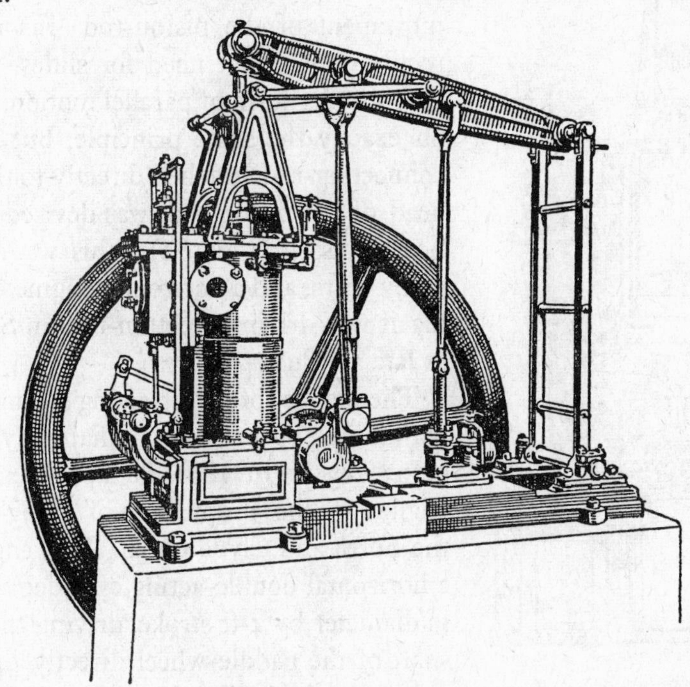

FIGURE 111—*The grasshopper engine of Easton and Amos, 1861. The name was suggested by the rocking links at the beam end.*

VI. DIRECT-ACTING ENGINES

Although when steam-engines were required for rotative duties there was no compelling reason for a cumbrous rocking beam, that type had the advantage of requiring only pin-joints for the guidance of the cross-head instead of slide-bars, which were far more difficult to make. To retain this advantage while eliminating the lengthy beam, the 'grasshopper' type was patented in 1803 by William Freemantle, the same principle being employed by Oliver Evans in America.

The grasshopper mechanism was based on the geometrical fact that if the mid-point of a straight link can move only in a circular arc by reason of a radius-rod attached to it, and if one end of the link be compelled to move in a straight path, the other end of the link will describe a second straight line at right angles to the first (figure 111). In practice, the piston-rod was attached to one end of the link, moving vertically, while the other end of the link was free to move in a small arc of circle, almost equivalent to a horizontal straight line. The mid-point of the link was held by a radius-bar. Thus the movement of the piston-rod was rendered rectilinear without need for slides.

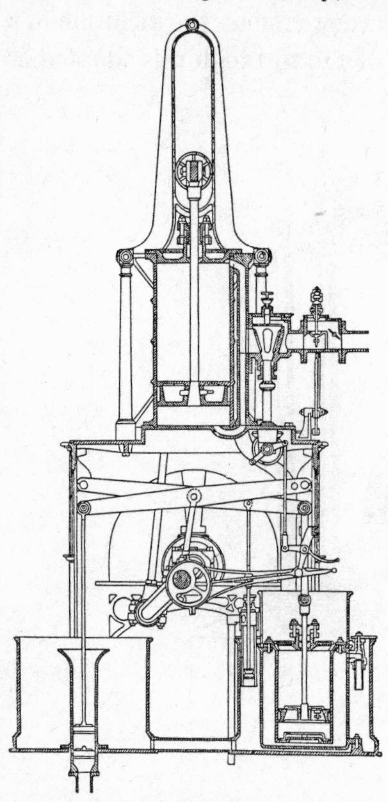

FIGURE 112—*Section of Maudslay's table engine, 1807. The beam was dispensed with and the crankshaft was driven by two connecting-rods from the cross-head above.*

A simpler form of parallel motion, working on exactly the same principle, but with the connecting-rod attached directly to the cross-head of the piston-rod, was devised by John Scott Russell (1808–82). This was used for many years, and a horizontal engine embodying it was driving a cotton-mill in Stockport as late as 1898.

The pioneer of direct-acting steam-engines without a beam was William Symington (1763–1831). In 1801 he applied such an engine to the propulsion of a tug-boat on the Forth and Clyde Canal. This engine had a horizontal double-acting cylinder 22 inches in diameter by 4-ft stroke, driving the crankshaft of the paddle-wheel directly through a connecting-rod. The simplicity of his design, however, made no appeal at the time, for the belief that a beam of some kind was essential to a satisfactory engine was deeply rooted. Stationary practice was therefore followed in marine work, though it was soon modified by replacing the overhead beam by a pair of lower beams, one on each side of the cylinder (see vol V, ch 7).

Direct-acting engines for industrial purposes had been built by both Trevithick and Evans early in the nineteenth century (p 189), but the first type to come into extensive use was the table engine of Henry Maudslay (1771–1831) patented in 1807. In this engine (figure 112) a vertical cylinder stood at the centre of a small cast-iron platform, its piston-rod carrying a cross-head having wheels running between vertical iron guides. A pair of connecting-rods from the ends of the cross-head drove a crank-shaft running on bearings beneath the platform. This engine was widely used in small factories for at least 40 years, and in a simplified form the type survived until the end of the century, especially for duties where its compactness was a consideration.

The belief that a cylinder placed otherwise than vertically would suffer undue wear from the weight of the piston was probably the reason for the tardiness in placing it horizontally. Such engines were hardly used before 1825, when Taylor and Martineau in London introduced the now familiar small open-type factory engine having its cylinder, slide-bars, and crankshaft-bearings on a horizontal cast iron bedplate of box-girder section.

To summarize the state of steam-engine practice about 1830 it may be said that the standard prime mover for the larger mills and factories was the Watt jet-condensing beam-engine using steam at little more than atmospheric pressure. In smaller establishments, the 'grasshopper' and the 'table' engines were commonly employed. For pumping at mines and waterworks the high-pressure Cornish engine of Trevithick, usually working at about 70 lb to the sq in, had no rival. For marine work, propulsion was by paddles always driven by side-lever engines, jet-condensing and working at about 4 or 5 lb to the sq in. Locomotive practice (vol V, ch 15) was in its infancy.

REFERENCES

[1] "An Account of Mr. Thos. Savery's Engine for raising Water by the help of Fire." *Phil. Trans.* **21**, no. 253, 228, 1699.
DICKINSON, H. W. 'A Short History of the Steam Engine', Pl. 1. University Press, Cambridge. 1939.
[2] *Post Man*, 19th–21st March 1702.
[3] DESAGULIERS, J. T. 'A Course of Experimental Philosophy', Vol. 2, p. 466. London. 1744.
[4] TRIEWALD, M. 'Kort Beskrifning om Eld- och Luft-Machin.' Stockholm. 1734. (Eng. trans. by R. JENKINS. Newcomen Society, London. 1928.)
[5] SWITZER, S. 'An Introduction to a General System of Hydrostaticks and Hydraulicks Philosophical and Practical', p. 342. London. 1729.
[6] FAREY, J. 'A Treatise on the Steam Engine, historical, practical and descriptive.' London. 1827.
[7] ROBISON, J. 'A System of Mechanical Philosophy' (4 vols). Edinburgh. 1822.
EWING, SIR JAMES ALFRED. 'The Steam Engine and other Heat-Engines.' University Press, Cambridge. 1926.
[8] LEUPOLD, J. *Theatri Machinarum Hydraulicarum* (2 vols). Leipzig, 1724, 1725.
[9] TREVITHICK, F. 'Life of Richard Trevithick with an Account of his Inventions', Vol. 1, pp. 153 ff.: Letter dated 22 August 1800. London. 1872.
[10] *Idem. Ibid.* Vol. 2, pp. 2 ff.: Letter dated 23 September 1804.
[11] JENKINS, R. *Trans. Newcomen Soc.*, **13**, 55, 63, 1932–3.
[12] MORSHEAD, W. *Min. Proc. Instn Civ. Engrs*, **23**, 46, 1863.

BIBLIOGRAPHY

BATHE, G. and BATHE, DOROTHY. 'Oliver Evans, A Chronicle of Early American Engineering.' Historical Society of Pennsylvania, Philadelphia. 1935.

DICKINSON, H. W. 'A Short History of the Steam Engine.' University Press, Cambridge. 1939.

Idem. 'James Watt, Craftsman and Engineer.' University Press, Cambridge. 1936.

Idem. 'Matthew Boulton.' University Press, Cambridge. 1937.

DICKINSON, H. W. and TITLEY, A. 'Richard Trevithick, the Engineer and the Man.' University Press, Cambridge. 1934.

EWING, SIR JAMES ALFRED. 'The Steam Engine and other Heat-Engines' (4th ed.). University Press, Cambridge. 1926.

FAREY, J. 'A Treatise on the Steam Engine, historical, practical and descriptive.' London. 1827.

JENKINS, R. "Savery, Newcomen, and the Early History of the Steam-Engine." *Trans. Newcomen Soc.*, **3**, 96–118, 1923; **4**, 113–33, 1924.

ROBISON, J. 'The Articles Steam and Steam-Engines, written for the Encyclopaedia Britannica.' Edinburgh. 1818.

SMEATON, J. 'Reports of the late John Smeaton' (4 vols). London. 1812–14.

TREDGOLD, T. 'The Steam Engine, its Invention and Progressive Improvement.' (2 vols). London. 1838.

See also *Transactions of the Newcomen Society.*

7

WATERMILLS *c* 1500 – *c* 1850

A. STOWERS

I. INTRODUCTION

THE origin and early history of water-power have been discussed and illustrated in chapter 17 of volume II of this work, where it was shown that the earliest form of water-wheel was the Norse mill. This had a horizontal wooden wheel with scoops rotated by a running stream; it developed, at the most, about half a horse-power. Roman engineers developed the Vitruvian mill with a vertical wooden wheel on a horizontal axle, producing up to about 3 hp. In western Europe the watermill and windmill were the main sources of motive power for many centuries until the steam-engines of Newcomen, Smeaton, and Watt were introduced in the eighteenth century.

The Vitruvian mill was constructed in two forms: (*a*) the undershot wheel, dipping into a river so that water flowed underneath and turned the paddles, and (*b*) the later overshot wheel, with a regulated stream of water directed on to the top of the wheel. These two main types revolutionized the grinding of corn, and when it was appreciated that they could be used or adapted for driving other machinery, technology was advanced on a new basis. This development took place especially after the fourth century, when the Christian religion was officially adopted in the Roman Empire and the long-established use of human power for the grinding of corn was discouraged.

Although technological progress was severely handicapped after the disintegration of the Roman Empire, the number of watermills increased, particularly in the eleventh and twelfth centuries, and by the fifteenth century they were being used for numerous industrial purposes, such as cutting and polishing marble, grinding powder and pigments, sawing timber, fulling cloth, tanning, crushing oil-seeds, and making iron and paper, as well as for irrigation.

The earliest known record of a watermill in England for grinding corn has been found in a charter granted in A.D. 762 by Ethelbert of Kent to the owners of a monastic mill east of Dover. But the most important historical landmark in this respect was undoubtedly the Domesday Survey, begun in 1080 and completed in 1086. In this were recorded over 5000 corn-mills, mostly south and east of the rivers Trent and Severn. The mills were probably of both types, Norse and

Roman, but the latter eventually predominated and most of them were situated on the eastern side of the country, which suggests that the utilization of water-power came from the European continent, first into Kent and then spreading into East Anglia, Lincolnshire, the midlands, and the south.

II. THE SIXTEENTH CENTURY

It is evident that at the opening of the sixteenth century the water-wheel was by far the most important source of motive power in Europe. It was the basis of mining and metallurgy, and hammers and bellows driven by the water-wheel were essential for the manufacture of wrought and cast iron. The hoisting, crushing, and stamping of ore, the drilling of gun-barrels, and the drawing of wire were carried out with the aid of water-wheels. Water-power had also been adopted in the mining of copper and silver.

In England, most villages and towns, which had naturally been established on favourable sites where water was available, possessed one or more corn-mills rented by the millers from the manorial lords. Towns grew in the river valleys—which appear to have been crowded with watermills—where industries, particularly those for producing iron and textiles, flourished. The expanding use of the water-wheel in industry obviously called for the concurrent development of methods of mechanical power transmission, especially the use of primitive gears for driving machines of different types in various ways and for increasing their speed and output.

In feudal times the manorial mill was a valuable source of income for the lord of the manor, providing a substantial rent from a comparatively small plot of land. Mill rentals varied considerably and the miller, who might be obliged to provide his own stones for grinding, often paid partly in cash and partly in kind. Eels from the mill pond were sometimes included in the rent. The feudal law of milling soke gave the lords the sole right of building and working mills on their estates. Peasants were theoretically compelled, according to the right of multure, to have their corn ground there. The miller levied a grist toll, usually one-sixteenth or one-twentieth of corn from every sack he ground, and this led to many grievances owing to the varying, and in some cases excessive, tolls demanded by unscrupulous millers. Penalties were imposed by landlords on peasants who secretly ground corn at home with hand-querns, or took it to a more convenient mill owing to the difficulties of transport or sometimes to shortage of water. The offending querns were frequently destroyed or confiscated.

Numerous watermills were owned by monasteries and priories, since the size of their establishments necessitated the grinding of corn on a comparatively large scale. Some mills belonged to the king and others to private owners. There are increasingly frequent references to watermills in conveyances, wills, and other legal documents. Whereas with windmills there could hardly be disputes about the use of air, many conflicting interests were involved in the ownership or use of streams and rivers. For example, men dependent on fishing for their livelihood complained that it was affected adversely by the mills; the owners of barges and boats protested that mills, weirs, floodgates, and suchlike obstructions introduced new dangers, and fatal accidents due to these causes are in fact on record. Then again, the construction of a new mill could affect the working of older mills lower down the river, especially in seasons of water shortage.

A valuable source of information is John Fitzherbert's 'Boke of Surveyinge and Improvements', published posthumously in 1539. He stated that it was common practice for corn-mills to be built not on large rivers, but at a more convenient site to which water was conveyed from the river by a man-made millstream to a weir, made of timber or stone or both, by means of which water could be stored just above the mill. P. N. Wilson considers that these mills were probably furnished with simple undershot wheels having flat unshrouded paddles rotated by the flowing water. They were convenient but very inefficient.

Fitzherbert refers in the same book to the importance of an adequate fall in the tail-race to minimize the disadvantages of back-watering, which caused the wheel to slow down owing to the building up of water below it. He wrote: 'Also there be two maner of corne mylnes, that is to saye a braste mylne and overshot mylne, and these two maner of mylnes be set and goe most commonly upon small brookes and upon greate pooles and meryres [meres] and they have always a brode bowe a fote [foot] brode and more, and the ladles be always shrouded with compost bordes on both sydes to hold in the water, and then they be called buckettes. And they most be set moche nerer togyther than the ladels be, and moche more a slope down wardes to hold moche water that it falls not out for it dryveth the wheel as well with the weight of the water as with the strengthe. And the mylner must drawe his water according to his buckettes, that they be always full and no more, for the longer that they holde the water the better they be.'

With the breast-wheel, water flowed into the buckets just above or below the level of the horizontal axle; it was consequently a type intermediate between the older undershot and overshot wheels. Fitzherbert wisely confirms the principle that more power can be produced by breast and overshot wheels, if their buckets are well filled, than by undershot wheels. The water was to a great extent prevented from leaving the buckets, before they reached the bottom position, by the building of a close-fitting breast of brick or stone, shaped to the profile of about a quarter of the wheel and only an inch or so from it. Working millers in the sixteenth century probably knew from experience that the weight of water in the buckets produced more power than the force of the same stream acting on the paddles of an undershot wheel, although there seems to have been some doubt about it. This principle was, however, confirmed 200 years later by Smeaton, whose experiments are referred to later in this chapter.

III. UNDERSHOT WHEELS

In its most primitive form the vertical wheel was used for the raising of water for irrigation of land in the Far East; the floats dipped into the river which turned them, at the same time filling bamboo tubes closed at one end, or earthenware pots lashed to the rim, the water from which flowed out at the top of the wheel into a trough or canal.

In western Europe a great advance was made, and increased power obtained, by building a dam or barrier across a stream to collect water and raise its head, as, for example, in hammer-ponds. A water-course or small canal was cut allowing the water to return to the river lower down. The wheel, which could be inside or outside the mill, dipped into the stream, and a sluice was built between the wheel and the pent-up water to regulate the flow. The water was confined between strong masonry walls supporting the bearings in which the horizontal axle turned, and was directed on to the paddles or float-boards. When the wheel was idle and the sluice shut, the level of the water rose until it reached the top of the dam, so provision had to be made for it to return to the river by overflowing a weir or waste-water sluice, which in later times was fitted with a self-acting balanced float.

These were the simplest watermills, easily made and managed. The undershot wheel supplied cheap mechanical power to drive corn-mills, fulling-mills, and forges. These were widely used by an agricultural population to supply themselves with bread, woollen cloth, and iron, the main requirements of a community where spinning and weaving were still domestic employments.

The undershot wheel was in many cases superseded by the breast-wheel in order to get the most value from the water available, but it was still useful even in the nineteenth century in remote places where water-power and timber were plentiful but mechanical skill and labour scarce. In the eighteenth century such eminent engineers as John Rennie (1761–1821) and Sir Marc Isambard Brunel (1769–1849) designed and built saw-mills with large undershot wheels and iron axles at Dartford and at Chatham dockyard. The wheel at Dartford was 16 ft in diameter by 4½ ft wide, and worked 16 saws of various types. The wheel designed by J. V. Poncelet (1788–1867) was virtually an undershot wheel converted into a kind of water turbine (figure 113). It was used for falls up to 6 ft and its efficiency approached 65 per cent.

IV. SMEATON'S EXPERIMENTS

At the time when John Smeaton (1724–92) was born, many industries were dependent on water-wheels for the power to drive machinery. Horse-mills were inadequate, and windmills were unsuitable for processes where stoppages would ruin production, but the demand for power was accelerating. Smeaton decided, when 27 years old, to investigate scientifically how the design and efficiency of water-wheels could be improved. Having been apprenticed to a mathematical instrument-maker, he made a really good model with his own hands and tested it accurately (figures 91, 92; pp 152 and 153).

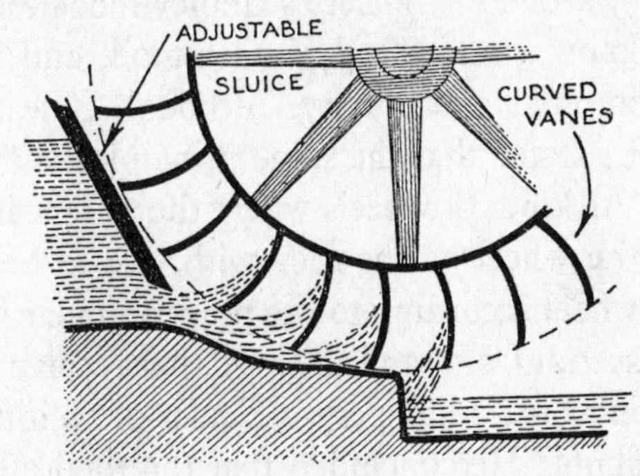

FIGURE 113—*Poncelet's water-wheel.*

The model, as originally constructed, had an undershot water-wheel, 2 ft in diameter, with flat paddles. By means of a hand plunger-pump, water was raised to a wooden storage tank, giving a 3-ft head, and then flowed through an adjustable sluice and along a channel until it struck the paddles. The output of power was measured by observing the height through which a scale-pan carrying weights was raised in one minute. The flow of water supplied to the wheel was measured by counting the number of strokes per minute of the piston in the pump needed to maintain a constant head of water in the storage tank. The water flowed round in a closed circuit, and was thus used again and again. In his second set of experiments, he employed instead a model overshot wheel with a trough to guide the water on to the top of it.

Smeaton found that the maximum overall efficiency which he could obtain from the undershot wheel was about 22 per cent and from the overshot about 63 per cent. He observed that there was a serious loss of power if a jet of water struck the flat paddles of the undershot wheel, and he proved that it was indeed more efficient to fill the buckets of the overshot wheel with water and develop power by gravity instead of by impulse. He also found there was no appreciable advantage in increasing the head of water over the top of the overshot wheel or in allowing water to strike the buckets with considerable velocity. He wrote: 'The higher the wheel is in proportion to the whole descent, the greater will be the effect;

because it depends less upon the impulse of the head and more upon the gravity of the water in the buckets. . . . It is desirable that the water should have somewhat greater velocity than the circumference of the wheel, in coming thereon; otherwise the wheel will not only be retarded, by the buckets striking the water, but thereby dashing a part of it over, so much of the power is lost.'

V. BREAST-WHEELS

On 3 and 24 May 1759 Smeaton presented two papers to the Royal Society, entitled 'Experimental Enquiry into the Natural Powers of Wind and Water to turn Mills' (published in London, 1794), detailing his results; for these he was awarded the Society's Copley medal. Before that time, the breast-wheel was little known, imperfectly understood, and regarded as a compromise by combining impulse and gravity. Although Smeaton did not test this type with a model, he stated that the same principles should be applied in these mixed cases, for: 'All kinds of wheels where the water cannot descend through a given space, unless the wheel moves therewith, are to be considered of the nature of an overshot wheel according to the perpendicular [that is, vertical] height that the water descends from; and all those that receive the impulse or shock of the water whether in a horizontal, perpendicular or oblique direction, are to be considered as undershots.' He concluded that the total effect or power of a breast-wheel would be the sum of (*a*) the effect of an undershot with a head equal to the difference in height between the surface of the water in the storage pond and the level where it struck the wheel, and (*b*) that of an overshot with a head equal to the difference between the level of impact and the surface of the tail-water. In actual practice, however, the total power was rather less than this.

VI. OVERSHOT WHEELS

If a stream flowing down a hill were directed into the earthenware vessels on the rim of a primitive irrigation wheel, they would be successively filled and the side of the wheel with the extra weight would be forced to descend, the vessels emptying themselves at the bottom. Thus rotary motion and mechanical power would be obtained, and this overshot wheel would rotate in the opposite direction to an undershot. Obviously vessels with a restricted neck would be inconvenient, so with larger streams a series of wooden troughs placed across the face of the wheel would be more effective. The stream was made shallow and nearly as broad as the wheel on to which it was directed. The wheel itself (figure 114) was constructed by fixing two sets of arms or spokes on the axle at a suitable distance apart and attaching to their outer ends wooden segments shaped to form the circumference. On to these, and across the face of the wheel, were nailed the sole-boards. On the ends of, and at right angles to, the sole-boards were fastened the two shroudings made of strong planks, a foot or more wide, and between these planks the buckets, made of lighter timber, were fixed with their ends let into the shrouding which closed them. The buckets thus resembled a triangular trough in section, with the third side open to receive the water. In later wheels only two boards were used, forming the front and bottom of the bucket. This shape was used for many years until curved iron plates were introduced.

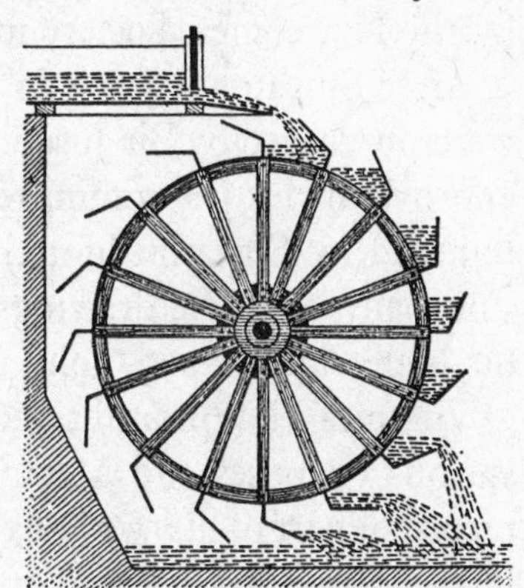

FIGURE 114—*Typical overshot water-wheel with side-shroudings removed. c 1600.*

Joseph Glynn, another civil engineer, who constructed numerous large water-wheels in the nineteenth century, wrote that 'Mr. Smeaton's experiments showed that the best effect was obtained when the velocity of the wheel's circumference was a little more than 3 ft in a second; and hence it became a general rule to make the speed of the overshot water-wheels at their circumference $3\frac{1}{2}$ ft per second or 210 ft per minute. Experience showed this velocity to be applicable to the highest water-wheels as well as the lowest, and if all other parts of the work be properly adapted thereto, it will produce very nearly the greatest effect possible; but it has also been practically shown that the velocity of high wheels may be increased beyond this rate without appreciable loss as the height of the fall and the diameter of the wheel increase, and that a wheel 24 ft high may move at the rate of 6 ft per second without any considerable loss of power.' Glynn adopted 6 ft per second in constructing several overshot wheels of iron, 30 ft in diameter or larger. By thus raising the velocity, the revolutions of a 30-ft wheel were increased from $2\frac{1}{4}$ to almost 4 per minute. The greater speed meant that less gearing was needed for driving machinery at the required rate, and reduced the load on the wheel and axle nearly in the inverse ratio of the speeds; furthermore there was a gain in the regularity of motion derived from the momentum of the quicker wheel. On the other hand, as Glynn stated, there was a limit to the diameter, for a very large overshot wheel was costly, cumbersome, and slow.

VII. SMEATON'S WATER-WHEELS

John Smeaton was one of the foremost engineers of the eighteenth century; his success in building the third Eddystone lighthouse (p 468) established his popular reputation, but during his busy working-life as a consulting engineer he carried out much work, less well known, in both civil and mechanical engineering. He was not primarily an inventor, but it was said of him that he could not touch anything without improving it. The Royal Society possesses about 1200 of his drawings, bound in 6 volumes, of which 'A Catalogue of the Civil and Mechanical Engineering Designs 1741–1792, of John Smeaton, F.R.S.' was published by the Newcomen Society in 1950.

After Smeaton's death in 1792, his manuscripts, drawings, and letter-books were purchased by Sir Joseph Banks, president of the Royal Society, with whose approval in 1795 a committee of the (Smeatonian) Society of Civil Engineers, founded by Smeaton himself, undertook to publish a selection of his reports. For many years the drawings were in the hands of John Farey (1760–1826) and his better-known son, John (1790–1851), who collected and arranged them.

Volumes I ('Windmills and Watermills for Grinding Corn') and II ('Mills for various Purposes and Machines for Raising Water') constitute a most valuable record of part of his work. From these drawings and the watermills they portray, P. N. Wilson has selected and analysed 60 schemes in a paper presented to the Newcomen Society in 1955 (see the bibliography at the end of the chapter). Where a corn-, oil-, gunpowder-, or fulling-mill was driven by a water-wheel, the plant was normally described as a 'mill', but it is interesting to note that water-wheels used for driving pumps or furnace blowers were usually described as 'engines'. The water-wheel drawings in volume III ('Fire Engines for Raising Water') are all 'engines' mainly working with a pumped supply and used for operating reciprocating machinery or for mine-haulage. 'Fire Engines' here refers to beam engines of the Newcomen type which pumped water from the tail-race to the top of the overshot wheel. Wilson has located the sites of many of the watermills but has stated that, so far as he is aware, no remains of any of Smeaton's water-wheels have been found. In many cases the mills have disappeared, but even where they still remain his original wooden wheels were probably replaced within fifty years.

Many of Smeaton's water-wheels were of the low breast type (figure 115) with flat paddles and no shrouds. The diameters varied from 12 to 18 ft, the widths from 2 to 7 ft, and the working head from 4 to 10 ft. Where the head of water was very low, the wheels were almost undershot. His only true undershot wheel was a very large example, 32 ft in diameter by 15 ft wide, constructed for London Bridge waterworks, on the Thames (p 491). It was turned by the water flowing through the arch of the bridge in which it was installed. The wheel had 24 floats, 4½ ft deep, and drove force-pumps through wooden gears. After working from 1768 to 1817 it was replaced by an iron wheel. The history of the London Bridge waterworks, originally installed by Peter Morris for supplying water to houses in the City of London, has been well described from 1582 onwards in 'Water Supply of Greater London' by H. W. Dickinson, published in 1954 by the Newcomen Society. It includes drawings of the water-wheels and pumps dated 1635, 1737, and 1768; the last was Smeaton's, referred to above.

A typical wooden breast-wheel built by Smeaton was that at Woodford Bridge artificial slate factory, Essex, with a working head of 6 ft. The wheel was 16 ft in diameter by 5 ft wide. The 6 wooden felloes on the circumference were fastened

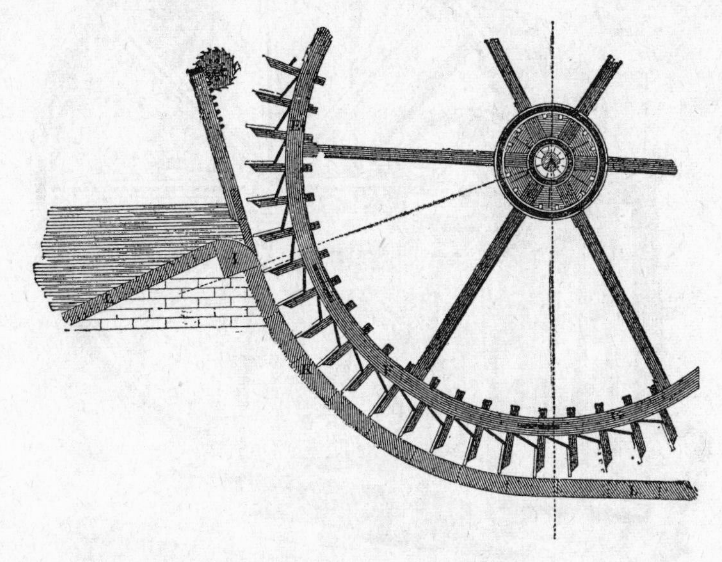

FIGURE 115—*Typical low breast-wheel, eighteenth century, designed by Smeaton. This wheel was controlled by a sluice operated by a rack-and-pinion gear.*

together with iron fish-plates and bolts. The 12 arms or spokes were mortised into the wooden axle, 2 ft in diameter, which rotated in two bearings, the iron gudgeons or journals at each end of the axle being 8 inches in diameter by 8 in long. An iron ring was fitted tightly round the axle, and 4 iron spokes, called the cross, were let into the axle and fixed by screws, the gudgeon being secured to the cross.

Smeaton built relatively few high breast-wheels, though this type became popular after 1800, but he gave much attention to overshot wheels and used them whenever circumstances permitted, owing to their higher efficiency, as proved by his experiments with models. He prepared two designs for the Carshalton corn-mill on the river Wandle, Surrey, one having two low breast-wheels 18 ft in diameter by 6 ft wide, and the other having two overshot wheels 7 ft

4 inches in diameter by 7 ft 6 in wide, for a head of 8 ft 6 in. The latter design was chosen and built.

Smeaton was consulting engineer to the Carron Company's ironworks, Falkirk, and was able therefore to experiment with, and develop the use of, cast iron parts for machinery, one of his greatest contributions to mechanical engineering. His

FIGURE 116—*Model of nineteenth-century iron breast-wheel. In this type the gearing of the wheel has been transferred to the circumference, allowing lighter construction of the axle and bearings.*

first cast iron water-wheel axle was made in 1769 for the Carron No 1 furnace blowing-engine, to replace one with a fractured wooden axle. A typical example was the cast iron shaft for the wheel at H.M. Victualling Office, Deptford, which was a single casting with two flanges to take the arms. Such shafts often ran for several years, but some gave trouble, as they were liable to break in cold and frosty weather. The fault was found to be due to the porous nature of the cast iron, in the parts where the relatively thin flanges joined the much thicker shaft. Smeaton also proposed cast iron for the rings or rims, built up in segments, of large low breast-wheels for driving boring-mills and rolling-mills. His intention was to provide a more constant speed of boring by increasing the fly-wheel effect. Cast iron gearing was used for Brook Mill, Deptford, in 1778 and frequently afterwards.

Smeaton's designs mark the end of an era of wooden water-wheel construction which had lasted for eighteen centuries. His numerous improvements enabled him almost to reach the limit of power that could be generated and transmitted by wooden wheels. His experimental and practical work marked a very important stage in the development of water-power, and fully justify his honoured place in the history of engineering and technology.

After his death, revolutionary improvements in design took place, the most important being all-metal construction (plate 11 A). Others were the fixing of the main driving gear-wheel on the circumference of the water-wheel (figure 116) so that the shaft did not have to transmit the power; ventilated buckets on high breast-wheels; and the sliding hatch or sluice of John Rennie (1761–1821), which admitted water over the top in a thin stream and thus enabled the maximum use always to be obtained from the available head.

Space does not permit the description of the relatively much less important tide mills and floating mills (vol II, pp 607–8, 610, 648), but descriptions of these, and fuller details of the types of watermill here considered, will be found among the works listed in the bibliography at the end of this chapter.

VIII. STRATFORD CORN-MILL, SOMERSET

Stratford Mill was formerly in the parish of West Harptree, Somerset, in the valley of the Chew. Originally it formed part of the manor of West Harptree Tilly, owned by Walter de Dowai at the time of the Norman Conquest. According to the Domesday Survey, this manor already had a mill for which the annual rental was 5*s*. It is not improbable that Stratford Mill was built on the site of this ancient Saxon mill. During the reign of Edward V, the manor passed out of the Tilly family and had a succession of different owners, but unfortunately the manorial records have not been discovered.

The first known reference to the present Stratford mill occurs in the local rate book of 1790, when the owner-occupier was John Collins. In 1861 Joseph Hassell became tenant and later the owner, being succeeded by his daughter. When she died in 1930, the mill was sold to the Duchy of Cornwall, and was purchased in 1939 by the Bristol Waterworks Company. The mill was very active during the war of 1939–45. The post-war construction of a large reservoir in the Chew valley made it necessary to demolish a number of buildings in the area, including the mill. Fortunately, however, a number of acts of generosity made it possible to dismantle the mill and re-erect it in the grounds of Blaise Castle House Folk

Museum near Bristol. It is in consequence possible to describe in detail the machinery of a highly developed watermill.

The existing mill machinery (figure 117) is worked by an external undershot

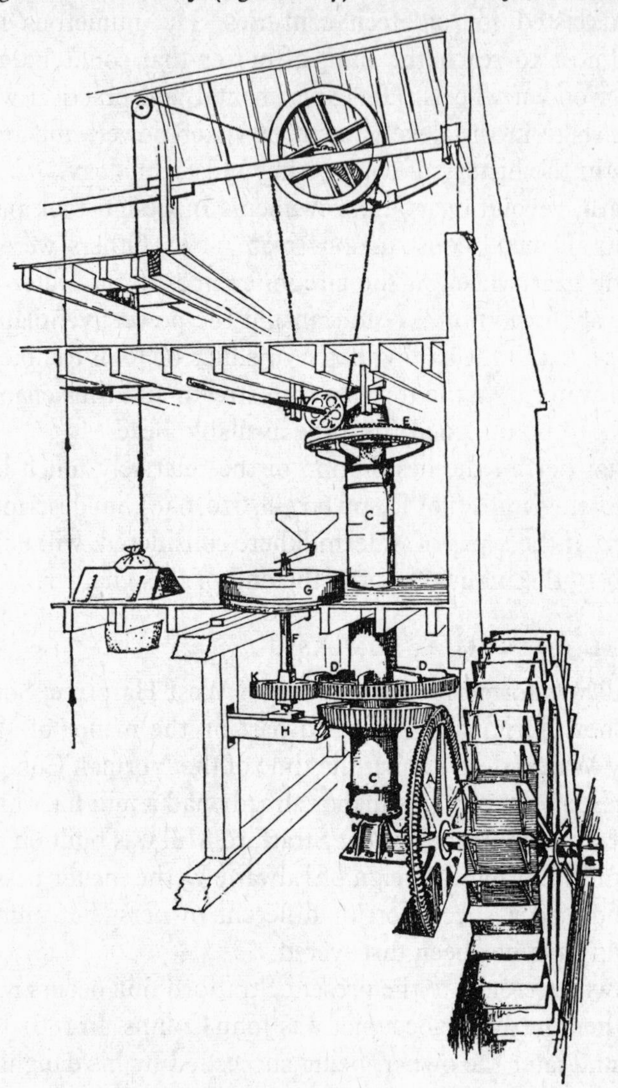

FIGURE 117—*Sketch of machinery, Stratford Mill, Somerset, showing undershot wheel and gears.*

wheel, 14 ft in diameter, with iron floats, made by Gregory of Flax Bourton, Somerset, about 1870 to replace the former wooden wheel. The flow of water, diverted from the main stream into the race, is regulated by a hatch, adjusted by a simple rod-gear operated by the miller within the mill. This in turn controls the speed of the wheel and hence of the machinery. When the hatch is in its lowest position the wheel is stopped. The horizontal iron shaft of the wheel also carries, inside the mill, the vertical pit-wheel A, driving by bevel cogs the wallower or horizontal wheel B on the main vertical shaft C. The latter is of apple wood, about 18 inches in diameter, and is supported in a bearing on the ground floor; it extends upwards through the first floor to a bearing secured to the joists of the second floor. It carries three horizontal wheels, the wallower B, the large spur-wheel D about 6 ft in diameter, and the horizontal gear-wheel E, near the top. It is interesting to note that throughout the driving mechanism the cog wheels are arranged so that metal cogs engage with timber cogs of apple or beech wood, which could be individually shaped and fitted, resulting in quieter running.

The vertical iron shaft F carries and drives the runner, that is, the upper one of the pair of stones G, and is supported in a bearing on the strong wooden bridge-tree H, adjustable at one end by a simple screw mechanism (not shown), which, by raising or lowering this beam relative to its fixed end, raises or lowers the vertical shaft and runner. The degree of fineness of the ground meal is determined by tentering, that is, adjusting the vertical gap between the runner G and the bedstone J at first-floor level. The shaft F is rotated by the stone-nut K, and can be disengaged by raising it clear of the spur-wheel D. The grain in the hopper flows down the shoe or chute and is shaken into the eye of the runner by the 'damsel' or extension on the top of the shaft F. After leaving the stones, the meal travels round inside the hurst or casing surrounding them, and originally descended inside timber chutes through the first floor to points where sacks were hung on adjustable cord supports for filling.

The hoisting of sacks is effected by the mechanism worked from the top of the vertical shaft C. Here the revolving wheel E is continuously engaged with a little vertical cog-wheel driving a horizontal shaft which carries a chain pulley. The chain passes up through the second floor and drives a large vertical wooden wheel at roof level, directly connected to a drum round which the hoisting rope is wound. The operation of this hoisting mechanism is controlled by a lever system which raises or lowers the large wooden pulley at roof level, thereby tightening the chain round the revolving chain pulley at first-floor level. The engaging of this mechanism can be effected from the ground floor by ropes passing through both floors to the levers. The hoisting rope, after passing over a small pulley mounted on the roof timbers, passes down through hinged wooden flaps in each floor which open when a full sack is hoisted and automatically close by dropping as soon as the sack has passed up. Sacks of grain can be hoisted to a platform at roof level, enabling the miller to spread the grain on the second floor, from which it can flow down timber or hessian chutes to the hoppers above the first-floor millstones. This mill originally had two pairs of stones but now has only one pair.

FIGURE 118—*Dressing millstones by hand. Some traditional designs are shown. Upper and lower stones were dressed similarly.* (A) *Late Roman;* (B) *eighteenth century;* (C), (D), (E) *nineteenth century.* (F) *and* (G) *right-handed and left-handed stones in 'four-quarter' dress.*

IX. VARIETIES OF MILLSTONE

Years ago there used to be three main varieties of millstone: (*a*) solid Peak stones, quarried in Derbyshire; (*b*) French burr stones, produced from French quarries in small blocks which were cemented together with plaster of Paris to form the required size; and (*c*) blue stones or cullin stones, which were solid German stones quarried at Cologne, whence their name. Today composition stones of emery and cement are widely used. After a long period of grinding, the millstones become dulled and have to be dressed or sharpened with double-ended steel picks and bills, wedged into the heads of wooden thrifts. There are standard patterns of master furrows running from the eye at the centre to the outer edge, with other furrows branching off from them (figure 118); the lands or grinding surfaces are either closely lined or untouched. Stone-dressing was usually done by the millers themselves, but sometimes by itinerant stone-dressers who walked from mill to mill and lived there until each job was finished.

Plate 11 B shows another old mill for grinding corn. This was Coldron Mill at Spelsbury, Oxfordshire, erected *c* 1800 and demolished in 1937.

BIBLIOGRAPHY

AGRICOLA, G. *De re metallica*, Books VI and VIII. Basel. 1556. Eng. trans. by H. C. and LOU H. HOOVER. The Mining Magazine, London. 1912.

BENNETT, R. and ELTON, J. 'History of Cornmilling', Vols 1, 2. Liverpool. 1898, 1899.

DICKINSON, H. W. 'Water Supply of Greater London.' Newcomen Society, London. 1954.

DICKINSON, H. W. and STRAKER, E. "The Shetland Water Mill." *Trans. Newcomen Soc.*, **13**, 89–94, 1932–3.

FAIRBAIRN, SIR WILLIAM. 'Treatise on Mills and Millwork' (4th ed.). London. 1878.

FITZHERBERT, JOHN. 'The Boke of Surveyinge and Improvements.' London. 1539. See also the edition of 1767.

GARDNER, EMILIE M. "Some Notes on Dutch Water Mills." *Trans. Newcomen Soc.*, **27**, 199–202, 1949–51.

GLYNN, J. 'Power of Water' (5th ed.). London. 1875.
HILLIER, J. 'Old Surrey Watermills.' Skeffington, London. 1951.
JESPERSEN, A. 'Gearing in Watermills in Western Europe.' Published by the author, Virum (Denmark). 1953.
REES, A. 'The Cyclopaedia; or Universal Dictionary of Arts, Sciences and Literature', Vol. 38: 'Water.' London. 1819.
ROSE, W. 'The Village Carpenter.' University Press, Cambridge. 1937.
SCIENCE MUSEUM. 'Historic Books on Machines', by C. ST. C. B. DAVISON. H.M. Stationery Office, London. 1953.
Idem. 'Pumping Machinery' by G. F. WESTCOTT. Part I: 'Historical Notes'; Part II: 'Catalogue.' H.M. Stationery Office, London. 1932–3.
SKILTON, C. P. 'British Windmills and Watermills.' Collins, London. 1947.
SMEATON, J. 'Experimental Enquiry into the Natural Powers of Wind and Water to turn Mills.' London. 1794.
Idem. 'Reports of the late John Smeaton (3 vols). London. 1812.
Idem. 'Catalogue of the Civil and Mechanical Engineering Designs 1741 to 1792 preserved in the Library of the Royal Society.' Newcomen Society, London. 1950.
SOMERVELL, J. 'Water-Power Mills of South Westmorland.' Wilson, Kendal. 1930.
WAILES, R. "Tide Mills in England and Wales." *Trans. Newcomen Soc.*, **16**, 1–33, 1935–6.
WILSON, P. N. "The Origins of Water Power." *Wat. Pwr.*, **4**, 308–13, 1952.
Idem. "Water Power and the Industrial Revolution." *Ibid.*, **6**, 309–16, 1954.
Idem. 'Watermills, an Introduction.' Society for the Protection of Ancient Buildings. Booklet No. 1. London. 1955.
Idem. "The Waterwheels of John Smeaton." *Trans. Newcomen Soc.*, **30**, 1955–6 (in the press).

Half-timbered watermill at Rossett, Denbighshire, built in 1661.

8

PART I

THE CHEMICAL INDUSTRY: DEVELOPMENTS IN CHEMICAL THEORY AND PRACTICE

E. J. HOLMYARD

FROM about the middle of the eighteenth century the chemical industry came to play an increasingly important role in industrial life generally, until towards the end of the period with which this volume deals it already promised to become the giant that we know today. The manner of this development was twofold. In the first place, increased demands for such commodities as glass, soap, soda, dyes, and textiles led to an intense *ad hoc* experimentation, as a result of which there were great improvements in the methods of manufacturing such fundamental substances as the mineral acids and the common alkalis. This aspect of the growth and influence of the chemical industry is dealt with in the second part of this chapter. There was, however, another development taking place simultaneously, and as this parallel line of advance gradually led to the decline of empirical methods, and finally to their almost complete abandonment in more recent times, some account of it is necessary for the balance of the picture.

The gist of the matter is that the period now under review saw a complete revolution in chemistry itself. Until the close of the seventeenth century chemistry had not outgrown alchemical ideas (vol II, ch 21), and although considerable scepticism existed about the possibility of transmuting cheaper metals into gold chemists nevertheless adhered to the basic habits of alchemical theory and practice. Thus they believed that the number of elements constituting all matter was either four (fire, air, water, earth), or three (salt, sulphur, mercury); they paid little or no attention to changes of weight occurring in chemical reactions; they did not recognize the existence of different gases; and they hardly realized the concept of chemical individuality. Such a background does not exclude the possibility of striking empirical discoveries, with which the period indeed abounds, but it is a limiting factor and, had it persisted, would have effectively prevented the astonishing development of chemical industry so characteristic of the nineteenth century and later.

The beneficial, and in the sequel exceedingly fruitful, change in chemical outlook did not take place all at once, but we can conveniently trace its first beginning to the publication in 1661 of 'The Sceptical Chymist' by Robert Boyle (1627–91). In this classic work, Boyle attacked the old ideas of 'elements' and stated that, in his view, chemists should hold no preconceived notions as to the number of elements existing but should rather regard as elements all those substances that they could not decompose into two or more other substances:

> I mean by elements, as those chymists that speak plainest do by their Principles, certain primitive and simple, or perfectly unmingled bodies; which not being made of any other bodies, or of one another, are the ingredients of which all those called perfectly mixt bodies are immediately compounded, and into which they are ultimately resolved . . . I must not look upon any body as a true principle or element, which is not perfectly homogeneous, but is further resolvable into any number of distinct substances.

This conception of a chemical element became a cardinal point of later theory, but for reasons easy to understand it did not gain adherents quickly. For one thing, it replaced the deceptively simple and elegant earlier schemes with a multiplicity of possible elements without providing or suggesting analytical means of investigation. For another, it appeared to contemporary chemists to serve no useful purpose. It thus aroused little discussion or controversy at the time, but though it lay dormant for a while it germinated in the following century when other developments had rendered conditions for its use more favourable. It was revived by Lavoisier (p 220) and then soon gained universal acceptance.

One of these new developments was an increasing interest in gases. To the alchemists there was only one gas, namely air; other aerial fluids were merely air more or less contaminated with poisonous, odorous, inflammable, or coloured impurities. Though they were certainly adept enough to have collected gases, the idea of doing so seems never to have occurred to them until towards the close of the alchemical age. The pioneering steps in the field of 'pneumatic' chemistry or the chemistry of gases were taken by the Flemish iatrochemist Jan Baptista Van Helmont (1577–1644), who was the first to perceive in these tenuous forms of matter a new and important class of substances and who in fact invented the word gas (from chaos) to designate them (vol II, p 745). Van Helmont showed that the *gas silvestre* (carbon dioxide) obtained by burning charcoal was also obtainable by fermenting sugary liquids, and he was able to detect it in the air of the Grotto del Cane, Naples. An inflammable gas from the intestines and from fermenting manure he called *gas pingue* (methane), and it is clear from his writings that he must have obtained several other gases in an impure state.

Though Van Helmont established a footing for gases on the chemical dais he did not succeed in collecting them. Boyle was more ingenious. He took a glass flask with a long neck and completely filled it with dilute sulphuric acid. He then dropped six iron nails into the flask and inverted it in a vessel containing more of the dilute acid. Bubbles of a gas (hydrogen) rose to the top of the apparatus, displacing the acid and soon filling the flask. Here was the germ of that invaluable device so familiar in the elementary laboratory, the pneumatic trough. A further advance in the manipulation of gases was made by John Mayow (1643–78), a Bath physician, who showed that a gas could be transferred from one vessel to another by filling the second one with water, inverting it in a trough of water, and bringing the mouth of the first vessel, containing the gas, under the mouth of the other: 'care being taken that the mouth of neither of the glasses is raised above the surface of the water'. Mayow further emphasized the importance, in work involving measurement of gaseous volumes, of levelling the water inside and outside a jar containing the gas, in order to get the latter at atmospheric pressure. This he accomplished by means of a siphon (figure 119, left).

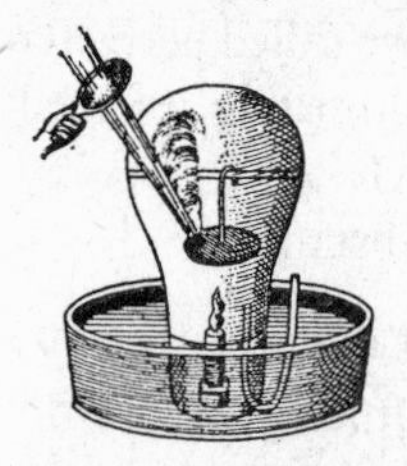

FIGURE 119—*Some of Mayow's apparatus for experiments with gases.* (Left) *Combustion in a limited volume of air. Note siphon.* (Right) *Collecting a gas (nitric oxide) obtained by the action of dilute nitric acid upon iron balls.*

The next improvement was made by Stephen Hales (1677–1761), parish priest of Teddington in Middlesex, whom Horace Walpole described as 'a poor, good, primitive creature' but who nevertheless was one of the founders of plant physiology. In his 'Vegetable Staticks' (1727) he gives an account of many experiments with gases, made in the course of his botanical work, and illustrates some of the apparatus he had devised for the purpose. Figure 120, taken from his book, shows the pneumatic trough used to collect gases evolved during the destructive distillation of vegetable matter. A final touch came with Joseph Priestley (1733–1804), who on occasion filled the trough and collecting-jars with mercury and was thus enabled to isolate several gases previously overlooked or little known owing to their solubility in water; among them were hydrogen sulphide, sulphur dioxide, ammonia, and nitrous oxide.

Investigation of the chemical properties of gases was accompanied by a determination of many of their physical and physico-chemical characteristics. Boyle had shown in 1662 that the volume of a given mass of gas varies inversely as the pressure upon it if the temperature is constant, and J. A. C. Charles (1746–1823)—the first man to make an ascent in a balloon filled with hydrogen (p 255)—discovered (1787) the complementary law that the volume of a given mass of gas at constant pressure varies directly as the absolute temperature. A few years later (1808) Joseph-Louis Gay-Lussac (1778–1850) was able to announce that, according to his experiments, gases react in volumes that at the same temperature and pressure bear a simple ratio to one another and to the volume of the product if that is gaseous: an observation that had a vital bearing on the development of chemical theory.

While the pneumatic chemists were thus establishing a new branch of chemistry,

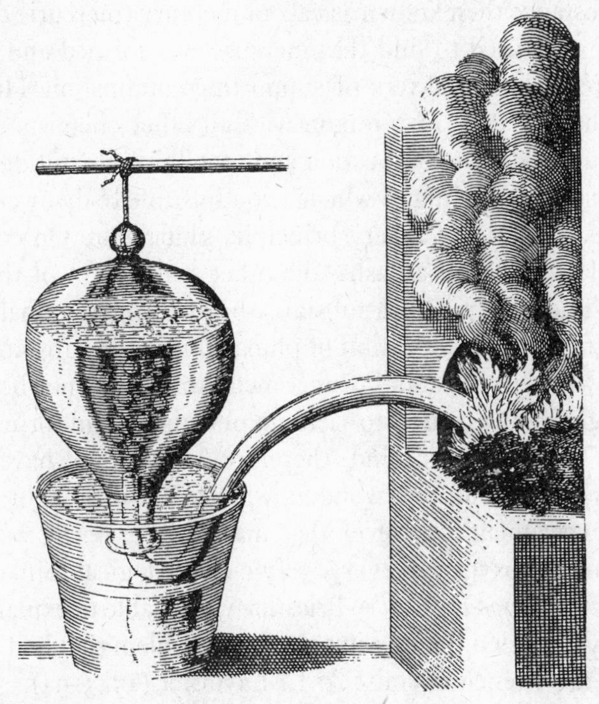

FIGURE 120—*Apparatus used by Stephen Hales to collect gases given off during destructive distillation of vegetable matter.*

fundamental progress was being made in other departments of the science. In the first place, it gradually became tacitly accepted by chemists that, in any and every chemical reaction, the total weight of the reactants is exactly equal to the total weight of the product or products—which is equivalent to postulating that matter is 'conserved', or indestructible and uncreatable. It is impossible to assign credit for this basal assumption to any single head, but the first to use it effectively was Joseph Black (1728–99). In 1756 Black published a paper entitled 'Experiments upon Magnesia Alba, Quicklime, and some other Alcaline Substances', in which, as the result of careful quantitative work, he explained the chemical relationship of limestone, quicklime, and carbon dioxide on lines that have stood the test of time. He relied on the balance at every step, and belief in the conservation of matter is implicit throughout his argument. Black's paper was indeed the first example of that logical, quantitative procedure that afterwards became the norm.

It was in a combination of pneumatic and quantitative chemistry that the modern science had its birth. In 1774 Joseph Priestley (p 216), a dextrous but dilettante experimenter, idly concentrated the Sun's rays through a burning-glass[1] on to a substance then known as calx of mercury (mercuric oxide), and was beyond measure surprised to find that mercury was formed and that a gas was given off with remarkable powers of supporting combustion. His surprise was occasioned by the fact that, in common with all other chemists of the time, he held an erroneous theory of combustion and metallic constitution. This was the theory of phlogiston, according to which a combustible body owed its combustibility to the presence in it of a fiery principle, phlogiston. On combustion, the phlogiston was lost and only an ash—the other constituent of the combustible body—was left. The more readily a substance burned, and the smaller the amount of ash left, the greater the proportion of phlogiston in the substance. The ash of a metal was known as its calx, and even a metal that could not be made to burn with a flame might yet be caused to yield its phlogiston and form a calx by continued heating. To Priestley's mind, therefore, heat should have had no effect on the calx of mercury, and one wonders what freak of thought led him to try this particular experiment. However that may be, the result was momentous, for he had discovered oxygen. Never a very clear or logical thinker—'*il se servit de ses mains, plus que de son cerveau*'—Priestley was unable to explain the reaction, but his discovery provided the missing clue to a problem that had been engaging the attention of the French chemist A. L. Lavoisier (1743–94).

Attracted by the phenomena of combustion, Lavoisier observed—as had indeed been observed many times before—that the calx of a metal weighed more than the metal from which it was obtained. Boyle, to whom this fact was well known, ascribed it to the passage of heat, which he regarded as a material substance, through the walls of the vessel from the fire to the metal. Lavoisier saw that this explanation was susceptible of experimental proof or disproof:

If [he says] the increase in weight of metals calcined in closed vessels is due, as Boyle thought, to the addition of the matter of flame and fire which penetrates the pores of the glass and combines with the metal, it follows that if, after having introduced a known quantity of metal into a glass vessel, and having sealed it hermetically, one determines

[1] Burning-glasses were quite often used to provide heat in chemical experiments. A large one made and mounted in France is shown in plate 8 A.

its weight exactly; and that if one then proceeds to the calcination in a charcoal fire, as Boyle did; and lastly that if one then reweighs the same vessel after the calcination, before opening it, its weight ought to be found to have increased by the whole of the quantity of the matter of fire which entered during the calcination. . . .

If, on the contrary . . . the increase in weight of the metallic calx is not due to the combination of the matter of fire nor to any exterior matter whatever, but to the fixation of a portion of the air contained in the space of the vessel, the vessel ought not to weigh more after the calcination than before, it ought merely to be found partly empty of air, and the increase in weight of the vessel should take place only at the moment when the missing portion of air is allowed to enter.

There could hardly be a more lucid statement of the problem, and Lavoisier proceeded to put his views to the test of experiment. He took a weighed glass flask, introduced a weighed quantity of tin, sealed the flask hermetically, and then heated it for some hours until no further calcination appeared to be taking place. He now allowed the flask to cool, after which he weighed it. There was no change in weight. Upon opening the flask, air was heard to enter, and when the apparatus was weighed once more, an increase in weight was found. This was clearly the weight of air that had entered the flask, and Lavoisier discovered that, to within about six parts in a thousand, it was equal to the increase of weight undergone by the tin on calcination. These results made it plain that calcination, far from being a decomposition, was on the contrary a combination of the metal with air or with a gas or gases forming part of the air.

Further experiments on the same lines enabled Lavoisier to conclude:

First, that one cannot calcine an unlimited quantity of tin in a given quantity of air.

Second, that the quantity of metal calcined is greater in a large vessel than in a small one. . . .

Third, that the hermetically sealed vessels, weighed before and after the calcination of the tin they contain, show no difference in weight, which clearly proves that the increase in weight of the metal comes neither from the material of the fire nor from any matter exterior to the vessel.

Fourth, that in every calcination of tin, the increase in weight of the metal is, fairly exactly, equal to the weight of the quantity of air absorbed, which proves that the portion of the air which combines with the metal during the calcination has a specific gravity nearly equal to that of atmospheric air.

Finally, that the portion of the air which combines with the metal is slightly heavier than atmospheric air, and that which remains after the calcination is, on the contrary, rather lighter. Atmospheric air, on this assumption, would form, relatively to the specific gravity, a mean result between these two airs.

These pregnant observations and deductions show how far chemistry was now moving from alchemy. The law of the conservation of matter was here again tacitly assumed, and the balance was the irrefragable arbiter. Instead of being one of the 'four elements', air was not an element at all but must consist of at least two gases, one active in calcination (and therefore in combustion) and the other inactive.

But at this point the work was still unfinished: the problem remained of separating the active part of the air from the inactive. Here fate intervened, by effecting a meeting between Lavoisier and Priestley at which Priestley told the Frenchman about the curious behaviour of calx of mercury on heating. Lavoisier instantly perceived that his problem was solved, the key being the facts (*a*) that when mercury is heated comparatively gently in air it gradually calcines, or combines with the active portion of the air, and (*b*) that the calx on being heated more strongly decomposes into its constituents, namely, mercury and active air. On this basis, Lavoisier carried out an operation so momentous in its results as to have become familiarly known by the simple title of 'Lavoisier's experiment' (figure 121). It consisted in moderately heating mercury in contact with a limited volume of air until no further calcination could be observed. During the calcination the volume of enclosed air diminished by about one-fifth or one-sixth, and the remaining air would not allow substances to burn in it. The calx was carefully collected, and more strongly heated in an apparatus suitable for receiving the gas evolved. Lavoisier found that this gas supported combustion much better than ordinary air, and that its volume was equal to the diminution in volume undergone by the air originally taken. When it was mixed with the inactive gas left in the first operation, the mixture was indistinguishable from ordinary air.

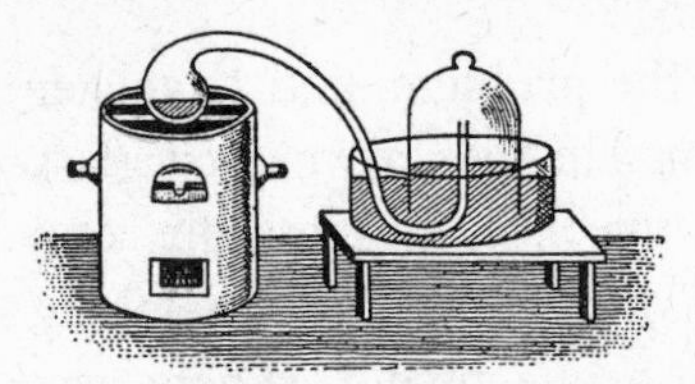

FIGURE 121—*Diagrammatic representation of the apparatus for 'Lavoisier's experiment'.*

Lavoisier had thus demonstrated the composite nature of atmospheric air in the most convincing way possible: by taking it apart and putting it together again. Further experiments firmly persuaded him, and later all other chemists, that combustion and calcination were combinations of active air with the combustible or calcinable body: phlogiston was overthrown and the modern theory of combustion established. A specific name for the active gas was obviously desirable, and since the products of combustion of sulphur, phosphorus, and carbon in the moist gas proved to be acid, Lavoisier framed the word 'oxygen', from the Greek words meaning 'acid-producer'.

In the meantime, H. Cavendish (1731–1810) had shown that when oxygen and the gas we now know as hydrogen were sparked together (figure 122), water was formed, but he put an erroneous interpretation upon his results. Lavoisier repeated and extended Cavendish's experiments and was able both to synthesize water by the explosion together of hydrogen and oxygen, and to liberate hydrogen from water by passing steam over red-hot iron. He had thus established the composite nature of two of the classical 'elements', and though 'fire'—heat or caloric—left him puzzled he had no doubt about the composite nature of 'earth'.

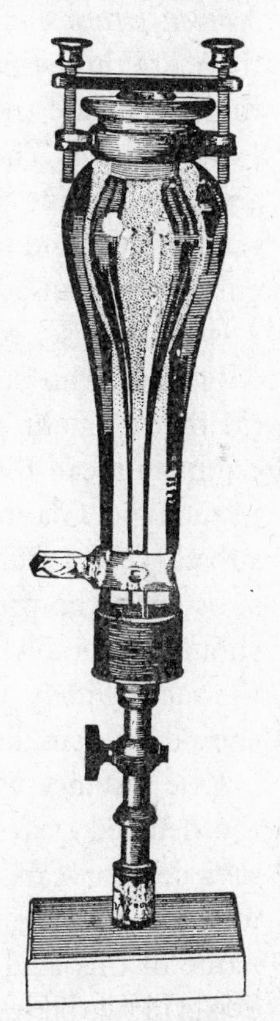

FIGURE 122—*Cavendish's vessel for the explosion of gases.*

While this revolutionary work was going on, great extensions took place both in the repertory of known chemical substances and in the field of chemical analysis. A Swedish apothecary, C. W. Scheele (1742–86), not only discovered oxygen independently of, and slightly earlier than, Priestley, but was the first to isolate chlorine and to prepare such valuable substances as hydrofluoric, lactic, oxalic, citric, tartaric, and uric acids, glycerol, and milk-sugar. He showed that graphite is a form of carbon, and invented new methods of preparing ether, calomel, and phosphorus. His contemporary, the German chemist M. H. Klaproth (1743–1817), elaborated reliable methods for the analysis of minerals and discovered the elements uranium, titanium, and zirconium. Gay-Lussac (p 217) laid the foundations of volumetric analysis, and C. L. Berthollet (1748–1822)—one of the first chemists to adopt Lavoisier's new theory of combustion—discovered hypochlorites and chlorates.

Such activity, of which these few examples must here suffice, impressed upon chemists the urgent need for a thorough revision of chemical nomenclature. The old nomenclature was completely unsystematic and had grown up piecemeal and at haphazard; it contained such absurd names as butter of arsenic, sugar of lead, flowers of zinc, and liver of sulphur, as well as other names—powder of algaroth, colcothar, aethiops, sal alembroth, sal mirabile, and so forth—that made excessive demands upon the memory without giving any information about the substances for which they were employed. There were in addition several alchemical names, which meant one thing to the chemist and another to the layman. Given the history of the science, such confusion was no doubt inevitable, but with the rapid advance of chemical knowledge it became apparent that an orderly and reasonable nomenclature was a prime necessity. Lavoisier's work on oxygen and water provided the requisite basis for such a system, and he, together with Guyton de Morveau (1737–1816), Berthollet, and A. F. de Fourcroy (1755–1809), undertook the preparation of a nomenclature based upon scientific principles. The report of the committee was published in 1787, under the title *Méthode de Nomenclature Chimique*, and in his prefatory memoir Lavoisier observes that there are three things to distinguish in every physical science: the series of facts that constitute the science, the ideas that recall the facts, and the words that express them. The word must evoke the idea, the idea must depict the fact: they are but three impressions of one seal. The perfect chemical nomenclature would render ideas and facts in their exact verity, without suppression and more particularly without addition.

This counsel of perfection was given a more practical turn by Guyton de Morveau, who suggested (*a*) that a chemical name should not be a phrase, (*b*) that it ought not to require circumlocutions to become definite, (*c*) that it ought to recall the constituents of a compound body, (*d*) that it should not be of the type 'Glauber's salt', which conveys nothing about the composition of the substance, (*e*) that in the absence of knowledge concerning the constitution of a substance, the provisional name should be non-committal, (*f*) that new names should preferably be coined from Latin or Greek, so that their signification could the more widely and easily be understood, and (*g*) that the form of such words should be assimilated to the genius of the language in which they are to be used.

One instance will be sufficient to show how these principles were applied in the detailed system proposed, which is basically that still employed. Sulphur, says de Morveau, in combining with oxygen produces an acid. To conserve the idea of this origin and to express clearly the first degree of composition, the name of this acid ought to be a derivative of the word sulphur; but this acid exists in two states of saturation and shows different properties in each. To avoid confusion, each state must be given a name that, while conserving the root, nevertheless marks this difference. Lastly, it is necessary to consider sulphur in other direct combinations, such as with alkalis and metals. Five different terminations, adapted to the same root, sulphur, are suggested to meet these requirements:

sulphuric acid will express sulphur saturated with oxygen as far as it can be, that is, what is called vitriolic acid.
sulphurous acid will express sulphur united to a less quantity of oxygen.
sulphate will be the generic name of all salts formed from sulphuric acid.
sulphite will be the name of salts formed from sulphurous acid.
sulphide will denote all the compounds of sulphur not carried to the state of an acid.

Guyton de Morveau remarks with justice that 'no-one will fail to perceive, at the first glance, all the advantages of such a nomenclature, which, while indicating various substances, at the same time defines them, recalls their constituent parts, classes them in their order of composition, and to a certain extent draws attention to the proportions that cause the variation in their properties'.

The work of the committee was completed by a dictionary giving the old and new names of about 700 substances, in which occur for the first time such familiar terms as potassium carbonate, copper nitrate, zinc sulphate, and ammonium molybdate. The enormous improvement of the new system does not need to be emphasized, but apart from its convenience it manifests that the idea of chemical individuality—altogether foreign to the alchemists—had become so generally accepted as to be taken as axiomatic. With the oxygen theory of combustion and with the ever-growing reliance on quantitative work, the systematic scheme of nomenclature had largely effected the chemical revolution on which so much of nineteenth-century technology was to be firmly based.

Largely, but not entirely: two or three other important factors had essential parts to play, and we may consider them in turn. The first was the establishment by John Dalton (1766–1844) of a serviceable atomic theory of the constitution of matter. The operative word is 'serviceable', for atomic theories were as old as classical Greece and Rome, and had been revived on sporadic occasions throughout the centuries. They bore, however, little fruit until Isaac Newton (1642–1727) used the atomic conception to explain certain physical properties. Thus in the *Principia* he stated that 'if the density of a fluid gas which is made up of mutually repulsive particles is proportional to the pressure, the forces between the particles are reciprocally proportional to the distances between their centres. And *vice versa*, mutually repulsive particles, the forces between which are reciprocally proportional to the distances between their centres, will make up an elastic fluid, the density of which is proportional to the pressure.' This argument provides a theoretical explanation of Boyle's law (p 216), and is typical of a new attitude towards atomic speculation. Greek philosophers, or some of them, had postulated a discrete constitution of matter but could not discover any way of testing their postulate; the advance of science had suggested some such ways, and it was for Dalton to apply them particularly in the field of chemistry.

This is not the place in which to describe in detail the chemical atomic theory that gradually shaped itself in Dalton's mind, but the main points of it must be briefly noted. First, Dalton assumed that all matter is composed of a vast number of extremely minute particles or atoms, and that chemical analysis and synthesis are nothing more than the separation of particles from one another, and their reunion: in other words, atoms are indestructible and uncreatable, whence comes a theoretical foundation for the law of the conservation of matter. Next, each element has its own distinctive kind of atom, and similarly each compound has its own distinctive kind of 'compound atom', or molecule as we now say. Dalton then went on to point out that it is important, and possible, to ascertain the relative weights of different atoms; and the fact that he suggested how this might be done is a sufficient mark of his genius. Quantitative chemistry was by now well established, and, as Dalton said, 'it has justly been considered an important object to ascertain the relative weights of the simplest elements which constitute a compound'. If, therefore, one knew the relative numbers in which the atoms of the different elements combined, the relative weights of those atoms could easily be calculated from the results of the quantitative analysis. The crux of the problem lay in the 'if', and Dalton's great achievement was that he saw how the difficulty might be surmounted. In effect, he applied Occam's razor—'entities must not be multiplied beyond what is necessary'—and assumed that when elements combine to form compounds, the molecules of the compounds consist of small whole numbers of the atoms of the elements concerned, the emphasis being on the small.

It was only an assumption, but it showed the way to experimental investigation, and if the results to which it led proved to be inconsistent it always allowed room for adjustment. We may take a few examples. At that time, water was the only known compound of oxygen and hydrogen; Dalton therefore assumed its molecule to consist of one atom of each element. But gravimetric analysis showed that in water eight parts by weight of oxygen were combined with one part by weight of hydrogen. Therefore the atom of oxygen must be eight times as heavy as the atom of hydrogen. Similarly, the only compound of nitrogen and hydrogen known to Dalton was ammonia, whose molecule he thus took to consist of one atom of each element. Analysis showed that the relative weights of hydrogen and nitrogen in the gas were as 1 is to about 5, hence the nitrogen atom must weigh about five times as much as that of hydrogen. Finally, Dalton knew of two oxides of carbon, carbonic oxide (carbon monoxide) and carbonic acid (carbon dioxide); the former he considered to be a binary compound of one atom of carbon and one of oxygen, and the other a ternary compound of one atom of carbon and two of oxygen. By quantitative analysis it was therefore a simple matter to arrive at the relative weights of the oxygen and carbon atoms.

Working in this way Dalton was able to construct a table of 'atomic weights' of the elements, that is, the relative weights of their atoms taking the weight of the hydrogen atom as unity. By an extension of the figures he was able to discover the relative weights, compared to that of the hydrogen atom, of the ultimate particles or molecules of various compounds. The significant outcome of the work, which was pursued not only by Dalton himself but—with greater analytical accuracy—by the Swedish chemist J. J. Berzelius (1779–1848), was that, though various discrepancies occurred, the 'atomic' and 'molecular' weights exhibited a remarkable degree of interdependent agreement. This showed that Dalton was at least on the right track, and in point of fact he had deservedly good luck in selecting for his early investigations substances whose molecules happen to be of a very simple constitution. But his guesses at their molecular structure were not always correct, and the figures he obtained for 'atomic' weights were merely what the modern chemist knows as equivalents. They could not be taken as definitive until the appropriate molecular structures were known with certainty, and then it might prove necessary to multiply them by an integer to get the true atomic weights. Dalton was never able to solve this aspect of the problem, which was later cleared up successfully by A. Avogadro (1776–1856) and S. Cannizzaro (1826–1910), but his provisional atomic weights played an incalculably valuable role in systematizing chemistry and in consolidating the experimental advances that were now being made in rapid succession.

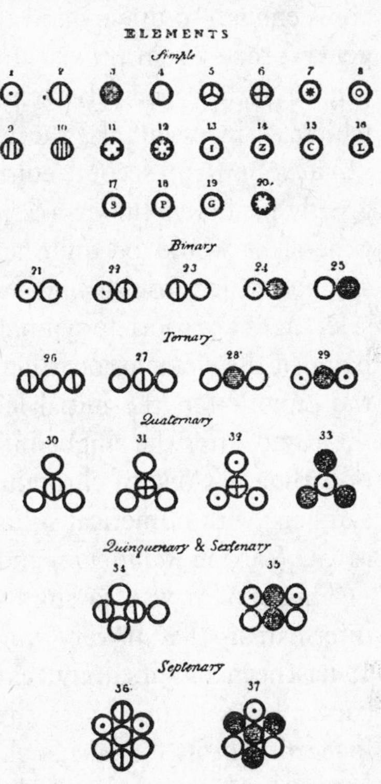

FIGURE 123—*Some of Dalton's symbols and formulae.*

Thinking always in terms of atoms, as he did, Dalton soon perceived the convenience of having a symbolic notation for them, and he constructed a scheme in which circles with lines, dots, shading, or capital letters in them were used to represent atoms of the various elements. Suitable groupings of these elementary symbols were used as formulae for the molecules of compounds. A list of some of Dalton's symbols and formulae is given in figure 123. The important difference between his signs and those in earlier chemical use is this: that whereas the old sign ♀, for instance, had signified copper in any quantity, Dalton's symbol © stood for one atom of copper and thus possessed a definite quantitative significance completely absent from the sign ♀. The formulae of compounds conveyed even more information; thus that of carbon dioxide, ○●○, showed that, in the opinion of those who adopted it, the molecule of carbon dioxide contains one atom of carbon and two of oxygen. And since (according to Dalton's reckoning) the atomic weight of oxygen is 6·5 and that of carbon 5, it is implicit in the formula that the composition of carbon dioxide is *carbon : oxygen* as *5 : 13*.

Dalton's symbols and formulae were adopted by those few chemists perspicacious enough to understand their potential value, but for the chemical world in general the system proved much too cumbersome. Fortunately, about 1814 or even a little earlier, Berzelius suggested a much more convenient notation, which is, in essentials, the one still employed. In his *Théorie des proportions chimiques* (1819; second edition 1835) he points out that the use of symbols greatly facilitates the expression of chemical facts. In order to render the usage general, it would be quite sufficient to give each element its own particular symbol, which would represent the relative weight of its atom. Berzelius then selected as appropriate symbols the initial letter of the (usually Latin or latinized) name of the element, or, when two or more elements had names beginning with the same letter, the initial letter together with another characteristic letter of the name, after the single initial had been allocated. Thus C signified one atom of carbon, Cr one of chromium, and Co one of cobalt. Juxtaposition of atomic symbols, with numerical suffixes when necessary, gave such molecular formulae as CO (carbon monoxide) and CO_2 (carbon dioxide).

This system was so simple to use, so easy to remember, and so concisely informative, that it very quickly gained universal currency among chemists. It has been modified and extended since the time of Berzelius, but his conception of a formula as a summary of experience still holds good. By a mere inspection of its formula, a chemist may gather as much about the constitution, preparation, properties, and reactions of a substance as might occupy two or three pages of prose description. Such formulae are indeed a principal medium for the expression and transmission of chemical knowledge.

All these striking upheavals in chemistry had been crammed into the space of comparatively few years—no more than a single life-time—and the tale is still not complete. On 20 March 1800, eight years before Dalton outlined the atomic theory in the first part of his 'A New System of Chemical Philosophy', the Italian physicist Alessandro Volta (1745–1827) announced his invention of the 'voltaic pile' or electric battery. The news of this invention aroused intense interest throughout Europe, and in the autumn of 1801 Volta was invited to demonstrate his battery before the Institute of France. Napoleon himself attended a demonstration and was so much impressed by what he saw that he not only made Volta a handsome gift in money, but offered a prize of 60 000 francs to encourage the study of electricity. An electric battery soon became an indispensable part of the equipment of a chemical laboratory, and in a few years it had proved its surpassing value as a scientific tool.

In May 1800, only a few weeks after Volta's original announcement, W. Nicholson and Anthony Carlisle showed that water could be split up into hydrogen and oxygen by the passage of an electric current through it. In the following September the German scientist Ritter effected an electrolytic copper-plating, and a little later Berzelius showed that, in general, an aqueous solution of a salt on electrolysis yielded the metal or its hydroxide at the cathode and oxygen or an acid at the anode. In 1806 Humphry Davy (1778–1829) advanced the hypothesis that chemical and electrical attraction are essentially identical, and expressed the belief that many substances that had hitherto resisted all attempts to split them up might possibly be decomposed if a sufficiently powerful current were passed through them. Two such substances were caustic soda and caustic potash. It is true that Lavoisier, with characteristic flair, had suspected them to be metallic compounds containing oxygen, but the suspicion had never been substantiated. In 1807, however, Davy passed a strong electric current from a battery (figure 124) through fused caustic soda and potash, and had the keen satisfaction of observing each of them to be decomposed: the soda into oxygen, hydrogen, and the soft white metal now known as sodium, and the potash into the same two gases and the similar metal potassium.

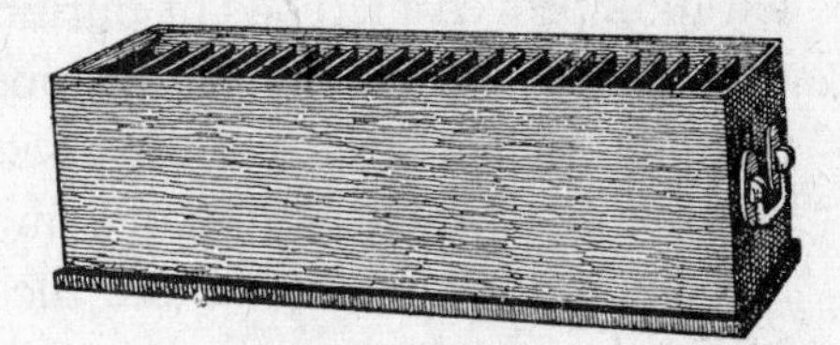

FIGURE 124—*Davy's battery at the Royal Institution, London.*

The qualitative importance of the electric battery was thus soon established, and towards the end of the period with which this volume deals the quantitative aspects of electrolytic phenomena were elucidated by Michael Faraday (1791–1867). In 1832–3 he showed that the mass of any individual product liberated in electrolysis is directly proportional to the quantity of electricity which has been passed through the electrolyte, and that the masses of the various products liberated in electrolysis by the passage of the same quantity of electricity are in the exact ratio of their chemical equivalents. These fundamental discoveries were the germ of the electrochemical industry that grew up in the second half of the nineteenth century (vol V, ch 11).

To describe or even to list any of the countless minor developments and discoveries made between 1750 and 1850 would be foreign to the purpose of this work. What this brief sketch of chemical history during that period has attempted to show is that, while the industrial revolution was taking place, chemistry was itself undergoing a revolution of comparable magnitude. The whole outlook of the science was metamorphosed. At the beginning of the period alchemy still lingered, empirical methods held undisputed sway, and such chemical theory as existed was sterile if not actually an obstacle to progress. Then a change began, at first slowly but later with gathering speed, and the foundations of the modern science were quickly laid one after another. The idea of chemical individuality led to improved methods of purification and analysis; the idea of the conservation of matter led to the establishment of quantitative chemistry; the work of the pneumatic chemists led to the discovery of the true composition of air and water and to a satisfactory theory of combustion; physical investigation of gases led to the enunciation of the atomic theory and chemical investigation to its acceptance; the atomic theory led to a better understanding of chemical reactions and to a convenient system of notation; and the discovery of the electric battery led first to wider qualitative discovery and subsequently to quantitative advances and to the development of fruitful chemical theory. From its very beginnings this spectacular growth reacted upon the chemical industry—even the mineral-water industry was initiated by Priestley—and little by little offered improvements upon old methods as well as suggesting entirely new ones. The conservatism of industrialists, still not unknown, was gradually broken down and more and more reliance was placed upon the knowledge that chemists provided. Many of the chemical manufacturers were themselves skilled in chemistry, and the ultimate importance of academic research to industry gained growing recognition. Conversely, the increased bulk and variation of industrial activity reacted upon the growth of pure chemistry by directing much research into specific channels, but the vital point is that the success of the chemical industry and in the long run of industry as a whole was very largely the result of the basic advances in pure chemistry here outlined. The history of technology since 1750 cannot be properly understood unless this fact is kept in mind. The detailed account of the chemical industry that follows shows how, in the branch most immediately affected, the new knowledge and philosophy made their influence felt.

BIBLIOGRAPHY

FREUND, I. 'The Study of Chemical Composition.' University Press, Cambridge. 1904.
HOLMYARD, E. J. 'Makers of Chemistry.' Clarendon Press, Oxford. 1931.
LOWRY, T. M. 'Historical Introduction to Chemistry' (3rd ed.). Macmillan, London. 1936.
MASSON, SIR JAMES IRVINE ORME. 'Three Centuries of Chemistry.' Benn, London. 1925.
MCKIE, D. 'Antoine Lavoisier.' Constable, London. 1952.
MEYER, E. S. C. VON. 'A History of Chemistry' (trans. from the German by G. MCGOWAN, 3rd ed.). Macmillan, London. 1906.
MUIR, M. M. P. 'A History of Chemical Theories and Laws.' Wiley, New York. 1907.
PARTINGTON, J. R. 'A Short History of Chemistry.' Macmillan, London. 1937.
THORPE, SIR THOMAS EDWARD. 'History of Chemistry' (2 vols). Watts, London. 1909–10.

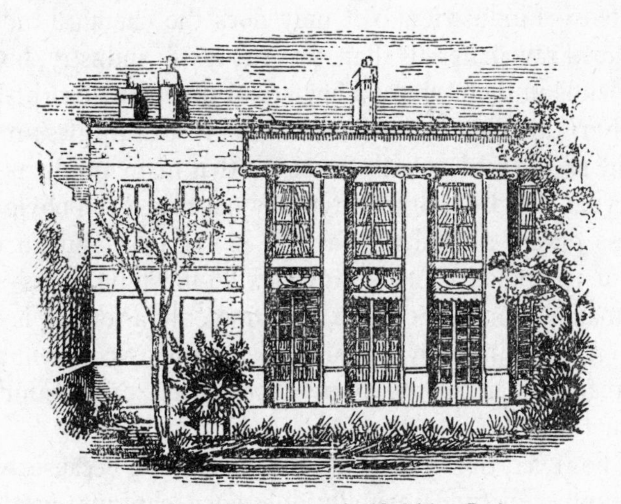

Lavoisier's house opposite the Madeleine, Paris.

8

PART II

THE CHEMICAL INDUSTRY: INTERACTION WITH THE INDUSTRIAL REVOLUTION

A. AND N. L. CLOW

THE chemical industry is the most polygamous of all industries—a description that pin-points a fundamental difference between it and practically all co-extensive industries. Not only does the chemical industry operate on a wider range of raw materials than, say, the textile industry, but its products are only rarely ends in themselves. They are in the main absorbed by other industries—sulphuric acid by the fertilizer industry, soda by glass-manufacturers, mordants by the textile trade—with the result that many products never appear as such in everyday life. But, although it may not have been obvious, chemistry has nevertheless played a fundamental role in the development of practically every branch of technology: metallurgy, textile-finishing, glass- and pottery-making, soap-making, and agriculture, to name only a few. It is this diversity that makes the chemical industry difficult to deal with in a coherent and summary form: its raw materials are many, its products varied, each manufactured by a process peculiar to itself.

Fortunately, however, this complexity can be reduced, because, while differing in detail, the number of fundamentally different techniques used is not great. These include: (*a*) furnace techniques, whereby the astonishing transformations of the metallurgical, glass, and pottery industries are brought about, (*b*) purification by crystallization, as in the production of salt and sugar, (*c*) distillation, and, as a later development, (*d*) the handling of gases. These processes enabled industrial chemists to progress towards the more sophisticated procedures of the twentieth century.

Furnace techniques go farther back than written records, and on them are centred the first observations that led to a body of chemical knowledge (figure 125): classical examples are the transformation of green malachite into red metallic copper, the firing of grey clay to give a red earthenware body, and so on. The ancients knew of six solid metals, but metallurgy was not the only furnace technique that industry of the industrial revolution inherited. The manufacture of glass and pottery (though for centuries neither product was widely used except among the upper classes) was established from China to the Baltic, and even at an early date some examples imply a high degree of technical competence. In making these products craftsmen cannot have failed to observe the profound changes taking place as their raw materials were transformed in the furnace, and they must have had the knowledge to search for, and to select, the proper materials—plant-ashes to supply alkali, sand to supply silica, and clays with the proper rheological properties.

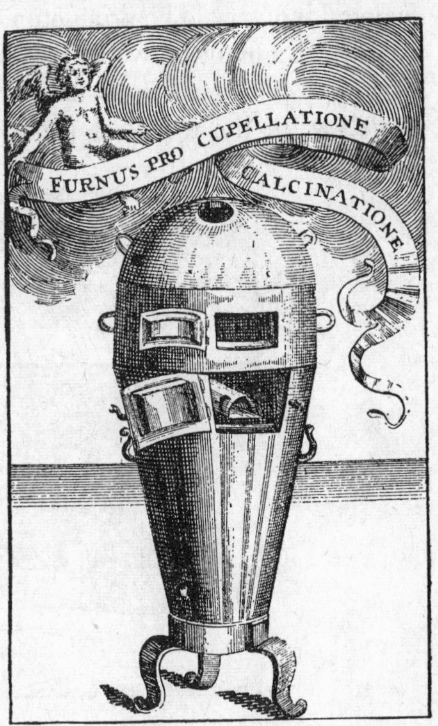

FIGURE 125—*Furnace for cupellation and calcination.*

In addition to the above (which by their use of fire undoubtedly have a dramatic quality), over many generations a body of knowledge comprising more subtle techniques was accumulated. These include tanning, involving knowledge of aluminium salts, and the production and use of mordants and dye-wares. Also, there is the part played by those chemists who saw their subject as the handmaid of medicine, the iatrochemists. By the beginning of the eighteenth century they, and the alchemists who were studying material bodies for a different purpose, had accumulated a collection of facts, as yet only loosely tied together by the most nebulous of theories, but nevertheless sufficient to play an important part in the subsequent development of chemical technology. To give only one example: there was the observation by J. R. Glauber (1603–70) of the resistance of lead to sulphuric acid, an observation that was utilized by John Roebuck (1718–94) when he began to make sulphuric acid in Britain in 1746. Glauber's observation may be considered a key discovery; its value was quite beyond reckoning. His 'Treatise on Philosophical Furnaces' was one of the outstanding collections of chemical and technological information published during the seventeenth century (vol III, ch 2).

Among the substances that attained importance in the chemical revolution were the following: *soda* and *potash*, mild alkalis derived until the end of the eighteenth century from plant-ashes (figure 126), or from natural deposits when geologic and climatic conditions were suitable. These alkalis may also have been known in the caustic condition, so rendered by the action of *lime*. By reaction with fats or oils the alkalis gave *soap* (vol III, pp 703–5), the manufacture of which, together with glass-making, may be taken as an index of an emergent chemical industry. The production of *salt* and *alum* must be similarly regarded, since the technique on which it is based, namely purification by recrystallization (figure 127), is of great importance throughout the whole of the chemical industry, as well as in the technical production of such substances as *sugar* (vol III, pp 7–8).

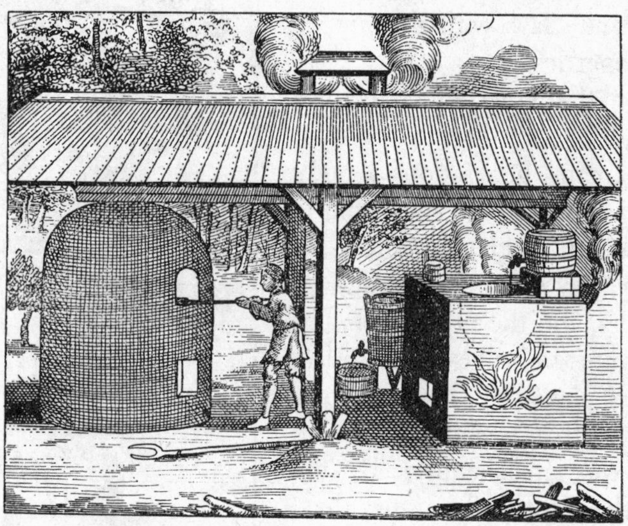

FIGURE 126—*Production of potash by the leaching of wood-ash.*

From our knowledge of the history of gunpowder it is clear that early technologists were familiar with two other chemical raw materials: *sulphur*, which occurs in the Mediterranean area and in Spain, and *saltpetre* (or nitre), mostly obtained from India and China through the East India trade, though knowledge that it could be made by neutralizing nitric acid with potash dates from the seventeenth century (vol II, pp 379–82).

The purification of sulphur and arsenic involved a knowledge of sublimation (figure 128), as also did the production of *sal ammoniac*, another substance which attained some importance from the seventeenth century onwards. Both sal ammoniac and borax were used as fluxes. A noteworthy list of substances then known was published by G. Roth in 1721.

To the above must be added an almost universal knowledge of the production of alcohol by fermentation, and the subsequent isolation of the alcohol by distillation (figure 129 and vol III, pp 11–12). Not only was it known how to produce alcohol but it was early realized that the fermentation could be taken a stage farther with the production of *acetic acid*, an acid which, together with citric acid and the salts of both, was much used in the textile industry. Glauber realized that the acids produced from wood-distillation and by fermentation were identical.

The more powerful mineral acids (sulphuric and nitric) were also known and found uses ranging from refining precious metals to the production of pharmacological nostrums. Glauber gives the preparation of hydrochloric acid from rock-salt and sulphuric acid, and fuming nitric acid from potassium nitrate and arsenious oxide.

FIGURE 127—*Crystallization of salt, illustrating early method of purification.*

The extent of the technological knowledge available at the beginning of what J. U. Nef calls the first industrial revolution may be judged by the publications then in existence. There was, for example, *De re metallica* by Georg Bauer (Agricola) (1494–1555) published at Basel in 1556. Bauer collected a mass of material about mineralogy, metallurgy, and chemical processes generally, and his work may be taken as the most complete on the chemical industry, such as it was, written before the seventeenth century. Then there is *Alchemia* of Andreas Libavius (1540–1616) of Halle, first published in 1597. The *Alchemia* is often described as the first real textbook of chemistry. It covers chemical technology, pharmacy, and metallurgy. In it the preparation of sulphuric acid from sulphur and saltpetre is rationally described. But it was a century before a publication that can justly be called a textbook of chemistry appeared. This was *Elementa chemiae* of Hermann Boerhaave (1668–1738). While professor of chemistry at Leyden, Boerhaave taught many of the men who subsequently made fundamental contributions in the application of chemistry to industry. To these works may be added four publications purely technological in origin. First is the *De la pirotechnia* of Vannoccio Biringuccio of Siena, which appeared in 1540 and is remarkable for its freedom from alchemical influence. Second comes the earliest handbook on the tinctorial arts, published by Rosetti of Venice in the same year; the sixteenth century saw new dye-wares introduced into Europe as the result of the discovery of America and the ocean route to the East, and the development of new methods of fixing dyes with, for example, iron, aluminium, and tin mordants. Lastly there are the *Art de terre* by Bernard Palissy (1510–88), in which great emphasis is laid on recourse to experiment, and the *De arte vitraria* by Antonio Neri of Florence, published in 1612.

Not only do the above treatises indicate the expansion and amassing of knowledge, but, with the founding of the Royal Society of London in 1660, we have

FIGURE 128—*Purification by sublimation, as in the preparation of arsenic.*

a further indication that time was ripening for the organized pursuit of natural knowledge. The 'Heads of Enquiries' issued by the Society shortly after its foundation reveal the interest of its founder members in the advance of technology, much of it chemical and metallurgical. This development was not confined to England: the *Académie Royale des Sciences* was founded in Paris in 1666 and its members displayed similar interests.

Among the topics of greatest interest were the substitution of coal for timber, and the need to deepen mines. The introduction of coal as a substitute for wood is a dominant factor both in the mechanical and in the chemical revolutions of the eighteenth and nineteenth centuries; it is therefore necessary to look at the position held by timber in the economy prevailing before the industrial revolution.

The structural use of wood on land and sea is obvious, but by-products of wood, particularly tar and pitch, were also essential to a maritime nation. Wood was also frequently the only fuel available. In domestic grates the substitution of coal gave rise to no particular difficulties, but for many generations wood continued to be used in industry because technologists were unable to prevent their products from being contaminated with the by-products of burning coal (vol III, ch 3).

The substitution of coal for wood in iron-smelting is associated with the name of the first Abraham Darby (1677–1717), founder of the Quaker dynasty of Coalbrookdale ironmasters, who solved this pressing economic and technological problem by converting his mineral fuel into coke before he used it in the blast-furnace (p 99). The year was 1709. The first to use coke in a blast-furnace in Germany was von Reden at Gleiwitz in 1796.

FIGURE 129—*Distillery. 1729.*

In glass-making the use of coal led to the closing-in of the top of the glass-pot, and that in turn to the evolution of flint glass, which was more easily fluxed in the covered pot (p 370). In pottery-making it led to the introduction of saggars.

The glass-maker, having solved his fuel problem, had still to face the fact that potash (the residual ash from timber or other plants) was an essential ingredient in the glass itself. So also was it indispensable to the manufacturers of soap, alum, and saltpetre. The latter when mixed with yet another timber by-product, charcoal, and with sulphur gave the only explosive known until nearly the middle of the nineteenth century. Thus we see that mining, metallurgy, and a variety of other industrial interests were competing for a dwindling supply of timber. As a result, from many quarters in the seventeenth century we have records of a timber famine, and the search for a substitute for wood was one of the dominant features in the development of eighteenth-century technology (vol III, ch 3).

The solution of the fuel problem was, however, only half the technological battle. As has been mentioned, plant-ashes supplied the alkali needed by glass-makers, soap-boilers, bleachers, and other manufacturers. Thus as a subsidiary facet of the search for an alternative to wood we have the search for a substitute for natural alkali. When the problem was solved at the end of the eighteenth century, the industries using alkali became the focus of practically the whole chemical industry, and so remained for some fifty years. At this point therefore it is necessary to discuss the rise of the alkali industry, and to consider the means whereby the solution of the problem was effected.

From an early date local supplies of alkali in Britain were insufficient to meet the growth of demand, and additional supplies were imported either in the form of crude weed- or wood-ash or as refined potash or pearl-ash. There were two sources of this alkali, namely *barilla* from the Mediterranean region, and wood-ash from northern Europe or America. But with the expanding economy of Europe, and particularly of Britain, demand continued to exceed supply. This directed the attention of technologists to possible solutions of the scarcity. Of these, four may be listed: (*a*) organized importation; (*b*) augmented domestic production of wood-ash; (*c*) the production of alkali from hitherto unexploited material, such as seaweed; and finally (*d*) synthesis. For nearly a century (1730–1830) the third of these possibilities made a major contribution to British economy, being superseded only when an adequate supply of soda came on the market as the result of the establishment in the 1830s, in the neighbourhood of the Cheshire salt-fields, of works operating the Leblanc process.

While kelping—that is, the production of alkali by the incineration of seaweed—is mentioned in Scotland as early as 1694, it is not till about 1730 that such production is generally noticed in contemporary records. Kelping is included here because it represents, in a sense, one of the roots of the British chemical industry. Its product, low-grade vegetable alkali, was absorbed by a range of manufacturers. It is in fact a good example of the point, made earlier, that most chemicals are not ends in themselves but are 'intermediates' absorbed in the manufacture of other products.

As a chemical raw material, kelp[1] was very different from the highly purified alkaline products of twentieth-century chemical industry, yet the technical skill of the era during which it was an important item of commerce was sufficient to make full use of its varied content. Kelp (ash) contains a mixture of sodium carbonate, chloride, and sulphate, magnesium sulphate and chloride, and a certain quantity of potassium chloride, and, while much of it was not alkali as such, as a chemical miscellany it was nevertheless useful to contemporary industry. Later it became of importance on account of its workable content of iodine.

From our point of view the development of the trade in kelp was nothing more than a palliative measure taken to lessen temporarily the difficulties arising from the shortage of other vegetable alkali. A more radical and scientific approach was to apply the increasing knowledge of the interaction of chemical substances in a frontal attack on the problem of making alkali.

[1] Kelp is a general name for brown seaweeds; it is also applied to the ash obtained by calcining the seaweeds.

The foundation and rise of the alkali industry represent the transition from an industry based on accumulated craft knowledge to one based on applied chemical knowledge. Although often represented as if the change happened more or less overnight, this is very far from true, and the significant events that took place in the third decade of the nineteenth century have antecedents going back for half a century at least. Moreover, while the principal product of the new industry was alkali, at the same time it yielded by-products which were absorbed by the bleaching industry and in turn revolutionized it. The new bleaching-agents also had a notable effect on the production of paper from rags. Indeed, Justus von Liebig (1803–74) described the synthesis of soda as the 'foundation of all our improvements in the domestic arts'.

At this point it is important to look at some of the antecedents mentioned above. As early as 1737 H. L. Duhamel-Dumonceau (1700–82), the originator of many technological improvements, who in the previous year had emphasized the distinction between soda and potash, was working on a process not unlike that on which the great alkali industry operated during its first century. Not long afterwards Joseph Black (1728–99) of Edinburgh (p 217) published his 'Experiments upon Magnesia Alba, Quick-Lime and Other Alcaline Substances', in which he made clear the interrelation between mild and caustic alkalis (p 217). Associated with Black in his experiments towards the synthesis of alkali were John Roebuck, the pioneer manufacturer of sulphuric acid, and James Watt (1736–1819) the engineer. Another interested investigator was James Keir (1735–1820), who was connected with the Rogers Amblecote glass-house at Stourbridge.

How successful these experimenters were we do not really know. It is reported that Black and his associates alleged that they would have gone into commercial production had it not been for the duty they would have had to pay on the salt they proposed to use as a raw material. They joined forces in 1771 to oppose a patent-application for the manufacture of soda from common salt by two London chemists, Alexander and George Fordyce. Evidence was produced that Keir had successfully synthesized soda, and at the same time Pierre Théodore de Bruges, a saltpetre manufacturer, also claimed that he had equipped a factory to make alkali.

These indications that some success had been attained in the synthesis of alkali are strengthened by the fact that in 1781 a British Act of Parliament reduced the duties on 'foul' salt 'used in the manufacture of fused fossil or mineral alkali'. That the problem was still current is evident from the remark in Richard Watson's 'Chemical Essays' (1782–7) that the subject was 'one of great national concern'. These references clearly reflect its economic importance, as also do the patents taken out for the manufacture of alkali about the same time by Richard Shannon (no. 1223 of 1779), Bryan Higgins (no. 1302 of 1781), John Collison (no. 1341 of 1782), and James Gerard (no. 1369 of 1783). A close study of these patents will repay those interested in the chemical background of the alkali problem. Some of the processes bear a marked resemblance to the Leblanc process; indeed, in 1789, Anthony Bourboulon de Boneuil referred in a patent (no. 1677) to sodium sulphate and charcoal as materials 'already used in the manufacture of alkali'.

Important though these developments undoubtedly were, it is questionable if any of them led to the real foundation of the alkali industry in Great Britain. For that it is necessary to turn to the activities of Archibald Cochrane, ninth Earl of Dundonald (1749–1831), and his associates in the Newcastle upon Tyne area.

In the 1780s Dundonald got in touch with two manufacturers, William Losh and Thomas Doubleday, who were trying to convert common salt into soda. Dundonald sent Losh to Paris in 1791. Guyton de Morveau had shown in 1782 that soda could be made from sodium sulphate. Armed with information collected in France, Losh and Dundonald, about 1796, with a number of partners, set up an alkali works at Walker upon Tyne, Dundonald having taken out a patent for the manufacture of mineral alkali (no. 2043). In essentials the process covers the production of Glauber's salt (Na_2SO_4, $10H_2O$) from salt ($NaCl$), and converting the former to sodium sulphide (Na_2S), from which soda, either mild (Na_2CO_3) or caustic ($NaOH$), could be prepared. At first their output was not high, but, considering the relatively low percentage of alkali in kelp, even a small output almost certainly had a considerable effect on the alkali market.

Following the establishment of the above co-partnership several other firms began to make alkali: Doubleday and Easterby of Bill Quay in 1808, Hutchinson of Felling *c* 1810, and Cookson of Jarrow in 1823. Similar developments took place in Scotland, particularly at Dalmuir in Dunbartonshire, where the development was associated with Lords Dundonald and Dundas (1795). From that focus the manufacture spread to several other centres in the neighbourhood of Glasgow, and to Ayrshire. In 1814 manufacture was started at Liverpool by Thomas Lutwyche and William Hill, who supplied alkali to local soap-makers.

All these developments antedate the founding of the first alkali works to operate the now much better known Leblanc process. To follow up the history of Leblanc it is necessary to return to the European scene and to the year 1775.

On the continent, as in Britain, there was an acute shortage of alkali, but the continental situation was aggravated by the warlike state of Europe. This being so, French scientists directed their attention to possible syntheses of soda. Malherbe devised a process involving the fusion of sodium sulphate, charcoal, and iron: Guyton de Morveau and Carnay were so confident of success that they erected a factory at Croisac in Picardy in 1782: de la Métherie heated sodium sulphate and coal in closed retorts: Athénas had yet another process. Then in 1787 Nicolas Leblanc (1742–1806) brought forward the process that became the core of the whole heavy chemical industry for nearly a century. Leblanc's process depended on the decomposition of common salt by sulphuric acid with the production of sodium sulphate (figure 130 (i)). This in turn was mixed intimately with chalk and charcoal and heated in a crucible. The resulting 'black ash' was leached with water (figure 130 (ii)) and the resulting soda recovered from the solution by evaporation (figure 130 (iii)). The process was patented in France in 1791, and a factory was built by Leblanc and Dizé at St Denis to work it. Unhappily the tide of revolution swept over Leblanc. His patron, the Duke of Orleans, was executed, his factory was confiscated, and a commission appointed by the *Académie des Sciences*, to award a prize of 2400 livres, decided that the processes put forward by Malherbe and Athénas were the most promising, but that none was satisfactory enough to be worthy of the prize.

As has been indicated, Leblanc's process hardly seems to have been unique in its fundamentals. It is curious therefore that the great efflorescence of industrial chemical activity in Britain in the 1820s and 1830s did not involve any of the workers or take place at any of the industrial foci so far described. In Britain, Cheshire, with its rich deposits of salt and ready access to supplies of coal and limestone, was the natural locus for the development of chemical industry, and there, and in the adjacent parts of Lancashire, in due course it did develop after an initial short phase at Liverpool. In addition to choosing perhaps one of the most favoured districts in Europe for the establishment of a chemical industry, its founder was able to benefit by the repeal of the salt-duties in 1823. The pioneer to avail himself of the opportunity was James Muspratt (1793–1886).

Muspratt was making prussiate of potash, acids, and solvents in Dublin in 1816. Six years later he settled at Liverpool, where he continued to make prussiate, and added sulphuric acid to his output. His chemical knowledge was small, but the capital acquired in the manufacture of prussiate was sufficient to enable him to embark on the manufacture of soda by the Leblanc process in 1823, a date often taken as the foundation of the alkali industry in Britain. In 1828 he was joined by J. C. Gamble (1776–1848), a Glasgow-trained chemist.

In 1825 the manufacture of Leblanc alkali was initiated at Glasgow, the pioneer in that region being Charles Tennant (1768–1838), who, as the developer of bleaching-powder, was already a chemical manufacturer of some substance.

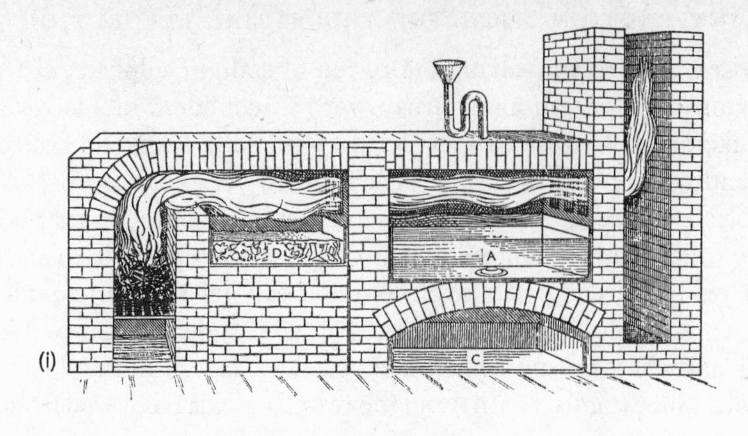

(i)

(ii)

(iii)

FIGURE 130—*Manufacture of soda by Leblanc's process.*

The St Rollox chemical works, the site of the development, was in time to become the greatest chemical factory in Europe.

After a somewhat slow start, due to the conservatism of the soap-boilers who constituted their principal market, the Muspratt and Gamble enterprise flourished. But in the very year that they joined forces (1828) they had the first of numerous encounters with the law. As first introduced, the operation of the Leblanc process gave rise to very large quantities of a noxious by-product, hydrogen chloride, which the pioneer manufacturers endeavoured to disperse simply by passing it up tall chimneys. In this way, their activities caused widespread devastation to vegetation and destruction of property. Muspratt was consequently arraigned in 1828 for causing a public nuisance. While legal action did not in fact close down the Liverpool works, it undoubtedly had a considerable influence on the subsequent locus of development of the alkali industry. Already Muspratt had started a second alkali works at St Helens, where the manufacture of bottle-, crown-, and plate-glass was established, and it was there, and in such other neighbouring places as Widnes, Warrington, and Runcorn, that the great development in Britain of the heavy chemical industry and its associated manufactures took place in following years. That these districts did not suffer from intolerable industrial pollution may be attributed to the fortunate invention in 1836 of a means of absorbing the offending hydrogen chloride. This was the utilization of an old windmill packed with wet brushwood, and subsequently of towers specially built for the purpose, by William Gossage (1799–1877) a Worcestershire alkali manufacturer (B.P. no. 7267 of 1836). Another factor was the realization by the manufacturers that they were allowing a valuable material to run to waste. From the hydrogen chloride could be produced chlorine, a bleaching-agent, a development that will be dealt with subsequently.

There is not space here to go into the detail of the evolution of the alkali industry during the middle years of the nineteenth century. Economics brought about the need for improved processes and attention to the utilization of waste products; social pressure resulted in a demand for the more careful operation of the industry; and these together produced in the end a process that finally superseded Leblanc's classic one. But the developments so far described set the pattern for the evolution of the heavy chemical industry till nearly the end of the nine-

---

FIGURE 130 (*cont.*). (i) *Section of a salt-decomposing furnace. The salt and sulphuric acid were brought together in* A, *which was lead lined. After several hours, during which time reaction took place and hydrochloric acid was driven off, the mass was pushed into* C. *The reaction was completed in* D, *the hottest part of the furnace.* (ii) *Black ash vats in which the sodium carbonate was dissolved out.* (iii) *Section of the crystallizing house in Chance's alkali works, Oldbury, Worcestershire, in which soda suitable for the production of plate glass was prepared.*

teenth century, a pattern that is succinctly described by Stephen Miall in his 'History of the British Chemical Industry', pp 5, 6:

> The works of the chemical manufacturer tended to become larger and more complicated; he began to make soda, using common salt and sulphuric acid and other raw materials. After a time he started to make his own sulphuric acid by burning sulphur or pyrites; if he used pyrites, it was probably a mixed sulphide of copper and iron, and it was comparatively easy to make copper sulphate and ferrous sulphate from the roasted pyrites. The process of making sodium sulphate produced large quantities of hydrochloric acid, and, as nitric acid was required in the manufacture of sulphuric acid, the alkali manufacturer easily developed into a manufacturer of hydrochloric, nitric, and sulphuric acids, and various salts of sodium, copper, and iron. It was a very common development for the alkali manufacturer to use the chlorine he recovered so as to make bleaching-powder, and in this way he became a maker of calcium chloride and bleaching-powder, and, as demands for them grew, he made other salts of sodium and calcium required in large quantities. The manufacture of all these 'heavy' chemicals became in this way an involved process, in which one part was dependent on the others and almost every effort to prevent waste involved the manufacturer in some new product.

With this picture of the heavy chemical industry in mind it becomes necessary to look at the history of the one substance that was the kernel of the whole structure, namely, sulphuric acid.

Knowledge of sulphuric acid, or oil of vitriol, was one of the legacies of the alchemical period. It is variously described in the works of the pseudonymous Basil Valentine, Paracelsus, and Agricola, and by 1570 we have a fairly accurate description of its preparation by the distillation of green vitriol (ferrous sulphate, $FeSO_4,7H_2O$) in the works of Gerard Dorn. In this method (operated at Nordhausen from 1755) ferrous sulphate was decomposed by heat to give oxides of sulphur which were absorbed in the water of crystallization. The yield of sulphuric acid was only of the order of 10 per cent of the weight of green vitriol used, and as this was insufficient to meet a growing demand attention was turned to other methods of production, in particular to the oxidation of sulphur, a method suggested by Cornelius Drebbel (1572–1634) and probably introduced into England about 1720. In this process the sulphuric acid was said to be made *per campanam*, the operation consisting of burning sulphur and saltpetre (potassium nitrate, KNO_3) together under a variety of bell-shaped vessels. Such vessels are illustrated in the works of Lefèvre and Lémery, where they are seen to consist of glass or earthenware.

There is no record of continuous manufacture of sulphuric acid in England until a good deal later, when Joshua Ward (1685–1761) and John White began to produce 'oil of vitriol made by the bell', first at Twickenham (1736), and then at Richmond (1740). Ward and White's venture represents a transition in the production of sulphuric acid from the laboratory scale to that of the factory. They still used glass vessels—of some 40 to 50 gallons capacity—but they produced acid at about a twentieth of the former price, and so presented to industry for the first time the possibility of procuring acid at reasonable cost. Unfortunately no detailed account of all the uses to which this early acid was put has survived. Andrew Brown, in his 'History of Glasgow', recorded that before 1750 Scottish bleachers procured their sulphuric acid from England or Holland; we know that it was used in pharmacy (in making the *sal mirabile* of Glauber); and there are good indications that it was used by tinplate-makers, brass-founders, button-makers, japanners, gilders, and the refiners of precious metals. They used it either for pickling and cleaning metals, or in the form of 'stripping-liquor' (sulphuric acid containing potassium nitrate) for removing silver from copper, and it is almost certain that it was to cater for this market among the metal-workers of Birmingham that the next English sulphuric acid works was established in 1746. The pioneers were John Roebuck and Samuel Garbett (1717–1805), the owners of a refinery for precious metals in Steelhouse Lane, Birmingham.

FIGURE 131—*Manufacture of sulphuric acid in glass vessels about the time of Joshua Ward.*

The Roebuck and Garbett enterprise was not, however, just one other sulphuric acid works in an ever expanding list. Roebuck had received the best possible scientific education of his time, by studying medicine at Edinburgh and Leyden, and having decided to abandon medicine for technology he made use of Glauber's observation that lead is not attacked by sulphuric acid and built his vitriol-producing plant of that metal. This substitution of lead for glass was one of the great forward steps in the history of chemical technology: it freed the manufacturer from the use of fragile laboratory-scale apparatus (figure 131) and brought about a further fall in the price of a valuable industrial commodity.

The Birmingham Vitriol Manufactory found a ready market for its products among the trades of Birmingham. There were, however, few outlets in the midlands for sulphuric acid until it was found useful as a substitute for sour milk—till then the only acid liquor available in quantity to the bleaching-trade. It happened that for several decades the Board of Trustees for Fisheries, Manufactures, and Improvements in Scotland (founded 1727) had been subsidizing the laying-down of bleach-fields, and a bleaching-trade that catered for weavers as far away as London had been built up. Roebuck and Garbett next established a sulphuric acid works at Prestonpans, on the Firth of Forth, a few miles east of Edinburgh. Once again they brought the manufacture of their product, always a difficult one to handle, into an area where there was a profitable market. In addition there may have been patent difficulties with Joshua Ward, and, Scotland then having its own patent law, they may have thought to avoid the consequences of litigation by moving north. This does not seem to be a very cogent reason, however, since, while Francis Home (1719–1813), professor of *materia medica* in the university of Edinburgh, published the first account of the use of sulphuric acid in the souring of linen, it is generally believed that Roebuck had earlier knowledge of it and had suggested the substitution to the bleachers.

The inviolability of patent rights being dubious in the middle of the eighteenth century, Roebuck and Garbett attempted to rely on secrecy to enable them to reap the advantages of their enterprise. For history this is unfortunate, as there is now no account of the way in which they carried out their operations. It is known, however, that they imported sulphur from Leghorn and bought saltpetre from the East India Company, and that in the year after they started manufacture they were exporting sulphuric acid to Holland at 3½*d* a pound.

Within a decade sulphuric acid works had sprung up in various parts of the country—that of Rhodes at Bridgnorth (1756); somewhat later that of Skey at Dowles in Worcestershire; and that of Benjamin Rowson at Bradford, which probably dates from 1750. There were others in Edinburgh and Govan—but the Prestonpans Vitriol Works was still the greatest in Britain in 1784. Other early vitriol works were founded in Holland and at Rouen. In Germany the first works to use lead chambers was that founded by von Waitz at Ringkuhl, near Grossalmerode, Hesse.

As the industrial revolution proceeded, more and more uses were found for the cheap acid, many of them connected with the textile trade. Bleachers found it admirable as a substitute for the sour milk formerly used, and after the discovery of chlorine it became an essential in the preparation of chemical bleaches. Calico-printers also used it as a sour and in the production of citric acid. It was used by dyers to render indigo soluble, in the preparation of mordants, and in many other ways. Just how useful it was to the expanding economy of the industrial revolution may be gauged by the fact that by 1820, that is, several years before sulphuric acid began to be absorbed on a large scale in the production of synthetic soda, there were some 40 vitriol works in Great Britain: approximately two dozen were in England, and half that number in Scotland.

In spite of this evidence of industrial activity few descriptions of the process have come down to us. The following, however, gives some idea of practice at the beginning of the nineteenth century. It describes the six chambers used by Bealy, of Radcliffe, Manchester.

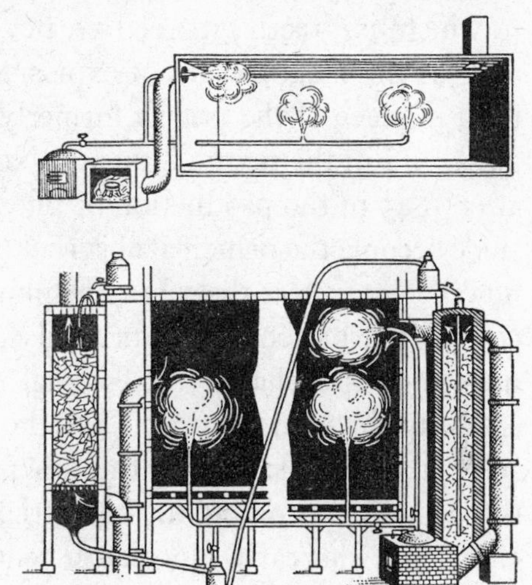

FIGURE 132—*Lead chambers in which sulphuric acid was made.*

They were ten feet square and twelve feet high, with a roof like a cottage, each house having a door, usually of mahogany, and a valve on top for ventilation between burnings. The floor was constructed to hold water to a depth of eight or nine inches. The 1 lb charge consisting of a mixture of seven to eight parts of sulphur with one of nitre was introduced upon two trays. This was lit and the doors shut for upwards of an hour until the combustion had taken place. Three hours from the time of lighting were allowed for condensation to take place, after which the doors and valve were opened to 'sweeten' the chamber. The operation was repeated every four hours day and night for about six weeks, after which the acid was withdrawn and concentrated in lead vessels. (Quoted in Clow, 'The Chemical Revolution', p 145).

We see that this is little more than the *per campanam* process writ large, with lead vessels in place of glass or earthenware. Soon, however, other changes were to be put in train. In 1803 Charles Tennant built the first lead chambers at St Rollox. These were constructed with a separate furnace for the combustion of the sulphur and saltpetre, and within ten years the water on the floor of the chambers had been replaced by jets of steam, so that the chambers remained as reacting spaces only (figure 132). The process having been made continuous by Jean Louis Holker (1770–1844), it remained virtually unaltered until the introduction of the catalytic or contact process many years later (vol V, ch 11).

Production of sulphuric acid in Britain just before the great expansion necessitated by the rise of the synthetic soda industry was of the order of 3000 tons a year. The cost of producing this sulphuric acid was about 2½*d* a pound, a figure that was further reduced when Chile saltpetre ($NaNO_3$) was substituted for the potassium salt after 1830. Pyrites was substituted for elementary sulphur after difficulties in procuring supplies of the latter had occurred about 1840.

The above account describes the manifold influences of sulphuric acid upon the European economy. Space does not permit a detailed description of the way in which, indirectly, it freed greater supplies of potassium salts for agriculture, and for the manufacture of explosives, by making available soda that could be used in place of the potash formerly absorbed in the manufacture of soap and glass, and in the textile industry. Nor is it appropriate to deal here with its use after 1845 in the production of phosphatic fertilizers (vol V, ch 11), which has since become the principal absorber of sulphuric acid. In spite of these omissions, however, it is clear that cheap sulphuric acid had a considerable influence on the cost of the bleached and printed cotton-goods that Britain exported in large quantities in exchange for colonial raw materials, and on the cost of the glass and soap she used at home. Thus the lead-chamber process for making sulphuric acid takes its place with the other great, particularly mechanical, inventions that helped to promote the industrial, chemical, and social revolution of the late eighteenth and early nineteenth centuries.

During the nineteenth century, mechanical technology radically transformed the production of textiles, by a series of ingenious devices operable on a large scale with the reliable power provided by James Watt's improved steam-engine (1769), and installed in mills lit by W. Murdock's gas-lights (1805). But there was little point in speeding up the production of textiles if the processes carried out by the finishing-trades, namely bleaching, dyeing, and printing, could not be hastened as well. Textile-printing was accelerated by the introduction of cylindrical printing by Bell in 1785, and, fortunately for the progress of the industrial revolution in Britain, her chemists also made conspicuous improvements in the chemistry of bleaching and dyeing.

Several references have already been made to improvements in the art of bleaching. Originally a domestic craft, much was done to organize it into an industry before chemical knowledge had any marked influence on the processes carried out. The different methods in operation throughout Europe do not merit discussion here, but it was at the instigation of the Board of Trustees in Scotland (p 244) that information was published which led to the first of two major revolutions in the technique of bleaching. The suggestions are contained in Francis Home's 'Experiments on Bleaching' (Edinburgh, 1754), where the author advocated the use of dilute sulphuric acid in place of the traditional sour or buttermilk. Although the change may seem somewhat trivial to twentieth-century eyes, supplies of cheap mineral acid enabled bleachers to reduce the time of souring to about a twenty-fifth of that formerly required. But even this increased rapidity of bleaching was not adequate to cope with the output of the mills, soon to be increasing by millions of yards annually.

Fortunately an entirely new bleaching agent was at hand. In 1774 chlorine was discovered by the Swedish chemist, C. W. Scheele (1742–86), and in 1785 the French chemist, C. L. Berthollet (1748–1822), discovered that it was a powerful bleaching agent. News of this was communicated to James Watt and to Patrick Copland (1748–1822). As a result, a second revolution in bleaching was initiated by the introduction of chlorine into industrial operations, first at Aberdeen in 1787, and then at Glasgow and Manchester within a matter of a year or so. From these centres the use of chlorine spread rapidly to the other textile producing areas, despite the difficulties inherent in handling the new reagent.

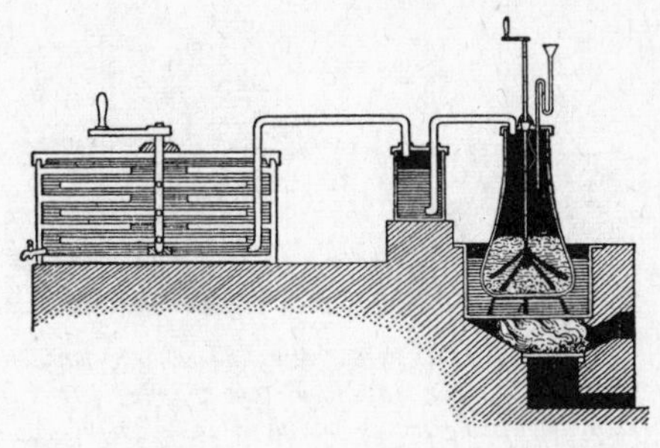

FIGURE 133—*The preparation of chemical bleach by the absorption of chlorine in water and alkali solution.*

Chlorine is a gaseous element and, at the date of its introduction into industry, pneumatic chemistry (p 215) had not emerged from the laboratory. Joseph Priestley's 'Experiments and Observations on Different Kinds of Airs' is dated 1774–7. On account of the difficulties contingent in handling gaseous chlorine, the first of a number of technical advances of great value was suggested by manufacturers at Javel,[1] who put forward the idea of absorbing chlorine in alkali with the production of dissolved hypochlorite (*eau de Javel*) (figure 133). In France the process did not succeed commercially, and its inventors emigrated to Liverpool, where lack of patent protection and the hazards of transporting their product to the bleach-fields led to the same result. In 1789 Charles Tennant (1769–1838), a bleacher of Darnley, Renfrewshire, took out a patent for the production of a liquid bleach made from chlorine and a sludge of slaked lime ($Ca(OH)_2$) (no. 2209), and simultaneously avoided the difficulty of transport by licensing manufacturers to work his patent at their own bleach-fields. He enjoyed the protection of this patent for only some four years, however, since proceedings in 1802 made it clear that the process was already widely used.

Meanwhile the Tennant company had registered a second patent, this time

[1] Javel (*not* Javelle) was a village on the outskirts of Paris, but now forms part of the XVth *arrondissement* of the capital.

for the production of an entirely dry bleaching-powder (no. 2312 of 1799) (figure 134), thus solving the transport difficulty. It was to operate this patent that Charles Tennant and Company established their chemical works at St Rollox in 1799. In the first year of its existence fifty tons of bleaching-powder were produced, which was sold at £140 a ton: by 1830 output had reached 1000 tons a year and the price had been reduced to £80.

Like the introduction of lead in the manufacture of sulphuric acid, and the production of soda from common salt, the development of bleaching-powder was one of the milestones in the evolution of Britain's chemical economy. Liebig assessed its significance in the following terms:

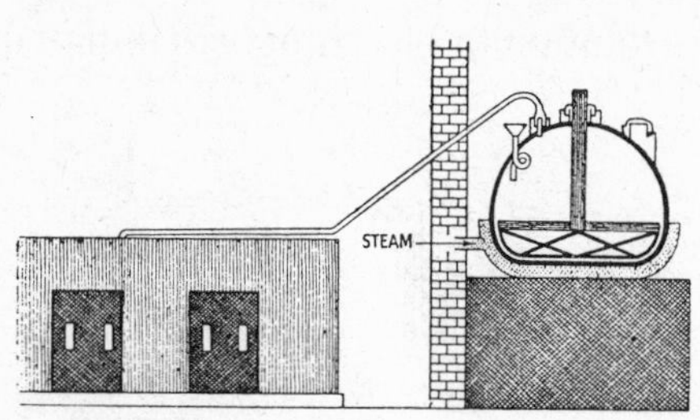

FIGURE 134—*The preparation of bleaching-powder. Lime is placed on trays in a stone chamber 8 to 9 ft high. The chlorine is produced in a large lead-lined chamber by the action of sulphuric acid on a mixture of common salt (sodium chloride) and manganese dioxide. It passes into a leaden chamber containing water (not shown) and so into the lime house. After 2 days the lime is stirred by rakes, and after another 2 days the reaction is complete.*

But for this new bleaching process it would scarcely have been possible for cotton manufacture in Great Britain to have attained the enormous extent which it did during the nineteenth century, nor could it have competed in price with France and Germany. . . . Had not chlorine bleaching been introduced, finding capital to purchase land for the old methods of bleaching would have presented a considerable problem, especially when it is realised that by 1840 a single establishment near Glasgow was bleaching 1,400 pieces of cotton daily throughout the year (J. Liebig, 'Familiar Letters', p 28).

Although in the period under discussion no revolution comparable with that in bleaching affected the art of dyeing, contemporary scientists did help to change dyeing from a craft into an industry. In the 1660s Boyle and Hooke performed experiments on dyeing before the Royal Society, and Sir William Petty listed the dyes then in use in England. They included madder, cochineal, saffron, anatto, weld, turmeric, woad, logwood, and indigo (vol V, ch 12), and these remained among the principal dye-wares used in Europe for many generations, in spite of the fact that many of them were fast neither to light, nor to washing, nor to alkali, even when improved by the simultaneous use of mordants (vol III, ch 25). In part the difficulty lay in the chemical complexity of most of the natural colouring-matters, the diverse chemical composition of the common fibres, and in the fact that there was no sound theory of the dyeing-process. E. Bancroft (1744–1821) distinguished substantive and adjective dyes in 1794. It was not till two of the directors of the French dye industry, P. J. Macquer

(1718–84) and C. L. Berthollet, became interested that any advance was made beyond a purely mechanistic conception. Macquer introduced Prussian blue (discovered by the Berlin colour-manufacturer Diesbach in 1704) as a dye, and the enthusiasm with which it was adopted, despite its shortcomings, is a measure of the weakness of the dye department of the textile industry.

Among the more successful innovations in this field during the period under discussion were (*a*) the perfection of the dye cudbear, discovered by Dr Cuthbert[1] Gordon and developed by George Macintosh (1739–1807), and (*b*) the solution, also by Macintosh, of the problem, which faced all the western nations in the eighteenth century, of producing a fast red cotton colour equal to the 'Turkey-red' produced from madder (*Rubia tinctorum*) in the orient. At the Dalmarnock dye works, Macintosh produced the best Turkey-red on a vast scale; 5000 looms were employed in 1796 in the neighbourhood of Glasgow making pullicates[2] for the Turkey-red dyers. These became known throughout Europe as monteiths, after Henry Monteith, who acquired Dalmarnock from Macintosh.

In addition to the introduction of new dye-wares, mechanical and chemical invention added to the variety of textiles available. Goods requiring only simple patterns were produced by resist-work, in which a resistant mixture, invented by a man named Grouse, was first printed on the fabric which was then dyed, often in a blue-vat, thus producing a white pattern on a blue ground. Another process in operation from the beginning of the nineteenth century was chemical discharge. In this the cloth was first dyed uniformly, and then a design was produced on it by clamping it between lead stencil-plates through which a bleaching-solution was forced, to discharge the colour in the exposed parts. Bandannas were produced in this way. When chromium compounds became available, about 1820, they were introduced to increase the range of colour-effects, though by modern standards they were certainly less satisfactory than one would judge by contemporary acclamation. Nevertheless these and the other chemical developments described above were important in the history of the industrial revolution. To quote Edward Baines, the historian of the cotton-industry: 'Chemical science has done at least as much to facilitate and perfect the processes, as mechanical science to facilitate and perfect the operations of manufacturing.' Together they brought about so great and so rapid an expansion that it is without parallel in the annals of industry.

Another essential part of the dyeing-process is mordanting, which improves, or indeed often effects, the adhesion of the dyestuff to the fabric. Further,

[1] Of whose name cudbear is a corruption. This dye is obtained from certain lichens.

[2] Bandannas. The name pullicate derives from Pulicat, a town on the Madras coast.

different mordants produce different colours, or lakes, with the same dye, and so increase the variety of colour that can be produced from a limited range of dyes. Supplying these ancillaries was an essential part of the early chemical industry. For the most part they consisted of alums (salts of the general formula $M'M'''(SO_4)_2,12H_2O$), or copperas, that is, ferrous sulphate ($FeSO_4,7H_2O$),

FIGURE 135—*Calcining alum shale at Hurlet, Renfrewshire.*

with the addition at a later date of lead acetate, iron acetate, and aluminium acetate.

Alum has been a commodity handled by eastern Mediterranean traders since the earliest times. Indeed, the manufacture of alum has been called the earliest chemical industry. There were alum-works in England in Elizabethan times at Guisborough, some ten miles south-east of Middlesbrough. Production depended on deposits of aluminous shale, which were calcined in the open air in vast heaps (figure 135). The resulting ash was extracted with water and the solution evaporated with alkali (figure 136). It was the existence of alum shale in waste from coal-mines that enabled Charles Macintosh (son of the George Macintosh already mentioned) to start an alum-works at Hurlet, Renfrewshire, in 1797. This soon became the largest in Britain. In 1808 Macintosh, Knox and Company started a second factory at Campsie, Stirlingshire, to utilize a very pyritous alum shale, found in the coal-measures, for the production of both alum and copperas. Their output of alum reached 1000 tons a year in 1812, and 2000 tons in 1835, in which year the price was £12 a ton. But this simple and lucrative method of making alum did not remain unrivalled for long. In 1845, Peter Spence (1806–83), who had been a chemical manufacturer in Dundee, London, and

FIGURE 136—*The manufacture of alum.* (Left) *Evaporating the solution;* (right) *removing the alum from the crystallizing pans.*

Cumberland successively, took out a patent (no. 10 970) for the production of alum and copperas by digesting roasted iron pyrites and burnt shale in sulphuric acid. A second patent followed in 1850 (no. 13 335), and having settled at Pendleton, near Manchester, the firm of Peter Spence became in time the largest manufacturer of alum in the world.

The history of copperas is similar to that of alum. It was being made in Elizabethan times at Queenborough in the Isle of Sheppey; then from the middle of the seventeenth century at Deptford; and from the middle of the eighteenth in the Newcastle upon Tyne area. From Newcastle it was exported in large quantities to French dye-houses. Macintosh, Knox and Company produced it at both Hurlet and Campsie.

Advancing chemical knowledge during the eighteenth century led to the introduction of new mordants, or to changes in the methods of producing those already in use. Lead acetate, formerly made in Holland with lead imported from Britain, was made in Britain from 1790; pyroligneous acid took the place of sour beer in the production of iron acetate for the 'red liquor' of the calico printers, and in time aluminium acetate was substituted for the lead salt.

Hitherto we have considered the core of the emergent heavy chemical industry —the applied chemistry of the industrial revolution. To leave the subject at this point would, however, be to present an unbalanced picture. There were other correlative advances which, if not part of the chemical industry proper, nevertheless were very relevant to it. Chief of these is the use of coal as a chemical raw material. In this capacity the first practical development was due to the versatile and active-minded Dundonald (p 238), who, in 1781, was granted a patent (described by a contemporary as of greater importance than Watt's for the steam-engine) for the production of tar by the destructive distillation of coal in tar-ovens (no. 1291). Earlier attempts had been made by Clayton in 1738. The economic and national significance of Dundonald's British Tar Company was that it could supply an alternative to wood-tar, hitherto produced from a dwindling supply of timber. Dundonald succeeded in establishing his tar-ovens at a number of places, usually where there were already ironworks; he also narrowly missed being the inventor of gas-lighting, through failing to see the possibilities, as an illuminant, of the inflammable vapours given off in the distillation of his tar. In this he was not alone, since several experimenters had observed and recorded that inflammable vapours are produced when coal is destructively distilled.

The first practical utilization of this observation came in 1785, when J. P. Minkelers (1748–1824) tried gas-lighting (ch 9) in the university of Louvain. Independently, William Murdock (1754–1839), manager of the Boulton and Watt interests in Cornwall, lit his house at Redruth with gas in 1792 (plate 12). The senior partners of the firm appreciated the possibilities of gas for lighting the mills in which they were installing their engines. Engines were capable of working long into the night without tiring, but the mills had to be lit, and by 1805 they had installed a thousand lights in one Manchester mill. For the conception of a public supply we are indebted to Frederic Albert Winsor (p 264), the holder of four patents for 'extracting inflammable air from all kinds of fuel' (nos. 2764 of 1804, 3016 of 1807, 3113 of 1808, and 3200 of 1809), who was granted a charter to found a Gas Light and Coke Company in 1812. A gas-works was erected in London almost at once, and very soon there were gas companies in the course of formation in most large cities (ch 9).

Gas-lighting advanced with great rapidity and it is said that the suppression of vice, consequent on the better lighting of the streets, was one of the minor social revolutions of the first half of the nineteenth century. This is merely incidental to our theme, but the early gas-industry did indeed have a far-reaching influence in two widely different branches of technology.

In the first place, it was the manager of a gas works, J. B. Neilson (1792–1865), who introduced the revolutionary 'hot blast' furnace into the iron-industry, as described elsewhere (p 109) in this volume. The preliminary stages of the second of the two developments took place in Glasgow. It added a new word to the English language—mackintosh—incidentally thus mis-spelled. For the preparation of the cudbear referred to on p 249 the Macintosh company required large quantities of ammonia. Before the development of the gas-industry they made it from human urine. Then in 1819 Charles Macintosh agreed to purchase all the by-product tar and ammonia from the Glasgow gas-works. He was already in a position to absorb the ammonia, and the pitch made from the tar, and it was in seeking an outlet for the low-boiling naphtha that he hit on the idea of using it as a solvent for rubber (introduced into Europe in 1736 by Ch. M. de la Condamine), and employing the resultant solution for making a waterproof fabric (B.P. no. 4804, 1822) (vol V, ch 31). After an experimental period at Glasgow, the process was developed by Charles Macintosh and Company at Manchester.

The broad pattern of the application of chemistry during the industrial revolution has now been outlined, but there are still several subsidiary developments to be recorded. For example, during the period under discussion the soap industry benefited greatly by cognate development in the chemical industry and by the advance of chemical knowledge; then towards the end of the period the availability of sulphuric acid made possible a supply of chemical fertilizer in the form of superphosphate, and also fostered the development of the match industry.

During the 1780s C. L. Berthollet and C. W. Scheele, continuing the earlier work of Tachenius, published papers on the chemistry of oils and fats; Scheele's work demonstrated that glycerine or glycerol ($C_3H_5(OH)_3$) is a by-product of the saponification reaction. In 1797 d'Arcet, Lelièvre, and Pelletier produced a report on the manufacture of soap, and the second decade of the nineteenth century saw the publication of the classical researches of M. E. Chevreul (1786–1889). These gave, for the first time, a clear understanding of the nature and reactions of the raw materials used by the soap industry and so made quantitative working possible. Thus, with adequate alkali coming forward in the form of Leblanc soda, soap-making (figure 137) expanded greatly, and in the expansion became closely connected with, and indeed dependent on, the chemical industry. The key material in its evolution was sulphuric acid.

The same is true of the initial development of the fertilizer industry. The importance of phosphates in the economy of vegetation was pointed out during the 1780s: guano was examined in 1805,[1] and bones to the value of several thousand pounds were imported by Britain during the first three decades of the nineteenth century. At first, to promote their absorption by vegetation, they were crushed or ground into a coarse meal, but about 1840 Justus von Liebig suggested that they might be rendered more soluble by treatment with sulphuric acid. This was tried by John Bennet Lawes (1814–1900) in 1840 and 1841, with

FIGURE 137—*Soap-making in the second half of the eighteenth century.*

very satisfactory results. As a result, in 1842 he took out a patent for the manufacture of 'superphosphate'. In 1843 he started to make it in a factory at Deptford, whence the manufacture spread throughout the world. Superphosphate manufacture has ever since provided one of the principal uses of sulphuric acid.

Another industry that derived impetus, both direct and indirect, from sulphuric acid was the match industry. In 1775 Carl W. Scheele first prepared phosphorus from bone-ash by treatment with sulphuric acid and subsequent reduction with charcoal. This led to the invention of a 'phosphoric taper' about 1781, and a *briquet phosphorique* by 1786. While neither safe nor satisfactory these 'instantaneous lights' nevertheless remained in use for upwards of forty years, being joined by Chancel's 'chemical matches' (depending on a mixture of potassium chlorate and sugar ignited by sulphuric acid) in 1805. Later, friction matches (prometheans, lucifers, and congreves), with heads of potassium

[1] The first large importation was in 1835.

chlorate and antimony sulphide—the first of the kind being invented by John Walker (d 1859) of Stockton-on-Tees—all involved the use of sulphuric acid, either directly or at some stage in the manufacture of the necessary raw materials. For a time yellow phosphorus was used, but after Schrötter's discovery of red phosphorus in 1847 Böttger reintroduced phosphorus-free match-heads.

Another collateral development depending on the availability of sulphuric acid, and by no means an insignificant one in the light of subsequent events, was the rise of aerostation (ballooning) in the 1780s. Following a short period of experimentation with hot-air balloons, J. A. C. Charles and the Robert *frères* released the first hydrogen balloon (unmanned) from the Champs de Mars in Paris in August 1783. On 1 December of the same year Charles and one of the Roberts ascended from the Tuileries Gardens in a gondola attached to a similar balloon. The connexion with sulphuric acid was that the acid was used to generate the hydrogen required to inflate the large envelopes which were the means of the first practical conquest of the air (vol V, ch 17).

Reference has been made earlier to the revolution wrought in the textile industry by the introduction of chlorine-bleaching. Similar changes were brought about in the manufacture of paper. In paper technology the introduction of chlorine made it possible for the paper-maker to avail himself of supplies of printed linen rags, which by chemical bleaching could be used in the production of white writing-papers, till then made exclusively from unprinted linen. A patent for bleaching, by hypochlorite solution, rags to be used in paper-making was granted to Clement and George Taylor in 1792, but four years later the patent was disputed when it came to light that J. A. Chaptal (1756–1832) and Joseph Black had demonstrated its use, and that it had been employed at Polton Mill, Midlothian, the year before that in which Taylor's patent was granted. An English patent for bleaching rags with gaseous chlorine was granted to Hector Campbell in 1792.

A second element in the halogen group, namely iodine, was discovered in 1812. A saltpetre manufacturer near Paris, B. Courtois (1777–1838), traced the corrosion of his copper vessels to an unknown substance in the kelp lye used to decompose the product of the nitre beds. He identified it as a hitherto unknown element, which was given the name iodine on account of its violet vapours (Greek, *īodēs*, violet-coloured). While the chemical properties of iodine were not such as to make it a commodity of industrial significance comparable with chlorine, its production (vol V, ch 14) is not without importance, if for no other reason than that it helped to retain kelp as a marketable commodity after the decline of its importance as a source of soda.

On reviewing the narrative here given, it will be clear that during the industrial revolution much of the expansion of the chemical industry was indeed conditioned by the prodigious growth of the textile industry. It is, however, important to recognize that it was far from being entirely so controlled. The glass industry absorbed thousands of tons of soda. Both glass and pottery created a demand for lead oxides, the former for the production of flint-glass, the latter for glazes. Red lead and white lead, much improved by Thenard (1777–1857), were manufactured for the production of paints; an oxide of lead and antimony gave Naples yellow; a copper hydrogen arsenite was sold as Scheele's green, and a similar composition as Schweinfurt green; lead in combination with chromium compounds gave the chrome yellows. Prussian blue (p 249) was being manufactured at Newcastle upon Tyne in 1770, and by the Macintosh concern at Campsie from about 1810. A synthetic ultramarine (the natural mineral lapis lazuli had been used as a pigment since ancient times) was developed by Gonelin, Guimet, and Tessaert between 1814 and 1828.

Thus did the application of chemistry bring a little colour into the drab lives of those who were being engulfed in the festering mushroom industrial towns. Not that the influence of chemistry was confined to any narrow sphere. In 1819 W. T. Brande (1788–1866) had confessed that it was difficult to select one useful art that was not immediately dependent on chemical principles for its improvement. How much more did that become true when the full impact of the chemical revolution became apparent during the ensuing decades of the nineteenth century!

BIBLIOGRAPHY

ALLEN, J. F. 'Some Founders of the Chemical Industry.' Sherratt and Hughes, London and Manchester. 1906.

ARMSTRONG, SIR WILLIAM (GEORGE), *et al.* (Eds). 'The Industrial Resources of the District of the Three Northern Rivers, Tyne, Wear, and Tees.' London. 1864.

ASHTON, T. S. 'Iron and Steel in the Industrial Revolution.' University Press, Manchester. 1924.

BANCROFT, E. 'The Philosophy of Permanent Colours' (2 vols). London. 1813.

BECKMANN, J. 'History of Inventions, Discoveries, and Origins.' London. 1797.

BERTHOLLET, C. L. 'Essay on the New Method of Bleaching' (trans. from the French by R. KERR). Dublin. [1790?].

BRITISH ASSOCIATION FOR THE ADVANCEMENT OF SCIENCE. 'Local Industries of Glasgow and the West of Scotland' (ed. by A. MCLEAN). [Glasgow Meeting of the British Association, 1901.] Glasgow. 1901.

Idem. "On the History of the Alkali Manufacture" by W. GOSSAGE, in 'Report of the 31st Meeting . . . held at Manchester in September, 1861': 'Notes and Abstracts', p. 80. London. 1862.

Idem. "On the most important Chemical Manufactures carried on in Glasgow and the Neighbourhood" by T. THOMSON, in 'Report of the 10th Meeting... held at Glasgow in August, 1840': 'Notes and Abstracts', p. 58. London. 1841.

CHAPTAL, J. A. C. 'Chimie appliqué aux arts.' Paris. 1807.

CLEGG, S. 'A Practical Treatise on the Manufacture and Distribution of Coal-gas.' London. 1841.

CLOW, A. and CLOW, NAN L. 'The Chemical Revolution: A Contribution to Social Technology.' Batchworth Press, London. 1952.

COCHRANE, A., NINTH EARL OF DUNDONALD. 'Account of the Quality and Uses of Coal Tar and Coal Varnish.' London. 1785.

DICKINSON, H. W. "Manufacture of Sulphuric Acid." *Trans. Newcomen Soc.*, **18**, 43, 1937.

GIBBS, F. W. "The History of the Manufacture of Soap." *Ann. Sci.*, **4**, 169, 1939.

HARDY, D. W. F. 'A History of the Chemical Industry in Widnes.' Imperial Chemical Industries, Liverpool. 1950.

HEAVISIDES, M. 'The True History of the Invention of the Lucifer Match, by John Walker, of Stockton-on-Tees, 1827.' Heavisides, Stockton-on-Tees. 1909.

HIGGINS, S. H. 'A History of Bleaching.' Longmans, London. 1924.

HOME, F. 'Experiments on Bleaching.' Edinburgh. 1754.

HUGHES, E. 'Studies in Administration and Finance, 1558–1828.' University Press, Manchester. 1934.

JARDINE, R. "An Account of John Roebuck, M.D., F.R.S." *Trans. roy. Soc. Edinb.*, **4**, 65, 1796.

KINGZETT, C. T. 'History of the Alkali Trade.' London. 1877.

LIEBIG, J. VON. 'Familiar Letters on Chemistry and its Relation to Commerce, Physiology and Agriculture', ed. by J. GARDNER. London. 1843.

LORD, J. 'Capital and Steam Power, 1750–1800.' King, London. 1923.

MIALL, S. 'A History of British Chemical Industry, 1634–1928.' Benn, London. 1931.

MORGAN, SIR GILBERT (THOMAS) and PRATT, D. D. 'British Chemical Industry. Its Rise and Development.' Arnold, London. 1938.

MUSPRATT, S. 'Chemistry, as Applied and Relating to the Arts and Manufactures' (2 vols). London. 1860.

NEF, J. U. 'The Rise of the British Coal Industry' (2 vols). Routledge, London. 1932.

PARKES, S. 'Chemical Essays' (4 vols). London. 1815.

PARTINGTON, J. R. 'The Alkali Industry.' Baillière, Tindall and Cox, London. 1918.

PROSSER, R. B. 'Birmingham Inventors and Inventions.' Birmingham, 1881.

SYKES, SIR ALAN (JOHN). 'Concerning the Bleaching Industry.' Bleachers' Association, Manchester. 1926.

TENNANT, E. W. D. 'One Hundred Years of the Tennant Companies.' Tennant, London. 1937.

URE, A. 'The Philosophy of Manufactures.' London. 1835.

WADSWORTH, A. P. and MANN, JULIA DE L. 'The Cotton Trade and Industrial Lancashire, 1600–1780.' University of Manchester, Economic History Series No. 7. Manchester. 1931.

WATSON, R. 'Chemical Essays' (5 vols). London. 1782–7.

9

GAS FOR LIGHT AND HEAT

SIR ARTHUR ELTON, Bt.

THE first public exhibition of gas for lighting and heating took place in Paris, in October 1801, at the Hôtel Seignelay (now 45–47 rue Saint-Dominique). The gas was generated by the destructive distillation of wood in two 'thermolamps', a name coined by their inventor, Philippe Lebon (1767–1804), an engineer attached to the *Service des Ponts et Chaussées*. One thermolamp warmed and lighted the interior of the house; the other lighted the garden with flames designed to take pleasing and fantastic shapes. A fountain in a grotto spouted flame instead of water.

The exhibition was continued at weekly intervals for some months, and was widely advertised in the Press. Lighting by gas thus came to be regarded as a practical possibility. Formerly, the generation and burning of 'inflammable airs' had seemed only a striking laboratory experiment. Lebon's great importance lies less in his inventiveness than in the fact that he demonstrated the practical application of principles already well known.

Ever since the discovery of *gas pingue* in the late sixteenth century by Van Helmont (1577–1644), natural and 'factitious' inflammable airs had attracted the attention of chemists and natural philosophers. In 1618 Jean Tardin studied a burning seepage of natural gas and concluded that it had something in common with the flames from burning oil or coal [1]. In 1667 Thomas Shirley (1638–78) sent a communication to the Royal Society, describing inflammable air issuing from coal-measures near Wigan. Johann Joachim Becher (1635–82) described coal-gas briefly in 1683 in his *Närrische Weissheit und weise Narrheit* or 'Foolish Wisdom and Wise Folly'.

Stephen Hales (1677–1761) stated in his 'Vegetable Staticks' (1727) that coal and other organic substances could be made to yield inflammable air by heating them in a closed vessel. In 1730 James Lowther led 'damp air' (fire-damp) through a pipe from the workings of one of his mines near Whitehaven to the surface, where it burned continuously (cf pl 6 A). He demonstrated samples of the gas, preserved in bladders, to the Royal Society, and showed that it would burn at the mouth of a tube. At about the same time, his agent, Carlisle Spedding (1695–1755), offered to light Whitehaven by exhalations from the pit, conducting the gas through pipes laid under the streets [2]. The offer was refused, but it is said that Spedding so lighted his office, and that the Whitehaven physician William Brownrigg (1711–1800) studied the gas chemically and physically.

The first detailed account of the production of gas by the destructive distillation of coal was by John Clayton (1657–1725), rector of Crofton near Wakefield. Though he made his observations in about 1684, it was not until 1739 that they were published in the 'Philosophical Transactions'. He says:

> I . . . got some Coal which I distilled in a Retort in an open Fire. At first there came over only *Phlegm*, afterwards a black *Oil*, and then likewise a *Spirit* arose, which I could noways condense, but it forced my Lute, or broke my Glasses. Once, when it had forced the Lute . . . I observed that the Spirit which issued out caught Fire at the Flame of the Candle, and continued burning with Violence as it issued out, in a Stream, which I blew out, and lighted again, alternately, for several times. I then had a Mind to try if I could save any of this Spirit, in order to which I took a turbinated Receiver, and putting a Candle to the Pipe of the Receiver whilst the Spirit arose, I observed that it catched Flame, and continued burning at the End of the Pipe, though you could not discern what fed the Flame: I then blew it out, and lighted it again several times; after which I fixed a Bladder, squeezed and void of Air, to the Pipe of the Receiver. The *Oil* and *Phlegm* descended into the Receiver, but the Spirit, still ascending, blew up the Bladder. . . . And when I had a Mind to divert Strangers or Friends, I have frequently taken one of these Bladders, and pricking a Hole therein with a Pin, and compressing gently the Bladder near the Flame of a Candle it [at] once took Fire, it would then continue flaming till all the Spirit was compressed out of the Bladder. . . .

The first person to take a firm step towards using coal-gas for illuminating a room seems to have been George Dixon, owner of a colliery near Newcastle upon Tyne. About 1760, using a kettle as a retort, he experimented with gas conducted through runs of tobacco-pipe to burners formed by piercing holes in the clay luting. He also attempted to estimate the amount of tar in a ton of coal by carbonizing it in a boiler. There was an explosion, and he decided that coal-gas was too dangerous for common use [3]. The 'Chemical Essays' (1781) of Richard Watson (1737–1816), bishop of Llandaff, contain an account of experiments made to determine the relative qualities of different varieties of coal and wood by distilling them in closed vessels. He bubbled the gas so obtained through water, and recommended converting the normal type of coke-oven into 'distilling vessels'.

Meanwhile others were studying the properties of hydrogen, which Henry Cavendish had discovered in 1766, and which was usually generated by the application of dilute sulphuric acid to chips of iron or zinc. In 1777 François Chaussier (1746–1828) stated that it could be made to burn brightly when squeezed from a bladder through a narrow pipe and ignited by an electric spark.

In 1780 F. L. Ehrmann suggested lamps using hydrogen as an illuminant, a method exploited as a novelty by James Diller, whose 'Philosophical Fireworks' were demonstrated in Paris before the *Académie Royale des Sciences* in 1787 [4], and subsequently in many parts of Europe.

In spite of Watson's suggestion, the coking industry had little influence on the development of gas-lighting, for early coking-ovens were not well adapted for the collection of gas. Nevertheless, in 1770 coke-ovens for carbonizing coal in closed retorts were erected at Sulzbach by the Prince of Nassau. They were described in detail by de Gensanne. The tar drained into a metal pot, and the gas is shown escaping to waste through a vertical pipe (figure 138). There is no indication that it was burned, though about twelve years later Archibald Cochrane, ninth Earl of Dundonald, ignited gas flames at his tar-ovens at Culross (p 252). He is said to have amused his friends by collecting the gas in a vessel 'resembling a large tea-urn', and igniting it at a nozzle [5].

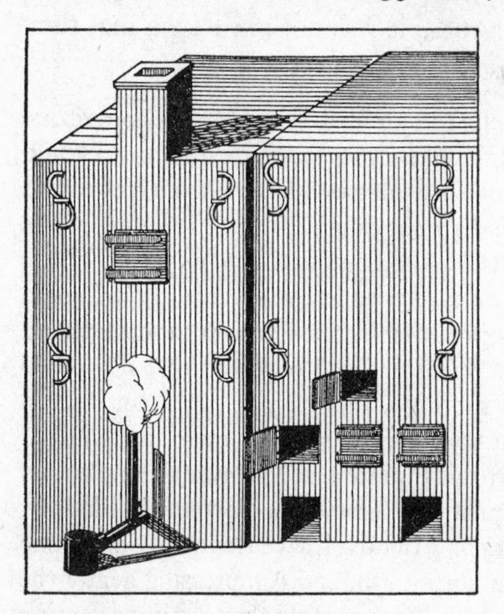

FIGURE 138—*Burning off gas from de Gensanne's coke oven at Sulzbach.*

Perhaps the first practical use suggested for coal-gas was for the inflation of balloons. This led to some early inconclusive experiments in gas-lighting. Charles Green, in 1821, appears to have been the first person to apply coal-gas on any scale to ballooning, but Faujas de Saint-Fond had suggested its use as early as 1783, though without conviction. He proposed to rid the gas of carbon dioxide by passing it through water to which lime had been added [6]. In the same year Lapostolle, an Amiens apothecary, noted that coal-gas prepared for balloons burned with a beautiful flame [7]. In 1784, Jean Pierre Minkelers (1748–1824), professor of natural philosophy at Louvain, published his *Mémoire sur l'air inflammable* on the preparation of gas for ballooning from coal and other organic solids. Many years after his death, it was stated that, at the same time, he lighted his class-room with gas, a practice he repeated for a number of years in succession. In consequence, he has sometimes been called the inventor of gas-lighting.

At about this time, a number of others began to make rudimentary experiments in gas-lighting. None appears to have presented his work to the public at the time it was carried out. Johann Georg Pickel (1751–1838), professor of pharmacology at Würzburg, lighted his laboratory with gas in 1786 [8]; John Champion, a Bristol copper-smelter, in 1790 contemplated taking out a patent for using gas in lighthouses [9]; J. B. Lanoix, of Lyons, experimented at some time before 1792 [10]; Christian Polykarp Friedrich Erxleben (1765–1831), apothecary of Landskron, lighted his laboratory in about 1795 [11]; Wilhelm August Lampadius (1772–1842) started experiments in 1796, and demonstrated gas-lighting in the castle of the Elector of Saxony in Dresden in 1799 [12].

However, the work of only two of the early experimenters with gas-lighting, Philippe Lebon and William Murdock (1754–1839), culminated in its commercial application. The former may have started investigating gas from wood as early as 1791; the latter began to study the illuminating properties of gas from coal in 1792.

Lebon was born and brought up among the charcoal-burners of Brachay, near Joinville, and doubtless this is why he developed an interest in combustion. In a thesis written at the age of twenty-four he stated that smoke consisted of particles suspended in a colourless inflammable gas, which he proposed to pass through water or to condense in a series of water-cooled pipes. In 1797 he subjected wood to destructive distillation in an iron retort and cooled the gas produced in a vat. He thought that it could be applied to lighting, heating, and the inflation of balloons.

In an effort to persuade the French government to apply gas to public buildings, Lebon moved to Paris in 1798, and conducted experiments on a bigger scale in a house on the Île-Saint-Louis. He took out a patent on 28 September 1799, *pour des nouveaux moyens d'employer les combustibles plus utilement, soit pour la chaleur, soit pour la lumière, et d'en recueiller les divers produits*, with an extension dated 1801. The French government, preoccupied with the war with England, was not interested. It was for this reason that Lebon decided to stage at the Hôtel Seignelay the more public demonstration which has already been described.

Lebon's patent contains a sketch (figure 139) of his gas-making plant. The sheet iron retort (AA) is encircled several times by the flue (FF) from the furnace (EE). The whole is set in fire-brick. The gas, conducted from the retort through G, is to be passed through water, and the by-products—oil, bitumen, and pyroligneous (acetic) acid—are to be collected. In spite of Faujas de Saint-Fond's proposal to use lime to remove carbon dioxide, it is unlikely that Lebon hit on the same idea to remove sulphureous impurities.

Lebon states that his gas was ready to extend everywhere the most sensible heat and the softest lights and could be conducted through the smallest and most fragile pipes. The latter could be embedded in the plaster of walls and ceilings. Provided that the nozzles were of metal, the pipes themselves could be made of varnished silk (*taffetas gommé*). He proposed to burn the gas in a glass globe into which three tubes were introduced; one conveying gas, one air, and the third carrying the waste products of combustion to the open air.

Lebon's contribution to the theory and practice of gas-lighting was great, not only because he was the first man publicly to demonstrate its possibilities, but because his imaginative grasp of its potentialities guided and inspired the men who came after him. In his few writings, Lebon anticipated nearly all the applications of gas in the hundred years succeeding his death.

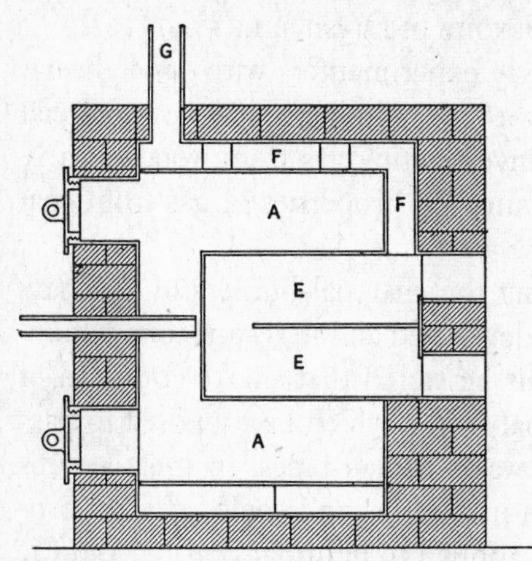

FIGURE 139—*Lebon's first gas-making plant.* (AA) *Sheet iron retort,* (EE) *furnace,* (FF) *flue,* (G) *pipe leading from retort. From his patent specification, 1799.*

William Murdock was trained as a mechanic by his father, a miller of Auchinleck, in Ayrshire. In 1777, at the age of twenty-three, he was engaged by the great engineering firm of Boulton and Watt. By 1790 he had become the firm's principal engine-erector in Cornwall. His interest in coal-gas was stimulated by a patent he took out in 1791 for 'treating certain Ores to obtain Green Vitriol, Pigments, and Compositions for preserving Ships' Bottoms'. This led him to study the destructive distillation of wood, peat, coal, and other substances. In 1792 he generated gas from coal and lighted a room in a house in Cross Street, Redruth. He began to make tests of its cost as an illuminant as compared with oil and tallow. In a paper communicated to the Royal Society by Sir Joseph Banks in 1808, he wrote:

> My apparatus consisted of an iron retort, with tinned copper and iron tubes through which the gas was conducted to a considerable distance; and there, as well as at intermediate points, was burned through apertures of varied forms and dimensions. The experiments were made upon coal of different qualities. . . . The gas was also washed with water, and other means were employed to purify it.

One burner had a number of small holes like the rose of a watering-can; in another, the gas burned in a long thin sheet. There was also a gas-burning Argand, the name at that time given to the normal type of oil lamp with a wick and glass chimney, invented by Pierre Ami Argand (1750–1803) and introduced into England in 1783. Boulton and Watt took it up in 1784. In a gas-burning Argand, air was introduced at the centre of an annular burner surrounded by a glass cylinder. In addition, Murdock collected the gas in vessels and bags of tinned iron and leather or varnished silk in an endeavour to make a portable light.

In 1798 Murdock moved to Birmingham to work in Boulton and Watt's celebrated Soho Foundry. There he continued his experiments on a larger scale,

FIGURE 140—*Two forms of Daisenberger's 'thermolamp' built to the design of Johannes B. Wenzler in 1802.* (A) *Furnace,* (B) *retort,* (C) *condenser,* (F) *pipe to relieve excess pressure,* (G) *receptacle for heavy fractions.*

using for retorts upright cast iron pots 30 inches deep and 12 inches in diameter with closely fitting lids luted with clay. A charge was 15 lb and the retorts were brought to a red heat. Though the principal building was lighted by gas 'during many successive nights', the evidence suggests that these experiments had been stopped by 1801 because of the firm's lack of interest.

Murdock's particular and important contribution to gas-lighting was that from the beginning, following Watson, he investigated systematically the comparative behaviour of different classes of coal under conditions of varying temperature and time of carbonizing.

Though no contemporary picture of Lebon's thermolamp is known, it probably resembled one built by J. M. Daisenberger in 1802 to the design of Johannes B. Wenzler, treasurer to the court of Passau [13] (figure 140). Decorated to take its place in the living-room, Daisenberger's thermolamp is in three parts. The furnace is in the lowest part. Above is a rectangular sheet iron retort, from which the heavier fractions drain away. Above the retort is a circular vessel containing a worm immersed in cooling water. The gas rises into a varnished silk pipe and is conducted to a lighting jet above a writing desk.

Zachaus Andreas Winzler (1750–*c* 1830), a Moravian chemical manufacturer living in Austria, who also derived his ideas from Lebon, gave a number of dinner-parties in December 1802, at which the food was cooked on a gas stove and the dining-room was heated by gas [14]. In 1803 he published a detailed account of his methods [15]. His retorts were based on the conventional laboratory equipment of the day, but above the one illustrated (figure 141) there are spaces for heating cooking-utensils. The gas was bubbled through water (lime was not added) and could be passed to a cooker with four burners and a small oven behind, or to a holder in the form of a bellows with a small weight on top. From the holder the gas could be led to a room, where it was used both to warm a radiator and in Argand lamps.

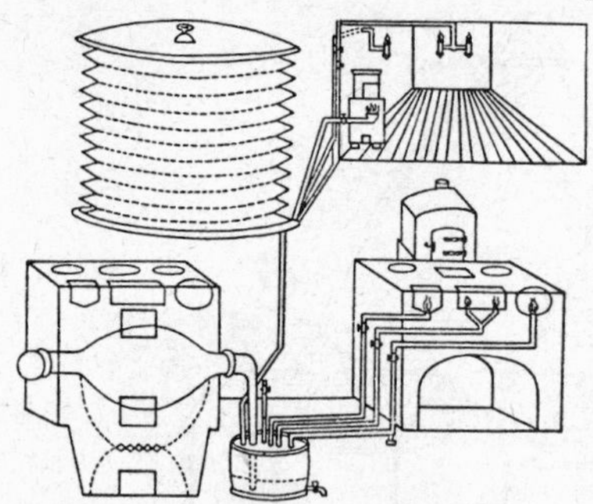

FIGURE 141—*Gas appliance of Z. A. Winzler. It is similar to the laboratory apparatus of the time and is adapted for cooking.*

Among the many people attracted to Lebon's demonstrations at the Hôtel Seignelay was an eccentric German 'professor of commerce', Friedrich Albrecht Winzer (1763–1830), who subsequently anglicized his name to Frederic Albert Winsor. Though he was in no sense a man of science and was without mechanical aptitude, he became infatuated with the idea of lighting houses and cities by gas. He failed to buy a thermolamp from Lebon, but after a great struggle succeeded in making one for himself. After attempting to peddle the idea of gas-lighting in various countries in Europe, he came to England at about the end of 1803: 'the thought of introducing the discovery, for the great advantage of the British realm struck me . . . like an electric spark'.

Another important visitor to the Hôtel Seignelay was Gregory Watt, James Watt's second son, who had managed to get to Paris even though Britain and France were still technically at war. He sent a report on Lebon's work to his brother James, stating that there was no time to lose if their firm was to gain any advantage from Murdock's experiments.

Lebon failed to persuade anyone to take up his proposals. On the evening of 30 November 1804 he was robbed and stabbed to death in the Champs Elysées. In spite of his vision, his murder at the age of thirty-seven had the effect of extinguishing for many years almost all interest in gas-lighting on the continent of Europe. Only in England was the situation favourable for its development. There were a number of reasons for this. The American and Napoleonic wars had interfered with the supply of whale-oil and Russian tallow, and the cost of lamp-oil and candles had risen steeply at the end of the eighteenth century. Further, cotton mills were peculiarly prone to fire, and insurance premiums were correspondingly heavy. In consequence, mill-owners were interested in any new source of light that was economical and safe. The incentive to overcome the difficulties in the way of generating, purifying, storing, and distributing gas was therefore great. In these circumstances the position of William Murdock was particularly favourable, for of the early experimenters with gas-lighting, he alone

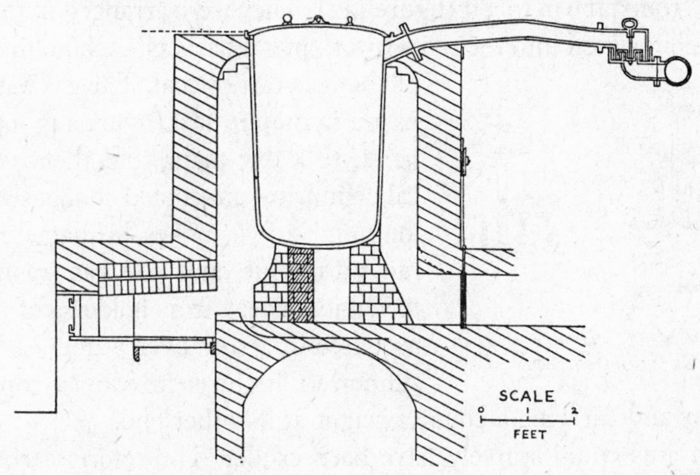

FIGURE 142—*Section of Murdock's first retort for Phillips and Lee, 1805–6. See also figure 143.*

was able to command the help of experienced mechanics and workmen. Without the Soho Foundry he would have been much handicapped.

As a result of the letter from Gregory Watt describing Lebon's demonstration, Murdock resumed his experiments late in 1801. When the Soho Foundry was illuminated to celebrate the Peace of Amiens, signed on 27 March 1802, the decorations included prominently two gas-flares, one at each end of the main building, supplied by pipes up a chimney from a small retort resting in an ordinary fireplace [16]. Statements that the whole front of the building was illuminated by gas are untrue.

From this time, encouraged by William Henry (1774–1836), the celebrated Manchester chemist, Murdock pursued gas-lighting experiments energetically, working with a variety of vertical, sloping, and horizontal cast iron retorts. Though trials were made to determine the best grades of coal to use, the relative efficiency of Argand and ordinary gas-burners, and the relative cost of illumination by gas and candles, little attempt seems to have been made to study the gas itself or methods of purifying it. By 1804 Boulton and Watt felt sufficient confidence in Murdock's apparatus to canvass for orders. Their first client was George Lee of the firm of Phillips and Lee, owners of one of the largest cotton-mills in the kingdom, at Salford, near Manchester.

The first test of the apparatus for Phillips and Lee took place with fifty lamps on the evening of 1 January 1806. Murdock reported a gratifying absence of 'Soho stink'. The first stage of the installation (plate 13 A) was completed in March. There were six retorts in the form of cast iron pots, 5 ft 6 in deep, and tapering in diameter from 3 ft 6 in to 3 ft (figure 142). They were arranged in threes under a crane which lowered into them openwork metal baskets, each holding a charge of about 15 cwt of coal. The gas was led away, past a hydraulic seal (figure 143) operated by hand, to a dry main, and thence to a vertical cylindrical air-cooled condenser about 6 ft long and 2 ft 6 inches in diameter. The tar ran into a pit, and the gas was conducted to cubical sheet iron holders, of 10-ft side, mounted in a row over water, each clumsily supported at the centre by a rope running over a pulley and carrying a counterweight at its other end.

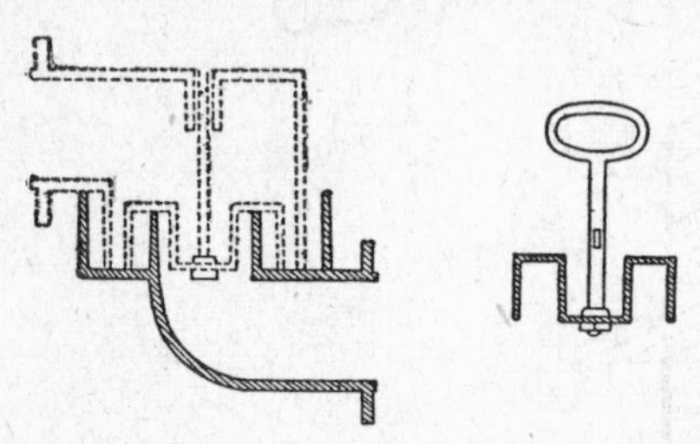

FIGURE 143—*Detail of hydraulic seal on Murdock's first installation.*

The apparatus could scarcely have been cruder. The retorts carbonized the coal badly and became encrusted with spent coke. Judging by the only available drawing, the gas was neither washed nor purified. Murdock's satisfaction at the absence of smell must have been short-lived. But, in spite of all its deficiencies, lighting-costs were much reduced and the plant was extended until, by 1807, it served the whole factory, a short stretch of private road, and Lee's residence. There were 271 Argands and 633 Cockspurs—burners consisting of three small holes in the closed end of a pipe. Single-hole burners were called Ratstails, and those with more than three holes Cockscombs.

Drawings in the Boulton and Watt collection in the Birmingham reference library show that, by 1808, Murdock had evolved what was to be, with minor variations, standard practice until the firm gave up making gas-plant a few years later. He used cast iron horizontal retorts (figure 144), 4 ft long, single-ended and elliptical in section, roughly 2 ft by 1 ft. In 1810 he also experimented with ear-shaped and other sections, but does not appear to have applied them in practice. The retorts were capped by a mouthpiece with a rectangular opening set at an angle of 45° and closed by a hinged flap. The heat from the furnace was applied to the retort through flues, and not directly as in his first designs. The crude gas rose from the front of the retort and passed to a dry main through a hydraulic seal. In some designs, the gas was led down to the seal from the front of the retort. There was no hydraulic main.

The gas was led to a vertical cylindrical condenser—sometimes air-cooled, sometimes water-cooled by the holder-water—where it met a jet of water introduced at the bottom, a design obviously based on the condenser of a steam-engine. Gas, water, and tar passed from the bottom of the condenser to a chamber whence the gas was conducted to the holder and the water and tar trickled away to a tar-pit or, in at least one case, into a canal. There was no chemical

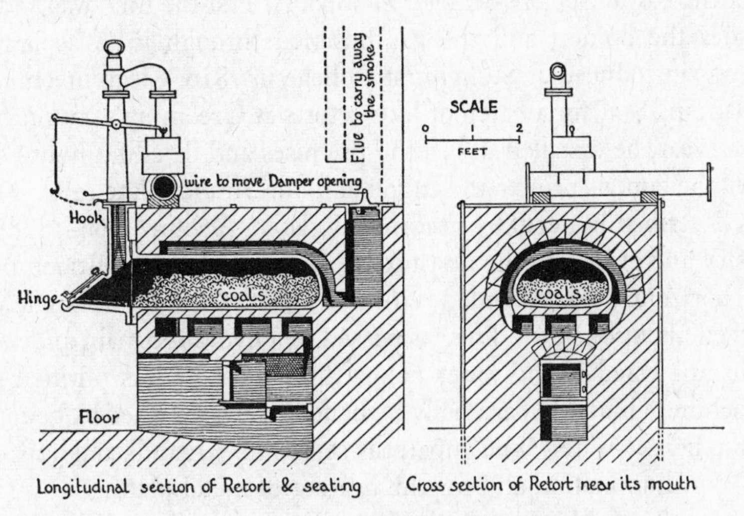

FIGURE 144—*Murdock's horizontal retort, 1808.*

purification by lime. The gas was introduced into or led away from the holder from below by vertical stand-pipes, or frequently directly through the side by pipes with unwieldy hydraulic valves at each end to allow the holder to rise and fall. The holders were rectangular, usually about 10 by 10 by 20 ft.

Though it has been said that Boulton and Watt gave up making gas-apparatus about 1814 out of pique occasioned by the success of their rivals, it seems as likely that their clients deserted them in favour of better equipment made by others. Their initial success may have been due not so much to the basic soundness of their ideas as to their prestige, their foundry and workshops, their command of capital, their salesmanship and, above all, to the well deserved reputation of William Murdock as one of the greatest mechanical engineers of his day.

At all events, Murdock was outdistanced by the first man to approach gas-lighting with something of the outlook of a chemical engineer. Samuel Clegg the elder (1781–1861), who had been educated under Dalton, soon became

Murdock's successful rival. Apprenticed to Boulton and Watt, Clegg worked on the illuminations for the Peace of Amiens, though he stated later that Murdock had refused to reveal his methods to him. He left the firm in 1805. After putting gas installations into a number of small factories, he was given an order to fit up Henry Lodge's cotton mill near Halifax, and claimed that on this contract he was a fortnight ahead of Murdock at Phillips and Lee. He was probably the first person to purify the gas by passing it through water to which lime had been added, an idea which gained him a medal from the Society for the Encouragement of Arts (later the Royal Society of Arts) in 1808. At first the lime was added to the water under the holder, and the gas bubbled through it. A separate liming machine was introduced at Stonyhurst College in 1810. Clegg invented the hydraulic main in 1811, for a batch of four retorts at Greenway's cotton mills [17]. In the next year, he installed gas in the premises and dwelling-house of Rudolf Ackerman, the famous printer and engraver in the Strand (plate 12 A). The equipment was described in detail by Fredrick Christian Accum (1769–1838), lecturer in chemistry and author of the first textbooks on gas-lighting. It comprised two cast iron, horizontal, single-ended retorts of circular section. A single charge of coal weighed about one cwt. The gas passed to a hydraulic main and was cooled in a worm immersed in the water below the holder. It was purified in a wet-liming machine, agitated occasionally by hand, and was washed by being bubbled through the holder-water. The apparatus served 48 Argands and 32 Cockspurs, used both for illumination and for the heating of metal plates.

Independently of Murdock and Clegg, Frederic Albert Winsor started to demonstrate gas-lighting in London in the autumn of 1804. From the first he realized that the Boulton and Watt idea of installing gas mill by mill and house by house was unsound. He saw that consumers would have to be supplied through mains radiating from central gas-generating stations. He realized, too, that the amount of capital required for such a purpose would be beyond the resources of any single individual or group of capitalists. It would be essential to obtain a charter from Parliament to form a joint stock company with limited liability.

In 1806 Winsor was sufficiently encouraged by the results of his demonstrations to canvass the formation of The National Light and Heat Company 'for providing our streets and houses with light and heat . . . as they are now supplied with water'. Though he promised, in extravagant language, preposterous profits to subscribers, he also had what Boulton and Watt lacked—vision and a grasp of the social and economic implications of gas-lighting.

He obtained permission to display his lights along the top of the wall separating the garden of Carlton House from the Mall on 4 June 1807, the birthday of George III. In December he lighted part of the south side of Pall Mall, opposite Carlton House. For the first time the public realized that there was something more behind Winsor's frenzies than megalomania. His committee of business men, bankers, and peers, headed by the Duke of Athol and Lord Anson, rashly announcing that anyone subscribing but £5 would receive an income of £5700 a year, decided to apply to Parliament for a charter.

To the ordinary trader, risking his private capital in manufactory and shop, such companies seemed an invasion of private enterprise, to be resisted at all costs. Boulton and Watt and many other interested parties used every trick to block the charter, but the case for a central supply of gas was too strong. The National Light and Heat Company, renamed The Gas Light and Coke Company, gained its charter early in 1812.

At the start, the chartered company was handicapped by the erratic conduct of its business by Winsor, who was neither administrator nor engineer, and whom the board ruthlessly drove out in a few months. Another failure seems to have been Accum, who had been engaged as a technical witness in the fight for the charter, and was given a position of importance as soon as the company was formed. He resigned in 1817.

The situation was saved by Samuel Clegg, who joined the company late in 1812, just in time to wrestle with the formidable problems created by the great and growing demand for gas-lighting. On 1 April 1814 the oil lamps in the parish of St Margaret's, Westminster, were discontinued in favour of gas, and crowds of curious people followed the lamp-lighters on their rounds. By May 1815 there were nearly fifteen miles of gas-main in London. By December, there were twenty-six miles. Even before this time, insurance premiums had been marked down for mills and public buildings illuminated by gas.

In Clegg's first installation for The Gas Light and Coke Company (plate 12B), the retorts were of cast iron, circular in section, and tapering from a diameter of 12 in at the front to 10 in at the back. They were single-ended and about 10 ft long. They carbonized the coal badly and were soon given up in favour of retorts of elliptical section, with one side flattened, charged and discharged by scoops and long-handled shovels and rakes, a method that remained in use for decades.

Clegg perpetuated the inconvenient method of cooling the gas in a worm immersed in the water of the holder. It was purified in a wet-liming machine, and washed in a compartment supported on a wooden framework under the holder, but now fed with an independent supply of water.

Though the liming-machine went some way towards ridding the gas of sulphureous impurities, it produced a foul-smelling, poisonous, and useless liquid known as 'blue billy'. Some companies poured it into the sewers, polluting the rivers and killing the fish. The Gas Light and Coke Company concentrated it by evaporation under the retorts, and removed the resulting stinking mess through the streets at night.

Clegg left the company in 1817 owing to a dispute about pay. He and Accum installed gas at the Royal Mint in the same year, and the plant was notable for including a semi-continuous carbonizing system, a semi-solid liming machine, a self-acting wet meter, and a gas governor.

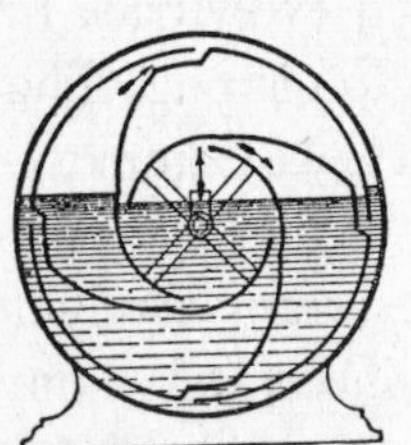

FIGURE 145—*Malam's wet meter. This consists of a paddle-wheel, with one inner and four outer chambers, revolving in a case. The gas enters the inner chambers and, in escaping through one outlet pipe in the outer case, forces the wheel to rotate.*

The carbonizing system comprised segmental trays, each charged with coal, and supported between the spokes of a horizontal wheel, rotated by hand, which carried them into the furnace. Though ingenious and in advance of its time, this apparatus was a failure owing to excessive wear in use. Clegg's wet meter took the form of a revolving cylinder divided at first into two, and later into three, compartments, alternately filled with gas and emptied as the cylinder revolved. Its complicated and mechanically unsound valve-mechanism caused it to fail, though its principle is still that used to measure the output from a works. It was greatly improved in 1819 by John Malam, Clegg's son-in-law, who was also employed by The Gas Light and Coke Company [18] (figure 145). The governor was virtually a miniature holder rising and falling with changes in pressure and actuating a valve according to its position.

Clegg's successor at The Gas Light and Coke Company, T. S. Peckston, wrote the first modern textbook on gas. He established principles that were to govern its manufacture for at least another seventy-five years. He mounted the retorts in benches of three, four, and five, though satisfactory designs to ensure even heating took years to evolve. In spite of their defects, he used cast iron retorts. Fireclay retorts, with cast iron mouths, did not become universal in Britain until the middle of the century. Presently, two banks of retorts were set back to back. By 1850, 'through' settings—that is, retorts open at each end and about 18 ft long—were coming into use at the larger works. At first they were charged and discharged through both ends by hand (plates 13 B and 14 A). Automatic and semi-automatic charging and discharging by machine were later introductions.

Reuben Phillips patented the dry-liming process in 1817. In 1823 John Malam patented the method of passing the gas through layers of quicklime, first in one direction, then in the other. This may have resulted in the marked improvement of gas said to have occurred at about this time. Lime was not given up in favour of oxide of iron till the end of the nineteenth century. Though oxide of iron stripped the sulphur from the free hydrogen sulphide, it left untouched certain other sulphur compounds, present in small quantities. Its use depended on the introduction of incandescent lighting, which led to a great reduction in the proportion of gas burned without flues.

At first, retorts were subject to back-pressure, and at high temperatures the gas was 'cracked', leaving a deposit of carbon that had to be chipped away by hand: a difficulty not overcome, by the introduction of exhausting-pumps, until the late thirties. Without these, it was impossible to lower the pressure on the retorts, and the gas could not even be passed through efficient washers and scrubbers. Before their introduction, large quantities of ammonia reached the mains, corroding copper and brass pipes and fittings, depositing a dangerous explosive compound, and giving the gas a nauseating smell.

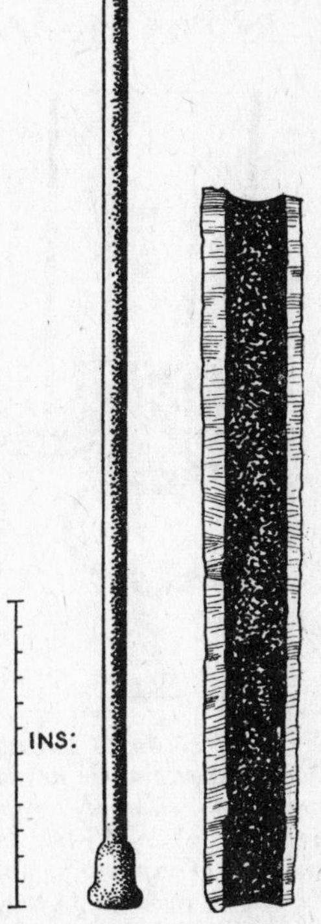

FIGURE 146—*A length of ¾-in iron pipe laid in 1836 by the Cupar Gas Company.* (Left) *External view*; (right) *section* (*magnified*).

Though wooden mains of tamarack (American larch) logs were in extensive use in the United States as late as 1878 [19], the London mains were of cast iron, first introduced for water in 1810. Their supply was less of a problem than that of the small-diameter service-pipe, which was known as 'barrel'. This term is still used by gas-fitters because the pipe was made in the same way as cheap gun-barrels, from 4-ft lengths of strip iron, bent over a mandrel and welded down the joint. For cheapness, old or rejected gun-barrels, in ample supply after the war with France, were often pressed into use. The problem of making barrel in quantity was not solved till Cornelius Whitehouse's patent of 1825 for making drawn wrought iron pipe, a process perfected in the following ten years. An early pipe for gas is shown in figure 146.

Meters were not supplied to consumers for many years, and dry meters did not become common till the fifties. Gas was often charged for not by volume, but by the number of burners in use for a given time—an arrangement leading to the theft of much gas. Some people simply lighted the gas at the open end of a pipe and let it rip; many fried-fish shops liked to have flares 10 in long. After a short time, the batswing and fishtail burners became standard. The former consisted of a long narrow slit, the latter of two jets of gas impinging upon one another, a system invented by J. B. Neilson about 1820. The greatly superior Argand never became popular. It was susceptible to changes in gas-pressure and was inclined to smoke when badly adjusted; it was expensive; and its glass chimney made it difficult to maintain (figure 147).

By 1823 three rival chartered companies were operating in London north of the Thames. Each invaded the territory of the other, and their mains writhed round each other like worms. The whale-oil interests, which had at first joined forces with those who wished to suppress gas altogether as dangerous, poisonous, or a defiance of Almighty God, later entered directly into competition with coal-gas. Animal fats and oils were cracked in heated cast iron retorts. The cast iron acted as a catalyst in the reactions, but soon became covered with carbon and so ceased to be effective. This was a fatal disadvantage, and all the oil-gas companies had failed by about 1830.

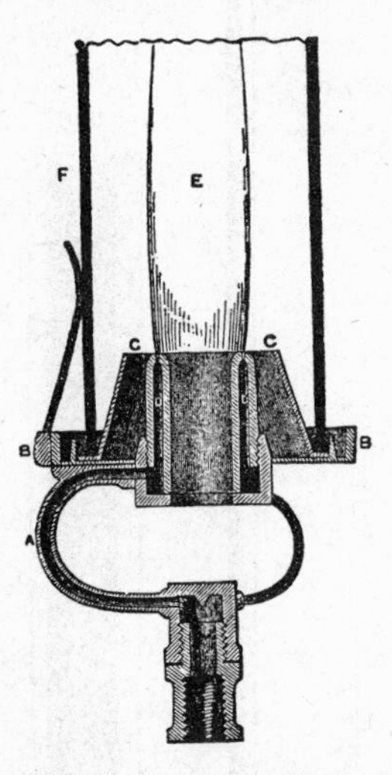

FIGURE 147—*Sugg's Argand burner, adopted as the British government standard burner in 1869.* (A) *Supply-tube to chamber of combustion;* (B) *support for chimney;* (C) *cone, outer air-supply;* (D) *steatite chamber of combustion;* (E) *flame;* (F) *chimney.*

Gas was adopted almost immediately by factories, public buildings, and shops. By 1825, churches, banks, 'The Times' printing-office, the Mechanics' Institution, East India House, Drury Lane theatre, and half a dozen London clubs were illuminated by gas. But a combination of imperfect purification, bungling fitting, leaky joints, and blackened ceilings made its use in a small room insufferable. John Martin, the allegorical painter, showed Satan presiding over the infernal council in a Hell illuminated by coronas of flaring gas-jets. Not even Accum's delightful Regency fittings, or the water-slide which William Caslon designed in 1818—a gas-bracket made of sliding tubes and a water-seal that could be raised or lowered—could dispel public prejudice. Though the Mansion House had 2062 gas lights in 1825, there was none in the Lord Mayor's parlour. As late as 1833, the 'Mechanics' Magazine' suggested that the proper way to use gas for domestic illumination was to reflect inwards light from a burner placed outside the window. In 1841 Samuel Clegg junior warned against 'sickness and oppressive headache' from gas-lights in an apartment not well ventilated, and Michael Faraday was called in by the Athenaeum in 1843 to mitigate the 'stupefying effects of gas' and to prevent the bindings of books from being spoiled. Gas was wholly excluded from the Crystal Palace in 1851 (it closed at sundown), and the industry had to have an exhibition of its own at the Polytechnic Institution [20]. It was for years common practice to fit a little ventilating pipe, called a perdifume, over each light.

FIGURE 148—*Sharp's gas-cooking apparatus, c 1851. It occupied a floor space 4 ft 6 in square and on top of the oven was a boiler to heat kettles and pans. It could cook dinner for 100 persons.*

Gas could not be applied efficiently till the atmospheric burner in which a supply of air was introduced into the gas stream just below the point of combustion was devised, surprisingly late, about 1840 [21]. The handy version to which R. W. Bunsen (1811–99) gave his name was designed by him for his new laboratory at Heidelberg in 1855. The gas-ring was introduced in 1867. Benjamin Waddy Maughan patented the geyser in 1865; he failed to protect the name and it came to be used by all manufacturers. Though John Maiben had suggested a gas fire in 1813, made by playing gas-flames on 'fancy figures' of cast metal, the gas fire with radiants of the type familiar today was not introduced until 1880. It did not become popular for another twenty years. Gas cooking was not common before the seventies, though the still familiar cast iron box with a hot plate over it was introduced about 1850 (figure 148). From 1880 the cooker changed hardly at all in fundamentals until thermostatic control became common about 1930.

The social and economic effects of gas can scarcely be exaggerated. Scoffing at those who claimed that sunlight was necessary for growth, Andrew Ure pronounced that children suffered no harm working twelve hours a day in mills lighted by gas. If gas must bear some of the responsibility for the intolerably long hours of labour in the early nineteenth century, it also gave the workman and his family a new life. For gas encouraged evening classes in the Mechanics' Institutes, and aided the new literacy and education. That people could congregate after their working hours in well lit halls encouraged the processes of popular government. The social, industrial, and communal life of the nineteenth century could not have developed as it did without gas-light.

So great was the impetus created by the rapid success of the early companies, that England became responsible for many of the installations on the continent of Europe and in America. An enormous export trade developed in gas-making appliances and pipes. From 1828 until the eighties the gas industry in Britain passed through a period of easy and complacent prosperity. A Board of Trade report in 1869 complained that the diversity of illuminating power from various burners and in various cities was incredible, and the waste of gas a disgrace.

Then, suddenly, gas undertakings were shaken out of their torpor, for between 1879 and 1884 the electric arc-light and the incandescent electric filament-lamp attained commercial success. Gas shares slumped, and the industry would have been in bad straits but for the Austrian inventor, Carl Auer von Welsbach (1858–1929), who patented the incandescent gas-mantle in 1885. An answer to the threat of electricity had been found, and gas was able to hold its own as a lighting-agent while the industry developed the techniques necessary for its prime function in the twentieth century—the flexible and convenient supply of heat-energy for domestic and industrial use, and of raw materials for the production of chemicals.

ACKNOWLEDGEMENTS

For much information or assistance the author is indebted to Dr M. Bouvet, President of the Society of the History of Pharmacology; Dr F. Klemm, of the Deutsches Museum; the Curator of the Boulton and Watt Collection at the Birmingham Reference Library; and the Assay Master of the Birmingham Assay Office. For information concerning Lebon he has drawn on papers quoted extensively by Amédée Fayol in *Philippe Lebon* and by Charles Gaudry in *L'Industrie du gaz en France, 1824–1924*.

REFERENCES

[1] TARDIN, J. 'Histoire naturelle de la fontaine qui brusle près de Grenoble.' Tournon. 1618.
[2] JARS, G. 'Voyages métallurgiques', Vol. 1, p. 248. Lyons. 1774.
[3] MACFARLAN, J. *Trans. Newcomen Soc.*, **5**, 53–55, 1924–5.
[4] *Obsns phys.*, **31**, 188–95, 1787.
[5] HART, J. *Mechanics' Mag.*, **40**, 410, 1844.
[6] FAUJAS DE SAINT-FOND, B. 'Description des expériences de la machine aerostatique de MM. de Montgolfier', p. 166. Paris. 1783.
[7] *J. Paris*, 24 Jan., 1784.
[8] "Über Thermolampen." *Verkündiger*, **6**, no. 35, 274, 1802.
FRIEDE, H. *Apothekerztg, Berl.*, **42**, no. 25, 369–70, 1927.
[9] Letter from John Champion to Matthew Boulton, 15 June 1790. Assay Office Collection, Birmingham.
[10] "Les premiers essais du gaz d'éclairage." *Chron. méd.*, **31**, 206*n*, 1924.
[11] FISCHER, W. "Geschichtliche Blätter aus der Apothekerfamilie Erxleben in Landskron in Deutschnöhmen" in 'Apotheker-Bilder von Nah und Fern', Pt 5, p 21. Vienna. 1912.
[12] LAMPADIUS, W. A. *J. Chem. Phys.*, **8**, 38, 1813.
[13] DAISENBERGER, J. M. 'Beschreibung der daisenbergerschen Thermolampe.' Stadtamhof. 1802.
[14] Letters from J. Du Mont de Florgy to Sir Joseph Banks. Woodcroft Collection, Patent Office Library, London.
[15] WINZLER, Z. A. 'Die Thermolampe in Deutschland.' Brünn. 1803.
[16] "Materials for a Memorium of Mr. Samuel Clegg." *Mechanics' Mag.*, **22**, 470, 1835.
[17] CLEGG, S., Sr. 'Description of an Apparatus by which Twenty-five Cubic Feet of Gas are Obtained from each Cauldron of Coal', p. 8. London. 1820.
[18] PECKSTON, T. S. 'The Theory and Practice of Gas-Lighting', pp. 322–36. London. 1819.
[19] KING, W. B. 'Treatise on the Science and Practice of the Manufacture and Distribution of Coal Gas', Vol. 2, p. 334. London. 1879.
[20] "Gas Apparatus and the Exhibition." *Expositor*, **1**, 275, 1851.
[21] ROBISON, SIR JOHN. *Edinb. new phil. J.*, second series, **28**, 291, 1840.

BIBLIOGRAPHY

ACCUM, F. C. 'A Practical Treatise on Gas-Light.' London. 1815.

Idem. 'Description of the Process of Manufacturing Coal Gas.' London. 1819.

BLOCHMANN, G. M. S. 'Beiträge zur Geschichte der Gasbeleuchtung.' Dresden. 1871.

CHANDLER, D. and LACEY, A. D. 'The Rise of the Gas Industry in Britain.' British Gas Council, London. 1949.

CLEGG, S., Jr. 'A Practical Treatise on the Manufacture and Distribution of Coal-Gas.' London. 1841.

CREIGHTON, H. "Gas-Lights." Article in Supplement to 4th, 5th, and 6th editions of 'Encyclopaedia Britannica'. Edinburgh. 1824.

KING, W. B. 'Treatise on the Science and Practice of the Manufacture and Distribution of Coal Gas' (3 vols). London. 1878–82.

MATTHEWS, W. 'An Historical Sketch of the Origin, Progress, and Present State of Gas-Lighting.' London. 1827.

PECKSTON, T. S. 'The Theory and Practice of Gas-Lighting.' London. 1819.

PECLET, E. 'Traité de l'éclairage.' Paris. 1827.

'The Gasman's Arms', from a lamp-lighter's Christmas broadsheet, c *1815.*

10

PART I

THE TEXTILE INDUSTRY: MACHINERY FOR COTTON, FLAX, WOOL, 1760–1850

JULIA de L. MANN

I. THE FIRST SUCCESSFUL MACHINES

THE industrial revolution is often thought of as having started in 1760. While this is a conventional date in a century that saw continuous change and growth in industry, it is at least true that the first successful spinning-machines, which were to transform the textile industry, were produced in the following decade. The cotton industry led the way, partly for technical reasons: of all the textile fibres cotton proved the easiest to spin by mechanical means. The industry was also experiencing a period of expansion in the early sixties and had adopted Kay's fly-shuttle in the previous decade, so that the demand for yarn stimulated a search for quicker means of spinning. As Paul's attempt was known in Lancashire, and Bourn's carding-engine (vol III, p 154) had been used there, it was natural that the possibilities of spinning by rollers should be canvassed. Arkwright was well able to take advantage of current ideas, but how far the machine that he patented in 1769 was his own invention need not concern us here; he deserves full credit for the persistence with which he carried it to success.

In 1760 the raw cotton, after being opened and cleaned, was carded by hand into a loose roll which was drawn out and slightly twisted on the spindle into a roving; the roving was spun into yarn by the same means. Arkwright's machine (figure 149) was a wooden frame at the top of which were four bobbins, placed horizontally across it, containing rovings. A roving from each bobbin passed through two pairs of rollers divided into four sections corresponding to the bobbins. The second pair of rollers moved more quickly than the first and so elongated the roving, which then passed down the arm of a flyer attached to a spindle at the bottom of the machine and was wound on the bobbin carried by the spindle. The speed of the bobbin was retarded in relation to that of the spindle by a brake in the shape of a piece of worsted twisted round its base. The winding was thus done on the same principle as that of the Saxony wheel from which Arkwright took the idea, even to the rather clumsy device of placing pins on the flyer so that the spinner could guide the thread evenly on to the bobbin. In Arkwright's specification the machine was designed to be worked by a horse, but the motive-power generally used at first was water: hence the name water-frame. Several improvements were made between 1769 and 1775, but little information about them has survived. One of the most important, patented in 1772 by Coniah Wood, one of Arkwright's workmen, was the introduction of a movable rail in place of the pins to guide the thread for winding; its movement

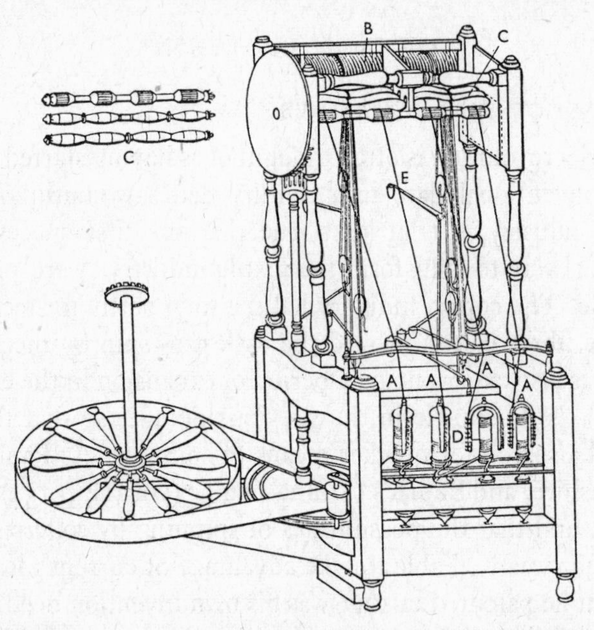

FIGURE 149—*Arkwright's original water-frame spinning-machine of 1769. The four threads* (A) *come from the roving bobbins* (B), *through the rollers* (C) *and on to the flyers* (D), *which are shown in different positions. The pairs of rollers* (*shown enlarged at the side*) *are pressed together by the weights* (E).

was later made automatic by means of a heart-shaped wheel or cam. Another pair of rollers was also added.

Almost contemporaneous with the water-frame was a hand-driven machine which owed nothing to previous experiments. This was the spinning-jenny, which reproduced the actions of the hand-spinner. James Hargreaves, a weaver of Stanhill near Blackburn, is said to have invented it in 1764, but he did not patent it until 1769, a few weeks after Arkwright. As he had sold some jennies before that date, his patent was held to be invalid. Bobbins filled with roving were placed at the bottom of a frame carrying several spindles, and a sliver from each was attached to a spindle, passing on the way between two rails forming a bar which slid back and forth on the frame. The spinner drew out the roving by moving the bar back a certain distance. The rails were then pressed together to hold the sliver fast while the backward movement of the bar, and the turning of the wheel which moved the spindles, were continued. When enough twist had been given, the bar was moved forward again and the spindles were turned slowly to wind the yarn; meanwhile the spinner pulled a lever which depressed a wire, called the faller, to push down the thread into a position where it could be wound. The jenny received several improvements, especially from Haley of Houghton Tower, soon after it came into use (figure 150).

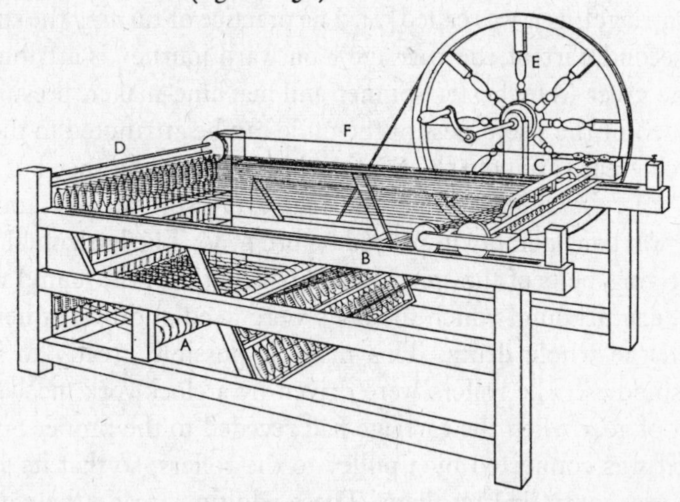

FIGURE 150—*Hargreaves's spinning-jenny after it had been improved by Haley, who made the roller* (A) *of sheet tin for the sake of lightness, and placed the wheel* (E) *in a vertical position. The thread passes from the roving bobbins* (B) *through the clasp* (C) *to the spindles* (D). *These are rotated by bands from the roller* (A), *which is turned by the large wheel* (E). *The faller cord* (F), *when pulled, presses down the transverse wire* (*below* D).

The water-frame produced a strong, well twisted yarn suited for hosiery and the warp of cotton goods. Jenny-spun yarn was at first used for warp and weft, but proved more suitable for the latter. The next machine, Crompton's mule, would spin yarn for either. It was never patented, and the only early model seems to be in France (plate 14 B). The earliest in England (in the Chadwick Museum, Bolton) dates from 1802 or later, and is a model on the lines of Kelly's patent (p 288) [1]. Crompton began experiments in 1774 and the machine was working by 1779. He combined the rollers of the water-frame with the movable carriage of the jenny by placing the spindles on the carriage and the rollers where the spindles had stood in the jenny. The spinner drew back the carriage at the same rate as the rollers gave out the sliver, until about five-sixths of the whole distance had been traversed. Then the rollers were stopped and made to act like the clasp on the jenny, while the carriage continued to recede at a much slower rate and the spindles continued to twist. At the end of the stretch the spindles were turned a few times in the opposite direction to disengage the yarn. The carriage was then pushed in again with the spindles turning slowly in the original direction to wind on the yarn with the help of the faller, as in the jenny.

For some time the great merit of the mule was thought to be the absence of strain on the roving, but in course of time spinners found that a slight stretch at this point was beneficial. Hence arose the practice, for certain types of yarn, of drawing out the carriage faster than the rollers gave out the roving—the 'gain of the carriage', as it was called [2]. The practice of turning the spindles faster during the second part of the carriage's outward journey is attributed to John Kennedy, the great Manchester spinner and machine-maker, presumably about 1790 [3]. Much of the usefulness of the mule can be attributed to the fact that it admitted such great variety in the relationship between the speed of the spindles and that of the rollers and carriage, so that every sort of yarn could be spun.

The mule was considerably improved before 1790. The horizontal roller round which the driving-belts of the spindles had passed (as in the jenny) was replaced by a vertical drum, round which the belts were fixed at different heights so that they covered the whole drum. This made it possible greatly to increase the number of spindles. The rollers were driven by a clockwork mechanism which dropped out of gear when the carriage had receded to the proper point, and the carriage itself was connected by a pulley to the rollers, so that its speed on the first stretch was controlled by them. These additions made the spinners' work easier and more accurate, but the mule was still a hand-driven machine.

The invention of spinning-machinery stimulated efforts to speed up the preparatory processes. The early carding-machines seem to have derived from Bourn's patent, and a machine of this kind is said to have been Arkwright's first model. He later substituted one on Paul's pattern, consisting of a large cylinder known as the 'swift' surmounted by a half cylinder or 'flat', the interior of which, like the surface of the swift, was covered with wire teeth. The carded cotton was removed from the swift by a doffer cylinder revolving in the opposite direction. The cards were arranged in strips across the cylinder, with spaces between each strip so that the cotton came off in short pieces. Arkwright's patent of 1775 shows him in process of experiments for making a continuous carding. By 1785 he had arrived at a solution by covering the whole of the cylinder with card-teeth, taking off the fleece of carded cotton by means of a comb working up and down on a crank, and passing it under rollers and through a funnel to narrow it to a sliver, which then fell in coils into a can. Some of his additions to the carding-engine had been made independently by others, notably the feeding-cloth for bringing the cotton to the swift, but it is now agreed that the crank and comb were his own invention, though they were claimed for Hargreaves in 1785. The machinery used for the further processes of drawing and roving was also shown in the patent of 1775, but the process was more intensive than would be guessed from the specification. The purpose of drawing was to take the place of the spinner's fingers in making the texture of the sliver uniform throughout. A number of cardings were drawn from their cans to unite and pass through two pairs of rollers, by which they were drawn out into one sliver of as many times the original length as there were cardings to be united. This process might be carried out several times, until, at the end, the sliver was given a slight twist to make the roving; this was done by rotating the can that received it (figure 151). The original model had a door through which the rovings were removed by hand, but, as handling exposed them to damage, later machines contained a box which could be lifted out.

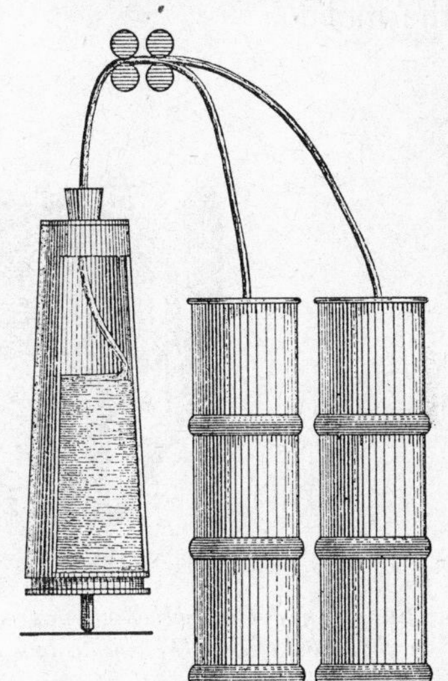

FIGURE 151—*Arkwright's roving-can, known from its shape as the 'lantern can'.*

Arkwright had thus a process for carding, drawing, and roving which was all but continuous, and his machines were driven by power. His patent of 1775 was infringed and was first declared invalid in 1781, but he persisted in challenging those who took advantage of this ruling, and the final decision against him was not given until 1785. Even so, his machines were expensive, and many attempts to find a satisfactory alternative were made in the late seventies and early eighties by men who were using the old carding-machine and the jenny. The one which proved successful, the billy, also a hand-driven machine, did not appear until 1786 (figure 152); it is not certain who was the inventor [4]. In form the billy looked rather like a jenny, but the spindles stood on the carriage and the twisting and winding took place as on the mule. In place of the rollers there was an endless cloth moving in a slanting position round two drums rotated by a weight which was attached to the upper one and wound automatically every time the carriage was moved in. The cardings, drawn in short lengths from cards arranged horizontally on the doffer cylinder, were placed side by side on this cloth and moved forward by its rotation, new lengths having constantly to be pieced to the backs of the old ones. As they moved forward they passed between two rails which acted like the clasp on the jenny to hold them while the spindles twisted them into rovings. This was a far cheaper method than Arkwright's, but it omitted the drawing and so gradually disappeared from the cotton industry—though not from the woollen—as his machines became more common. In the nineties there were many manufacturers possessing carding- and roving-machinery on Arkwright's model who sold rovings to others for spinning on the mule.

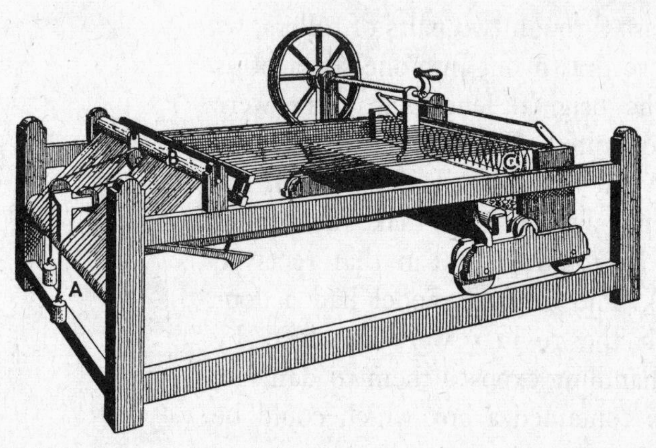

FIGURE 152—*The slubbing-billy—a combination of the jenny and the mule. The cardings were placed on the endless band of cloth* (A) *which is in a sloping position and which leads them under the roller* (B) *and so to the spindles* (C).

II. THE DEVELOPMENT OF SPINNING-MACHINERY UP TO 1850

The machines of 1790 were still crude, and the yarn they produced was imperfect. In discussing their development the different fibres must be treated separately, for it was often necessary to alter a machine invented for cotton in order to make it suit another fibre. From 1800 inventions not only in Britain but in France and the United States must be taken into account. In spite of British prohibitory laws, France acquired the first machines very quickly, mainly through emigrants, and the United States came not far behind. French contributions were made for linen and worsted, but in America attention was concentrated on designing machines of simple construction which would produce quickly and so offset high wages. Most of these machines would not spin fine yarn, but British superiority in this department was in any case too great for effective competition. Skilled mechanics, scarce in England, were even scarcer in France and America [5], and at least up to 1840 it was not uncommon for machinery invented in the last two countries to be greatly improved in Britain [6]. Early machinery was mainly constructed of wood, often by the manufacturer himself. The use of cast iron for machine-frames began in the first decade of the nineteenth century [7]—though much wooden machinery continued in use—and specialized machine-makers became more common. Steam as the motive-power was first used at Arkwright's factory at Shude Hill, Manchester, but this worked on the Newcomen principle by pumping the water which drove the machinery. The first steam-driven factory was at Papplewick, Nottinghamshire, where Boulton and Watt set up an engine in 1785. From 1790 the use of steam-power spread rapidly

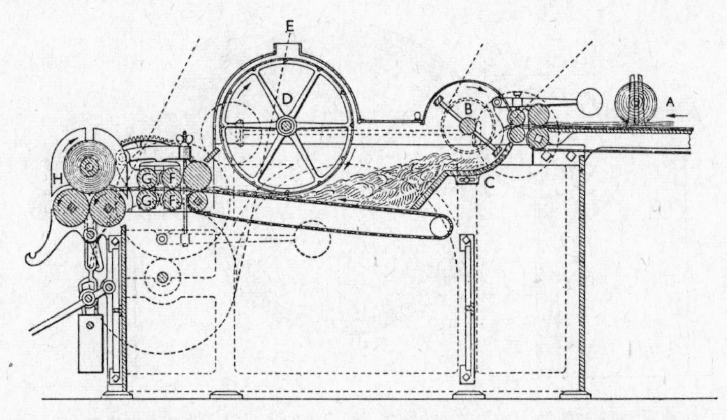

FIGURE 153—*Scutching and lap machine. The cotton was fed to the machine at* (A), *and led past the beaters* (B), *which removed the dust through a grid* (C). (D) *was a revolving cage through which more dust was sucked up the pipe* (E). *The layer of beaten cotton was then led between the rollers* (FF) *and* (GG) *and round the lap cylinder* (H). *When* (H) *was full it lifted a crank and the sliver was cut between rollers* (F) *and* (G). *In the full-scale model the parts from* (A) *to* (F) *might be repeated four to five times.*

and had the effect of concentrating mills in towns instead of dispersing them over the countryside: but many water-driven mills survived.

(*a*) COTTON. Power seems to have been applied about 1800 to the preparatory processes of willowing and batting the cotton to remove impurities and open it thoroughly. Various forms of machine were made for willowing and were found to suit different types of cotton. They all involved teasing the cotton between spikes set in a container, which was quickly rotated while the dirt fell through a grating at the bottom of the machine. For the next process, that of batting, a power-driven machine, the scutcher, was produced in Scotland by Neil Snodgrass in 1797 and improved at the mills of Arkwright and the Strutts, but it was not used at Manchester until 1808. The cotton was again beaten by revolving arms and subjected to a draught to suck up impurities. A given weight of cotton was then put on the feeding-cloth of a lap-machine, where it was passed under rollers to reduce it to a fleecy mass; this was delivered to another cloth ready to feed the carding-engine. In 1814 Crighton attached a lap-machine to the scutcher, but in the majority of factories in England the processes continued to be separate [8] in spite of the fact that by the thirties an efficient combined machine had been evolved (figure 153). In this machine the lap-cylinder revolved on friction-rollers placed below it, and was progressively lifted by a crank to allow for its increasing diameter. When it had reached a certain size the machinery behind it was thrown out of gear, thus cutting the sliver.

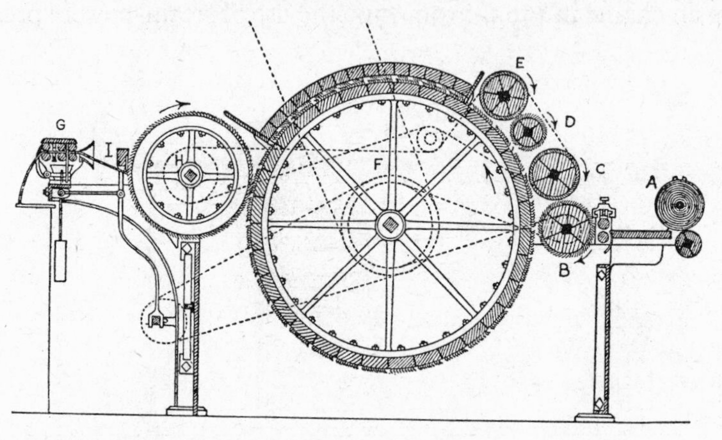

FIGURE 154—*Carding-machine.* (A) *Feeding cylinder;* (B) *licker-in;* (C), (D), (E) *urchins;* (F) *main carding-cylinder or swift;* (G) *metal plate with slit to round sliver after drawing;* (H) *doffer;* (I) *crank and comb or doffing knife.*

The carding-machine became larger and more complicated (figure 154). The cotton was fed to the swift by a small, slower-moving cylinder, the licker-in, and then carded between a series of small cylinders or urchins working on the swift. It next passed under the flats, from which it emerged with the fibres roughly parallel. The doffing took place as in Arkwright's machine, but the sliver received its first drawing, and was rounded by passing through a vertical slit in a metal plate before falling into the can. The drawback of this carding-engine was the trouble of cleaning the flats, which had to be done twice a day by hand. Various automatic cleaning processes were produced, but none was very successful owing to the delicacy of adjustment needed. A patent for revolving flats, to be cleaned by a brush attached to the machine, was taken out by James Smith of Deanston in 1834, but it succeeded only after 1850, when many improvements had been made to it.

This carding-engine was essential for fine yarns, for which the cotton was carded twice. The first machine, known as the breaker, had coarser cards than the finisher. Another type of machine, the roller-and-clearer card, without flats but with a number of smaller cards round the swift, was also in use for coarse yarns (figure 155). The cotton was carded by the action of successive cylinders placed on top of the swift; next to each large cylinder was a smaller one which cleared the cotton from it and returned it to the swift.

Arkwright's drawing-frame remained unchanged, but his system of roving was not entirely satisfactory because the coil had to be wound on a bobbin before spinning, and might be damaged in the process. It was finally superseded by the bobbin-and-fly frame (figure 156) introduced by the machine-making firm of Cocker and Higgins in 1815 and perfected by Henry Houldsworth of Glasgow in 1825 (figure 156). This machine, in appearance like the water-frame, revived Arkwright's first idea of winding the roving straight on to the bobbin by means of a flyer, but the problem of doing so with such a tenuous thread was much more difficult than with yarn. To avoid straining, it must be wound at exactly the same speed as that at which it is given out from the front rollers, but if the angular velocity of the bobbin is constant its peripheral velocity will increase as it grows larger with winding. It was therefore necessary to find a means of keeping the relative speeds of the spindle and the surface of the bobbin constant, so that winding might always go on at the same rate. This was achieved by driving the bobbins separately from the spindles by means of a strap sliding on a conical drum, an idea which Arkwright had patented but was unable to bring into action. As the strap moved from the smaller to the larger circumference of this cone, it moved at a gradually increasing speed. The cone was connected to a wheel which, by coming alternately into gear with other wheels, raised and lowered the copping-shaft on which the bobbins stood, for the rovings were too delicate to move up and down them. By the changing speed of the strap the velocity of the bobbins was gradually increased by the difference between the new speed and the constant velocity of the driving-shaft. Through a chain of wheels set in motion when the copping-shaft reached the top of its upward journey, the pulley round which the strap of the cone passed was moved backwards at each double traverse (up and down) of the copping-rail by just so much as was necessary to allow a tooth to move from one rack to the next. When the bobbin was full the tooth had reached the last rack, and by doing so set in motion a mechanism that stopped the machine.

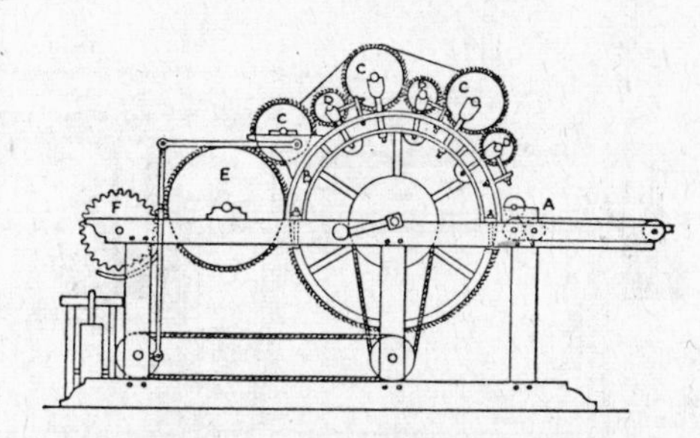

FIGURE 155—*Roller-and-clearer card.* (A) *Feed rollers;* (B) *main cylinder or swift;* (C) *rollers;* (D) *clearers;* (E) *doffing-cylinder;* (F) *fluted cylinder used for wool but not for cotton.*

This was satisfactory as long as the spindles always turned at the same rate, but if more or less twist was needed very intricate adjustments had to be made, which might involve much waste before the right relationship was achieved. Henry Houldsworth, working on an idea patented in 1823 by Green, a tinsmith of Mansfield, solved the problem by introducing a differential motion which kept the velocity of the bobbins in constant relation to that of the spindles whatever the speed of the latter might be. The same device is claimed for an American in-

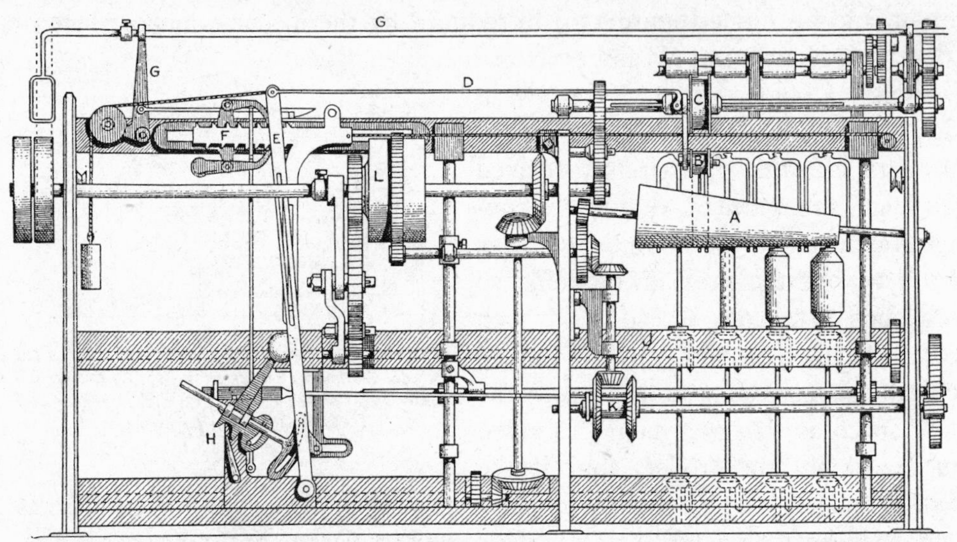

FIGURE 156—*Back view of the bobbin-and-fly frame.* (A) *Cone;* (B) *strap attached to pulley* (C), *which is connected by rod* (D) *to lever* (E); (F) *toothed shaft;* (G) *mechanism for stopping machine;* (H) *mechanism connecting copping-shaft* (J) *with lever* (E); (K) *wheels for raising and lowering copping-shaft;* (L) *Houldsworth's differential box.*

ventor, Asa Arnold, who patented it in 1822. A model of his invention was brought to England in 1825, but it is quite possible that Green and Houldsworth arrived at their solution independently.

Almost at the same time as Houldsworth's patent, an American invention—the tube roving-frame, patented by G. Danforth of Massachusetts in 1824—was introduced into England by J. G. Dyer, who obtained another patent for an improvement in it in 1829 (figure 157). In this machine the place of the spindles was taken by revolving tubes through which the roving passed. Their revolution twisted the rovings backwards to the rollers, but the twist was only transitory, serving to make them hold together on their way to the bobbins. These were placed horizontally below the tubes on iron drums which moved at the speed of the front drawing-rollers and carried the bobbins round, the change in their circumference being provided for as in the lap-machine. The tubes moved to and fro across the bobbins, and the rovings were untwisted in the act of being wound on. This frame produced a very soft roving, suitable only for coarse yarn. It was one of several speed-frames produced in the United States, of which only one other, the Eclipse Roving Frame, in which the roving was temporarily twisted by revolving leather bands, appeared in England. Both were simpler and cheaper than the bobbin-and-fly frame and gave far quicker results, but they made more waste and were eventually abandoned. The fly-frame gained much ground during the thirties, though some manufacturers continued for a time to

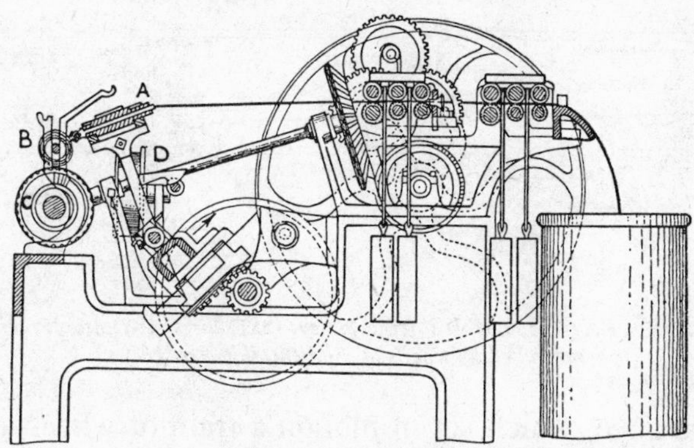

FIGURE 157—*Danforth's or Dyer's tube roving-frame. The sliver passes from the can through the two sets of drawing rollers, through the tube* (A), *and so round the bobbin* (B); (C) *friction rollers which turn the bobbin;* (D) *mechanism giving transverse motion to* (A).

use Arkwright's 'lantern' supplemented by a stretcher-frame, worked by hand on the lines of a mule, which further attenuated the roving.

The credit for making the process from carding to spinning continuous has often been given to J. G. Bodmer, a Swiss inventor who lived for many years in Lancashire [9], but Bodmer's inventions were very little used there, being found 'too complicated to be practical' [10]. This did not prevent their adoption on the continent and in America, but in Lancashire the carrying of cans from one machine to the next has always been preferred.

Spinning. There is no evidence that the jenny was ever power-driven, but for cotton it was soon superseded by the mule. Efforts to apply power to this machine were made from 1790 onwards, but the achievement of a fully self-acting mule was the work of many years. In 1790 William Kelly, manager of Dale's New Lanark Mills, applied water-power for driving the clockwork mechanism which turned the rollers and drew out the carriage for the first stretch. Immediately afterwards Wright, of Manchester, formerly an apprentice of Arkwright, doubled the number of spindles by putting the driving-gear or 'rim' in the middle of the machine. In 1792 Kelly took out a patent for a completely self-acting mule, but abandoned it on finding that it was cumbrous and brought no economic advantage, since only a comparatively small number of spindles could be used.

From 1793 onwards, John Kennedy experimented with driving the mule by steam, and in 1800 he succeeded in doing so up to the point when the spindles finished twisting at the end of the outward stretch. The change of speed for the carriage and the spindles was automatically effected by levers acted upon by the

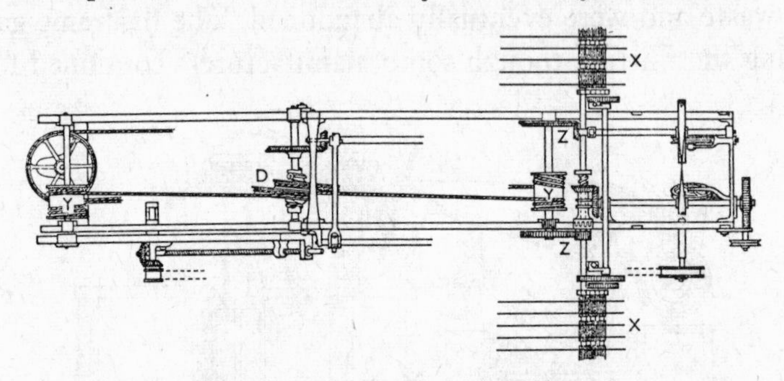

FIGURE 158—*Headstock of Roberts's mule.* (D) *Scroll pulley;* (XX) *rollers;* (YY) *drums taking carriage out and controlled by wheels of different diameters* (ZZ).

passage of the carriage, which set in motion a train of wheelwork coming into gear alternately with wheels of different diameters. The machinery was set so that the spindles continued twisting after the carriage had stopped for a length of time depending upon the twist required; the spinner then took over the winding-on, as in the hand-mule. This invention made the mule a factory-machine, but it required skilled operators, who could command high wages. Several self-acting mules were produced between 1818 and 1825, but none was successful enough to come into general use until, during the spinners' strike of 1825, Richard Roberts was asked to solve the problem. Roberts, the son of a Welsh shoemaker, had established himself as a machine-maker at Manchester after having worked with Maudslay, the great engineer, as a turner and fitter [11], but, although he was recognized as an ingenious mechanic, his works was not on a large scale. The machine that he patented in 1825 did not entirely succeed, but his second patent of 1830 was much more satisfactory. In 1828 he entered into partnership with the firm of Sharp Brothers, who had been established at Manchester as machine-makers since 1806, and they spent £12 000 in perfecting this second patent (figures 158 and 159).

The movements to which Roberts had to apply power were those of reversing the spindles to 'back off' the yarn, and of sending in the carriage and turning the spindles, both at varying speeds, in order to build up the cop in the double cone which was necessary to make it hold together: in the mule, as distinct from the water-frame, the cop was built on the spindle itself without a bobbin. He furnished the machine with three driving pulleys and two driving belts, one of the latter moving in the opposite direction to the other. Until the twisting was finished one belt drove two pulleys, which between them moved all the machinery

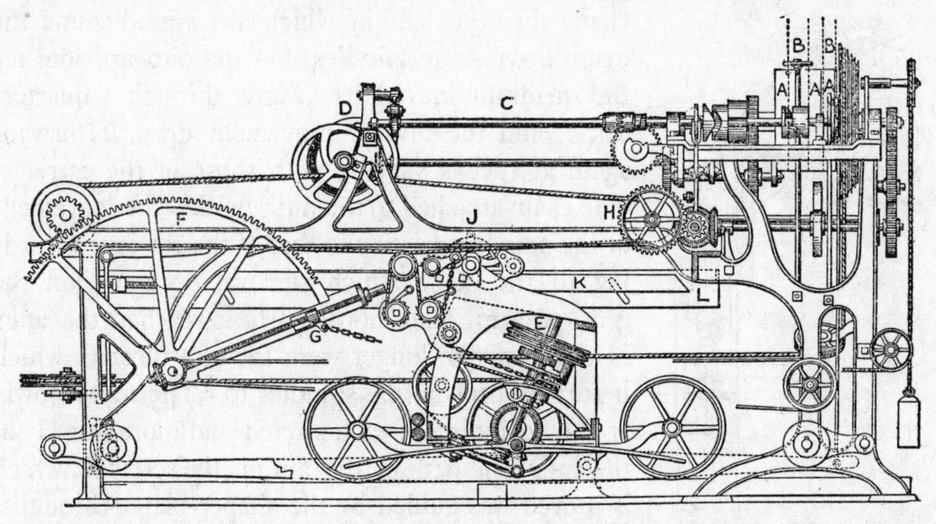

FIGURE 159—*Side view of headstock of Roberts's self-acting mule.* (AA) *Steam-driven pulleys;* (BB) *driving belts;* (C) *driving shaft;* (D) *scroll pulley for inward journey;* (E) *drum driving spindles;* (F) *toothed quadrant;* (G) *nut sliding on radial arm from which chain is attached to carriage;* (H) *wheel driving drum which takes carriage out;* (J) *self-actor governing path of faller through rail* (K), *which is guided by shaper-plates attached to the frame* (L).

needed, while the other belt revolved idly on the loose pulley. In backing off, the first belt was shifted to the first pulley and the second to the other, which drove the spindles, so that they turned in the opposite direction. When backing-off ended, the belts shifted back to their former positions. The moving-in of the carriage was done by a spiral 'scroll' pulley; this took over its control from the pulleys which moved it outwards and pulled it in, at first at an increasing and then at a decreasing speed, according to the diameter of the groove from which the rope was being unwound. To maintain the proper tension of the yarn Roberts introduced a counter-faller wire underneath it, which moved up towards the faller as soon as backing off began, to take up any slack in the yarn. Both faller and counter-faller were operated automatically by mechanism set in motion by the carriage when it reached the end of the stretch. The path of the faller, which determined the point on the spindle where the winding-on should begin, was regulated by a rail moved up and down by pins moving on two shaper-plates, which lowered the faller and raised the counter-faller to the proper position.

The problem of how to vary the speed of the spindles, which must be in accordance with the speed of the carriage and must also vary according to the state of the cop, was not solved until 1830, when Roberts added the 'quadrant' (figure 159), which finally made the machine a success. The quadrant was a segment of a toothed wheel with a grooved arm in which slid a nut attached to a chain, the other end of which was wound round the drum driving the spindles. On the outward journey the quadrant moved backwards through a quarter-circle, and the inward movement drew it forward again at speeds varying with those of the carriage. The chain attached to the nut retarded the movement of the spindles relative to that of the carriage according to the place which the nut occupied on the grooved arm. The more nearly it reached the apex of the arm, the longer were the arcs through which it turned, causing the spindles to rotate more slowly at the beginning of each stretch and more quickly at the end. The path of the nut on the screw on which it moved was guided by the shaper-plates through a connexion between the screw and the faller. When the ends of the cop were formed the range of the faller was lessened, and the nut remained fixed while the body of the cop was built up.

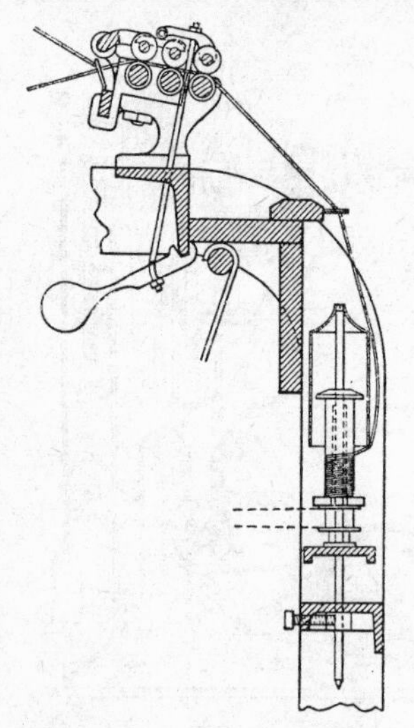

FIGURE 160—*Danforth's throstle for cap spinning; cross-section of spinning parts.*

All the motions of the self-acting mule were governed by making the driving-shaft turn through a quarter-circle at successive points in the operation. At each turn the mechanisms governing the motions which were to stop were thrown out of gear, and those which governed the next motions were engaged. When the carriage reached the roller-beam the shaft returned to its original position.

The self-actor was acclaimed as an almost perfect machine, but it did not spread quickly. By 1839 the profits had not exceeded £7000 [12], and the patent was extended for another seven years. By 1850 counts up to fifty were being spun on it. Another self-actor, invented in 1834 by J. Smith of Deanston, was also being used to some extent for counts up to thirty, but the older mule was still in use for fine yarns. Improvements in the latter, simplifying the putting-up action, made by Evan Leigh in 1832, had enabled two mules to be coupled together on either side of the headstock, thus increasing to a possible 1200 the number of spindles that one spinner could drive.

Throstle-spinning. When the mule became a factory-machine its ability to spin all kinds of yarn led to a decline in the use of the water-frame for spinning cotton. After the Napoleonic wars, when the spread of power-looms created a demand for strong yarn, the water-frame returned in the enlarged and more economic form of the throstle. Instead of having the spindles grouped four or six to a head, each head being separately driven, the frame now consisted of two long lines of spindles set back to back, all driven from one driving-belt. A copping-rail was introduced, as in the bobbin-and-fly frame, and the method of winding was simplified by allowing the thread to drag the bobbin round by its own weight, a method possible only when the yarn is strong and thoroughly twisted. The throstle therefore would not spin fine yarns. An even simpler contrivance, known as Danforth's throstle frame after its American inventor (p. 286), was patented in England by J. Hutchinson in 1829 (figure 160). There was no flyer, and the spindles were stationary but covered by a conical cap which revolved at a high speed. The bobbin, which moved up and down the spindle, and the cap rotated together, and the thread was conducted to the bobbin under the rim of the cap, the friction of which retarded its speed relative to that of the bobbin so that winding-on could take place. The value of this machine was its simple construction and its speed. It produced yarn softer and more fleecy than that spun on the throstle, but it also made more waste. In the cotton industry it never conquered more than a small part of the field held by the throstle, but it was eventually adopted for worsted spinning. There were other attempts in the thirties to speed up the process of spinning, but none survived. Ring-spinning, which was ultimately to triumph, was invented in America in 1828 and introduced into England in 1834, but it soon disappeared and did not return until after 1850.

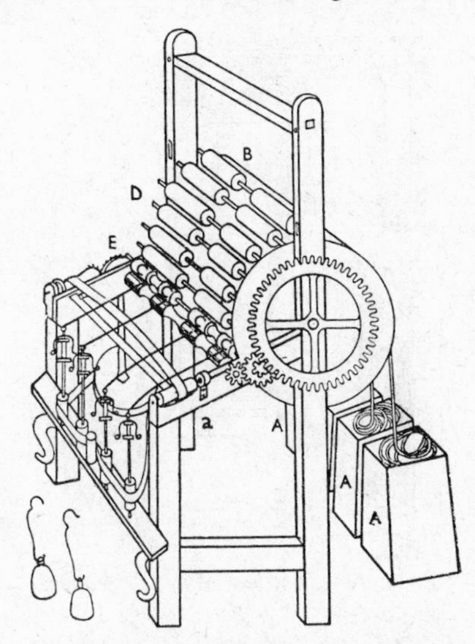

FIGURE 161—*Kendrew and Porthouse's machine for spinning flax. The slivers are drawn from the bins* (A) *over the roller* (B) *and under the heavy rollers* (D). *Weights* (a) *are hung on the rollers* (C). *The thread passes over the damp band of material* (E) *before reaching the spindles. The drawing-frame is similarly weighted.*

(*b*) FLAX. The fibres of flax are longer than those of cotton: they consist of short filaments held together by a gummy substance which must be loosened before fine yarn can be spun. Drawing and spinning flax for coarse yarn became a factory-process long before heckling, which corresponds to carding in cotton and separates the 'line' or long fibres from the 'tow' or shorter ones, which can be spun like cotton. The first patent for adapting Arkwright's machinery to spinning line was taken out in 1787 by J. Kendrew and A. Porthouse of Darlington (figure 161). The pairs of drawing-rollers had to be placed much farther apart than for cotton, and both in drawing and in spinning the flax was subjected to the pressure of heavy weights. In spinning, the thread was passed over a wet cloth just before it reached the spindles, in order to soften the gum. This machinery was worked at Darlington and in Scotland, but much greater success was gained by the commercial genius of John Marshall of Leeds, who soon substituted for it the machines patented by Matthew Murray, at that time his foreman mechanic. Murray, whose first patent was taken out in 1790, drew the flax between leather straps revolving round a pair of rollers tightly pressed together and placed in a vertical position at right-angles to a second pair (figure 162). No provision was made for wetting the thread, but dry-spun yarn proved to be more elastic and filled the web better. Both methods were in use later for coarse yarns, wet-spun being stronger and more silky in appearance.

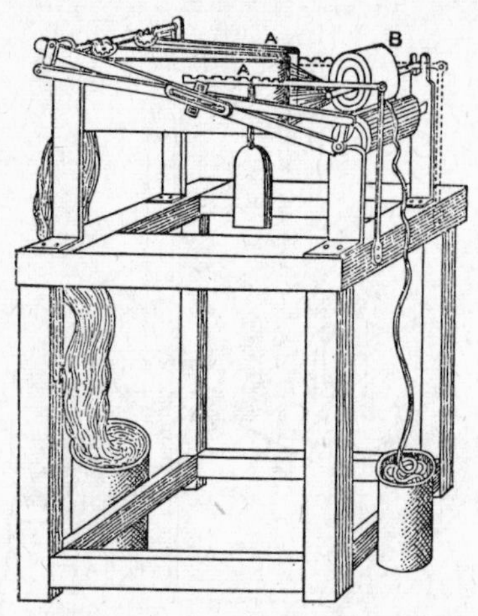

FIGURE 162—*Matthew Murray's drawing-frame for flax. The flax is drawn between the vertical leather bands* (A), *which are tightly pressed together. It is then drawn out to the proper size under the weighted roller* (B) *and drops into the bin. The spinning-frame is similar, but the first pair of rollers is placed vertically above the second set.*

These methods of applying pressure to the fibres could not produce a perfectly regular yarn. The discovery of a superior method of preparation was the work of a French inventor, Philippe de Girard (1775–1845). At the beginning of the century there had been unsuccessful efforts in France to rescue the linen industry from the competition of cotton by applying machinery to its manufacture, and in 1810 Napoleon offered a prize of a million francs for a successful process. P. de Girard produced his solution too late for the prize, and the official opinion of his methods was unfavourable. Like most new inventions, his machines needed many adjustments before they would produce good results, and his French factories were not successful. He later started others in Austria and finally in Poland, where he was employed by the government. His processes were brought to England by two of his associates and sold to Horace Hall, who patented them in 1814, but it was only several years later that his whole system was adopted.

Philippe de Girard's three innovations were the use of a hot alkaline solution to separate the fibres before drawing; the drawing of them when dry through combs or gills (probably from the French *aiguilles*); and the immersion of the roving in another alkaline solution on its way to the spindles. Of these, gill-drawing or something like it had been patented by an English inventor in 1801 but had never come into use. It straightened and levelled the fibres and produced a more even sliver by placing between the drawing-rollers a succession of bars carrying combs fixed to revolving cylinders, over which the fibres were drawn more quickly than the comb-bars moved. This process began to be employed in England between 1816 and 1820. de Girard's other processes were neglected.

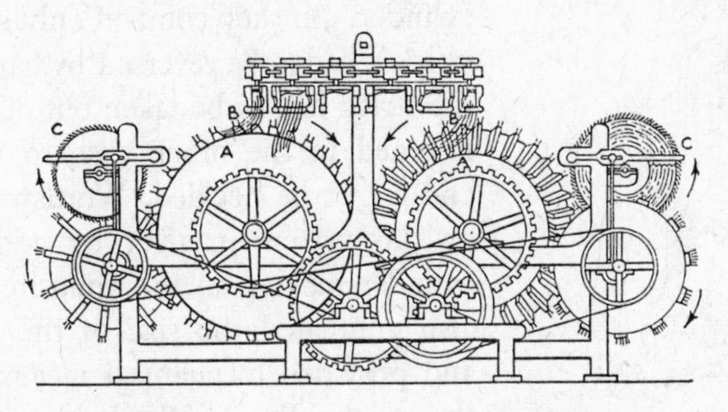

FIGURE 163—*Wordsworth's flax-heckling machine.* AA *are the two cylinders revolving in opposite directions, and the stricks of flax are held at* BB. CC *are brush cylinders to remove the tow from the machine.*

In 1825 James Kay of Preston took out a patent for macerating the roving by soaking it in cold water for about six hours before spinning, thus softening the gum so that the shorter filaments held together by it could be loosened for drawing and spinning, after which the gum would harden again and preserve the original strength of the flax. Since the spinning was done while the fibre was soft, the rollers were placed nearer to each other, as in cotton-spinning, to support the short filaments. This lost Kay the action which he brought against Marshall for infringement, since it was held not to be original and invalidated that part of the patent which dealt with maceration. de Girard pointed out that he had been the first inventor of maceration, and his claim seems to be justified. In the forties, the method of steeping the flax in hot water before drawing, and wetting the roving again on the spinning-frame by making it pass through a trough of hot water before reaching the rollers, seems to have been the general practice for finer yarns.

Gill-drawing was improved by the screw-gill patented in 1833 by Lawson and Westly, and improved by Fairbairn in 1846 and 1848. The comb-bars were made to travel forward on a pair of screw-shafts so that they might present a flat surface and approach as near as possible to the back of the drawing-rollers, each bar as it came to the end being knocked down to a lower level and carried back to the beginning by another pair of shafts.

Good spinning depended, however, on the thoroughness with which the flax was heckled. All the early heckling-machines had in common the suspension of a series of stricks (bundles) of flax, each in its own holder, to be brought into contact with a series of heckling-teeth, generally fixed on a revolving cylinder. As they combed only one side of the strick it had to be reversed by hand; and finally the strick had to be taken out of its holder and fastened in the other way, so that the other end might be heckled. Wordsworth improved on this system in 1833 by adding a second cylinder moving in the opposite direction. He also graduated the size of the heckling-teeth and provided mechanical means for reversing the stricks. Brush-cylinders at the side of the machine removed the tow remaining in the teeth of the comb, so that this had no longer to be done by hand (figure 163). In 1832 de Girard produced a machine which was brought to England by a mechanic named Decoster and patented in the name of T. M. Evans; the patent included some improvements, possibly made by Decoster [13]. The stricks of flax were hung between two vertical sheets of combs which moved in opposite directions. As they moved they drew nearer to each other and then again receded (figure 164). There was an arrangement for taking off the tow similar to that in Wordsworth's patent. In England this machine was often known as Wordsworth's heckler, as he patented an improvement to it giving an up-and-down movement to the holder which enabled the teeth to penetrate progressively deeper into the flax [14]. It was widely used, and formed the basis for several improved hecklers, but a great variety of machines was in use in 1850. At that date, however, manual labour still remained universal for flax intended for fine yarn.

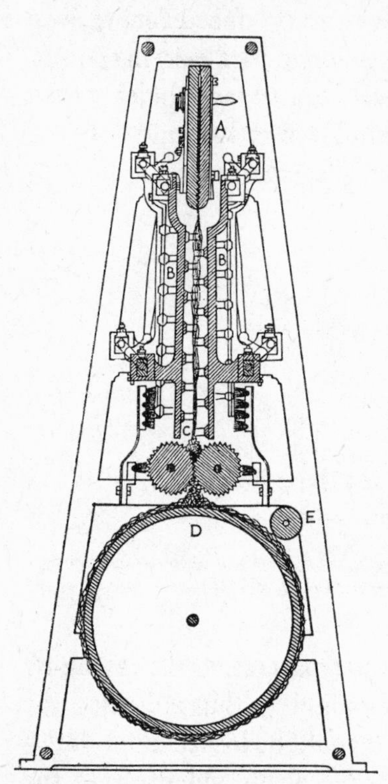

FIGURE 164—*Heckling machine derived from de Girard's.* (A) *Holder for strick;* (BB) *section of comb cylinders moving in opposite directions;* (C) *tow deposited on fluted rollers and falling to drum* (D), *round which, under pressure of roller* (E), *it forms a lap.*

(*c*) WOOL. The staple, or length of fibre, in wool ranges from under 1 inch up to 10 in or more. All wool has small curly hairs branching out from the main stem, but the number of them to an inch in a short-stapled wool is far greater than in a long-stapled one. Short wool, therefore, will felt but long wool will not; these differing properties account for differences during this period in the method of manufacture (now largely superseded by modern machinery), beginning with the fact that long wool was combed while short was carded.

Combing wool. In spinning long wool for worsted the fibres must be laid as straight as possible to produce an even thread, and Arkwright's machinery was well suited for this purpose. The first mill was at Dolphin Holme near Lancaster in 1784, but more successful attempts were made in Yorkshire from 1787 onwards. The only change in the spinning- and drawing-frames was the placing of the pairs of rollers at a greater distance from each other to suit the longer staple. For roving, the bobbin-and-fly frame was used, but without the cone or differential, the roving being strong enough to pull the bobbin round, as in spinning. In France, methods of roving without twist were preferred, and a way of rubbing the sliver to make it cohere had been invented by Dobo in 1815; but the importation of American roving-frames, as described on p 286, in the late twenties seems to have led to a greater extension of the practice. French manufacturers had also adopted gill-drawing from the linen industry in 1820 or earlier. In England an operation of this kind was in use in 1835 in what was called the breaking-frame, to which the wool was taken after being combed [15], but it was not introduced into the actual operation of drawing until the late forties. A similar difference prevailed in methods of spinning. In France the mule, and in England the throstle, were the prevailing machines, to the virtual exclusion of the other in each case. Cap-spinning (p 291) does not appear to have been adopted in England until after 1850 [16]. Many writers assume it to have been introduced in 1831, but an illustration published by James in 1857 shows merely the ordinary throstle. It was not universal even in 1870. The French use of the mule, together with their better preparatory methods, gave them a superiority in the finest worsteds.

Combing, corresponding to the heckling of flax, was the most difficult process to mechanize, and up to 1850 hand-combing held its ground for all but coarse worsteds. The first machine-comb was invented by Edmund Cartwright, of power-loom fame, in 1792 (figure 165). Slivers of wool made by hand were drawn through a tube in an oscillating frame and delivered by rollers to the teeth of a circular revolving comb; this carried them under a smaller cylinder-comb moved to and fro across it by a crank. The short fibres, called noils, were

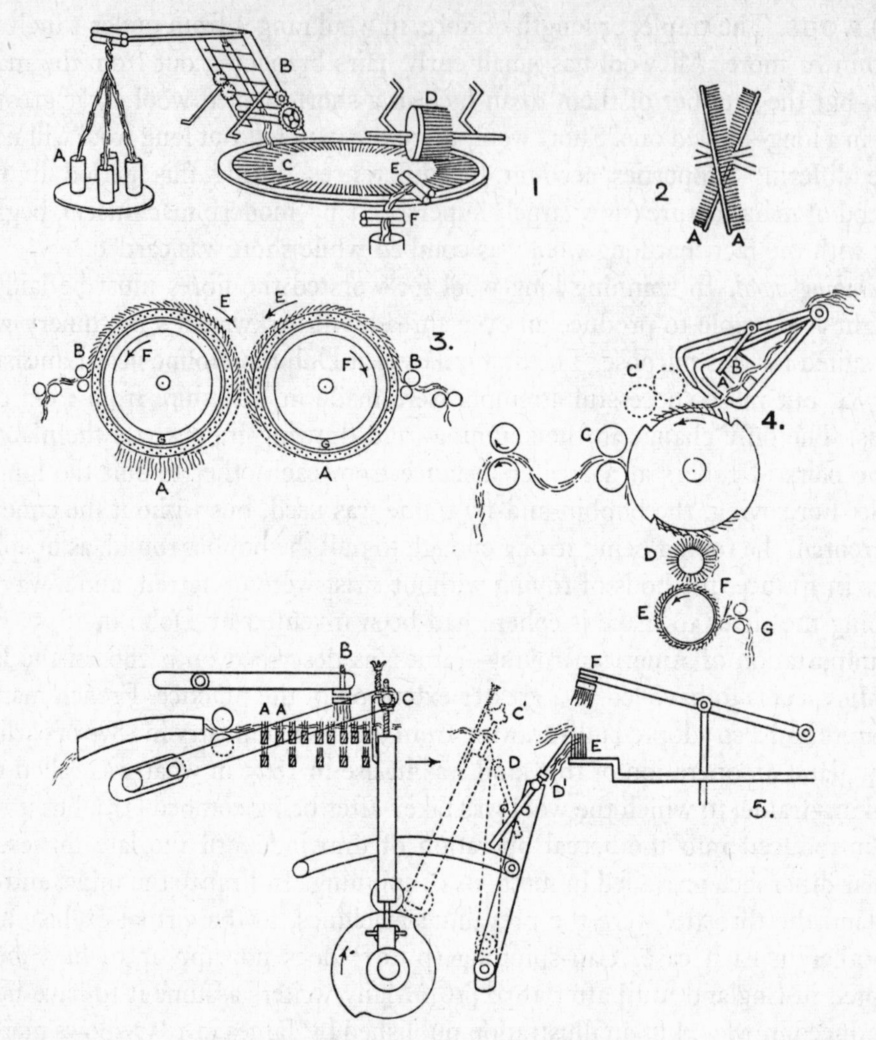

FIGURE 165—*Various combing-machines.*

(1) *Cartwright's, 1792. Slivers of wool are drawn from the cans* (A), *through a tube by the oscillating frame* (B), *into the teeth of working comb* (C), *and so to working comb* (D). *From there it is pulled through the rollers* E *and* F *into the can below.*

(2) *and* (3) *Platt and Collier's, 1827. The machine consists of two circles of combs* (A). *Wool is fed on to one comb and, as the combs are made to approach each other and rotate in the direction* E, *it is equally distributed between them. The angle at which the combs are set can be seen in figure 2. The combs are then separated and by moving in the direction* F *the top can be slipped off at* B.

(4) *Heilmann's, 1846.* (A) *The nip;* (B) *intersecting comb;* (C) *rollers which move down from* C^1; (D, E) *brush cylinders for removing noils;* (F) *knife which pushes the noils off the brush cylinder to pass through rollers* (G).

(5) *Lister and Donisthorpe's, 1851.* (A) *Gill comb;* (B) *brush;* (C) *nip moving to* C^1; (D) *porter comb moving to* D^1; (E) *section of circular comb;* (F) *brush. The taking-off rollers are not shown.*

teased out and remained in the small comb, from which they had to be removed by hand, while the long fibres which make the 'top' were carried off by rollers into a can. Cartwright himself was not successful with this comb, but it formed a basis for better machines, at which there were many attempts. None was widely used until that patented in England by Platt and Collier in 1827. This embodied a French invention by a manufacturer named Godard, of Amiens, who had obtained a first patent in 1816 in conjunction with Collier, an English machine-maker established in Paris [17]. The machine arrived in England with improvements patented in France in 1825 (figure 165). It consisted of two circles of combs, one of which was filled by hand. They moved in opposite directions and were so placed that the teeth of one circle worked into those of the other. The combs began their revolution when they were only just touching each other, and were brought closer until half the wool from the first comb was transferred to the second. Then drawing-rollers, placed on each side, were brought into contact with the combs and carried off the top. The noils remaining in the teeth had to be cleaned off by hand. This comb was not entirely superseded in France until 1845, and not in England until after 1851, though many inventors were in the field; these included Noble, whose comb was successful after 1850, and a German named Wieck, of Chemnitz, whose comb was patented in England by Preller in 1852.

In 1845 Josué Heilmann of Mulhouse produced a comb on a new principle, in response to a suggestion that if fine cotton could be combed as well as carded a much finer thread could be produced. The comb proved equally suitable for wool (figure 165). The wool was passed through a frame furnished with two jaws to nip the sliver when a sufficient length had passed through. The comb-teeth, covering a quarter of the combing-cylinder, then revolved through the sliver presented to them and were succeeded by the flat surface of the next quarter; this carried the sliver to the drawing-rollers which moved down to receive it. These in turn held it fast by the combed end while the jaws opened, allowing the other end to pass over the succeeding comb-teeth; an intersecting comb descended to comb the middle section of the sliver, which escaped the teeth of the cylinder. As the combing-cylinder revolved the noils were cleared off by a brush-cylinder at the bottom and finally by a knife and doffing-rollers. A patent for this machine was taken out in England in 1846 but it did not become generally known until it was exhibited at the Great Exhibition of 1851.

Meanwhile, in England, G. E. Donisthorpe, who had been experimenting with combing-machines from 1835, produced in 1842–3 an improved model on Cartwright's principle; this attracted the attention of S. C. Lister, a large worsted manufacturer at Bradford, who bought the patent rights. Together they arrived at a machine that resembled Heilmann's in using the nip (figure 165). The wool was fed through rollers across a gill-comb to a nip placed at the top of a crank which carried it to a porter-comb, and this again fed it to a circular revolving comb. Brushes placed above both the gill and the circular combs descended to force the wool into the teeth, and the top was taken off the latter by rollers. The noils were removed in the same way as in Heilmann's comb. Lister and Donisthorpe had several patents, but the final one, in which the use of the nip was specified, was not taken out until 1851, and Heilmann won an action against them for infringement. Subsequently he sold his rights to other Yorkshire manufacturers who resold them to Lister. Lister suppressed Heilmann's comb in favour of his own, which held the field for a considerable time in England, as Heilmann's did in France. The rights in the latter for use in cotton had, however, been bought by a group of manufacturers at Manchester, where it opened up a new era in fine cotton-spinning.

Two other innovations deserve mention. Wool was carded before combing as early as 1814 in France and 1829 in England. Cotton warps for worsteds were introduced into Yorkshire in 1834 [18] and led to a great extension of the worsted-industry.

Carding wool. The first power-driven machine in the cloth industry was the carding-engine, which was set up in Yorkshire in the early 1770s, often in existing fulling-mills where it could be turned by water. This machine was of the type patented by Bourn, which developed into the roller-and-clearer card, since the short fibres must be thoroughly interlaced and not laid straight as would be done in a machine with flats. The process was duplicated, the first carding being known as scribbling. From this machine the wool came off in a fleece; it was then weighed and put on the feeder of the carding-engine proper. Here the old arrangement of placing the cards on the doffer cylinder in parallel strips was retained, so that the carding came off in flat pieces about 3 ft long, which passed under a fluted roller to make them round. In the early twenties there were several attempts in both England and America to produce a machine that would make a continuous movement of carding and slubbing (roving). The experiments that finally succeeded were begun by John Goulding of Massachusetts about 1822. He used a ring-doffer, on which strips of card were placed round instead of across the cylinder, and the latter was given a traversing motion so that it might clear the whole of the swift. Later, a second doffer below the first, with strips of card to take off the wool in the gaps left by the first doffer, was sometimes employed. The flat, continuous strips obtained in this way were rounded by passing through revolving tubes, and wound on bobbins ready for spinning. This machine was patented in England in 1826, but neither it nor any of the machines patented by English inventors for the same purpose came into use there. Goulding's machine, with some variations, appeared in France in 1834, and in Germany after 1839; it was not used in England, and only to a small extent in Scotland [19], until it arrived in a much improved form as the condenser, after 1850.

Since short wool cannot be drawn, Arkwright's machinery was useless in this connexion, but the billy and the jenny proved to be admirably suited for slubbing and spinning. The rolls obtained from the carding-engine were placed on the feeding-cloth of the billy, where they had constantly to be pieced up by children; but in the forties this was increasingly being done by a piecing-machine known as the 'tommy'. The billies were, in general, hand-machines like the jenny. The mule could be adapted for wool by dispensing with one pair of rollers and using the other to pay out the slubbing and then to hold it during the second stretch. It was introduced at Leeds in 1816 but it did not spread quickly. In 1843 spinning was 'most often' performed by it [20], but this was either the hand-mule or the semi-power-driven one. The self-actor was not used until well after 1850. In the remoter places the use of the jenny continued, in some cases right into the twentieth century.

III. WEAVING

Apart from the Jacquard loom (p 318) only one significant improvement was made in the hand-loom after 1760. This was Radcliffe's arrangement for taking up the woven cloth by means of a ratchet-wheel connected with the batten, so that the cloth beam moved automatically. It was patented in 1805 in the name of Radcliffe's employee, Thomas Johnson, and besides speeding up the action of the hand-loom it provided a contribution towards the power-loom. The dandy-loom, as hand-looms equipped with this action were called, came into general use during the nineteenth century.

The obvious problems in applying power to the loom were to devise means of performing the motions made by the hand-weaver, namely, opening the shed for the passage of the shuttle, driving the shuttle, beating up the weft, and winding up the woven cloth. But in a power-loom further devices are necessary to stop the loom in case a thread breaks, to keep the cloth stretched in width, and to size the warp, which the hand-loom weaver did at intervals as necessary. The first English attempt to put a power-loom into action came from outside the industry and owed nothing to previous models. Cartwright made his first attempt in 1784, and after producing an unworkable model in 1785 he patented in the following year a power-loom which, with improvements patented in 1787 and 1792, was worked in his factory at Doncaster, as well as by licensees at Manchester until their factory was burnt down. He provided means for dealing with all the points noted above, and attached the warping to the loom so as to size the threads mechanically before they reached the warp-beam. Considering the primitive state of engineering technique at that time it is not surprising that the loom would not work economically. It had some serious disadvantages. The shuttle was propelled by a spring, which made its action too sudden, and the driving-force was provided by a single shaft, which made all the movements too harsh. Its great merit was to show that weaving by power was not impossible. Further attempts were made by several inventors, especially by Robert Miller of Glasgow in 1796. His loom is said to have derived not from Cartwright's but from that of Jeffrey of Paisley, who had designed a model at almost the same time. Miller's loom, known as the wiper-loom from his use of excentric wheels or wipers to drive the shuttle, was used in Scotland in the early 1800s.

The problem of sizing the warp was satisfactorily solved by Thomas Johnson, who in 1803 produced a machine that sized the threads in the warping-mill by passing them through rollers one of which was impregnated with size. The size was worked in by a series of brushes and dried by passing the threads over a current of hot air driven upwards by fans at the bottom of the machine. This machine, improved by later inventors, was not abandoned until after 1850, though it was partly superseded by the tape-sizing machine of Hornby and Kenworthy patented in 1839. In this machine the warp, divided into bands or tapes of relatively few threads, passed into a trough of size and was dried by being rolled round two heated cylinders.

Of the different looms produced during the early years of the nineteenth century the most significant was that of William Horrocks of Stockport who, among other improvements, introduced in 1813 a method of varying the speed of the batten so as to increase the period for which the shed remained open for the shuttle to pass through. He also adopted Radcliffe's method of taking up the cloth. Between 1813 and 1820 the number of power-looms in Britain increased from 2400 to 14 150, a growth that seems to have been mainly due to the merits of this loom—although there was great variety in detail. The model that appears finally to have emerged as the most practical was one constructed by Roberts, the inventor of the self-acting mule, based on Horrocks's loom. About 1822 Roberts set up a partnership for loom-making under the title Roberts, Hill and Company, and the loom he produced was known by his name, although the patent that he took out in that year was chiefly concerned with weaving twilled fabrics.

Roberts's loom (figure 166) had two shafts, the main one driving the batten while the second, known as the tappet-shaft, drove both the treadles for raising the healds and the pickers for throwing the shuttle. The main shaft had at its end a toothed wheel connected with another wheel, having twice as many teeth, at the end of the tappet-shaft, so that the latter revolved only half as fast; hence the batten moved twice (once forward and once back) for every movement of the

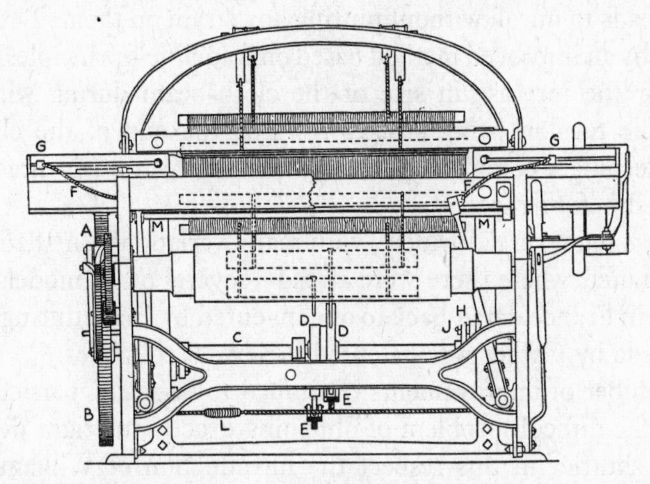

FIGURE 166—*Roberts's power loom, front view.* (A) *Wheel on main shaft, driving wheel* (B) *on tappet or wiper shaft* (C); (DD) *tappets or excentric wheels working on treadle levers* (EE); (FF) *picker cords driving pickers* (GG) *and attached to lever* (H); H *is moved by rollers* (J) *in connexion with excentrics* (DD) *and brought back by spring* (L); (MM) '*swords of the lay*' (p 302).

healds and the shuttle. The healds were connected by cords passing over the roller-beam and were raised by treadle levers moved by excentric wheels or cams set opposite each other, so that the larger side of each wheel raised its lever in turn while the heald that was drawn downwards automatically drew the other one upwards. The cords attached to the pickers which impelled the shuttle were drawn to and fro by other levers moved by rollers fixed in a slot on the excentrics; by shifting their position in this slot the point at which the shuttle began to move could be adjusted to any point in the movement of the healds, thus ensuring co-ordination in weaving any type of cloth. These levers were restored to their original position by a spring mounted on a cord uniting them. There was an automatic stop-movement, in case the shuttle was caught in the shed, consisting of a small shaft under the batten connecting with levers partly entering the shuttle-boxes. If the shuttle did not enter the box it failed to raise the other end of the shaft, which in consequence came into contact with a projection and moved it forward, stopping the machine.

The batten was supported from below by two cranks, 'the swords of the lay', attached to a mechanism moving on the driving-shaft. By adjusting the cranks the velocity of the batten could be varied to suit different types of cloth. In the model shown in the accompanying diagram (figure 167) the warp was unrolled by an arrangement of weights on the warp-beam in the same way as in the hand-loom, but several attempts were made to provide means of turning the beam to allow the threads to unroll without putting any strain on them. The woven cloth was taken up by an improved method based on Radcliffe's principle. No allowance was made for the increase in size of the cloth-beam during winding, which resulted in the tension being slacker towards the end of the cloth; but the problem of keeping a completely even tension between warp-threads and cloth was not solved before 1850.

The Roberts loom spread widely, with many variations. In 1826 it was introduced into France, where there were already several other models [21]. Loom construction in France dated back to one invented by Biard during the Empire; later, one made by Collier was patented in several countries.

A large number of improvements continued to be made, particularly in connexion with the difficult problem of obtaining exactly the right degree of force to drive the shuttle; in this respect the introduction of William Dickinson's 'overpick' or Blackburn loom in 1826 marked a step forward. Among other inventions it is possible to mention here only those relating to the two points in which Roberts's loom was deficient, namely, the lack of any device for keeping the cloth stretched in width, and of an automatic stop-motion in case of the breakage of a weft-thread. For the latter, the first successful device was patented by Ramsbottom and Holt of Todmorden in 1834; it was improved by Kenworthy and Bullough in 1841, and again in Bullough's brake, which made stoppage immediate, in 1842. In its later form it consisted of a small fork projecting through the reed over which the weft passed. If the weft failed to pass the fork fell back and set off a train of motion which stopped the machine. Out of the many devices produced for an automatic stretching-mechanism or temple, that which proved most satisfactory was the trough-and-roller temple patented by Kenworthy and Bullough in 1841, an improvement on a method that had been introduced earlier. It consisted of two small rollers with a roughened surface placed one at each side of the cloth-beam and moving with it in a trough. The cloth passed between the rollers and the trough, and was kept stretched by the adhesion of the roughened surfaces.

The above description applies to the power-loom for weaving plain fabrics, but its adaptation for a twill or fancy weave, in which the pattern is formed by the raising at intervals of different sets of warp-threads, had been made quite early. Improvements were patented by Bowman in 1820 and by Roberts in 1822. All systems involved the substitution for the excentrics of a number of circular wheels (or rollers mounted on one wheel, as in Roberts's patent) corresponding to the number of healds to be raised by means of projections on the wheels, which moved the appropriate levers. Of later patents the most important was that of Woodcroft in 1838. It was claimed that up to eight pairs of healds and eight changes of pattern could be worked by this method. It took longer to mechanize the working of the drop-box, by which shuttles containing weft of different colours could be used at will by the hand-loom weaver. The final solution was found in the endless chain, patented by Squire Diggle of Bury in 1845. This was composed of a series of plates of different thicknesses which revolved at the end of the loom under a pulley attached to a rod carrying the drop-box at its other end. As the chain revolved, the plates raised the rod to the height determined by the thickness of each plate, thus bringing the appropriate shuttle into place. These contrivances eventually gave way to the Jacquard loom, which for worsted was worked by power from about 1833. In cotton, however, where cheapness was important, the use of the 'dobby', a simpler form of Jacquard, does not appear to have become common until after 1850.

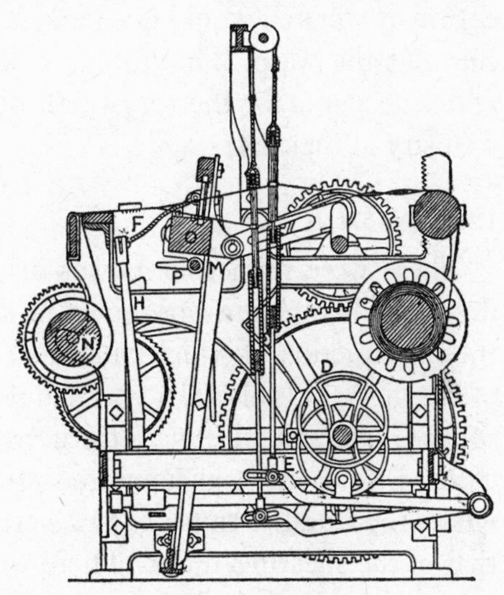

FIGURE 167—*Roberts's power loom, side view.* D, E, F, H, *and* M *as in figure 166;* (N) *cloth beam;* (O) *batten;* (P) *lever to stop loom if shuttle is caught in the shed.*

By the middle forties, therefore, the power-loom had been brought to a state which made its use much more economical. The weft-breakage stop-motion and the automatic temple eliminated the necessity for constantly watching each loom, and made it possible for one weaver to look after a number at the same time. Other inventions in the forties, especially Bullough's 'loose reed' by which the reed was dissociated from the batten when the shuttle stuck in the shed, and was thus prevented from driving it against the warp, made it possible to work with increased speed. By 1850 the power-loom was well on the way to superseding the handloom-weaver in cotton and had almost completely done so in worsted, where it had been introduced in 1824. For wool, however, the fragility of the thread made it impossible for the shuttle to move at a higher rate than in the hand-loom, so that there was little to be gained by employing it until after the improvements of the forties; but it was spreading in 1850. For linen, the lack of elasticity in the yarn meant that the thread would break under a strain where cotton or worsted would give, and a different method had to be adopted for letting out the warp. This problem was not seriously attacked until after 1850, which accounts for the very small number of power-looms at work in the linen industry at that date.

IV. FINISHING

There were numerous power-driven machines for finishing that cannot be described here, but a word must be said about the machinery for cloth-dressing, the introduction of which caused so many riots. It seems probable that the use of the gig-mill (vol III, p 172) had never been quite abandoned, and in the 1790s some Gloucestershire manufacturers began to use it with great success for fine cloth. Elsewhere it encountered stubborn resistance, especially in Yorkshire, where the Luddite riots of 1812 were mainly concerned with its destruction and that of the shearing-frame. There were a large number of patents for gig-mills, some using teasels and some wire cards, the object of the latter being to provide a more durable material than teasels, which were often scarce and dear, though they had not been superseded by 1850. There were also attempts to make the gigs work in different directions, either across the cloth or with a circular motion, but the original lengthwise direction proved to be the right one. The gig-mill was imported into France in 1802 and spread widely there after 1807, receiving many improvements. In England its success varied in different parts of the kingdom. In the west it seems to have been universally employed during the 1830s, but in 1850 there was still some hand-raising in Yorkshire.

In the production of machinery for shearing the nap, France preceded England, since the machine supposed to have been invented by Everett of Heytesbury in 1758 is a myth [22]. This machine appears in most continental histories of textile technology, owing to misleading information given to Roland de la Platière (1734–93) and embodied in the *Encyclopédie Méthodique*. The first shearing-machine was that of Delaroche of Amiens in 1784, but J. Harmer of Sheffield, who patented his in 1787, was not far behind. In these machines several pairs of shears were united by a crank and moved by power. Harmer improved his device in 1794, and there were several later patents. In some types the shears travelled across or along the cloth; in others, the cloth was drawn under them by means of rollers. At first this machinery seems to have spread more widely in France than in most parts of England, where opposition to it was strenuously maintained until the great depression of 1816. The first rotary machine was invented by an American, Samuel Dorr, and patented in England in 1794, but nothing more was heard of it here. It was improved in America, where other machines on the same principle were also produced. Introduced into France in 1812, it was improved by Collier, who patented it in England in 1818, where it was sometimes used [23]. More widespread in England, however, was the rotary machine patented by J. Lewis of Brimscombe, near Stroud, in 1815. This has generally been regarded as his own invention, though it is possible that he may have seen or heard of the American model, drawings of which were brought to England in 1811 [24]. These machines and others produced later differed in details, but all included a cylinder furnished with blades placed spirally round it, so that when the cylinder rotated they came into contact with a fixed blade underneath. The carriage on which the blades were mounted was drawn over the cloth either lengthwise or from list to list; and there were contrivances for keeping the cloth stretched and for bending it sharply at the point of contact, so that the blades might encounter the nap at the best angle. Rotary shearing-frames spread widely after 1820, but hand-shearing was not quite extinct even in the forties.

REFERENCES

[1] DOBSON, B. P. 'The Story of the Evolution of the Spinning Machine', p. 81. Marsden, Manchester. 1910.

[2] MURPHY, W. S. 'The Textile Industries', Vol. 3, p. 54. Gresham, London. 1910.

[3] FAIRBAIRN, W. "Rise and Progress of Manufactures and Commerce in Lancashire and Cheshire" in BAINES, T. 'Lancashire and Cheshire Past and Present', Vol. 2, p. 197. London. 1869.

[4] WADSWORTH, A. P. and MANN, JULIA DE L. 'The Cotton Trade and Industrial Lancashire, 1600–1780', p. 496, note 2. University of Manchester Economic History Series, No. 7. Manchester. 1931.

[5] 'Report of the Committee on Artisans and Machinery', pp. 102, 300, 327, 384. London, Parliamentary Papers, Session 1824, Vol. 5.
MONTGOMERY, J. 'A Practical Detail of the Cotton Manufacture of the United States of America', pp. 151–2. Glasgow. 1840.

[6] *Idem. Ibid.*, pp. 60, 61, 70.
'Report of the Committee on Artisans and Machinery', p. 327. London, Parliamentary Papers, Session 1824, Vol. 5.

[7] *Ibid.*, p. 385.

[8] MONTGOMERY, J. See ref. [5], p. 28.

[9] BROWLIE, D. *Trans. Newcomen Soc.*, **6**, 86, 1925–6.
URE, A. 'Ure's Dictionary of Arts, Manufactures and Mines', ed. by R. HUNT (5th ed. re-written and enl.): Spinning. London. 1860.
[10] LEIGH, E. 'The Science of Modern Cotton Spinning' (2nd ed.), Vol. 1, p. 145. London. 1873.
[11] DICKINSON, H. W. *Trans. Newcomen Soc.*, **25**, 123–37, 1945–7.
[12] WEBSTER, T. 'Reports and Notes of Cases on Letters Patent for Inventions', Vol. 1, p. 573. London. 1844.
[13] BALLOT, C. 'L'introduction du machinism dans l'industrie française', pp. 241 ff. Marquand, Lille; Rieder, Paris. 1923.
[14] PICARD, A. 'Le bilan d'un siècle, 1801–1900', Vol. 4, p. 199. Le Soudier, Paris. 1906.
[15] URE, A. 'The Philosophy of Manufactures' (3rd ed., with additions by P. L. SIMMONDS), p. 151. London. 1861.
[16] BAINES, SIR EDWARD. "The Woollen Trade of Yorkshire" in BAINES, T. 'Yorkshire Past and Present', Vol. 2, p. 682. London. 1877.
[17] BALLOT, C. See ref. [13], p. 206.
[18] BAINES, SIR EDWARD. See ref. [16], p. 684.
[19] CLAPHAM, SIR JOHN H. 'An Economic History of Modern Britain', Vol. 2, p. 13. University Press, Cambridge. 1932.
[20] TAYLOR, W. C. 'The Handbook of Silk, Cotton and Woollen Manufactures', p. 154. London. 1843.
[21] DOLFUS, E. *Bull. Soc. industr. Mulhouse*, **3**, 323, 1830.
[22] PILISI, J. *Industr. text.*, no. 818, 51, 1955.
[23] 'Report of the Committee on Artisans and Machinery', p. 21. London, Parliamentary Papers, Session 1824, Vol. 5.
Ibid., p. 44. 1825.
[24] URE, A. See ref. [15], p. 141.
WEBSTER, T. See ref. [12], Vol. 1, p. 126.

BIBLIOGRAPHY

ALCAN, M. 'Essai sur l'industrie des matières textiles' (2nd ed.). Paris. 1859.
BAINES, SIR EDWARD. 'History of the Cotton Manufacture in Great Britain.' London. 1835.
BALLOT, C. 'L'introduction du machinism dans l'industrie française.' Marquand, Lille; Rieder, Paris. 1923.
BARLOW, A. 'The History and Principles of Weaving by Hand and by Power.' London. 1878.
BURNLEY, J. 'The History of Wool and Woolcombing.' London. 1889.
COLE, A. H. 'The American Wool Manufacture' (2 vols). Harvard University Press, Cambridge, Mass. 1926.
DOBSON, B. P. 'The Story of the Evolution of the Spinning Machine.' Marsden, Manchester. 1910.
DODD, G. 'The Textile Manufactures of Great Britain.' London. 1851.
HORNER, J. 'The Linen Trade of Europe during the Spinning Wheel Period.' McCaw, Stevenson and Orr, Belfast. 1920.
JAMES, J. 'History of the Worsted Manufacture in England, from the Earliest Times.' London. 1857.
KENNEDY, J. "Rise and Progress of the Cotton Trade of Great Britain" in 'Miscellaneous Papers on Subjects connected with the Manufactures of Lancashire.' Privately printed. 1849.

Idem. "Brief Memoir of Samuel Crompton." *Ibid.* 1849.
LEIGH, E. 'The Science of Modern Cotton Spinning' (2nd ed., 2 vols). London. 1873.
LIPSON, E. 'A Short History of Wool and its Manufacture.' Heinemann, London. 1953.
MARSDEN, R. 'Cotton Spinning.' London. 1884.
Idem. 'Cotton Weaving. Its Development, Principles, and Practice.' London. 1895.
MONTGOMERY, J. 'A Practical Detail of the Cotton Manufacture of the United States of America.' Glasgow. 1840.
Idem. 'The Theory and Practice of Cotton Spinning' (3rd ed. enl.). Glasgow. 1836.
MURPHY, W. S. 'The Textile Industries' (3 vols). Gresham Publishing Company, London. 1910.
PICARD, A. 'Le bilan d'un siècle, 1801–1900', Vol. 4. Le Soudier, Paris. 1906.
PRIESTMAN, H. 'Principles of Woollen Spinning' (2nd ed.). Longmans, London. 1924.
Idem. 'Principles of Worsted Spinning' (2nd ed.). Longmans, London. 1921.
REES, A. 'The Cyclopaedia; or Universal Dictionary of Arts, Sciences and Literature.' London. 1819.
TAYLOR, W. C. 'The Handbook of Silk, Cotton and Woollen Manufactures.' London. 1843.
URE, A. 'The Cotton Manufacture of Great Britain.' London. 1861.
Idem. 'The Philosophy of Manufactures' (3rd ed., with additions by P. L. SIMMONDS). London. 1861.
Idem. 'Ure's Dictionary of Arts, Manufactures and Mines', ed. by R. HUNT (5th ed. rewritten and enl., 3 vols). London. 1860.
WADSWORTH, A. P. and MANN, JULIA DE L. 'The Cotton Trade and Industrial Lancashire, 1600–1780.' University of Manchester Economic History Series, No. 7. Manchester. 1931.
WARDEN, A. J. 'The Linen Trade, Ancient and Modern' (2nd ed.). London. 1867.

Penny token issued by Jackson and Lister of Barnsley, c 1811.

10

PART II

THE TEXTILE INDUSTRY: SILK PRODUCTION AND MANUFACTURE, 1750–1900

W. ENGLISH

THE period from 1750 to 1850 saw appreciable progress towards more scientific methods in the culture of the silkworm (*Bombyx mori*), and this coincided with the transfer of more of the work from peasant homes to the filatures, or larger silk-producing establishments. In Italy, in particular, a number of painstaking scientists and agriculturists carried out experiments and made numerous observations concerning the life and habits of the silkworm—more correctly, the silk-caterpillar—in relation to the qualities and quantities of the silk produced by it, and their findings contributed largely towards increasing the efficiency of the silk-producing industry, not only in Italy but in other parts of the world.

The selection of those cocoons from which moths were to be allowed to emerge for breeding was made chiefly by reference to their shape and size, and the fineness of the silk filaments. No attempts seem to have been made to develop strains from which eggs could be obtained, although some producers preferred to buy eggs from other sources rather than continue using eggs from their own stocks. Experiments had shown that artificial heating of the compartments in which the worms were reared, in order to avoid excessive variations in temperature, was extremely beneficial. Ample ventilation and a relatively dry atmosphere were also found to be important factors in maintaining the health of the worms, and means for obtaining these conditions were provided. Count Vincenzio Dandolo (1758–1819), one of the most prominent members of the group of experimenters mentioned, did much to improve the conditions under which the silkworms were reared. He was particularly zealous in the matter of ventilation and cleanliness, having noted the unhealthy conditions under which the worms were reared in the dwellings of the Italian peasantry. He widely disseminated the knowledge he had gained from his experiments, both in his writings and in lectures. His book was published in an English translation [1] in 1825 by a chartered company—The British, Irish and Colonial Silk Company—which had the avowed purpose of developing the culture of the silkworm in Great Britain, Ireland, and certain colonies.

Disease amongst silkworms was then common; this was not surprising in view of the conditions under which silkworm culture had been carried on for centuries. One very prevalent disease was known as jaundice because of its effect on the colouring of the worms; the application of powdered lime was found to be a satisfactory preventive, if not a cure. It was about the middle of the nineteenth century that another disease, which was later given the name *pébrine*, began to cause considerable anxiety amongst the French producers. There was indeed justification for this concern, since between 1853 and 1865 the output of silk cocoons in France was reduced, through this disease, from 26 000 000 kg to a mere 4 000 000. *Pébrine* also spread to other European silk-producing countries, and even to the east, but the story of Pasteur's successful investigations of it, resulting in the restoration of the silk-industry to its former prosperity, belongs to a later period (p 320).

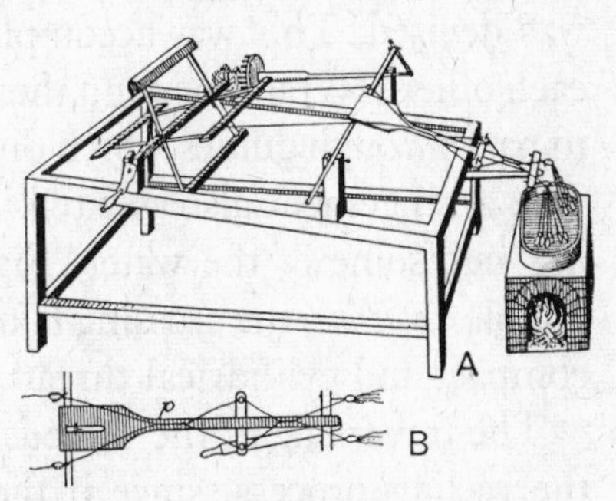

FIGURE 168—(A) *Eighteenth-century silk-reeling machine.* (B) *The double* croisure *on the silk-reeling machine.*

The East India Company was responsible for developing silk-production in India. Up to the middle of the eighteenth century Bengal silk was of extremely low quality—it was worth only one-third to one-half as much as raw Italian silk—and the quantity available for export was insignificant. In 1772 the Company sent a number of experts to Bengal, with the result that in a few years satisfactory qualities were established and exports considerably increased. The basis of most of this work appears to have been instruction in, and the adoption of, Italian methods of sericulture. Even by 1828, however, and 'notwithstanding all the attention and care which the East India Company have devoted to an amelioration of their filatures' the silk was not good enough for 'the richest qualities of broad goods' [2].

I. THE REELING OF SILK

From the viewpoint of quality, reeling—that is, the unwinding of the silk cocoon—is almost as important as the health and development of the silkworm. Careful attention on the part of the operative is a major factor, but improvements in the reeling-machines have contributed towards better results. These machines were turned by hand, and usually two separate skeins were reeled at the same time. Figure 168 A shows a side-view of the type of reel in use in the period. The water in which the cocoons were placed was heated by a fire below the basin (seen on the right of the figure), and one of the difficulties arising from this method of heating was that of maintaining a suitable temperature. The operative kept a vessel of cold water by her side to cool the heated water when necessary. Subsequently the water was steam-heated, and the expression 'steam-filature' was evolved. The filaments, collected together from several cocoons to form one group, were taken over a kind of bobbin on their way to the reel. This tended to flatten the thread, and in order to prevent the flattening, and to preserve a circular cross-section and compact construction, the *croisure* or crossing of the threads was devised. This was accomplished either by twisting adjacent threads round each other several times and then separating them, or by arranging for one thread to pass through guides which diverted it and allowed it to be twisted round itself. The arrangement also assisted in the quicker drying of the filaments by squeezing out some of the water. Figure 168 B shows in plan an enlarged view of a double *croisure*, the crossing taking place at *p*; this improvement gave a still more compact and cylindrical thread.

The traversing of the threads across the face of the reel was necessary during the reeling process, since if they had been allowed to pile up over preceding layers before the threads were dry they would have become gummed together. There were several methods of providing this traverse. In some cases a wheel on the axis of the reel drove, through a band or cord, a wheel which actuated the traverse-guide—usually referred to in the eighteenth century as a guide-stick. In other examples cog-wheels (figure 168 A) were used, giving a positive drive without risk of slip, as might happen with a band-drive. The ratio of the diameters of the wheels, or of the numbers of teeth in the cog-wheels, determined the rate of spread of the threads along the reels; S. Pullein devised a ratio which provided that the threads were not laid again in the same part of the reel until nearly 600 yds had been wound. This was at a time when the usual interval was 150 yds, and the method therefore greatly reduced the risk of threads adhering because of insufficient drying [3].

Italian reeled silks were considered much superior in quality to French silks, but so far as the reeling process affected these standards it would appear that the difference was not due to any constructional superiority in the Italian machines, or even to better technique amongst the reelers, but rather to the stricter control enforced by the Piedmontese government over those responsible for the reeling processes [4]. In 1825 John Heathcote, an Englishman already famous as the inventor of a lace-making machine, patented a cocoon-reeling machine that was later copied and used in the Italian silk industry.

II. SILK-THROWING

The introduction of silk-throwing machinery (plate 15) into England, and its rapid early development by reason of the enterprise of John and Thomas Lombe, belong to an earlier period than the one under consideration. It is, for example, not generally realized that Lombe's silk-mill at Derby preceded Arkwright's first cotton-mill by over fifty years. What does concern us here, however, is the fact that once Thomas Lombe's patent lapsed, in 1732, and others began to use his processes, various improvements were applied to the machines. This was a somewhat gradual operation, largely because import duties on thrown-silk yarns protected the new English industry, and it was not considered necessary to aim at greater efficiency. One authority stated that very few improvements took place before 1824, and that before that year 'no machinery in Great Britain was so barbarous as that in the throwing trade' [2]. The duties were relaxed in 1826, and new and improved machines began to be installed more generally. But if British throwsters were tardy in modernizing their equipment, continental throwsters seemed to have remained at a standstill. As late as the 1830s the Piedmontese were still using the same types of machines as Lombe had copied in 1718; in France, too, at the same date, no improved machinery had 'up to a very recent period' been made for throwing silk.

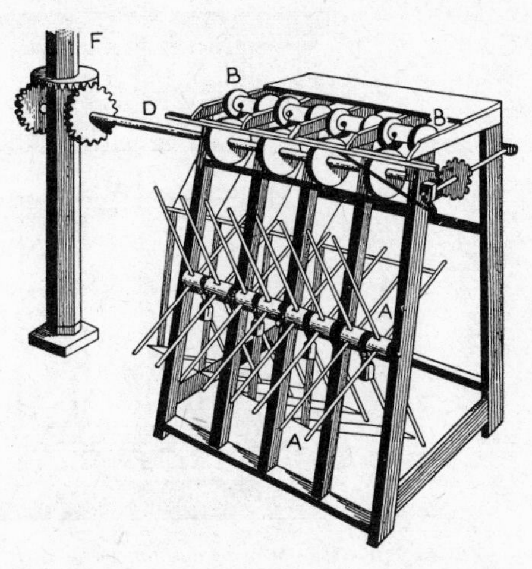

FIGURE 169—*Silk-winding machine of the early nineteenth century.* (AA) *reels or swifts, upon which skeins of silk were placed;* (BB) *bobbins for winding silk.* (D) *the layer, a light wooden rod with holes in it through which the silk was guided on to the bobbin; it was moved to the right and left by a crank.*

The improvements did not involve any fundamental changes in the throwing processes, and were mainly constructional alterations in the machinery. For example, wood was replaced by cast iron in the making of wheels, and crudely made wrought iron spindles were superseded by turned steel spindles. Similarly, metal bearings for the spindles replaced wooden shoulders. Elementary though these changes appear to be, they made an enormous difference to the performance of the machines: spindle-speeds reached 3000 rpm (the Italian and French machines operated at only about 300 to 800 rpm) and costs were reduced by almost 50 per cent.

Throwing in the wider sense of the term involves winding and doubling operations as well as the actual throwing or twisting. Figure 169 shows an early winding-machine, in which the skeins of silk, mounted on swifts (light revolving frames) AA, were transferred to the bobbins BB. Generally the machines were much longer than the one shown. Figure 170 shows a simple form of throwing-machine, in this case arranged for manual operation; by extending shaft R and gearing it to a vertical driving-shaft similar to shaft F in figure 169 the machine could be power-operated. The bobbins wound on the preceding machine now

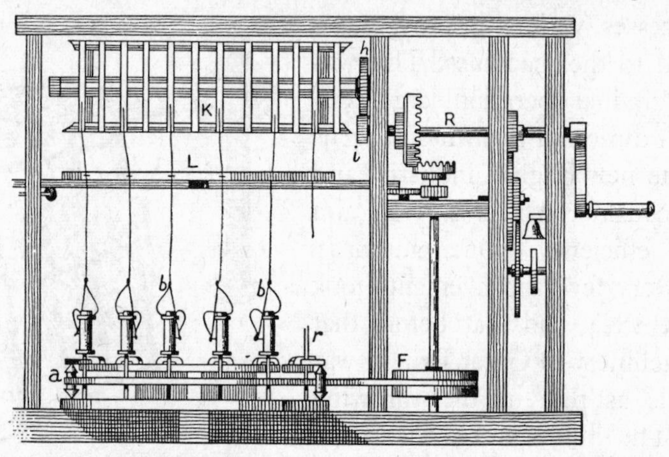

FIGURE 170—*Silk-throwing machine of the early nineteenth century, as used in the home. From the arrangement of spindles it was known as 'the oval'; normally it contained 13 spindles, of which only 6 are shown. Bobbins were placed on spindles* (r) *and thread was led through a piece of bent wire called the flyer* (b) *with an eye at each end. The thread was then led through an eye in the oval frame* (L), *which was given traversing motion by a crank, and so to the reel* (K). *As spindle and flyer revolved, twist was given to the thread, the tightness or hardness being regulated by the size of wheels* (h) *and* (i), *which were changeable.*

supplied the thread, and withdrawal of the yarn was aided by the wire flyers *b* which were free to rotate. The bobbins were mounted on spindles, which were rotated by the belt *a* driven by the pulley F. As the reel K rotated it withdrew the yarn from the bobbins and re-formed it into a skein. During the process the rotation of the bobbins caused the yarn to twist, and the degree of twisting could be varied by changing the gear-wheels. As bar L was given a rapid side-to-side motion, and as the yarn guides were fixed to this bar, the yarn was wound round the swift in a crossed formation. This spreading of the threads made the skeins easier to handle. The mechanism was patented by Nouaille in 1770. In his specification he claimed that this quick crossing of the yarn 'had never been done before' [5].

The doubling-machine was in effect another winding-machine, in which two or more single yarns on separate bobbins were transferred to one bobbin. This process was necessary when organzine[1] yarns, intended for the warp threads in

[1] From the town of Urgenj, in Turkestan, an early market for Chinese silks.

the loom, were being produced, and was a preliminary to the process of throwing or twisting the two or more yarns together. It was important that the full complement of single yarns should always be maintained, and to assist in this object a stop-motion was applied to the machine to interrupt the winding process when any of the single yarns failed. This may or may not have been applied to Lombe's original machine, although it is clear from his patent specification that there was a stop-motion on his winding-machine, where it was not so important a requirement. The stop-motion of the doubling-machine is shown in figure 171, where A is one of the supply bobbins and B is the receiving bobbin driven by the disk F, as in the winding-machine described. It will be noticed that the yarn passes through a guide *e*. This guide is free to slide up and down in a hole in the frame *f*, and the tension of the yarn is such that it keeps the guide out of contact with a lever *t*. If the yarn fails, however, the guide falls, and depresses lever *t*, so that its other end *v* enters the teeth of the ratchet formed in the flange of the bobbin B and arrests its motion.

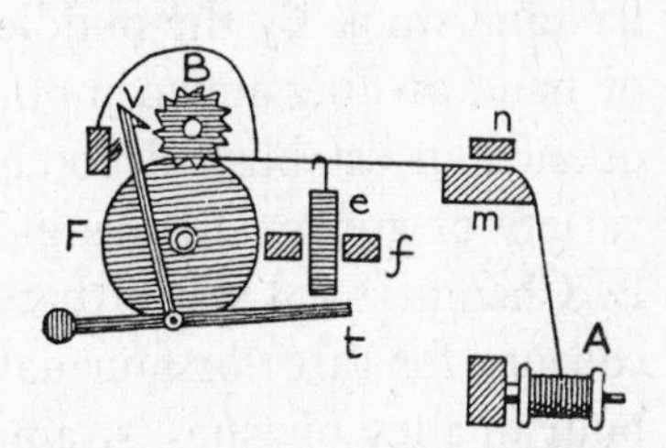

FIGURE 171—*Stop-motion silk-doubling machine, early nineteenth century. Thread from bobbin* A *is first cleaned by passage between* m *and* n. *It then passes under the hook in* e, *which slides up and down in* f. *If the thread breaks,* e *falls and depresses* t, *which allows pawl* v *to enter teeth of ratchet and prevent the receiving bobbin* (B) *from turning.*

The setting or stabilizing of the twist in thrown yarns was effected by immersing the skeins in boiling water. During the period under consideration, steaming replaced this method. This was quicker and more effective than immersion.

III. THE SPINNING OF WASTE SILK

Even today rather more than half the silk produced by the cultivated silkworm is unreelable, and it is probable that this proportion was even greater when silkworm culture and silk-reeling were less efficient. It is this unreelable silk, consisting of cocoon-remains after reeling, damaged cocoons which will not unwind continuously, and the ordinary processing-wastes resulting from silk-throwing and so on, which is described as 'waste' silk. Given suitable preparation, however, this so-called waste can be spun, the products being known as spun silk yarns to distinguish them from the thrown or nett silks. Because a specialized form of spinning has been developed within the last hundred years it is sometimes thought that silk-spinning in general is a modern conception, but this is not so. In fact, some authorities say that silk-spinning originated before silk-throwing, and in support of this view state that the moths of the wild (uncultivated) silkworms would break through their cocoons before the latter were collected. Such cocoons would of course be unreelable.

The possibilities of spinning became obvious once it was discovered that fermentation—or, alternatively, steeping in certain hot aqueous solutions—removed much or all of the gummy matter in the silk, leaving a soft, fibrous, and lustrous mass; for the fibres could then be cleaned, carded, dressed, and spun much as flax and wool. By the middle of the eighteenth century silk-spinning by means of hand carding and combing, followed by the distaff and wheel, was in consequence an established cottage industry, and the yarns were used for a wide variety of goods, such as gloves, stockings, shawls, neckerchiefs, and ribbons. E. Chambers [3] states that the degumming process consisted in steeping the cocoons for three or four days, with frequent changes of water, boiling half an hour in a ley of ashes, straining, washing, and drying in the sun. The combing or dressing operation consisted in passing heckles or combs through the silk while it was held at one end. When the fibres were sufficiently near to parallel, with short fibres and impurities removed, the tuft was reversed so that the processed portion was held whilst the other end was combed.

The gradual mechanization of spinning processes in Great Britain naturally led to attempts to spin waste silk by machinery. A number of patent specifications issued during the latter half of the eighteenth century, while primarily relating to processes involving the preparation of flax and wool for spinning, also mentioned the suitability of the machines for the corresponding treatment of silk. Amongst these were Thomas Wood's combined carding and spinning machine [6], Cartwright's comb [7], and Axon's cleaning and fining machine [8].

But although the preparatory processes of breaking, opening, and heckling required little modification to render them suitable for operating on waste silks, combing methods in use were not satisfactory. This was due to the excessively tangled and matted condition of the fibres and to the action of the combers, resulting in excessive losses of expensive silk as 'waste'. Another difficulty lay in the fact that the silk fibres were present in a variety of lengths, from very short to very long. In the successful spinning machines of the day—Arkwright's throstle-frame and Crompton's mule—the attenuation of the loose strands of fibres was done by drawing-rollers, and these rollers were spaced apart to correspond with the average length of the fibres. Any fibres that were too long would break or otherwise disturb the flow of attenuation, while those too short would tend to accumulate and create thick places in the yarn. This explains why cotton, having relatively short fibres, not too variable in length in a given quality, was successfully spun on these machines.

The obvious solution was to cut the silk fibres to shorter lengths. This was in fact done on machines made somewhat like chaff-choppers, which cut the fibres to lengths varying from 1 to 2 in, corresponding to cotton-fibre lengths.

The mechanical spinning of waste silk began in 1792 at a factory near Lancaster, and subsequently a number of other concerns were started both in Lancashire and in Yorkshire. In one or two instances existing cotton-spinning mills began spinning waste silk. These developments were confined at first entirely to Great Britain, and it was not until about the second decade of the nineteenth century that other countries began mechanized spinning, although on the continent in particular there was a very large cottage industry.

The cutting of the fibres into such short lengths was necessary in order that they could be spun on cotton machinery, but it was not long before attempts were being made to spin the material without such drastic treatment. Machinery for preparing and spinning long fibres was being developed in the flax and wool industries and it was to these sources that inventors turned for ideas. The first of them were Gibson and Campbell [9], of Glasgow (1836). In their specification they were frank enough to say that the machinery described was the same as that used by flax-spinners, and it is therefore not surprising to find that, following an action at law [10], a disclaimer regarding some sections of the patent was issued. The case also brought to light the fact that a number of spinners had been using flax machinery more or less openly for spinning waste silks before 1836. It was in connexion with Gibson and Campbell's process that the term 'long-spun' or 'long-spinning' was first applied to spun silk, to distinguish it from the cotton-system where the cut fibres were used.

Other attempts to prepare and spin the fibres without cutting them were made by Iveson [11] in 1838 and by Templeton [12] in 1841. To obviate the old method of cutting and carding the former used fluted drawing-rollers to tear the fibres apart, afterwards subjecting them to further pressure to render them softer and more pliable. It was Templeton, however, who seemed to hit on the right idea—that of carding or combing the fibres in such a way that at least two separate groups of fibres were formed, one group containing long fibres and the other short fibres.

An improvement in spinning-machines made in 1833, and intended for all long-fibre processing, ultimately proved extremely valuable in the spinning of long-fibred waste silk. This was the invention by Lawson and Westly [13], in 1833, of the screw-gill. Gills or fallers are essentially combs that move along between two pairs of drawing-rollers, so assisting in carrying forward the shorter fibres. They are an important part of the drawing operation, and the inventors applied a worm-gear drive instead of the unreliable chain-and-sprocket drive hitherto used to move the fallers along between the rollers.

Fully satisfactory preparation of waste silk for the spinning process was not achieved until a mechanical dressing-machine was devised by which the silk was separated into a number of groups, known as drafts, according to their fibre-

FIGURE 172—*Loom for weaving silk brocade, worked by a draw-boy.*

lengths. These developments took place mainly during the second half of the century.

IV. WEAVING

Nearly all improvements to looms have ultimately been applied to the weaving of more than one kind of textile material. This has been true of the Jacquard machine, but as it was originally specifically applied to the silk-loom it will be dealt with here; accounts of other developments will be found in the first part of this chapter. The weaving of more or less elaborate designs was a natural development for the enhancement of fine and lustrous silk fabrics, even though such weaving was a slow and laborious process involving the use of a draw-boy to select and lift the correct warp threads for each insertion of weft (figure 172 and vol III, ch 8). A diagram of the draw-loom apparatus is given in figure 173. It shows the comber-board, below which the cords carrying the heald[1] eyes,

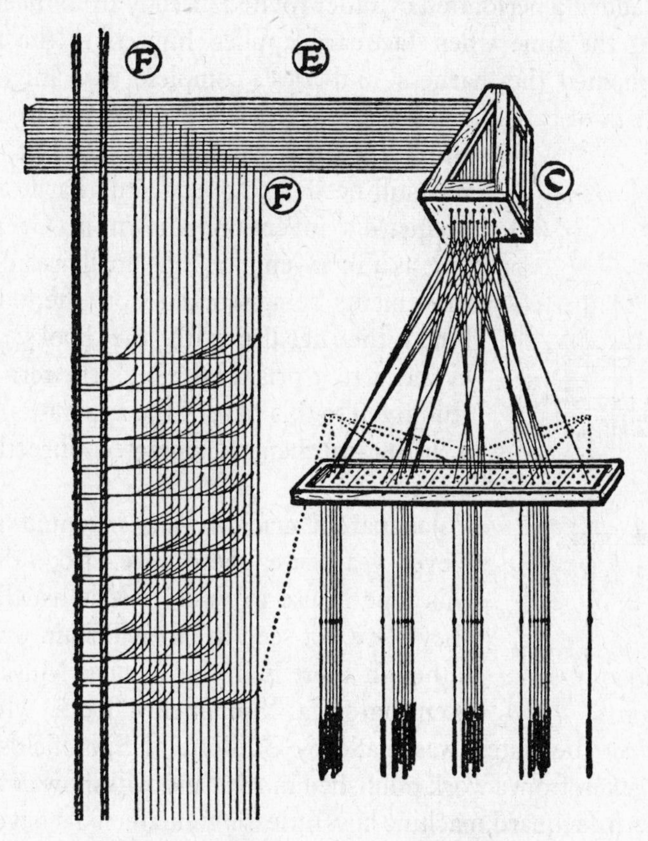

FIGURE 173—*Mechanism of the draw-loom apparatus.*

through which the warp-threads pass, are held taut by lingoes (p 318). Inside the triangular frame C are pulleys over which cords E move, the other ends being fastened to, say, a wall. It will be seen that when the draw-boy pulls one of the cords F, the corresponding heald eyes and warp-threads will be lifted. There had been attempts before that of J. M. Jacquard (1752–1834) to provide mechanism which would do the work of the draw-boy. One was patented by Joseph Mason as early as 1687, and another by William Cheape in 1779. In the meantime a number of inventors continued to apply modifications and improvements to the apparatus for selecting and lifting the warp, without actually making it automatic.

[1] Heddle.

Thus Bouchier had provided needles and hooks in 1725, and three years later Falcon replaced perforated rolls by a series of cards linked together. In 1745 Vaucanson transferred the apparatus from the side of the loom to an overhead position, and added a perforated cylinder rotated directly from the loom (vol III, pp 165–7). At the time when Jacquard applied himself to the problem, the apparatus embodied the 'harness' and 'ties', complete with lingoes,[1] comberboard, and chain of cards; the designs were transferred to squared paper, from which the cards were perforated. But the draw-boy was still needed to operate the harness, and it was Jacquard's invention, known in Great Britain at first as a draw-engine, that finally resulted in all the movements being worked from the loom. He combined the needles with the hooks, changed the cylinder to a prism (although the term 'cylinder' is still given to this part of the apparatus), and applied a lifting-mechanism operated directly from the loom.

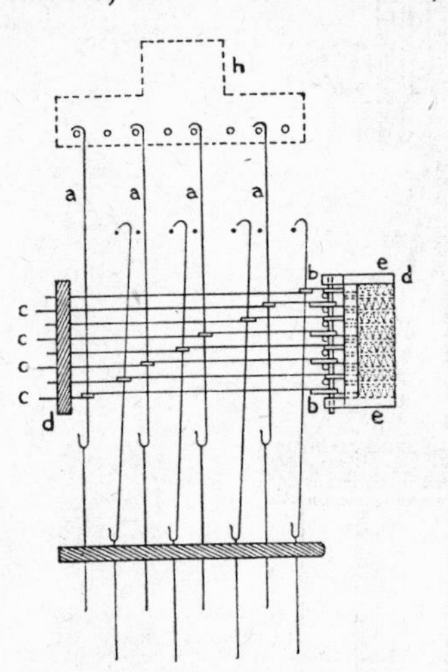

FIGURE 174—*Diagram showing the principle of the Jacquard loom.*

Jacquard's machine was invented in 1801, and eleven years later there were 11 000 draw-looms of this type in use in France. It is usually stated that they were not seen in Great Britain until the 1820s, although there is in the Science Museum at South Kensington a 'Spitalfields loom with Jacquard' which, the catalogue states, was made by Guillotte of Spitalfields about 1810. Figure 174 is taken from a work published in 1831 and will show to those familiar with the modern Jacquard machine how little the fundamentals have changed [4]. This apparatus is fitted to the top of the loom. The hooks *aa* pass perpendicularly through eyes in the needles *bc*, which are fixed in the frame *dd*. (Eight are shown but there may be many more.) The needles protrude at *c* and are kept in that position by springs *ee*. Above the frame *dd* is another frame *h*, which is alternately raised and lowered. The hooks are lifted by the bars in the frame *h* if they are retained in a vertical position. If they are thrust out of this position (as shown by the four lower hooks) the bars miss them and they remain down. The pattern of the perforations in each card as it is pressed against the needles at *c* determines which needles are thrust back and which are not; that is, a perforation allows a needle to remain stationary, and its hook vertical, so that the hook and the corresponding series of warp threads are raised. A blank in the card

[1] Pieces of lead or wire hung on the bottom of each coupling to maintain the tension.

thrusts a needle backwards, its hook remains lowered,, and the warp threads controlled by the hook remain below the weft.

In the meantime, and while Jacquard's machine was being kept a close secret, several British inventors had been working on the problem. The fillover loom developed by John Harvey in the early years of the nineteenth century, which produced the Norwich fillover shawls, required the assistance of a draw-boy but appears otherwise to have been a great improvement on existing looms. Other inventors, however, worked directly on the warp-selecting mechanism; they included Clulow (1801), Birch (1804), Duff (1807), and Sholl. A few years later they were followed by Jones and Hughes (1820), and Richards (1821). Some of these draw-engines are described and illustrated in the work already referred to [4].

One important improvement devised in Great Britain was that of W. Jennings, who so rearranged the ties in the Jacquard harness that with other alterations it became possible to place the machine in a much lower position over the loom. This was a useful modification not only in connexion with factory construction, but for what was still also a cottage industry. In Coventry, for example, where there were about 600 Jacquard machines in 1832, steam-engines behind rows of cottages supplied power to the looms inside.

V. THE PERIOD 1850–1900

No outstanding developments in silk-throwing took place after 1850, while the developments in weaving were common to textiles in general. However, a political action having far-reaching consequences for the British silk industry, and important advances in three branches of the industry other than throwing and weaving, will be considered here in order to complete the picture for the nineteenth century. This political action was the Franco-British treaty of 1860, by which silk goods manufactured in France were to be imported into Britain duty-free, while similar goods made in Britain were to be subject to a duty not exceeding 30 per cent *ad valorem* at the French ports. Before the ratification of the treaty, French silk goods were subject to an import duty in Britain, while British goods were completely prohibited in France. The immediate effects on the British silk-industry were disastrous, particularly among the Spitalfields weavers and the ribbon-manufacturers of Coventry. On a longer view, however, it is probable that technical improvements were, as a result, developed in the industry at a faster rate than would otherwise have been the case.

The important advances made in the sections of the industry other than throwing and weaving were concerned with Pasteur's work on silkworm diseases, the weighting of silk during dyeing, and the development of long-spinning in the production of yarns from waste silk.

VI. THE WORK OF PASTEUR

It was in 1865 that Pasteur (1822–95) began his investigations into the causes and prevention of silkworm diseases, particularly *pébrine*. After three years' work on the problem, he had isolated the bacilli of two diseases, and expressed the opinion that these diseases were of long standing, the then recent epidemic condition having arisen owing to the unhealthy conditions under which the worms were reared. The preventives he recommended were mainly based on the adoption of small, isolated rearings of the worms with frequent checks on their condition, including the opening and microscopic examination of selected chrysalides. Having established that a satisfactory condition of health existed, the eggs from such rearings were to be used by the commercial breeders. The adoption of these methods brought about a rapid improvement in the health of the worms, and Pasteur's work restored the prosperity of the silk industry not only in France but in other silk-producing countries.

VII. THE WEIGHTING OF SILK

The dyeing of textiles is dealt with elsewhere in this work (vol V, ch 12), but there is one aspect of the dyeing of silk which may be appropriately mentioned here. This is the weighting of silk, which is usually carried out as part of the dyeing process. Weighting is possible because silk has a chemical affinity for certain metallic salts, a discovery made in the early part of the sixteenth century. Other substances also have been used, such as sugar, which was employed in England, if not elsewhere, during the first half of the nineteenth century. Metallic salts, however, remain the principal ingredients, and when they are used with discretion the resultant weighting gives to the silk fabrics fullness and firmness in handling.

In 1857, in a small dyeworks at Crefeld, a skein of silk to be dyed black was by mistake immersed in a vat prepared for dyeing a Prussian blue. It was subsequently passed on for dyeing black, and was afterwards found to be more lustrous and much heavier than it would have been had it been dyed black by the methods then normal. Further experiments confirmed that this offered a means of weighting silk far in excess of other known methods, so that ultimately black dyed silks were often weighted up to 40 oz per lb, and some spun silks as much as 150 oz per lb. For many years it was only in black dyeing that silks were so heavily weighted, but by the 1880s the practice had spread to coloured silks;

salts of iron and tin, and a number of tannin compounds, were used for the purpose.

These developments took place chiefly in Germany and France, and, since they brought about a considerable reduction in the price of silk goods, the British silk industry suffered a serious decline. Lack of technical knowledge of the processes of weighting, and in some cases refusals to attempt such weighting on the grounds of commercial morality, were the principal reasons why British dyers did not at once follow the continental practice. As to the second reason, there was a gradual acceptance of the position that not only was limited and controlled weighting not injurious to the silk, but that in fact it improved the 'handle' and appearance. On the other hand, excessive weighting, carried out mainly to cheapen the goods, was extremely injurious, and many of the imported silks were soon looked upon with suspicion by the public after some experience of their poor serviceability. In the end, British dyers had in self-defence to begin the weighting of coloured silks, and the position was well summed up by one authority, who in 1885 wrote: 'It is absolutely necessary for a dyer to be a good chemist . . . but I am sorry to say the dyer's chemistry is almost wholly needed nowadays for the weighting of silk, not for the dyeing of it. Nothing is more difficult than to weight silk to the same extent the French do. The tinctorial part, since the introduction of aniline dyes, is easy in comparison' [14].

VIII. THE SPUN-SILK INDUSTRY

The preparation and spinning of waste silk is now almost entirely done on the long-spinning system, and the outstanding developments took place mainly during the second half of the nineteenth century. Not all sections of Gibson and Campbell's patent (p 315) were invalidated, and certainly some of the sections retained in the specification were subsequently applied with success. A number of spinning concerns adopted and improved upon the processes described in the specification, and it was not long before the spinning of long-fibred silk wastes became a recognized and established business.

As has been indicated, however, the combing of silk waste on machines similar to those used for combing wool and other fibres was not a satisfactory operation, and although many improvements were made in the processes preparatory to combing which further softened and disentangled the material, the combing operation continued to be performed by hand-dressing. The wool-comber S. C. Lister (1815–1906; he became Lord Masham) and J. Warburton invented a combing-machine in 1859 intended especially for the combing of silk, but although it was possible to spin high-quality yarns from its products much expensive fibre was rejected as waste, and commercially the machine was a failure.

IX. LISTER'S SELF-ACTING DRESSING MACHINE

Some nine years earlier, Greenwood and Warburton had introduced the intersecting gill, in which two sets of gills or fallers were used, one set working upwards and the other downwards, so acting on both sides of the sheet of fibres

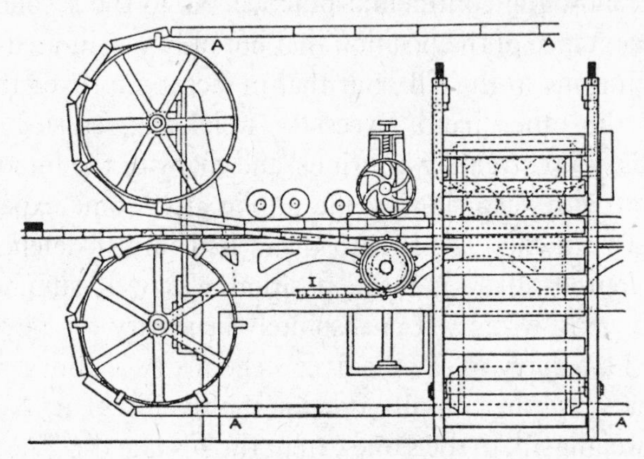

FIGURE 175—*Side view of Lister's self-acting silk-dressing machine, from the original specification.*

at the same time and ensuring better control during the attenuating process. Subsequent improvements and their application to the processing of silk waste ultimately resulted in Lister's comb becoming redundant, and Lister himself, now well established as a silk-spinner, installed the intersecting gills and reverted to hand-dressing. At the same time he began working on a dressing machine that should be automatic in operation, and in 1877 his efforts met with success. Although Lister himself claimed that his machine was the first self-acting dressing machine, de Jongh of Alsace had invented a machine of this type in 1856, and at least one authority [15] has stated that Lister's patents of 1877, 1878, and 1891 were mainly improvements on de Jongh's ideas. Certainly they made the machine workable and commercially successful. Figures 175 and 176 are taken from Lister's specification. These figures show respectively a side view and a plan of part of the machine. AA are two moving endless belts formed of wood blocks hinged together, and the silk is fed between these two belts, which hold it firmly while another endless belt carrying the cards or combs I moves alongside, as shown in the plan, and combs out the projecting tufts, straightening the longer fibres and removing the shorter ones. The cards are positioned in relation to the 'nips', as they were termed, so that the combing action is graduated, the teeth penetrating more deeply into the tufts as the combing proceeds.

An ingenious device on the machine provided for a transfer of the nips from one end of the tuft of silk to the other, so that the silk previously held could now be combed. An additional set of nips was provided for this purpose. The shorter fibres gradually accumulated on the cards; these were removed at intervals and subsequently again fed to the machine or to a similar machine. This process

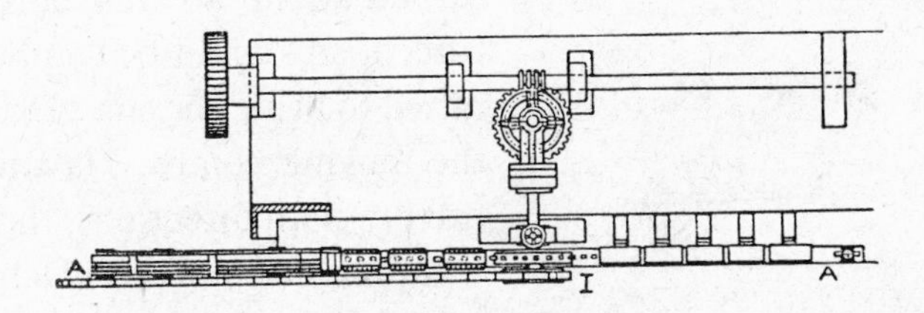

FIGURE 176—*Lister's silk-dressing machine, seen in plan.*

could be repeated as often as necessary so that finally a series of drafts of different qualities was produced.

A number of improvements were made on the machine from time to time. Fairbairn and Newton in 1856 devised an addition whereby the cards or combs operated alternately on both ends of the silk tufts 'during one passage of the holders through the machine'. Three years later they provided an intermittent feeding arrangement, while in 1865 Warburton replaced the travelling combs with cylinders. In 1889 Priestley patented an apparatus for automatically reversing the 'books' of silk, and for releasing the tufts on completion of the combing and transferring them to a delivery apron.

X. THE FLAT DRESSING MACHINE

It is not certain how many other spinning-mills adopted Lister's dressing machine. Certainly the flat dressing frames that came into general use in British mills bear very little resemblance to Lister's machine. They were probably so called to distinguish them from the circular dressing machines, which were being mainly used on the continent and for which a patent was first granted to Quinson in France in 1856, although they did not supersede the flat machine until after 1870. Greenwood and Batley, of Leeds, were making flat dressing machines as early as 1860.

A typical flat dressing machine, as used in Great Britain in the 1890s, is shown in sectional side-elevation in figure 177, the large drum and its adjacent parts being applied about 1880. An endless moving belt A carried a number of combs B and cards C. The silk, after preliminary preparation, was fed to the combs from the box or 'in-frame' E, consisting of a series of holders with screw adjustments so arranged that the silk was firmly held in position for combing. The whole box was movable vertically by the cams KK, and could be swivelled completely round on the pivot H, the whole being carried on a carriage J mounted on rails RR. The box could therefore be withdrawn from the machine for refilling; it could be turned round so that both sides of the tufts of silk could be combed; and it was raised to bring the silk gradually closer to the moving combs. Having combed the tufts in both directions, the in-frame was withdrawn from the machine while the tufts were taken out by hand and reversed in the holders so that the silk previously held could now be combed. The tufts were then removed and passed on to the next process. In the meantime the silk retained by the combs and cards was removed and prepared for further dressing, to constitute another draft with shorter fibres than the preceding one.

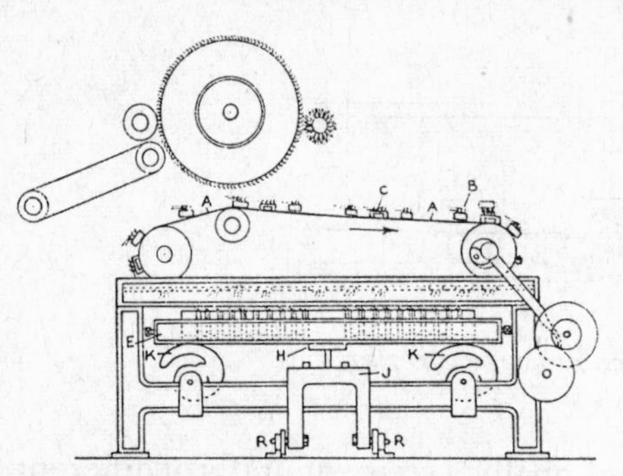

FIGURE 177—*Flat dressing machine, 1890.*

XI. BAUWENS AND DIDELOT'S DRESSING FRAME

The originators of this form of dressing were undoubtedly Bauwens and Didelot, who patented their process in France in 1821. Reference to figure 178, taken from the specification, clearly shows the similarity. The endless band *f* carries the cards or combs, while below is the table G with its nips or grippers pressed together by screws and holding the silk. The table is mounted on wheels for easy withdrawal; it is pivoted to reverse the combing action, and can be raised and lowered through the levers shown. Repetition of the operation produced several drafts. The inventors used the machine in their own factory in Paris, the motive power being a steam-engine.

Among British patents for improvements in this type of dressing machine was that of Molineaux in 1840, who, however, adapted his machine for flax and tow. Another improvement was that of Greenwood, who in 1862 introduced a variable-speed drive to the endless belt carrying the combs. It is generally accepted, however, that the main features of Bauwens and Didelot's patent remained unchanged to the end of the century—a remarkable achievement in view of the difficulties met with by the early inventors of silk dressing machines.

Although the circular dressing machine was not largely adopted in Britain until the turn of the century, it is worth noting that British inventors were concerned with improving it before that time. Thus in 1864 Greenwood and Hadley devised an arrangement of holders, mounted on a large revolving cylinder in the circular machine, which automatically slackened their grip on the silk as they approached the position where the operative was required to remove the combed tufts and replace them with uncombed ones, and then automatically tightened as they moved to the combing position. In 1881 Greenwood, with Schule, patented further improvements.

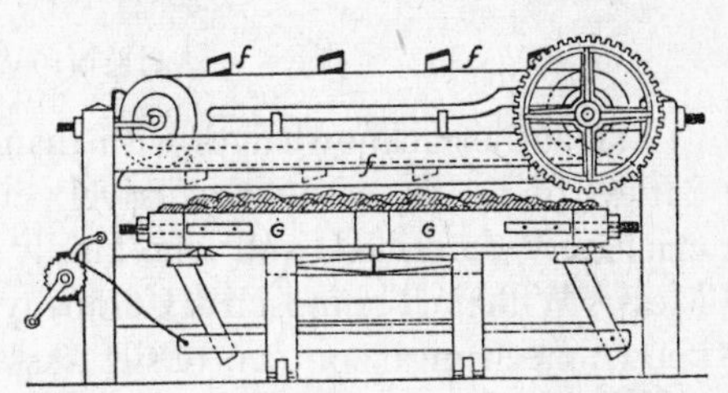

FIGURE 178—*Bauwens and Didelot's silk-dressing frame.*

XII. PROCESSES BEFORE AND AFTER DRESSING

As has been indicated, there were processes that preceded the dressing operation, and these were developed throughout the second half of the century. Thus improved degumming or discharging methods were adopted, and subsequent processes included suppling, for softening and freeing matted fibres by applying soap solutions; cocoon-beating, to free the silk of portions of chrysalis and other foreign material; and opening, to disentangle the fibrous masses further and partially to straighten the fibres. This was followed by a coarse combing operation on the filling machine, where the silk was spread uniformly over the periphery of a cylinder. This layer was next cut into strips about 7 inches in width, so that all excessively long fibres were shortened, and as these strips were removed from the cylinder they were placed between hinged boards termed book-boards, where they were firmly held and transferred to the in-frame of the dressing machine.

Processes following dressing were similar to those used in spinning other long fibres such as wool, and need not be described here. Spun-silk yarns being of a more hairy character than nett silks, it was necessary in many cases to remove these projecting fibres. Neps (very small bunches of tangled fibres) and foreign matter were also found to adhere to these yarns, and a combined gassing and cleaning machine invented by Lister in 1868 proved very effective in removing them. Each yarn was passed rapidly several times through a Bunsen flame, the yarn moving backwards and forwards round a series of bars so as to rub against itself at the crossing points; in this way the singed fibres were removed and the yarn cleaned.

About 1880, various types of the so-called wild silks, that is, silks produced by worms not cultivated and reared in the manner of the *Bombyx mori*, began to be used in the British silk-spinning industry. Tussore silk in particular, from wild Indian silkworms, was spun and woven into a popular range of fabrics. On the continent these and other waste silks were only partially degummed by a process of fermentation, the product being known as Schappe silk. The process was never adopted in this country and in fact has almost died out.

ACKNOWLEDGEMENTS

The author acknowledges with thanks the assistance given by Messrs Greenwood & Batley, of Leeds, who were actively engaged in the development of the silk-spinning machinery described, and who kindly supplied information from their early records; Messrs William Thompson & Company Limited, of Galgate, near Lancaster, the earliest known mechanical spinners of silk waste; the Textile Institute, Manchester; and Messrs T. M. M. (Research) Limited, of Helmshore, Lancashire.

REFERENCES

[1] DANDOLO, COUNT VINCENZIO. 'The Art of Rearing Silkworms. Translated from the Work of Count Dandolo.' London. 1825.
[2] BADNALL, R. 'A View of the Silk Trade.' London. 1828.
[3] CHAMBERS, E. 'Cyclopaedia.' Edinburgh. 1784.
[4] LARDNER, D. 'Cabinet Cyclopaedia': 'A Treatise on Silk Manufacture.' London. 1831.
[5] British Patent, No. 960, 1770.
[6] British Patent, No. 1130, 1776.
[7] British Patent, No. 1787, 1790.
[8] British Patent, No. 1935, 1793.
[9] British Patent, No. 7228, 1836.
[10] Law Journal Report. New Series. Common Pleas, p. 177. *Gibson* v. *Brand.*
[11] British Patent, No. 7600, 1838.
[12] British Patent, No. 9169, 1841.
[13] British Patent, No. 6964, 1833.
[14] WARDLE, SIR THOMAS. 'Report on the English Silk Industry.' Manchester. 1885.
[15] MANGOLD, F. and SARASIN, H. F. 'Société Industrielle pour la Schappe: Origines et Développement, 1824–1924.' Delchaux et Niestlé, Neuchâtel. 1924.

BIBLIOGRAPHY

BADNALL, R. 'A View of the Silk Trade.' London. 1828.
DANDOLO, COUNT VINCENZIO. 'The Art of Rearing Silkworms. Translated from the Work of Count Dandolo.' London. 1825.
HOOPER, L. 'Handloom Weaving: Plain and Ornamental.' Hogg, London. 1910.
HOWITT, F. O. 'Bibliography of the Technical Literature on Silk.' Hutchinson, London. 1946.
LARDNER, D. 'Cabinet Cyclopaedia': 'A Treatise on Silk Manufacture.' London. 1831.

MASHAM, LORD. 'Lord Masham's Inventions. Written by Himself.' Argus & Lund, Bradford and London. 1905.
RAYNER, H. 'Silk Throwing and Waste Silk Spinning' (2nd rev. ed.). Scott, Greenwood, London. 1921.
SILK AND RAYON USERS' ASSOCIATION. 'The Silk Book.' Silk and Rayon Users' Association, London. 1951.
WARDLE, SIR THOMAS. 'Report on the English Silk Industry.' Manchester. 1885.
Idem. 'A Paper on Silk read before the Society of Chemical Industry (Manchester Section).' Manchester. 1887.
WARNER, SIR FRANK. 'The Silk Industry of the United Kingdom.' Drane, London. 1921.

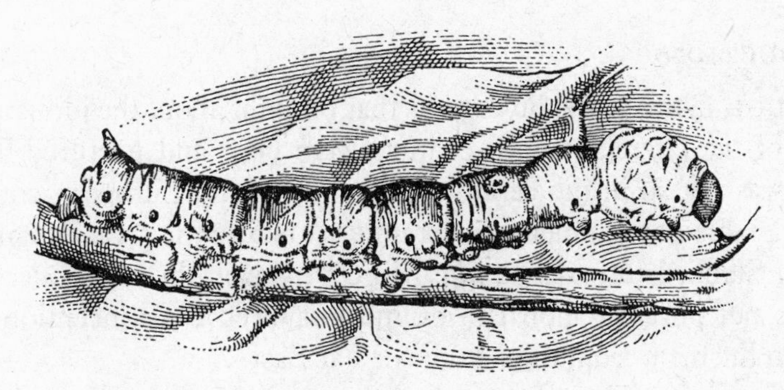

Silkworm (Bombyx mori).

11

CERAMICS FROM THE FIFTEENTH CENTURY TO THE RISE OF THE STAFFORDSHIRE POTTERIES

A. AND N. L. CLOW

I. INTRODUCTION

ALTHOUGH many of the inventions that brought about the industrial revolution of the late eighteenth century were born and nurtured in England, this was not so in the ceramic industry; several European countries had witnessed notable developments in ceramic art before the great expansion of the potteries in Staffordshire after 1750. Moreover, even these European developments were not purely regional in origin, but owed their inception to stimuli that came in the main from the Middle or Far East.

During the fourteenth century a knowledge of the materials and techniques of pottery-making, dating from the beginning of the Christian era at least, percolated into the Mediterranean area along the trade-routes of Syria and Persia. By the sea-route, the Portuguese, who had a trading-centre at Macao at the mouth of the Canton river, brought knowledge of the ceramic achievements of China to Europe, and following the establishment of the Dutch East India Company in 1609 a flood of oriental wares appeared in the European markets. Importation by the British East India Company dates from 1631. This imported china had a profound influence both on the technology and on the aesthetics of European pottery. Not only did the physical properties of the imported wares derive from techniques then unknown in Europe, but the idiom in which they were decorated became a standard of style that was widely copied and adapted to European taste. Attempts to copy both the quality and the style of the imported products stimulated experiment over many generations, and this led not only to the invention of new and discrete types of European ceramics but to the rediscovery of methods of manufacture used in the east. Thus in Europe pottery-making evolved over many centuries from a humble craft producing local ware for everyday use into a highly skilled industrial activity employing power-driven machinery and, particularly in the hands of Josiah Wedgwood (1730–95), such scientific knowledge of materials as was available. Not until this happened—and the whole process took several hundred years—did ceramic products appear in place of wooden and pewter furnishings on the tables of the artisan classes as well as on those of the wealthy. When the change did take place, Staffordshire—where potting of a sort, European in feeling, had been carried on since the middle of the seventeenth century—rapidly evolved into one of the principal pottery centres of the world. It used local coal and clay, but also imported raw materials over considerable distances even before the advent of railways. Its products were sold by English traders in all accessible parts of the world.

Wherever there was clay there were potters, and from the beginning of the fifteenth century rudely fashioned and simply decorated ware was widely made for local use. Nevertheless, without seeking to over-simplify the history of ceramics in Europe, one pre-eminent line of development can be singled out. It extends from the Hispano-Moresque pottery of fifteenth-century Spain, the best pottery in Europe from 1425 to 1475, through the tin-glazed *maiolica*[1] of Italian Tuscany (1475–1530), the hard-fired Rhenish stoneware of Germany, and the ware made by the alchemist Bernard Palissy (1510–88), to the dominant position occupied by delft, which was made at the Dutch town of that name, throughout practically the whole of the seventeenth century. In the following century Delft gave place in turn to Meissen (1710–56) and to Sèvres (1738–75). By this time European pottery was beginning to take on its modern form, and in due course the principal focus moved to Staffordshire (1775 onwards).

To pretend that this outline represents the whole development of ceramic art in Europe would be grossly misleading. While the dates given above denote the periods of pre-eminence of the types and localities named, the tradition of peasant pottery continued everywhere, with the possible exception of England, and the earlier great centres continued to operate, in some instances even to the present day. Thus, while for half a century Italian *maiolica* enjoyed an unrivalled position based on the quality and skill of its production, this position was one that, considering the universality of ceramic materials, it could not expect to occupy indefinitely. So one observes the spread of the manufacture to France, Germany, Switzerland, and the Netherlands, and its continued operation there, also over long periods. There was in fact parallel development everywhere, although—not unnaturally—success varied greatly from centre to centre, some regions being more favoured than others by the fortuitous existence of deposits of superior raw materials.

[1] The name *maiolica* is derived from Majorca, a source of the present Hispano-Moresque ware. Italian *maiolica* was made at many centres, including Orvieto, Faenza, Urbino, Deruta, Castel Durante, Gubbio, Caffagiolo, Florence, Pesaro, Forlì, Venice, Siena, Padua, and Castelli.

II. CLAYS

Unlike ores of metals, which often occur in relatively isolated lodes, the raw materials from which ceramic objects are produced are of extremely wide distribution. Moreover, it is on their rheological properties rather than on their chemical composition that the selection of clays for potting depends, although the composition decides the quality of the final product, its texture, refractoriness, colour, and so on. Even so, few clays can be used just as they are dug from the ground.

FIGURE 179—*The 'blunging' of clay. This was done by mixing the clay and water with a long-handled blade having a cross-bar as handle. These blades were usually made of ash. In the background is a sieve, through which the liquid was strained into the evaporating trough.*

The clay, or a mixture of clays, has first to be purified by levigation, that is, it is 'blunged' with a large quantity of water and the resulting suspension of fine particles sieved and run off (figure 179). The sludge has to be concentrated and dried until sufficient water has been removed to enable the potter to handle it properly. The stiff, but still plastic, clay is next wedged, that is, large pieces are slapped one on the top of the other to remove air-bubbles, which would cause deformation during firing, and to improve the rheological properties of the clay (figure 180). For countless generations all these operations were carried out by hand under exceedingly primitive conditions. Gradually, however, artificial heat was introduced for drying the clay in the vat or sun-pan, and power-operated machinery was used to mix it.

Having obtained his clay in a proper state for working, the potter can proceed in three ways. He can press the clay into a previously prepared mould (figure 181); he can throw it on the wheel (figure 182); or he may obtain the required shape by casting in a mould from a sludge of clay kept in liquid form by the addition of some such substance as water-glass. This method, introduced into England about 1750, gave the potter greatly increased facilities for the production of more complicated objects.[1]

Profound chemical and physical changes are brought about by firing. The temperature at which this is carried out, and the amount of free oxygen in the

[1] For the treatment of clays and general methods of manufacture and finishing see vol I, ch 15, and vol II, ch 8.

atmosphere of the kiln, determine the nature of the final product. In the Mediterranean area, where fuel was scarce and fuel economy important, firing did not bring about the same degree of vitrification of the clay as characterizes, for example, the stoneware of northern Europe, where abundant forests provided sufficient fuel to enable the kilns to be heated to 1200–1400° C, or even higher temperatures. It was this difference in the technique of firing that produced the distinctive Rhenish stoneware of Renaissance Germany, which was imported in

FIGURE 180—*The clay is wedged by throwing one lump of it on to another to expel any air-bubbles. The potter's wheel was turned by the man at the large wheel.*

large quantities into Elizabethan England. This ware later had an important influence on the technology of potting in Staffordshire although, as it happens, the first examples of it to be made in England did not come from Staffordshire but from the pottery of John Dwight (fl 1671–98) of Fulham, London.

While the vitrification of stoneware is sufficient to render it impermeable to water, impermeability is not achieved when products are fired at lower temperatures. Thus from very early times additional processes had to be carried out, on the one hand to render the vessels aesthetically more pleasing, and on the other to make them more serviceable.

III. DECORATION AND GLAZING

Slip decoration, the simplest of all treatments, is of great antiquity. A wash of clay-sludge is applied to the moulded or thrown article to improve its surface, and, if the slip is of a different clay, to produce a simple decorative effect by a variety of colour contrasts. A common practice was to use a whitish clay on the common red (plate 16 D). Fine early French, German, and English tiles were produced in this way, the decorative effect depending entirely on the use of different coloured clays. Designs could also be produced by scratching through the slip, thus exposing the clay of the body, and also by manipulating the clay while still wet with combs and brushes. These constitute the earliest forms of decoration.

A more satisfactory way of rendering pottery vessels impermeable to liquids is to coat the primary body with glaze, in essence a clear or coloured glass (vol II,

FIGURE 181—*Clay is moulded by first rolling it on to cloth, as by the workman on the right, and then placing it in or over a mould. The woman is fixing handles on to a moulded shape.*

chs 8 and 9). The origin of glazing is hopelessly obscure, but a siliceous glaze, consisting virtually of soda-glass, was certainly known in Egyptian times, and indeed Egypt may well have been the site of its origin; lead glaze, which had a greater adhesive power than the earlier siliceous glaze, was known from China to Rome as early as the time of the Han Dynasty (*c* 206 B.C.). In the more primitive method galena (lead sulphide) was simply applied by insufflation to the ware before firing, during which process the lead reacted with the silica in the clay body to produce on its surface a strongly adhering fusible glass. With the progress of chemical technology, artificially prepared lead compounds, such as litharge and red lead, were substituted for galena, and the production of lead compounds for potters became an important ancillary to the pottery industry.

Glazing opened up new fields for aesthetic exploration, and in time glazes became nearly as varied as the clays of the bodies they covered. The clear colourless glaze produced by the fusion of pure silica and lead oxide can be coloured by the addition of natural coloured earths containing iron, manganese,

FIGURE 182—*Clay thrown on a wheel turned by foot. An apron was fastened beside the wheel to catch the wet clay and slip thrown off as the wheel turned.*

and cobalt. Although the only colours available in the Mediterranean area were yellow and brown (from iron and possibly antimony), green (from copper), purple and brown (from manganese), and blue (from cobalt), ceramic artists evolved between the ninth and the sixteenth centuries a palette of surprising diversity, and with it produced wares of the highest artistic merit.

In addition to the property of taking up traces of iron, manganese, and cobalt to form coloured glazes, lead glaze has also the useful property that it can be rendered white and opaque by the addition of tin ash (stannic oxide). The resulting tin glaze, or enamel, hid most effectively the natural dark colour of many clay bodies and produced an attractive canvas, as it were, for increasingly subtle decoration; it also satisfied a social demand for a whiter ware and in many regions took the place of the earlier slip-coated ware. This property of tin oxide was known to the ancient civilizations of the Near and Middle East, and knowledge of it was probably brought to Europe by Mohammedan invaders. Certainly in the fourteenth century the Muslim countries from Spain to Egypt, and possibly beyond, were using it to coat a body made of whitish clay and sand which was subsequently decorated with vivid pigments and lustres. The use of tin glaze was much improved by Luca della Robbia (1388–1463). Its development and perfection gave us the Italian *maiolica*, an enamelled earthenware which was the pre-eminent ceramic product of Europe throughout the period 1475–1530 (plates 16 A and C). Tin glaze was also the basis of the delft ware of the Netherlands, which held the field throughout most of the seventeenth century.

The introduction of tin enamel had, however, one disadvantage: it caused difficulties in decoration, and at first only copper-green and cobalt-blue could be used, because manganese gave black and brown instead of purple, and iron unacceptable yellows.

The problem of colour in relation to ceramics is worth considering here, since, for chemical reasons, the range of materials suitable for the ceramic artist's palette is very limited. Unlike the colours used in any other branch of art, with the exception of enamelling, those employed in pottery must be stable at temperatures of the order of at least 1000° C, a requirement that severely limits the range of suitable materials. In spite of this difficulty, the four high-temperature colours, purple, yellow, green, and blue, used alone or in combination, have enabled the ceramic artist throughout the centuries to achieve a wonderful range of decorative effects.

Most pottery clays burn to a yellowish-red, owing to the almost universal presence of iron in them. This iron-produced colour can be transmitted to lead glaze, giving the type of effect that characterizes so much peasant pottery. But, as has been mentioned, lead glaze will dissolve several metallic earths to give coloured compounds of great permanence. The production of green glaze by the addition of copper is of great antiquity: some natural copper minerals are highly coloured and so may have attracted the notice of an observant early experimenter. The fact that copper dissolves in vinegar was recorded in Roman times. In the fifteenth century copper contributed conspicuously to the decoration of the Spanish Paterna ware, and three centuries later it was again used in the production of the early green ware that was the first of Josiah Wedgwood's successful productions.

The blues, so characteristic of ceramic decoration, are produced by cobalt. Their popularity rests entirely on a technological basis, and the reason for the predominance of cobalt blue in the decoration of the 'china' of the Ming Dynasty (1368–1644) was that cobalt was the only pigment that would stand the high temperatures used in firing the true porcelain of the east.

The Egyptians knew that blue could be produced with cobalt, and purple with manganese. Oxide of manganese occurs widely as the mineral pyrolusite, but the source of early cobalt is not known. The Chinese obtained their cobalt minerals from Persia; later supplies came from the Erzgebirge, on the confines of Saxony and Bohemia, and from Sweden. Besides giving purple, manganese when suitably applied will also yield a black: it was used, for example, by Wedgwood in the production of his black basalt ware.

The fourth of the high temperature colours, yellow, is produced by antimony, which with the addition of iron oxide yields an orange. These elements furnish the brilliant colours seen on Italian *maiolica* of the latter part of the fifteenth century.

The one conspicuous omission from the early high-temperature ceramic palette is red, the reason being that no stable compound possessed this colour. For a long period the only method of producing red was by the use of Armenian bole. Usually, however, red was omitted altogether from the decoration, or was applied at a subsequent firing as a muffle colour (p 336). From late in the seventeenth century ferric oxide, obtained by calcining ferrous sulphate, was used to produce red.

The use of the above materials indicates no little skill in prospecting for raw materials to produce the required colours, since in no case does the naturally occurring oxide bear any marked resemblance to the final pottery colour. Similar skill is evidenced in the production of the copper-red lustred Hispano-Moresque ware. How this ware came to be invented is not known; it is found in the Mediterranean region from the ninth century. The interesting technological point is that its production implies an empirical recognition of the difference between an oxidizing and a reducing atmosphere in the kiln. For the latter, smoke-producing material such as damp brushwood was introduced into the kiln at the appropriate stage in the firing. The carbon particles in the smoke acted as a reducing agent upon copper oxides applied to the body, forming a film of free metal on its surface, usually of a pale or dark copper colour (plate 16 B). Produced in Spain with great, if somewhat fortuitous, success during the Hispano-Moresque period, and decorated with coats of arms or texts from the Koran, it has a continuous history up to the rise of the Staffordshire potteries.

IV. DELFT WARE

The foregoing is in outline the technical knowledge available when one of the major events in the history of ceramics took place, namely the rise of the Dutch town of Delft as a dominant centre of European pottery production. The stimulus to this expansion of potting was provided by the greatly augmented importation of blue and white Chinese porcelain into Europe during the early years of the seventeenth century. Sporadic imports had occurred earlier, but it was the development of the Dutch trade with the east, following the foundation of the Dutch East India Company in 1609, that brought about the change in fashion and established the ideal aimed at by European pottery-makers for many years to come. Imported porcelain had properties then unattainable by European techniques, but within a few years (1615) Dutch potters were imitating it, albeit crudely, in tin-enamelled earthenware, virtually a *maiolica* (cf plates 17 A, B).

By the middle of the seventeenth century the tin-enamel industry had become centred on the town of Delft (though the Italian potteries continued to flourish) and for the next century the industry there enjoyed great prosperity. Historically, delft, a soft clay body covered with tin-enamel, forms a link between the medieval Italian and Spanish wares and products deriving from the technical discoveries that led to the manufacture of true porcelain in Europe.

Chinese porcelain, as has been said, was characterized by a quality and whiteness not previously known in Europe. To emulate such excellence, Dutch potters turned their attention to the more careful preparation of their clay and to the quality of their glaze, and this new degree of refinement affords a technical distinction between *maiolica* and delft. Originally the process consisted of throwing a carefully prepared fine buff clay, drying it, and baking it to give an unglazed and absorbent biscuit. The biscuit was then dipped in tin-enamel and dried; decoration in high-temperature colour was applied to the unfired enamel, a glaze applied, and the ware fired a second time.

By the end of the seventeenth century, a similar ware was being produced in England at Lambeth, Liverpool, and Bristol, and at various centres on the continent. Of these, Lambeth was the most Italianate (plate 17 C); Bristol was characterized by its chinoiserie; and Liverpool was celebrated for its punch-bowls decorated with representations of ships. This was the first painted English pottery.

V. OTHER IMITATIONS OF PORCELAIN

In attempting to imitate some of the effects seen on imported porcelain, the delft-makers had to turn from the use of true high-temperature colours as described above to the more elaborate palette produced by muffle colours; these are applied on top of the already fired glaze and fused at a lower temperature. Careful attention to detail, and the occasional application of an additional glaze, enabled the Delft potters to maintain a leading position in European ceramics until their production fell away in the face of competition from the superior ware produced at Meissen (p 338), and from the English salt-glazed stoneware and lead-glazed white and cream earthenware.

Up to this point the line of ceramic evolution is comparatively straightforward, but from the end of the seventeenth century it takes on a new complexity. There are two main streams of development: (i) the improvement of ceramic objects generally, and (ii) the avowed attempt to produce in Europe a ware comparable

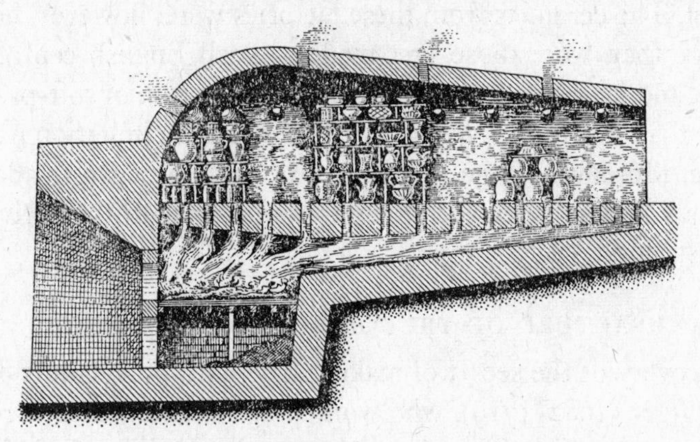

FIGURE 183—*Wood-fired furnace for porcelain.*

with imported porcelain. As a result of this latter activity ceramic evolution took place in three directions: (*a*) the production of a glassy (soft paste) substitute porcelain; (*b*) the production of a true porcelain from European materials; and (*c*) the evolution of bone-china, a peculiarly English innovation.

The introduction of porcelain into northern Europe was the result of Dutch and Portuguese trade, but knowledge of porcelain may also have reached Mediterranean Europe even earlier by the land route through Persia or Egypt. Certainly the first porcelain of any sort to be made in Europe was the famous Francesco de' Medici 'porcelain' which was made at Florence from about 1575 to 1585 (plate 17 E). It was a soft translucent paste composed of sand with Faenza and Vicenza clay fused together with a glassy frit made of rock-crystal and soda, and coated with a thick creamy lead glaze. The product was in fact more akin to opaque glass than to porcelain. After the Medici porcelain there is a long interval before the next record of any other glassy porcelain being made in Europe. This brings us to Rouen (of which the products are very rare) and St-Cloud, the first important French porcelain factory, founded in 1693. The St-Cloud body was formed from an ivory-white paste, which was inclined to crack during the process of firing. The glaze, which was greenish-white, was of good quality but prone to be marred by black specks derived from the wood used as fuel in firing it (figure 183). The manufacture of porcelain had spread to Chantilly by 1725 and to Vincennes-Sèvres by 1738 (p 339).

The Chantilly ware was made of a fine soft body. This was glazed for the first ten years with tin-enamel, but from then on with ordinary lead glaze. By contrast, the first productions of Vincennes were of a slightly grey paste covered with a good clear glaze. *Pâté tendre* was substantially a glassy frit containing chalk or marl. The ceramics from these factories were, however, not true porcelain any more than were those first made in such English centres as Chelsea, Bow, Derby, and Longton Hall, where the manufacture of soft-paste was begun slightly later than in France. Worcester ware also is an imitation porcelain based on soapstone. Moreover, these English factories soon began to add bone-ash to their clay body and so to evolve along a line peculiar to themselves, to be discussed later (section VII).

VI. THE MANUFACTURE OF TRUE PORCELAIN IN EUROPE

The rediscovery of the secret of making true hard porcelain is due to Johann Friedrich Böttger (1682–1719), who worked at Meissen, near Dresden: hence the name Dresden china. The story of how the Meissen factory with which Böttger was associated came to take the lead during the period 1710–56 is the next part of the history of European ceramics to be considered.

The porcelain factory at Meissen owes its inception to the association from 1707 of the mathematician E. W. von Tschirnhausen with Böttger, alchemist to Augustus II (the Strong), Elector of Saxony and King of Poland. First, Böttger succeeded, in 1708, in making a fine red stoneware like that imported along with tea from China, and esteemed as the proper ware in which to infuse tea. His successful technique derived from his realization that it was necessary to add a fluxing agent (alabaster or marble) to the naturally infusible Saxony clay. So hard is this red stoneware that it can easily be mistaken for jasper. By varying his raw materials, and particularly by using an earth from Aue, in the Erzgebirge, he soon succeeded in making a similar white porcelain body and so achieved the success that had eluded other European potters for many generations. Within a year he had also devised an appropriate glaze for his new ceramic body.

Founded on these important technological innovations, the Meissen porcelain works was established in 1710 and the new ware marketed in 1713. Böttger managed the works till his death in 1719, when he was succeeded by J. G. Herold (1696–1765). Herold made conspicuous contributions to the technology of ceramic production. He altered the composition of the body in 1722, making it correspond more closely to the Chinese ware it was devised to imitate, and developed suitable colours with which to decorate it.

In Böttger's method china clay (kaolin) was fused with the calcareous flux (marble or alabaster) at from 1300 to 1400° C in improved kilns. This calcareous flux was later replaced by a felspathic flux of petuntse or china-stone, which takes up the insoluble kaolin to give a translucent matrix rendered opaque by the infusible kaolin. This true porcelain is known as 'hard porcelain' to distinguish it from the earlier glassy or 'soft' porcelains of St-Cloud and elsewhere. It has a hardness of between 6 and 7 on Mohs's scale of hardness. The secrets of porcelain-manufacture were closely guarded, and Meissen was virtually a state prison.

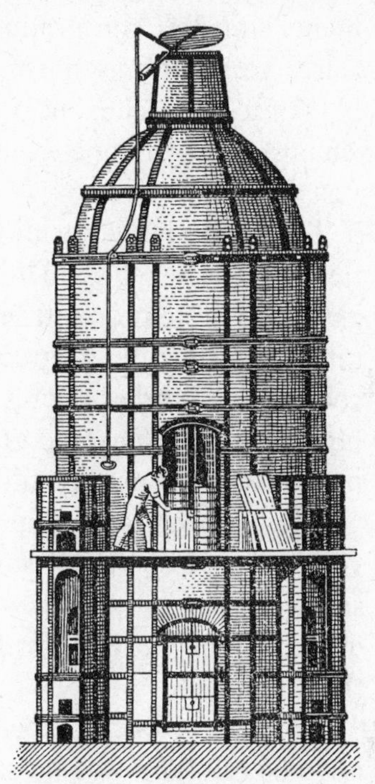

FIGURE 184—*Porcelain furnace used at Sèvres.*

Böttger was by no means the only chemist trying to make porcelain. Only a few years after Meissen porcelain came on the market, the famous French scientist R. A. F. de Réaumur (1683–1757) was experimenting towards the same end, starting with ground and powdered glass as his raw material. We also know that he received specimens of the true porcelain raw materials, kaolin and petuntse, from Père d'Entrecolles, superior-general of the French Jesuits in China, but at the time he was unable to distinguish kaolin from talc, and his publications do not indicate that he attained any decisive success. The first French hard-paste was made about 1758 in the laboratory of L. F. de Brancas (1733–1824), Comte de Lauraguais, scientist and Academician, with clay from Alençon. Having fled to England for religious reasons in 1763, he secured an English patent in 1766 (B.P. No 849) and promptly tried to sell it to Matthew Boulton of Birmingham. Only a couple of years later the manufacture of porcelain was started at Sèvres and the supremacy of Meissen came to an end.

Sèvres, the Manufacture Royale de Porcelaine de France, had been founded at Vincennes in 1738 under aristocratic patronage and utilizing technical knowledge brought by absconding workmen from earlier porcelain works. Success was long in coming, and may be said to date from the appointment of Academician Jean Hellot (1685–1766) to be chief chemist in 1745, a position he retained till 1757/9, when he was succeeded by P. J. Macquer (1718–84).

Although from the start the aim at Sèvres was the production of true hard porcelain, only soft-paste was made till about 1770, and costly experiments aimed at the production of hard porcelain were carried out for nearly thirty years. It was not till 1768, when Macquer began to use the kaolin of St-Yrieix-la-Perche, near Limoges, discovered some years before by the chemist Jean-Étienne Guettard (1715–86), that a successful hard-paste body was assured (figure 184).

The Sèvres body was difficult to work and very liable to fracture, two properties that may be reflected in the shapes that characterize this ware (plate 17 D). The glaze was extremely soft and easily fused, so that the over-glaze enamels sank into it to a greater degree than in almost any other porcelain. The ground-colours produced at Sèvres were outstanding: yellow, rich cobalt, and turquoise blue from 1753, an apple-green from 1756, and rose-pink from 1757. Many of the pieces were elaborately gilded with gold taken up in honey (p 356).

The discovery of kaolin and its exploitation by Böttger and Macquer afford yet another instance of simultaneous independent discovery in the history of science, for in the same year, 1768, William Cookworthy (1705–80), a Plymouth chemist, took out the first English patent for the manufacture of true porcelain (B.P. No 898).

Cookworthy began experimenting with Devon and Cornish clays about 1745, but not till 1768 was he satisfied that he had produced a true porcelain. His patent covered the manufacture of a ceramic body from 'moorstone' or 'growan', and 'growan clay', with a glaze made of china-stone to which lime and fern-ashes, or magnesia alba (basic magnesium carbonate), were added. With a company of Quakers, including Lord Camelford, he established a factory to exploit his discovery at Coxside, Plymouth. This was the first of the kind in England. At Plymouth, however, Cookworthy had to fire his pieces with wood, a convenient supply of coal not being available, and it was the difficulty of securing adequate supplies of fuel locally that led to his removal to Castle Green, Bristol, in 1770, only two years later.

Cookworthy's scientific skill exceeded his business acumen, and after some three years he was forced to make over his patent to Richard Champion (1743–91). Champion, however, encountered difficulties when he tried to renew and register an extension of Cookworthy's original patent in 1775 (B.P. No 1096).

This patent defines porcelain made from a wide range of proportions of clay and china-stone, and for the glaze suggests additionally magnesia, nitre, lime, gypsum, fusible spar, arsenic, lead, and tin-ash. Wedgwood and others challenged Richard Champion's patent and, following litigation, the use of kaolin and china-stone was thrown open to general use. The newly won freedom was eagerly seized by the Staffordshire potters, who applied it to improve their stoneware. In 1781 Champion himself was forced to sell the patent to a group of five potters in Staffordshire who, in the following year, began to make hard-paste porcelain at New Hall, near Shelton. This centre, and its two predecessors at Plymouth and Bristol, represent the only factories at which hard-paste porcelain, comparable with that made on the continent at Meissen, Sèvres, and other less important works, was produced in Britain. New Hall continued to operate till 1825, but from about 1810 it was turning out a product to which bone-ash had been added.

VII. ENGLISH SOFT-PASTE WARES

Having traced the evolution of true porcelain from its importation into Europe during the fifteenth and sixteenth centuries to the establishment of the small group of factories that made it in England, it is now necessary to go back a little to follow up another line of ceramic evolution: one that ultimately had a profound effect, particularly in Staffordshire. Soft-paste porcelain had been made in England considerably before 1768 as a result of experiments in which ground glass and other materials were added to the basic clay. In the successful substance, frit-porcelain, or soft-paste porcelain, the additional materials included kaolin of a sort, various calcareous minerals, and, at one particular group of English factories, ground bone-ash. These factories were at Stratford-le-Bow, Lowestoft, Chelsea, Derby, Longton Hall, and Worcester (plate 18), and while they may not be important in the history of European ceramics as a whole, they are of technological significance in that the developments they initiated led to the evolution of a hybrid ceramic species characterized by its content of bone-ash, and thus differentiated from contemporaneous continental wares.

The origin of the first English soft-paste factory, at Stratford-le-Bow, is obscure, but it is known that a patent for the production of 'a certain mineral whereby a ware might be made equal to porcelain' was registered in December 1744 (B.P. No 610) by Edward Heylyn, a Bristol copper-merchant, and Thomas Frye (1710–62), a painter and engraver from Dublin. The mineral, imported from the American colonies, is presumed to have been some sort of kaolin; it was known as *unaker* to the Cherokee Indians. A second patent was registered in the name of Frye alone in 1749 (B.P. No 649). The material patented was an earth 'the produce of the Cherokee natives' in America.

In his patent specification Frye refers to the use of 'virgin earth', derived from the calcination of animals, vegetables, and fossils. A. H. Church identified it as bone-ash (calcium phosphate). It was used to fabricate a soft-paste porcelain which was fired with wood 'in cases' (saggars) at about 1100° C. True porcelain, by contrast, requires a temperature of about 1300 to 1400° C. The Frye patent is important in that it appears to cover the first actual use of bone-ash in the production of a porcelain, although the idea had certainly been mooted in Germany a century earlier. Macquer, at Sèvres, adopted it some six or seven years after Frye.

At first the Bow paste was thick and heavy, subject to fire-cracking and warping. The yellowish glaze was soft, and so became abraded in use. It also tended to flow in the process of firing and to collect in pools round the foot of the article. With regard to decoration, the Bow blues had a greyish appearance: over-glaze printing was carried out in red, black, and puce.

The Chelsea Porcelain Works is believed to date from about the same time as Bow: bone-ash was first incorporated in the soft-paste there about 1755. Managed by a French potter, Charles Gouyn, and patronized by the Duke of Cumberland, until the 1770s Chelsea was the principal porcelain works in England, at first frankly imitating Meissen, but later developing its own style.

The Chelsea paste was soft, fragile, and creamy-white in colour, with a particularly vitreous glaze. The ingredients of the body were often badly mixed and when fused gave areas of increased translucence, which are highly characteristic of early ware. Both fire-cracking and warping are common. Most of the specimens are decorated in over-glaze enamels; following Sèvres, blue ground-colour was used from 1755, green from 1759, turquoise and crimson lake from 1760. Yellow was seldom used by the Chelsea decorators.

The Chelsea works was acquired by William Duesbury of Staffordshire in 1770. He had taken charge at Bow ten years earlier, but in 1775 he closed it down, transferring operations to Derby. Chelsea shared the same fate in 1786. The history of Derby porcelain, and of the celebrated Chelsea–Derby productions of the 1770–84 period, though well documented, does not concern us here, but one might add a note on Longton Hall, another factory with which Duesbury was associated, on account of the pioneering activities of its founder, William Littler. Longton Hall was founded in 1750 and operated till 1760, by which time it appears to have become associated with Duesbury. Its products were similar to those of Chelsea, but technically are not without interest in that

Littler was the first in Staffordshire to use cobalt blue—the so-called Littler blue, an under-glaze put on rather unevenly.

The production of the next porcelain manufactory, Worcester (founded 1751), is characterized by the presence in the paste of soapstone or steatite (a hydrated magnesium silicate). The introduction of this mineral into ceramics is associated

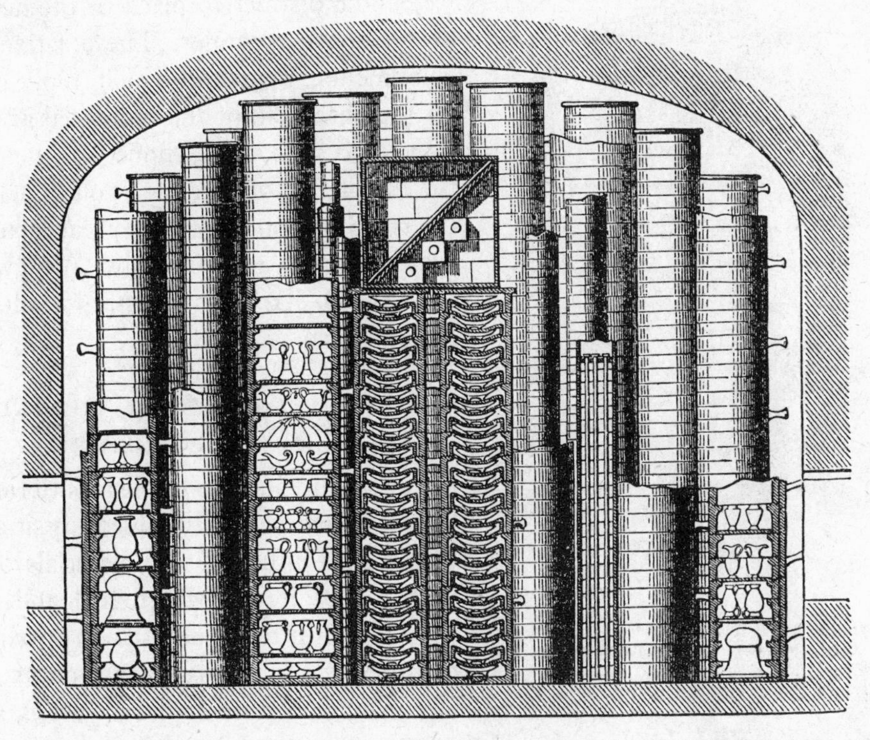

FIGURE 185—*Section of a porcelain kiln as charged at Sèvres, showing the use of saggars to prevent the smoke from coming into contact with the ware.*

with William Cookworthy, the first use of it in soft-paste having been made at Lowdin's Bristol Glass-house founded about 1700. This glass-house was an experimental one; it was transferred to Worcester in 1752 and with it the use of the new material. The resulting paste, which had a greenish tinge, was used till 1823, products of the period 1768–83 being characterized by a high proportion of steatite. On this ware an exceptionally fine glaze, containing a trace of cobalt, was brushed instead of being applied by dipping. Transfer-printing was introduced early, first in over-glaze black, red, and purple, and later (1756) in under-glaze blue (p 354).

To sum up the history of ceramic developments in England, the principal centres for delft were Lambeth, Bristol, and Liverpool; for true porcelain, Bristol, Plymouth, and New Hall (Shelton); for soft-paste, Bow, Chelsea, Derby, Lowestoft, and Longton Hall; for soapstone-paste, Worcester, Caughley, and Liverpool. The manufacture of bone-china started at Bow, spread to the other soft-paste potteries, and in time became the standard English paste, thus giving England a distinctive place in the history of European ceramics. These latter developments, many of which took place on the threshold of the industrial revolution, were, however, none of them in the direct line of ceramic evolution from the small pot-houses to the great factories such as those organized by Wedgwood and Spode. To this industrial evolution we now turn.

FIGURE 186—*Placing the saggars in the biscuit kiln. These kilns were 12 to 14 ft high and had eight fireplaces.*

VIII. THE EXPANSION OF THE INDUSTRY IN STAFFORDSHIRE

Few, if any, of the English potteries so far mentioned were advantageously situated with regard either to raw materials or to timber, and it was where fuel and clay were found in reasonably close proximity that the great industrial expansion of pottery manufacture took place. Just as with other contemporary industries, potting was influenced by the timber famine of the early eighteenth century, which in time made a shift to the coalfields inevitable. Not only did the need for coal determine the ultimate location of the great potteries, its adoption also brought in its train such technical changes as the necessity for firing wares in saggars (figures 185 and 186), which prevented the combustion products of coal from coming into contact with the ware in the oven.

The district of England in which pottery manufacture expanded most considerably was north Staffordshire, a region favoured by the occurrence of many kinds of clay, adequate supplies of coal, and an ancient potting tradition. Even in the late sixteenth century a considerable trade was carried on from Burslem and Hanley with ware made from local red-burning clay glazed with galena. Output in the early days consisted in the main of jars, bottles, and butter-pots, fired with coal dug by the potters themselves. About 1680 a second method of glazing became available when salt glazing was introduced into England from the continent, where it had been known in the Rhineland and the Low Countries since the beginning of the sixteenth century. It was introduced, it is said, although the attribution is doubtful, by David and John Philip Elers, two potters of Saxon stock who are reputed to have come to England from Delft with William of Orange. There are thus two lines of evolution, lead-glazed wares, and the salt-glazed. On the common brown clay, however, neither lead nor salt gave a product with the appeal of oriental porcelain or European delft.

The first step towards a white-bodied ware was the utilization by Thomas Miles of a pale Shelton clay to give a crude whitish stoneware. Experiment continued, and by adopting the Derbyshire crouch clay already in use in Nottingham, a brownish ware, known as crouch ware, was evolved. It dates from the end of the seventeenth century and was of a brownish or drab colour. All these wares were given a single firing which lasted for about three days, on the last of which, if salt-glaze was being produced, salt was thrown into the red-hot kiln. In the heat of the kiln, the salt reacts with the silica and alumina of the clay to form a coating of fusible glass on the surface of the hot primary body.

To the Elers brothers are also due the first attempts to improve form and finish, and to establish new standards of excellence in Staffordshire. Originally they had been silversmiths and it was probably to their previous skill in metal-working that their desire for refinement in ceramics may be attributed. According to A. H. Church the careful attention they gave to the levigation of the clay, combined with the fact that they turned the clay bodies on the lathe before they were fired, and their introduction of salt-glazing, were 'precious legacies to the Pottery District'; their technique brought about a complete revolution in potting methods in England.

From crouch ware, a white-dipped or slip-ware was evolved by treating the insides of vessels with a slip of white pipe-clay. This ware was in great demand from about 1710–40. Not only was the slip used to coat the whole inner surface of the vessel, but by slip-trailing or applying thinned-down clays of different colours, as in icing a cake, decorative effects of considerable charm were produced. This ancient technique, practised considerably in Kent, perhaps received its most perfect expression in the hands of two potters, probably father and son, both named Thomas Toft, of Leek, Staffordshire, in the second half of the seventeenth century (plate 19 A). Thirty-four of their dishes are known, two of them dated 1671 and 1677; they have been described as follows:

They were made from common clay, presumed to have been dug in the locality where the Tofts worked, to which fine sand may have been added. The pieces were wheel thrown and turned. All the decoration was executed on the ware before firing while the clay was still moist. A coating of white slip was first applied over the entire upper surface of the dish to provide a clay coating of pleasant colour and texture. The design was then drawn in by means of a trailer, resembling an oil-can, from which the liquid slip was directed. The initial outline of the design was executed in a dark brown slip made by colouring the red slip with an oxide of iron or manganese. Such decoration appears far too spidery in character unless enhanced by broad masses of another colour, and for this reason Toft filled in the main passages of decoration with slip made from different clay which fired an orange-brown colour. Finally white dots were added to the original dark brown outlines, producing a certain scintillating effect that enhances the whole design....

When the decoration had been completed a coating of pulverised galena, or similar lead compound, was dusted over the ware, which was then ready for firing. There is evidence that this type of pottery was fired to 1050° C.[1]

This was a further step in the direction of a light coloured ware as a substitute for the oriental porcelain or European tin-enamelled delft which, in London and the foreign markets, was then the most sought-after table furnishing. That pipe-clay, in the first instance, was used only as a slip was almost certainly a matter of cost, since it had to be brought to the potteries from a distance, for example from Bideford in Devon, no light undertaking in the absence of cheap transport.

So obvious, however, were the advantages of this white-burning clay that it was soon incorporated in a mixture with fine grit and sand, and a light coloured stoneware was made for the first time. Its invention is commonly associated with the name of John Astbury (1688?–1743). This fine salt-glazed stoneware (plate 19 C) enjoyed great popularity from about 1710 to 1780, its evolution contributing greatly to the subsequent prosperity of The Potteries.[2] In thin pieces it was translucent and its hardness rivalled that of quartz (Mohs's scale 7): it was, indeed, almost a porcelain. Macquer described it as having 'all the essential properties of the finest Japanese porcelain', and for many years it was a fashionable substitute for that ware, particularly as it brought some of the grace and amenities of the well-to-do within the reach of those less wealthy. It is interesting to note that the production of the other substitute for imported porcelain, namely tin-enamelled earthenware, never gained a footing in The Potteries. Instead, the continued striving towards a light-coloured body, and the invention of white salt-glaze ware, anticipated one of the major changes in the whole history of ceramics. This was the abandonment, at the behest of fashion, of the common red

[1] Cooper, Ronald. 'The Pottery of Thomas Toft.' Leeds and Birmingham, 1952.

[2] The Staffordshire potteries are mostly grouped in the six towns forming the county borough of Stoke-on-Trent, and this district is commonly described as The Potteries or the Five Towns.

and buff clays rendered white by slip or tin-enamel, and their replacement by a mixture of white-burning clay and calcined flint, giving a ware that was white throughout the whole body.

The practical utilization of ground flint (silica) in the ceramic body is also attributed to John Astbury. It was effected by him in 1720, although the idea had been mooted about 1698 by John Dwight (1637?–1703) of Fulham, secretary to the bishop of Chester, and himself the owner of patents for the 'mystery of transparent earthenware' dated 1671 (B.P. No 164) and 1684 (B.P. No 234), against the infringement of which he took action against the Elers and three of the Wedgwoods. Two of Dwight's notebooks, covering experiments from 1689–98, were discovered at Fulham in 1869. Thomas Heath of Lane Delph is also said to have made the suggestion before Astbury. The flint was calcined and ground to a fine powder (plate 20 A); the first flint-mill was built at Hanley in 1726. Added to native or imported clay, it lightened the colour of the fired vessel and gave it a more refractory body, in consequence of which it could be fired at a higher temperature and so rendered harder. The body was finished by glazing with salt or lead, of which the latter became ultimately the more important.

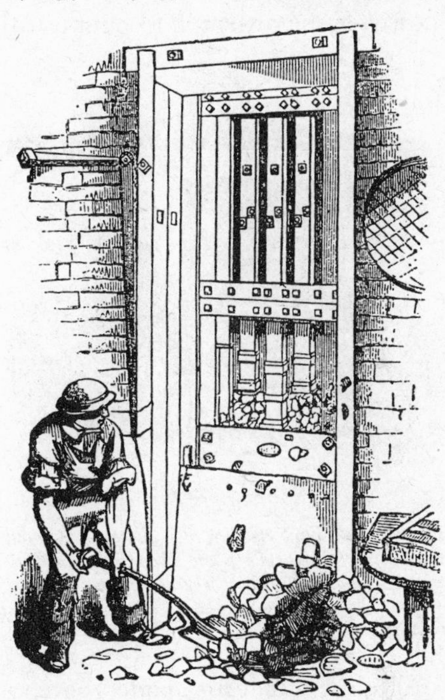

FIGURE 187—*Flint-crushing. After being crushed, the flint was sieved and mixed with water.*

There was, however, a disadvantage in the industrial use of ground flint. It was in time realized that flint-grinding had introduced a very dangerous new industrial hazard into pottery-making. At first the flint was calcined in kilns and ground by hand in primitive stamp-mills or in large iron mortars, after which the fine powder was sieved through lawn (compare figures 187, 188). The result was that, in spite of all precautions, silica got into the lungs of the operatives. This led Thomas Benson to apply his knowledge of colour-grinding to the problem and to take out a patent in 1726 for grinding under water (B.P. No 487). Initially the grinding was effected by iron wheels and balls, but traces of iron contaminated the flint and coloured the ware in which it was used, so in 1732 Benson took out a further patent covering the use of stone balls instead of iron ones (B.P.

No 536) (figure 189). The large potteries set up their own mills, while the smaller Staffordshire establishments bought their flint as slip from mills in the Moddershall valley that specialized in this trade. These mills, together with the extended use of the lathe in the production of more accurately finished wares, mark the advent of the demand for mechanical power in the pottery industry, to be met in due course by the adoption of James Watt's improved steam-engine. It would, however, be an error to suppose that mechanical power was unknown in The Potteries before the introduction of steam. Indeed, water-power was an important prerequisite of a successful pottery: in this respect Whieldon and Wedgwood were favourably placed, and to it may be attributed some of their early successes. Wedgwood employed James Brindley (1716–72)—who was later renowned as the engineer of the Duke of Bridgewater's canals, and whose brother John had a pottery at Longport—to construct flint-mills. Many generations were to pass, however, before power was to be applied to the throwing-process and to the manufacture of flat and hollow ware.

FIGURE 188—*Flint-grinding. The flints were ground by massive stone rollers and then transferred to vessels containing water, where they were mixed to a cream.*

According to John Thomas:

Like every industry, pottery, even in the peasant stage, needs raw materials. These must be suitably prepared, or the finished article will be poor. All these peasant potters had raw materials prepared in water-mills. These were often converted corn-mills. These flint water-mills have persisted from the seventeenth century to this day in the potteries.[1]

As changes were made in the basic raw materials, corresponding improvements were introduced in pottery processes generally. Ralph Shaw of Burslem is reputed to have introduced the drying of clay in a shallow kiln heated by flues from an external fire. This eliminated much of the contamination that inevitably accompanied the preparation of clay in the primitive sun-pan. About 1750 Enoch Booth of Tunstall introduced double firing into Staffordshire. A preliminary firing produced the biscuit stage, which was followed, after glaze and decoration had been applied, by the glost or glazing firing. Easier to operate, the double firing began to oust salt-glazing, which suffered from the additional disadvantage

[1] Thomas, John. 'The Pottery Industry and the Industrial Revolution.' *Econ. Hist.*, 3, 399, 1937.

that it was less economical. Among the first to follow Booth in the production of a cream-coloured ware were Ralph and John Baddeley of Shelton, and John Warburton of Hot Lane, Cobridge. Booth also pioneered the glazing of wares with slip instead of merely dusting them before firing with powdered galena. Unfortunately the lead glaze used increased the risks to health. Booth progressively altered his glazing process from a simple dusting with lead ore to dipping in a slip of red- or white-lead with clay and flint, and finally to lead compounds and flint according to William Littler's method. The ware was dipped in this glaze after the biscuit-firing (figure 190). The body of Booth's ware was composed of local clay to which he added white-burning clays from Devon and Dorset, as well as ground flint, as suggested by Astbury. These changes took the evolution of cream-coloured earthenware one stage nearer the form in which it superseded salt-glazed ware and tin-enamelled delft and secured a world market under royal patronage. Production expanded rapidly between 1750 and 1760.

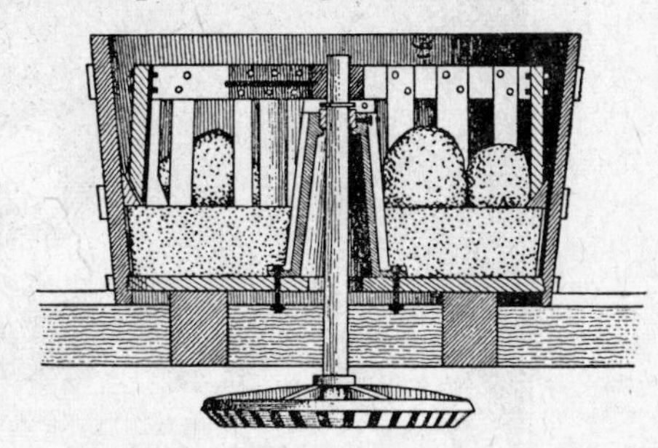

FIGURE 189—*Ball-mill for grinding calcined flints under water. The flint was burnt in a kiln like a lime-kiln and while still hot was quenched in water. The foot of the mill was a large block of chert (a flint-like quartz or siliceous rock), and large stone balls were moved round on it by oak paddles, thus grinding the calcined flints.*

A minor invention that contributed to increased output was the introduction, attributed to Ralph Shaw, of pieces of sharp-edged stoneware to separate vessels during the firing process. Several pieces could thus be stacked one inside the other and fired in the same saggar. This simple device considerably increased output from a given number of ovens.

By 1770 local clays had been abandoned in spite of transport difficulties: Staffordshire was still served by the same roads that had sufficed in the seventeenth century.

These roads were narrow, rutty lanes, along which hard-working horses and donkeys, muzzled to prevent them from eating the hedges, carried packs or panniers filled with crates of pottery or balls of clay. It is almost incredible that five hundred separate potteries employing 7000 persons could import their clay and export their wares along such routes, for, according to the petition presented to Parliament in 1762, these wares were sent in vast quantities to London, Bristol, Liverpool, and Hull, for despatch to America, the West Indies and almost every port in Europe. The clay and flints came to Liverpool and Hull. From Liverpool they were brought by the Mersey and Weaver to

Winsford in Cheshire; from Hull to Willington in Derbyshire. From Willington and Winsford they were brought on the backs of horses and donkeys to the Five Towns.[1]

The popularity of Enoch Booth's cream-coloured ware led to a further improvement in its quality about 1765, when he adopted a glaze devised, but not

FIGURE 190—*Dipping biscuit or once-fired ware in liquid glaze.*

patented, by John Greatbach, and also when, about 1768, he added china-stone as well as china-clay to the body. It was this improved body that Josiah Wedgwood began to make when he set up as an independent potter.

Improvements were not, however, confined solely to the ceramic bodies and glazes. Ovens increased in size and were repeatedly rebuilt to modified designs in an attempt to secure an easier control of temperatures; and whole banks of ovens in due course replaced the older and more primitive single units. In 1740, John and Thomas Wedgwood invented 'pyrometric beads' which changed colour with rising temperature. Whitehurst (1749), Ellicott (1750), and Smeaton (1754) all made contributions in the same field, and Josiah Wedgwood in-

[1] Hammond, J. L. and B. 'The Rise of Modern Industry' (4th edn.), p. 169. Methuen, London. 1930.

vented the 'pyrometric cones' that have been used by the pottery industry ever since.

The revolution in the potteries consisted in the discovery by constant experiment of new bodies, new glazes, and new methods of decoration; a greater division of labour, a growth of the factory and a development of methods of control, i.e. the beginning of scientific management, cost accounting; the improvement of transportation and the opening up of new markets at home and abroad.[1]

We shall now see how this was effected at the hand of one of the greatest potters of all time, Josiah Wedgwood.

FIGURE 191—*Mechanical power was introduced for lathe-turning as the output of the mass-produced articles increased.*

IX. JOSIAH WEDGWOOD

Josiah Wedgwood (1730–95) came of a family already well known in The Potteries. At the age of nine he started work in the family pottery, and after twenty years of work there and in partnership with Thomas Whieldon (1719–95) of Fenton, he set up in 1759 on his own account at Burslem. One of his first successes was the production of a fine green-glazed ware, but he made all varieties of Staffordshire ware. Within a few years he had evolved an improved stoneware from the older cream-coloured ware of Booth and Warburton and, having secured royal patronage, dubbed it Queen's ware. The body consisted of roughly 4 parts of ground flint and some 20 to 24 parts of the whitest Dorset, Devon, or Cornish clays. Following Booth's practice it was fired twice, and glazed with what was virtually flint glass. Production of this fine ware increased very rapidly, and in 1764 Wedgwood moved to larger premises at the Bell House. Queen's ware was easy to manufacture, was as cheap as the other wares then in use, and as a result of Wedgwood's attention to form was of considerable aesthetic appeal even in the almost total absence of applied decoration. Wedgwood having shown the way, the ware was soon being made in a hundred other potteries, and as the years passed it became one of the major products of The Potteries. Every form of table-

[1] Bladen, V. W. 'The Potteries in the Industrial Revolution.' *Econ. Hist.*, 1, 117, 1926.

furnishing was made from it, and in the course of time Queen's ware was in use throughout England, displacing the clumsier delft and also the much older pewter which was then still in use in many districts. With its universal acceptance the full tide of the industrial revolution had come to Staffordshire. Power was required in quantity to turn the lathes on which the refined shapes were finished (figure 191); flint had to be crushed and ground in large quantities; and the various ingredients had to be incorporated mechanically in a homogeneous mix (plate 20 B).

After the legal fight with Richard Champion in 1775 over the china-clay patent (p 341), Wedgwood visited Cornwall in company with John Turner of Lane End. In Cornwall they saw Newcomen engines in operation, and so impressed was Turner with the possibilities of steam-power that, on his return, he installed an engine to pump water back over an existing water-wheel, exactly as Matthew Boulton did at the Soho Manufactory at Birmingham. When Spode took over Turner's pottery, the engine probably passed to him. Wedgwood arranged for James Watt to survey flint-mills at Trentham and Lane End, and in particular directed him to examine the engine and mill at Spode's works. As a result, in 1782 Wedgwood ordered his first steam-engine. It was designed to supply power for grinding flint and enamel colours, to operate a saggar-crusher, and to temper or mix clay. This first order given by Wedgwood was fortunate for Boulton and Watt, since their engines had displaced many of the older Newcomen type in Cornish mines, and Staffordshire was now ripe for mechanization. The market for engines in the mills of Lancashire, and later Yorkshire, developed after the general adoption of mechanical power in The Potteries. In the pottery industry, as elsewhere, the steam-engine changed the whole pattern of activity and led to the evolution of the modern type of factory equipped with power for the preparation of the raw materials, and for facilitating the mechanical operations.

It was at Wedgwood's Etruria that these changes were first put into operation, but it must not be thought that Wedgwood's activities were confined to the scientific management of the production of vast quantities of Queen's ware, and of *objets d'art* for his royal patrons. He was an indefatigable experimenter and freely availed himself of such scientific information as he could get in the search for improved ceramic raw materials. According to John Thomas 'he elevated pottery manufacture from a matter of guess-work and procedure by rule of thumb to a matter of scientific measurement and calculation'.

By the end of the eighteenth century, as a result of Wedgwood's activities and those of many less well known potters, a wide range of ceramics was being produced in Staffordshire, which had become the leading pottery area in the world. Scientific experiment had covered all the readily available refractory materials, and kaolin, china-stone, flint, and bone-ash had found established places. The last quarter of the century saw salt-glazed stoneware, in the production of which Staffordshire had been pre-eminent, give way to fluid-glazed cream-coloured ware. The production of stoneware did not by any means stop, but it was gradually excluded from the homes of the well-to-do, who showed a preference for wares more directly inspired by oriental porcelain. Throughout Europe this preference was met by the production of a true hard-paste porcelain; only in England, with its special tradition of porcelain-making, was the new taste served by the hybrid bone-china (p 341), which became the standard English body. When Josiah Spode II (1754–1827) took over his father's works at Stoke-on-Trent in 1797, he is reputed to have established this standard body by adding both felspar and bone-ash. It is still in use today, since it is easy to work and lends itself to mass-production. Similarly, the composition of Queen's ware today is very much as the first Josiah Wedgwood left it.

In 1725 the output of The Potteries had not reached a value of £15 000, but by 1777 it had increased to £75 000. Ten years later there were no fewer than 200 master-potters with 20 000 employees.

X. TECHNICAL AIDS TO POTTING

There now remains to be discussed the introduction of several techniques, such as pressing and casting, that supplemented the changes already discussed. The first of these is the introduction of moulds. As has been described above, in making a pottery vessel the appropriate clay was initially formed by the potter's hands. In Staffordshire, about 1740–50, this simple form of throwing was supplemented by the use of moulds. The innovation is attributed to Ralph Daniel of Cobridge. The first moulds were of cast metal, from which small vessels of high precision could be stamped. It was soon found, however, that moulds of plaster of Paris had the additional advantage of absorbing moisture from the clay and so expediting the drying of the primary body. Lightly baked clay moulds, called pitcher moulds, were also used for the same reason. These were often cut in intaglio and used to make the small flower motives which were attached with slip in the production of the characteristic wares of Thomas Astbury and Thomas Whieldon. At a higher level of technical competence they were used by Wedgwood in producing his 'jasper' portrait-medallions and other similar pieces (plate 19 B).

The usual technique was to prepare in alabaster a master of the design or article required, and to make a stoneware duplicate or block of this, from which the plaster moulds were subsequently made (plate 19 D). So important was this innovation in promoting the speedy reduplication of a standard design that the block-cutter became one of the most important workers in the pottery industry. Many potters made their blocks themselves, but demand was sufficient for some designers to set up on their own. The most celebrated mould-cutter of his day was Aaron Wood (1717–85). Wood started life with Thomas Wedgwood, and his work had a lasting influence on the style of the moulded Staffordshire wares. Moulding not only called for makers of moulds, but in time caused the 'flat hollow-ware presses' (figure 192) to outnumber the traditional 'throwers'.

FIGURE 192—*Presses for flat hollow-ware such as plates and saucers were introduced to speed up the production of cheaper ware. The balance was to weigh the piece of clay to be pressed, and so standardize the finished product.*

Apart from other advantages, the use of moulds enabled the potters of the industrial revolution to move in the direction of mass-production, so converting the small craft-pottery into the factory. At the same time, moulds introduced a considerable degree of standardization, since each vessel was a copy of the master.

The necessity for increased production similarly led to the invention of a method for the rapid reduplication of decoration. This was effected by transfer-printing, one of England's principal contributions to ceramic technique. As with so many inventions in the ceramic industry, the name of the innovator is not certainly known. It may have been an Irish engraver John Brooks (1720–60), or Simon-François Revenet (1706–74) of Battersea, *c* 1752. Another possible inventor is Robert Hancock (1730–1817), who was associated successively with Battersea, Bow, Worcester, and Caughley. It is clear, however, that the new art was in use by the early 1750s, and by 1756 there was an important printed ware works at Liverpool. Its owners were John Sadler (1720–89) and Guy Green, who claimed that they had invented the transfer-printing process as early as 1749, but no patent in their names has been recorded. Printing was at first in black, red, and purple: under-glaze blue dates from 1756. John Wall (1708–76) was using it at Worcester in 1757, and Wedgwood by 1760.

The technique was to engrave the pattern on a metal plate which was then 'inked' (figure 193); the design was taken up on paper and transferred to the articles to be printed (figure 194). Initially the pattern was applied over-glaze, but after a few years it was being used for under-glaze as well. When stipple engraving replaced line drawing, 'bats' made of sheets of glue were substituted for paper. In bat-printing the design was transferred by a thick oil which was then dusted with colour and fired.

To these cheap yet reliable processes we may attribute the enormous market enjoyed by Staffordshire under-glaze blue landscapes in the early nineteenth century, when England had a clear lead over other European countries in this particular development.

FIGURE 193—*In transfer-printing the design was first engraved on a copper plate. This was heated and rubbed with a mixture of metallic oxide and oil. The surplus was scraped off and an impression taken on special paper which had been moistened with soap and water.*

A modification of transfer-printing proper enabled potters to keep pace with the growing demand for their products and yet retain some of the qualities of craft potting. This was the printing of nothing more than a faint outline guide for the artist, who subsequently developed the full pattern by hand-painting. From the 1830s this method was used particularly at Coalport (Coalbrookdale in Shropshire), and at the Rockingham works at Swinton in Yorkshire. Further developments in this field are outside the period under discussion in this chapter.

In the above discussion numerous ways in which the primary body can be decorated, and made aesthetically pleasing and technically sound, have been described: slip decoration, high-temperature and muffle colours, glazing, printing, and painting. It now remains to say something about decoration in metals, particularly gilding—an indispensable adjunct to the production of many fine ceramic products.

By far the most important of the decorative metals was gold. It was first used in the early eighteenth century in the form of size-gilding; the ware to be decorated was painted with a varnish made of linseed-oil and litharge and the gold leaf was applied to it. Being unfired, the gilt was naturally much weaker than most ceramic decorations and was easily abraded. An improvement was effected by incorporating the gold in a lacquer. In Europe a fired decoration dates from the introduction of honey-gilding. In this process gold leaf mixed with honey was painted on, a method in use throughout the greater part of the eighteenth century. This 'fired gold' was one of Europe's few ceramic contributions to the east.

Yet another method was, it is true, introduced about 1780, but it involved a serious industrial hazard in that it depended on the use of gold amalgam, from which the mercury was driven off in a low-temperature oven, to the detriment of the workers' health.

FIGURE 194—*The design was transferred from the paper to the ware by rubbing with a roller. The paper was then washed off in cold water. The ware was heated to drive off the oil, and finally glazed.*

Another process involving the use of metals in the late eighteenth and early nineteenth centuries was the production of lustre wares. Often the avowed intention of the eighteenth-century potter was to imitate a metal article. To do so, pigment containing copper, silver, gold, or platinum was applied over the glaze and the ware was fired in a reducing atmosphere. In Staffordshire, Wedgwood made particular use of this process (*c* 1800), employing the then comparatively new metal platinum. Incidentally, Josiah Wedgwood's only patent (B.P. No 939, 1769) is concerned with encaustic gold bronze. In 1810 Peter Warburton took out a patent for printing in platinum and gold, which was actually one of the earliest industrial uses of platinum.

The gradual multiplication of the processes whereby ceramic products could be produced led, as in other industries, to a marked division of labour. Josiah Wedgwood's Etruria, where the principle of specialization was first introduced, was divided into departments according to the type of ware produced: useful, ornamental, jasper, basalt, and so on. In 1790 some 160 employees were engaged in the 'useful' branch, in the following categories: slip-house, clay-beaters, throwers and their attendant boys, plate makers, dish makers, hollow-ware pressers, turners of flat ware, turners of hollow-ware, handlers, biscuit-oven firemen, dippers, brushers, placers and firemen in the glost oven, girl colour-grinders, painters, enamellers and gilders, and, in addition, coal getters, modellers, mould makers, saggar makers, and a cooper.

This long list emphasizes the contrast between the mechanized production of the textile industry where, from early in the industrial revolution, one operative had been able to concentrate on tending, say, a machine producing simultaneously a large number of threads, and the pottery industry, where, despite mechanical aids, each article has still to be handled many times in the course of production.

BIBLIOGRAPHY

BLADEN, V. W. "The Potteries in the Industrial Revolution." *Econ. Hist.*, **1**, 117, 1926.
BRONGNIART, A. 'Traité des arts céramiques, ou des potteries, considerées dans leurs histoires, leur practique et leur théorie' (2 vols and atlas). Paris. 1844.
BURTON, W. 'A History and Description of English Earthenware and Stoneware.' Cassell, London. 1904.
Idem. 'A History and Description of English Porcelain.' Cassell, London. 1902.
CHURCH, A. H. 'English Earthenware of the 17th and 18th Centuries.' Victoria and Albert Museum Handbook. Wyman, London. 1904.
CLOW, A. and CLOW, NAN L. 'The Chemical Revolution.' Batchworth Press, London. 1952.
FORTNUM, C. D. E. 'Maiolica, Historical Treatise.' Oxford. 1896.
HANNOVER, E. 'Pottery and Porcelain: a Handbook for Collectors' (3 vols, trans. from the Danish edition by B. RACKHAM). Benn, London. 1925.
HARRISON, G. 'Memoir of William Cookworthy . . . By his Grandson.' London. 1854.
HAVARD, H. 'La céramique hollandaise.' Éditions Vivat, Amsterdam. 1909.
HONEY, W. B. 'European Ceramic Art from the end of the Middle Ages to about 1815' (2 vols). Faber & Faber, London. 1949, 1952.
JEWITT, L. 'The Ceramic Art of Great Britain from Prehistoric Times down to the Present Day' (2 vols). London. 1878.
LORD, J. 'Capital and Steam-power, 1750–1800.' King, London. 1923.
MACKENNA, F. S. 'Cookworthy's Plymouth and Bristol Porcelain.' Lewis, Leigh-on-Sea. 1946.
MARRYAT, J. 'History of Pottery and Porcelain, Medieval and Modern.' London. 1857.
PARKES, S. 'Chemical Catechism' (8th ed.). London. 1818.
PLOT, R. 'Natural History of Staffordshire.' Oxford. 1686.
SHAW, S. 'A History of the Staffordshire Potteries, and the Rise and Progress of the Manufacture of Pottery and Porcelain.' Hanley. 1829.
SOLON, M. L. 'Brief History of Old English Porcelain.' Bemrose, London. 1903.
THOMAS, J. "The Pottery Industry and the Industrial Revolution." *Econ. Hist.*, **3**, 399, 1937.
TURNER, W. 'Transfer Printing on Enamels, Porcelain and Pottery.' Chapman & Hall, London. 1907.

12

GLASS

L. M. ANGUS-BUTTERWORTH

I. OPTICAL GLASS

In the middle years of the eighteenth century both Chester Moor Hall (1703–71) and John Dollond (1706–61) were working on the solution of the optical problems resulting from the dispersion of light that, as Newton realized, always occurs on refraction (vol III, p 233). They found that by combining two types of glass in a single lens the disturbance caused by the formation of differently coloured images could be greatly reduced. The original discovery was made by Moor Hall, but its development was due to Dollond, a practical optician: he apparently learnt of the invention from George Bass, who ground the lenses for Moor Hall's achromatic combination. Following reasoning similar to that advanced in 1695 by David Gregory, Moor Hall became convinced, from a study of the human eye, that achromatic lenses were possible. After various experiments he found, in 1729, two kinds of glass of dispersions sufficiently different to enable him to realize his idea. Accordingly, about 1733, a number of truly achromatic lenses were constructed according to his specifications. The concave component was of flint glass and the convex of crown glass.

Although controversy later arose about the credit for the invention of the achromatic lens, the patent was awarded in 1758 to Dollond after he had read a paper in that year to the Royal Society under the title of 'An Account of some Experiments concerning the different Refrangibility of Light'. The mathematical theory of the achromatic objective was apparently not worked out until later, being published by Samuel Klingenstierna (1689–1785) of Uppsala in 1760. Klingenstierna had written to Dollond in 1755 to tell him that he had doubts about Newton's views on refraction and dispersion and believed further experiment to be desirable.

These discoveries were of great practical value. Until this time the lenses of telescopes and microscopes had been relatively small, and ground from thick crown or plate glass; chromatic aberration severely limited their performance. It was now found that if a convex lens of crown glass was cemented to a concave lens of flint glass, which had a higher refractive index, the chromatic effect was largely absent in the combination. Unfortunately, however, there remained a great lack of suitable glass, partly because the small demand for glass of optical quality meant that the cost of production was very high. It soon became evident that the time was ripe for advances in glass-making technology, and attention was therefore turned in that direction.

A discovery of prime significance in connexion with the manufacture of optical glass was made by Pierre Louis Guinand (1748–1824), a Swiss, at the close of the eighteenth century. His career was remarkable. He began life as a wood-worker, specializing in the making of clock-cases. From this he turned to the then very profitable work of casting bells for clocks. The metal used in bell-founding was stirred during the operation to make it homogeneous, and Guinand had the brilliant idea that in the same way the homogeneity of glass might be improved by stirring it in the crucible while still in the molten state, and that in this way better glass for making lenses might be obtained.

Guinand began to take an interest in optical glass as early as 1768, when he undertook small-scale experimental foundings. At the start, his methods did not differ from those of his contemporaries, and success eluded him. He built his first full-scale furnace in 1775, but as the stirring device had not yet occurred to him little progress could be made. It was not until the summer of 1798, after thirty years of effort, that Guinand first used a stirrer. The original form was mushroom-shaped, and was not fully effective. Other patterns followed, and in 1805 he devised the type that became universally adopted, namely a hollow cylinder of burnt fireclay, moved through the molten glass by means of a hook-ended iron rod.

The value of Guinand's discovery lay in the fact that it helped to solve many of the intractable problems associated with the making of optical glass, which calls for a higher degree of homogeneity than any other kind. If it is not of the same composition throughout, its refractive power is variable and a distorted image is formed. Thus in a flint glass—of which the essential constituents are silica, lead oxide, and potash—the relatively high density of the lead oxide causes it to be unevenly distributed through the molten material. This variation may cause veins or striae to be present, and no control of the defect was possible until the introduction of stirring.

The chief advantage of stirring was that it enabled much higher proportions of relatively heavy materials to be used in the batch mixtures, and this in turn ultimately led to a great extension of the range of composition available for optical glass. Another advantage of stirring the molten metal was that, if the operation was long continued, it became possible to release very completely the air-bubbles generated during the founding. In this way the proportion of light transmitted was increased, because previously some had been scattered and dispersed at the surface of the bubbles.

Guinand's own resources being limited, he established contact with the German manufacturer Utzschneider, founder of the Munich optical institute, and agreed to produce lenses for him. For this purpose he removed to Benediktbeuern in Bavaria, and in conjunction with Joseph von Fraunhofer (1787–1826), who was acting as Utzschneider's manager, he made considerable progress in perfecting the stirring process. Guinand returned to Switzerland in 1814.

The stirring process remained a secret one, but glass-manufacturers in a number of countries were anxious to learn details of it, especially after the death of Guinand in 1824. In France, in 1827, Georges Bontemps, a glass-maker, and J. N. Lerebours, an optician, agreed to purchase the secret from Henri Guinand, the eldest son of the inventor, for 3000 francs. Trial melts were made at the Bontemps factory at Choisy-le-Roi, and by the following year good lenses were being produced.

In England it was not until 1837 that Lucas Chance, of the Chance Brothers glass company at Birmingham, made an agreement with Bontemps to acquire particulars of his manufacturing technique. Bontemps was paid immediately a fee of 3000 francs, the same amount that he himself had paid Henri Guinand, and was to receive five-twelfths of the profits resulting from the business. Chance took out an English patent for the Guinand process in 1838, but for various reasons the invention was not fully exploited for a further decade.

In 1848 Bontemps, by then the most celebrated glass-technologist of the day, had to leave France because of the revolution. He made an agreement with Chance Brothers to devote himself exclusively to their service, and in particular 'to carry out the manufacture of Optical glass in accordance with Lucas Chance's patent of 1838'. A new plant was built for him, and in a short time the firm was producing optical glass of a very high standard in the form of 'hard crown' and 'dense flint' for telescopes, and 'soft crown' and 'light flint' for camera lenses. By 1849 London opticians were reporting that the Chance flint glass was superior even to Swiss flint, not being so easily altered by the atmosphere. In 1850 glass was sent to a number of the principal opticians in Germany and Austria, and from that time onwards steady improvements were effected in the size and quality of the lenses made.

While the main line of advance in the manufacture of optical glass has now been traced, reference should be made to the work in this connexion of Michael Faraday (1791–1867). In 1824 the Royal Society appointed a committee to consider the improvement of optical glass, especially such as would be suitable for telescope objectives. It was proposed to carry out investigations on the melting of optical glass, and Faraday took charge of this undertaking, with the assistance of Sir John Herschel, who was to determine the refractive indices, and G. Dollond (1774–1852), who was to make up the glass into lenses.

When Faraday began his investigations the glass-melting was done at the Falcon glass works of Green and Pellatt (plate 21 B). This proved inconvenient to Faraday, however, as the works was three miles away from the Royal Institution. Accordingly, in 1827, a small furnace was built at the Institution, and during the following two years Faraday devoted much of his time to the work. He left careful records of this research, which was discontinued in 1830 when supplies of optical glass began to be more freely available from other sources.

The Herschels, father and son, were greatly interested in lenses in connexion with their astronomical work. The father, Francis William Herschel (1738–1822) was a native of Hanover, a kingdom which during his lifetime was still united to the British Crown; he made four surveys of the sky of the northern hemisphere with instruments of his own construction. The son, Sir John Herschel (1792–1871), who co-operated with Faraday, extended the surveys to the southern sky.

In the first half of the nineteenth century two men were responsible, in the main, for the advances that were made in the art of optical glass manufacture, namely Fraunhofer in Germany, and William Vernon Harcourt (1789–1871) in England.

Joseph von Fraunhofer was born at Straubing in Bavaria, and at the age of twelve was apprenticed to a glass cutter and polisher at Munich. He became the manager of the optical institute at Benediktbeuern in 1818. In conjunction with Guinand he did valuable work in extending the range of dense flint and crown glasses. This investigation was on well established lines, and did not include the use of any new fluxes, but spectrometric examination of the glasses produced showed that in two cases there was decided diminution of the secondary spectrum.

Fraunhofer also spent much time on the improvement of optical instruments. He invented ingenious machines for polishing lenses and mirrors without altering their curvatures, a spherometer, a heliometer, and a micrometer. He produced some of the finest object glasses of the early nineteenth century, including the 9½-in objective of the Dorpat equatorial.

Vernon Harcourt devoted more than a quarter of a century to experiments on the composition of optical glass, making 166 trial meltings. He was greatly handicapped by lack of proper equipment and by the necessity of working on a small scale, but was finally able to produce two nearly flawless disks of titanium glass and two of borate glass. His work demonstrated the possibility of abolishing the secondary spectrum.

II. MIRRORS

The earliest mirrors were of copper, bronze, or brass. Mirrors of glass were being made at Venice at the beginning of the fourteenth century (vol III, p 238), but their manufacture was not introduced into England until early in the seventeenth century. In 1623 Sir Robert Mansell (1573–1656), in applying for a renewal of his general glass-making patent, claimed to have brought from abroad experts to make Murano crystalline glasses, spectacle glasses, and mirror glasses, the last two being new businesses. He further claimed that he then had 500 Englishmen engaged in 'making, grinding, polishing and foyling looking glasses'. Forty years later, in 1663, the Duke of Buckingham, in a petition to Charles II, asked for a further renewal of the patent, with a clause therein 'for the sole makinge glasse-plates, glasses for coaches and other glasse plates'.

In the manufacture of mirrors the first stage was preparation of the polished plate glass (plate 21 A), used also for other purposes and described elsewhere (p 368). As regards the 'silvering', the process used throughout the eighteenth century was the one using tin and mercury discovered by the Venetians. The glass plate, after being polished on both sides, was laid on a perfectly flat table or base, usually of stone and of great strength and solidity. As the mercury used was very costly, the table had a raised edge so that none of it could escape, and guttering leading to receptacles so that as much as possible of it could be recovered.

After being carefully cleaned, the upper surface of the glass was covered with sheets of tinfoil, which were rubbed down smooth. Mercury was then poured on, some of it at once forming an amalgam with the tin. Part of the excess mercury having been run off, a woollen cloth was spread over the whole surface and square iron weights were applied. A day and a night were allowed for setting, after which the weights and cloth were removed. The glass was then taken to a wooden table which could be set at a gradually increasing inclination. The object of this was to allow such mercury as had remained unamalgamated to drain completely away. The draining was allowed to continue for about twelve days. In the final product only a film of amalgam remained, coating the glass and adhering perfectly to it.

The mercurial process is still used to a small extent for the reproduction of 'antique' mirrors. Apart from this limited application, however, it became obsolete about 1840, when the chemical deposition of silver was introduced. In its early form this method of making mirrors consisted of treating the glass with an ammoniacal solution of a silver salt, such as silver nitrate, to which tartaric acid and sugar-candy had been added.

Greater care began to be taken to see that the plates used had surfaces that were truly flat and parallel, in order to avoid the distortion visible, for example,

FIGURE 195—*Drawing glass tubing.* (A) *The ball of glass is attached to the post-iron.* (B) *The glass tube or rod is drawn out, and is laid on a ladder which prevents it from being contaminated with grit or dirt from the floor.* (C) *The glass is cut into lengths and made up into bundles.*

in the Galerie des Glaces at Versailles. The layer of silver deposited was very thin and delicate, and therefore had to be well protected. This was done by giving it a coating of shellac, followed by a backing of red lead, turpentine, and japan gold-size. This method continued until the introduction of copper coating in recent times.

The size of mirrors was limited by that of the blown or cast glass plates from which they were made, and until the close of the eighteenth century it was necessary to build up large wall mirrors in sections. Where the plates joined they were sometimes serrated for security; in other cases the sections had between them strips of wood supporting metal strips that overlapped the glass and held it in position—the wood was below the joint and the metal above it. The plates frequently had their edges bevelled by hand with pumice-stone, thus increasing the decorative effect,

III. GLASS TUBING AND ROD

Glass was considered such difficult material to handle in the molten state that mechanization was introduced later than in most industries (vol V, ch 28). During the early part of the industrial revolution no attempt was made to draw glass tubing and rod mechanically, and the traditional method of drawing by hand accordingly remained standard practice (figure 195).

FIGURE 196—*'Glory-hole.' A ball of glass is shown inserted into the reheating furnace. While manipulating the gathering of molten metal, the glass-maker supports his blow-iron on an iron stand.*

The process consisted of taking a gathering of glass from the crucible on a blow-iron. As gathered, the gob of glass was roughly spherical, and had to be rolled on a small iron table or marver[1] to give it a symmetrical and slightly conical shape. When hollow tubing was required the glass-maker blew air down the blow-iron, but when solid glass rod was needed the blowing was omitted.

If the draught of tubing or rod was to be long or heavy the first gathering needed to be coated with two or three layers of fresh glass to build up the quantity of metal needed, and between each gather the ball had to be marvered afresh. During these operations the glass lost heat and tended to become too stiff to work. A subsidiary furnace or 'glory-hole' (figure 196) was thus provided in which the ball could be reheated. The ancillary furnaces were fired originally with beech-wood and the like, but later with wood mixed with cobs of coal.

When reheated, the glass, retaining its symmetrical marvered form, was mounted on an iron post carried by an assistant. The gathering of glass, in its compact cylindrical form, was now supported at both ends and was drawn out by the tube-drawer, who walked backwards from the post-holder (figure 195 A, B), usually a youth. During the draw the glass was twisted slowly, and by intermittent blowing the operator maintained the air-cavity in the tubing and kept it circular.

[1] The marver was so called because when first used in France the top was of marble (*marbre*).

While being drawn the tubing was gauged by a third man armed with calipers. This assistant noted when the tube had reached the required diameter at a particular point, and then cooled it by flapping the air near it with a sheet of leather, thus causing it to set. In this way the gauger followed the drawer at a short distance, repeating his gauging and cooling operation as required. Glass rod was made in exactly the same way, except that the gathering was on a solid iron.

Drawing tubes by hand was highly skilled work, but by varying the size and shape of the job, and by regulating the speed of drawing, an experienced man could draw tubes of various diameters with a fair measure of accuracy. Much depended upon having the glass at just the right temperature, and the drawer needed to have instinctive appreciation of the glass he happened to be working with, the behaviour of which varied according to its composition. The gathering might be from 4 to 8 inches in diameter, and from 6 to 12 inches in length. From this could be drawn tubing of $\frac{3}{32}$ to 6 inches in outside diameter, and of lengths up to 150 ft for the smaller diameters.

IV. CROWN WINDOW-GLASS

The crown window-glass process was the earlier of the two chief methods of making sheet glass by hand (figure 197), and was in common use until shortly after the end of the eighteenth century. The procedure was somewhat elaborate, the work being shared among a team of as many as ten men and boys. The earlier and simpler stages of the operation were undertaken by the younger members of the group, thus permitting the senior men to concentrate upon the stages where more skill was required, and at the same time giving the boys experience in handling the metal. Because the glass was blown, it was necessarily thin, in contrast to cast plate glass (p 368).

After the glass had been founded overnight and brought to a liquid state, it had to be cooled before working. When cooling had reduced it to a consistency something like that of treacle it could be gathered on a blow-iron. As clarity and transparency were important, a fireclay ring was floated in the melting-crucible to keep back scum or stringy metal. An assistant glass-blower dipped his pipe inside this ring, thus ensuring that he gathered only the best of the glass.

The quantity of the glass required being considerable, it could not be taken from the crucible in one operation. The first gathering after removal was accordingly cooled and a second gathering taken upon it by another assistant. Meanwhile the pipe had become too hot to handle with comfort, and so was trundled in a trough of cold water, care being taken not to splash the ball of glass. Marvering of the glass followed, the ball being rolled on an iron table or in a hollowed block of wood until it acquired a conical form.

The marvering was a two-handed operation. While a man rotated the pipe, a boy blew down it to expand the globe. As the glass was setting rapidly during this work it had to be reheated from time to time according to the judgement of the operator. Finally, when the globe was ready a pontil or solid iron rod was

FIGURE 197—*General view of a glass-house, showing the manufacture of crown glass. In the background is seen a disk of glass which has been 'flashed' from the molten metal. Note the protective masks.*

attached to it by a nodule of the molten metal directly opposite the original blow-iron, which was now broken free. The removal of the blowpipe left in the sphere an opening with slightly jagged edges.

In the final and most spectacular stage a highly skilled glass-maker took the globe and spun it in a reheating furnace. The man wore a veil or mask because great heat was required and he therefore had to stand very close to the furnace. The glass was rotated rapidly and vigorously. When it was reduced to a very soft and semi-molten state, a moment came at which centrifugal force caused it to flash into a flat disk, still adhering to the pontil by the boss in the centre (figure 197).

After flashing, the glass-maker had instantly to remove the disk from the reheating furnace. The thin, brilliant disk of fire-polished glass being still very soft when removed, he had to keep whirling it at the end of his pontil until it became cooler and stiffer. An assistant then cut it free from the pontil with shears, so that it could be taken to a kiln for annealing.

Every sheet made by this method had in the middle the bull's-eye or 'crown' from which it took its name, this being the point where the pontil had been attached. The sheets were comparatively small, and as they were circular the size was still further reduced if they were cut square after making. The sizes of the pieces of glass yielded by this process were thus severely restricted.

After the 1830s crown glass became obsolete except for a few special purposes. A limited amount, for example, continued to be made for the small slides upon which microscope specimens were mounted, as the quality of the glass was considered to render it particularly suitable for this purpose.

V. MAKING SHEET GLASS BY THE HAND-CYLINDER PROCESS

In the early years of the nineteenth century the hand-cylinder process was already well established in both Lorraine and the German states. This method of manufacturing sheet glass was brought to England in 1832 by Lucas Chance (p 360), with the help of Georges Bontemps of Choisy-le-Roi and a team of foreign workmen.

The making of sheet glass by the hand-cylinder process was essentially a development from the crown glass method. From 20 to 40 lb of glass was gathered on a particularly strong blow-iron about 5 ft long, the weight being regulated according to the size of the sheet required. After preparation of a globe of glass, as in the crown method, a further process was introduced. This consisted of swinging the hot glass in a trench up to 10 ft deep. While being swung the globe assumed an elongated form, the blower keeping it inflated meanwhile.

The cylinders produced were normally 12 to 20 inches in diameter and 50 to 70 inches in length. To form them into flat sheets two methods were adopted, the removal of the ends being the first stage in each. In one case the resulting cylinder was allowed to cool somewhat and was then slit lengthwise with a diamond tool. Reheating in a flattening kiln then caused it to fall into a flat sheet. A more careful method was to reheat the cylinder after slitting, and then pass it to a flattening-stone covered with glass, where it opened into a rather wavy sheet. A flattener rubbed the sheet with a *polissoir* or block of wood mounted on an iron rod, after which it was taken to a kiln for annealing.

The operations called for great skill and judgement on the part of the glass-makers. The gatherer had to gauge just how much metal was needed to make cylinders which, when split and flattened, would give sheets of a given size and thickness. The blower had to manipulate the molten metal by swinging and rotating it so as to ensure even thickness throughout the cylinder as well as correct overall size. For fashioning a sheet of glass in this way five types of skilled workers were required: gatherers, blowers, snappers, cutters, and flatteners. The sheets were larger than those of crown glass and were free from the boss in the centre, besides being lower in cost.

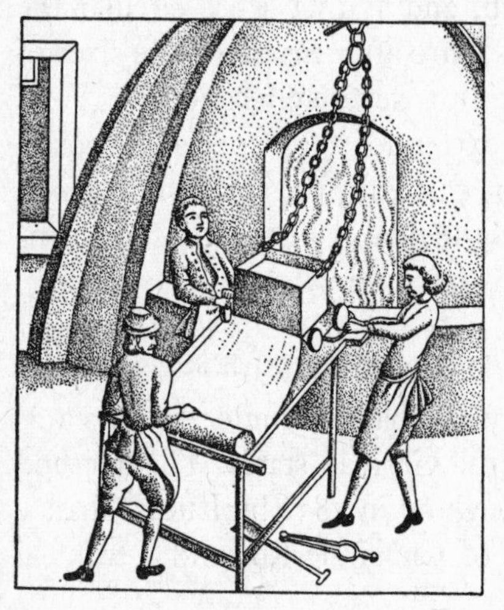

FIGURE 198—*Casting and running plate glass. c 1780.*

In 1839 Sir James Chance (1814–1902) invented a method of grinding and polishing sheet glass, thus giving it the brilliance and transparency of plate glass that had been similarly treated. The patent declared that his object was 'to remove the irregularities of surface without grinding away irregularities arising from any bending or curves which may exist in the general substance of the glass'.

This aim was achieved by supporting the sheet during operations upon a bed of moistened leather mounted upon slate, and causing it to adhere by applying suction. The adequately firm but not rigid background enabled the finishing-work to be done without the strain that was otherwise imposed through the more or less bent or buckled sheet being pressed against a hard, flat base, and also without the risk of grinding the glass thin in places.

VI. CAST PLATE GLASS

Casting was first introduced into France in 1688 when a company was given a monopoly of the home market (vol III, ch 9). The manufacture eventually settled at St-Gobain in Picardy, where the wood necessary for fuel was plentiful. By 1760 the output exceeded 1000 tons a year. A great part of the demand was for glazing houses—a practice then becoming increasingly popular among the wealthy—and carriages. In England the manufacture of plate glass by casting was introduced by Huguenots in 1773, though there had been an abortive attempt in 1691. In 1776 a British cast plate glass company began operations with a works covering about 30 acres at Ravenhead, near St Helens in Lancashire. The great casting-hall, 113 yds long by 50 yds wide, was one of the largest industrial buildings of the period. The technical processes were for a very short time under the control of Philip Besnard, but he was very soon replaced by Jean B. F. Giraux de la Bruyère (1739–87), who had received his training in France; and at the start most of the experienced workmen also were French. This firm had a very

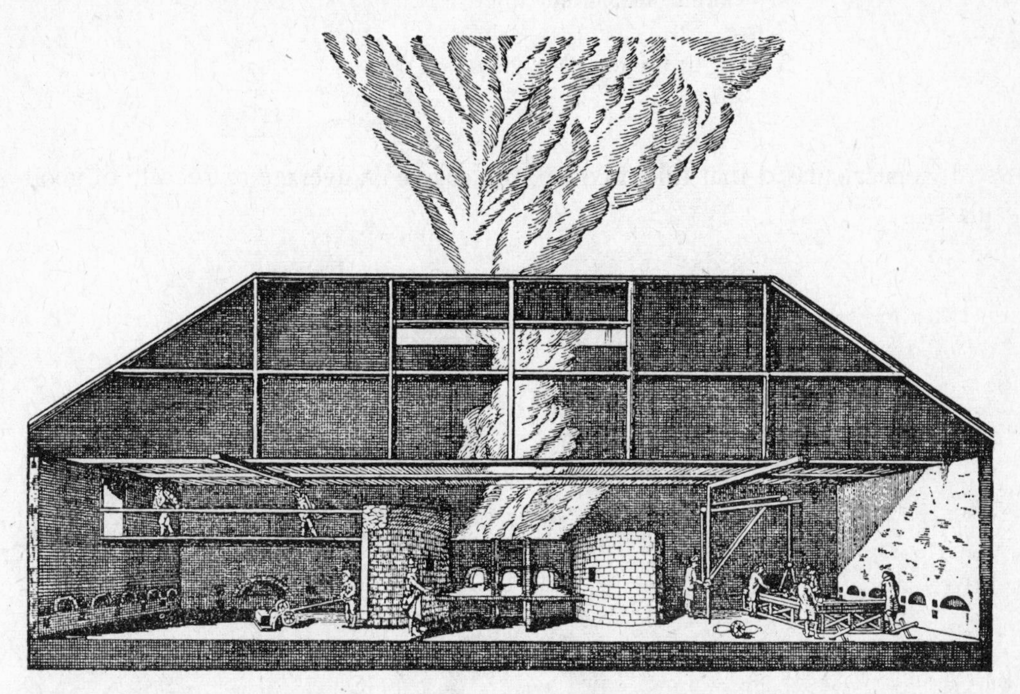

FIGURE 199—*Plate glass factory of* c *1800. Smoke from the wood-fired furnace escaped through a vent in the roof. On the right is the casting-table, with the crane for inverting the container of molten glass. Along each side of the glass-house are the openings to the annealing chambers. On the left is a man with a hand-trolley for removing the hot container after it has been emptied.*

unpropitious infancy and in its early years nearly failed, the main difficulties being poor management, heavy excise duty, and—above all—a very high rate of breakage. Complete reorganization, and the removal by war of competition from St-Gobain, eventually brought it great prosperity.

The French system of casting plate glass was quite different from the method of blowing it (figure 198, and vol III, pp 238–9). Casting had the advantage of enabling larger plates to be produced. The largest plates that could be made by blowing were 50 in by 30 in, while by casting it was possible to obtain plates 160 in by 80 in. A plate glass factory of about 1800 is shown in figure 199.

At Ravenhead the first task was to decide upon a batch-mixture which would produce a good plate of glass, capable of resisting the action of air, water, and the common mineral acids. The following was chosen:

	lb
Siliceous sand, washed and sifted . .	720
Alkaline salt	450
Quicklime, slaked and sifted . . .	80
Nitre	25
Cullet, or broken plate glass . . .	425
	1700

It was calculated that this mixture would give an average of 1200 lb of good glass.

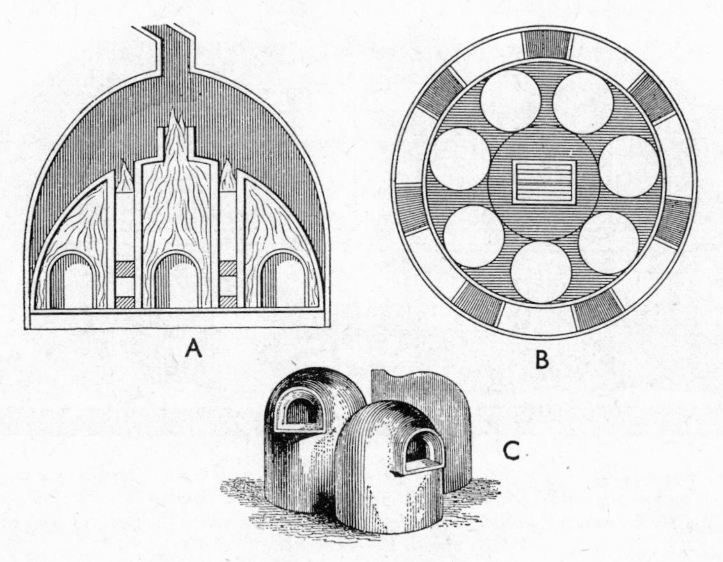

FIGURE 200—(A) *Section of the interior of a glass-furnace, and* (B) *ground plan;* (C) *covered pots for melting glass.*

The materials were prepared for use by a process known as fritting. This consisted of calcining to a sufficient extent to drive off moisture and to reduce the whole to a uniform mixture of paste-like consistency. The resulting frit was cut into square cakes, which were fed into the crucibles at intervals. This rather tedious operation was necessary because the frit was more bulky than the fused metal, and thus no new charge could be added until the preceding one had melted down. During the melting process an opaque white scum, known as glass-gall, rose to the surface, and had to be carefully skimmed away.

The materials were fused in earthern pots or crucibles standing in a high-temperature furnace (figure 200). These crucibles had to be very carefully prepared in order to withstand not only the intense heat of the fire but the solvent action of the molten glass. They were commonly made of five parts of the finest Stourbridge clay in a raw state, and one part of 'grog' or burnt clay, the latter being old crucibles ground to powder.

Until after the middle of the eighteenth century both plate and sheet glass

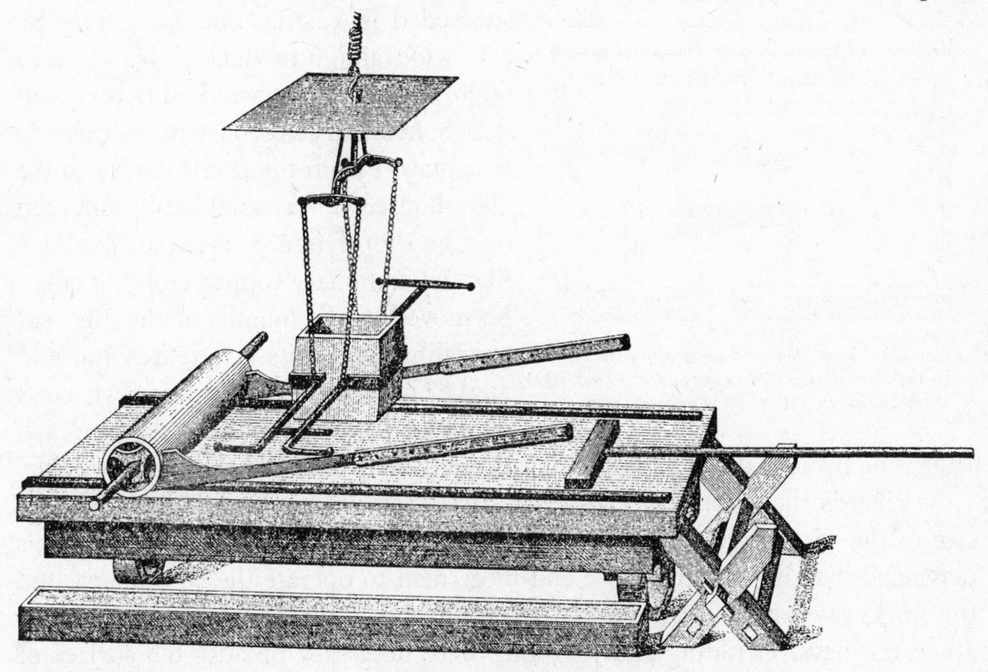

FIGURE 201—*An early form of casting-table, with the roller used for flattening the mass of molten metal. Above the table is suspended the crucible holding the glass; this container is in an iron framework with handles on either side to permit pouring.*

were founded in furnaces fired with wood. In 1763 attempts were made at the St-Gobain works to substitute coal for wood, but with such little success that as late as 1819 this French company purchased further large forests to maintain their normal fuel supplies. By 1829 the company had succeeded in melting the glass in a coal furnace, but it still needed fining in a wood furnace. At Ravenhead, Robert Sherbourne, who was appointed manager in 1792, introduced 'caped' or covered pots (figure 200 (C)) for use with coal fuel; by this means the spotting of glass by furnace soot was avoided.

The original casting-tables at Ravenhead, like those in France, were made of copper supported by solid masonry. It was considered that copper would have less effect in discolouring the molten glass than iron, but the copper was found liable to crack when the mass of molten glass was poured upon it. When this happened the tables were rendered useless—a serious matter, for great labour and expense were incurred in grinding and polishing them.

About 1843, after several accidents of this kind, the British Plate Glass Company—as it was known after reincorporation in 1798—made a trial of cast iron, although it was hard to obtain an iron plate of the dimensions required. They succeeded in casting one 15 ft long by 9 ft wide and 6 in thick. This massive table, with its frame, weighed 14 tons, and it was necessary to construct a carriage to convey it from the iron-foundry to the glass-house. It was afterwards mounted on castors (cf figure 201), so that, unlike the stationary copper tables, it could be moved to the mouths of the different annealing chambers (cf figures 199 and 203). These ovens, placed in two rows on each side of the glass-house, were each 16 ft wide by 40 ft deep, and had their floors exactly level with the casting-table.

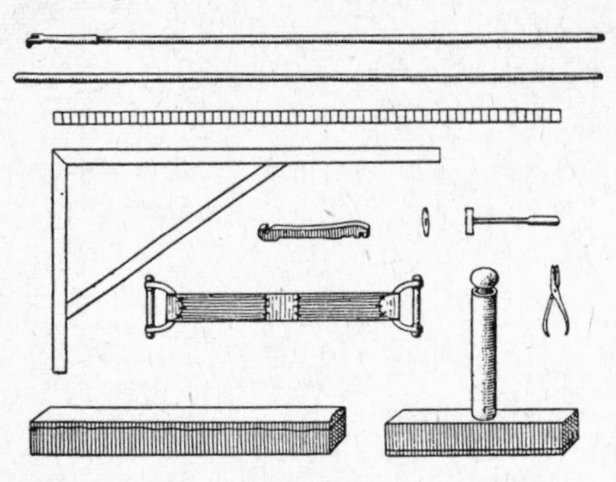

FIGURE 202—*Some tools and equipment used in the making of plate glass, including appliances for moving it, measuring it, and breaking it into sections.*

As regards the actual casting of the glass, there was a steady advance in the size of the plate produced, but while manual handling remained in force this depended mainly on using more and more men to operate the equipment, and the work was slow and laborious. Annealing, too, continued to be slow, taking about ten days. Grinding and polishing were necessary because the surface of the glass was roughened during manufacture by contact with the roller above and the casting-table below. Some of the appliances used for moving, measuring, and cutting the cast plate are shown in figure 202.

To grind plate glass it was laid on a table of fine-grained freestone, and plastered down with lime or stucco to prevent movement during the grinding. Upon the glass to be ground was laid another piece less than half its size, this upper plate being cemented to a wooden plank which in turn was fastened to a horizontal wheel made of light but hard wood. By means of the wheel the upper plate could be turned or moved backwards and forwards, thus causing constant attrition between the two glasses. To aid the process water and sand were poured in, being retained within the framework of the grinding table by a rim. Coarse sand was used first, then finer, and finally powdered smalt. This manual method continued until 1789, when for the first time a steam-engine—made by Boulton and Watt—was used to grind and polish the plates of glass.

After the grinder had done his work the polisher took over, using finely powdered tripoli stone or emery applied by a small felt roller with a double handle at each end. According to long-established practice the roller was mounted on a wooden hoop, which acted as a spring and by bringing the roller back to its original position helped the actions of the workman's arms (plate 21 A).

In Britain a great expansion in building took place in the early 1820s. Between

FIGURE 203—*Annealing arches. The doors to each annealing chamber were made to open in sections. Thus when small ware was being made the heat could be conserved by using the minimum size of opening. The lower archways were used for firing the ovens. Similar chambers were used for plate glass.*

1821 and 1825 brick-production rose from 900 m annually to 1950 m, and the demand for flat glass rose proportionately. To the existing works at Ravenhead and on Tyneside a number of others were added to meet the new demand. Thus the St Helen's Crown Glass Company was formed in 1826, and in 1832 the Smethwick firm of Chance and Hartley brought glass-makers from the continent to blow cylinder-glass. In 1836–7 the great Union Plate Glass Works (figure 204) was built at Pocket Nook, St Helens. Its casting-hall (figure 205) was nearly as big as that at Ravenhead and the equipment included two founding and two firing furnaces and twenty annealing kilns.

VII. COLOURS IN GLASS

Great advances were made in the chemistry of glass coloration between 1750 and 1850. Surprisingly good results had previously been obtained by empirical means, but subject to a wide margin of error; this, however, was of no consequence in such applications as stained glass windows, and might even prove advantageous from the artistic point of view. In the period in question the scientific basis of the colouring agents was explored much more fully than ever before, and in consequence a much closer control over their uses was gained.

Glass was coloured blue with cobalt at a very early date, but the metal was not identified until 1733, when Georg Brandt (1694–1768) named it after the German *Kobold*, a kind of malicious gnome that delighted in frustrating the work of miners. T. O. Bergmann (1735–84) examined the properties of the metal in 1780,

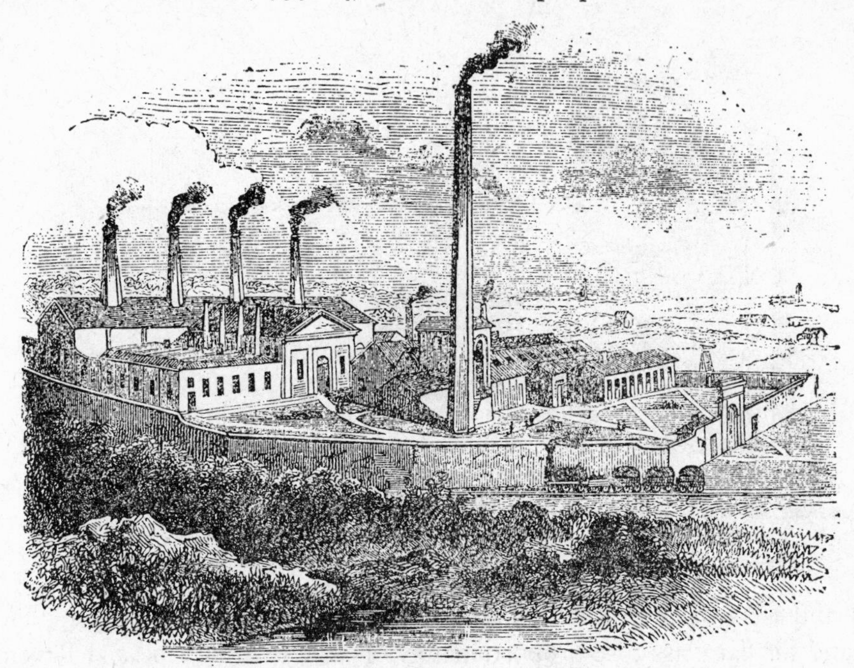

FIGURE 204—*The Union Plate Glass Company's works at Pocket Nook. c 1843.*

and in 1802 Thénard (1777–1857) began systematic research into the chemistry of cobalt compounds.

Nickel can be used to produce a variety of colours that range, according to the composition of the glass, from brown, green, and grey to an attractive purple. The name is a shortened form of *Kupfernickel*, or copper-goblin: the nickel ore looked like copper ore but yielded no copper, suggesting the interference of a mischievous sprite. A. F. Cronstedt discovered the metal in 1751, and Bergmann investigated its properties in 1774.

In his 'Travels Through England', R. Pocoke mentions that in 1751 he came to Stourbridge, 'famous for its glass manufacture, which is here coloured in the liquid of all the capital colours in their several shades'. In spite of this tribute it appears that there was one important exception, in that no good ruby glass was available. In a patent specification of 5 December 1755, for making transparent red glass, the applicant proposes to colour flint glass by melting with it an equal quantity of *Braunstein* and adding 20 grains of dissolved Dutch gold. As *Braunstein* is an impure form of manganese dioxide, and Dutch gold an alloy of copper and zinc, the resulting colour would be purple rather than ruby. The way of making true copper ruby glass seems to have been rediscovered in 1826 by Georges Bontemps.

FIGURE 205—*Casting Hall, Union Plate Glass Company, Pocket Nook.* c *1843.*

In 1779 J. F. Gmelin noted that glasses containing iron became blue when founded under strongly reducing conditions, but no explanation was then possible. The colour was later attributed to a modification of ferric oxide which is stable only in the presence of ferrous oxide. This involves the existence of the metal in its two states of valency in the glass.

In 1789 M. Klaproth (1743–1817) identified a new element, uranium, in the mineral pitchblende. He obtained sodium uranate as a bright yellow solid, which soon came to be used as a colouring-agent for glass and glazes.

Glass can be given a bright green colour with chromium, discovered in 1795 in the Russian mineral crocoite, a form of lead chromate. Chromium has been used for colouring glass from early in the nineteenth century.

In 1831 Sir David Brewster (1781–1868) investigated changes of colour with temperature, and since then several studies have been made of this relationship. For example, a glass coloured with cadmium sulphide is nearly colourless when submerged in liquid air, is yellow at room temperature, and when heated changes first to orange and then to red.

Carbon is commonly used for the manufacture of yellow glasses, being introduced in the form of powdered coke, graphite, or anthracite. The true source of the colour is to be found in the sulphur compounds contained as impurities in the carbon. D. K. Splitgerber demonstrated this in 1839 when he melted two carbon-containing batches, the first of which had 1·75 per cent of sodium sulphate but the other none, and only the former developed a yellow colour. J. T. Pelouze (1807–67) was able to confirm these results by experiments he conducted shortly afterwards.

As regards the colour of glass in general use there were two well marked categories in the period under review. Bottles intended merely as containers were black or very dark green, through excess of iron and other impurities in the raw materials. In evidence before the commissioners at an excise inquiry in 1831 it was stated that the materials employed in the making of common bottles were sand, soap-makers' waste, lime, common clay, and ground bricks. For flint glass, from which table-ware was produced, a much higher standard had to be maintained, and it was stated that the materials used to give a colourless glass were pearl-ash, litharge or red lead, with Lynn or Alum Bay sand or 'Yorkshire stones burnt and pulverized'.

VIII. GLASS-CUTTING

For the making of English cut-glass the great period was from 1750 to 1810, after which the art declined until recent times. The fame of the English product was based partly on the excellence of the workmanship, but to an important extent also upon the quality of the metal. The early crystal glass consisted of sand, lime, and soda, with some potash and a very small proportion of lead oxide added as a flux.

By gradual stages more lead oxide was substituted for the lime, and in the same way the soda was gradually replaced by potash. There was no question of any sudden change or invention by one man, the development taking place slowly. In the event, however, the result was brilliant, for the power of breaking up light into its constituent colours is in proportion to the optical density of the translucent material through which the light passes.

The process of glass-cutting by hand, as carried on until the mid-nineteenth century, was simple in its elements but required a high degree of skill. Three operations were involved, namely grinding, smoothing, and polishing. For the grinding (figure 206), an iron disk was mounted on a horizontal axis and was rotated by power supplied originally by the human foot, then by water, and afterwards by steam. The wheels, larger on the average than those used for engraving, ranged from 3 to 24 inches in diameter.

The glass to be cut was pressed against the iron wheel, and was grooved by the movement of the wheel combined with the abrasive action of sand. When the patterns were completed they were smoothed with wheels of fine sandstone fed with water. Finally, the polish was restored by treating the surfaces of the cuts on a wheel of willow- or pear-wood supplied with putty-powder and water. The designs were chiefly geometrical, and interesting effects were obtained by leaving some parts of the pattern in the smooth state and bringing others back to the original brilliant fire-polish.

FIGURE 206—*Grinding cut-glass vessels.*

IX. GLASS-ENGRAVING

The engraving of glass was a handicraft skill that flourished in the earlier half of the nineteenth century but has since become almost extinct. It was found that engraving could be applied to thin blown glass-ware that was unsuitable for the deeper penetration of cutting. The treatment of the surface of the glass was lighter than in the case of cut glass, and greater freedom of design was possible. Engraved designs were delicate but sharply defined in form, and had easy-flowing curves that contrasted with the straight lines normal in cutting.

The engraver worked before a small copper wheel or disk rotating in a lathe, and used fine grades of emery made into a paste with linseed-oil as the abrasive medium. Engraving-wheels were of many different sizes, and had a variety of bevelled edges. For one design the engraver might use fifty different wheels, varying in diameter from $\frac{1}{8}$ to 4 in or more.

BIBLIOGRAPHY

ANGUS-BUTTERWORTH, L. M. 'The Manufacture of Glass.' Pitman, London. 1948.
Idem. 'British Table and Ornamental Glass.' Hill, London. 1956.
CHANCE, SIR HUGH. "Centenary of Optical Glass Manufacture in England." *J. Soc. chem. Ind., Lond.*, no. 52, 795, 1947.
DICKSON, J. H. 'Glass.' Hutchinson, London. 1951.
DIDEROT, D. and D'ALEMBERT, J. LE R. (Eds). 'Encyclopédie ou dictionnaire raisonné des sciences, des arts et des métiers.' Paris. 1751–72.
FISCHER, J. L. 'Handbuch der Glasmalerei.' Hiersemann, Leipzig. 1914.
HENRIVAUX, M. J. 'Le verre et le cristal.' Paris. 1897.
JEANS, SIR JAMES. 'The Growth of Physical Science.' University Press, Cambridge. 1947.
KRUYT, H. R. (Ed.). 'Colloid Science', Vol. 1. Elsevier, Amsterdam. 1952.
LE VIEIL, P. 'Art de la peinture sur verre, et de la vitrerie.' Neuchâtel. 1781.
MCGRATH, R. 'Glass in Architecture.' Architectural Press, London. 1937.
MARTIN, B. 'An Essay on Visual Glasses (vulgarly called Spectacles).' London. 1756.
MASON, S. F. 'A History of the Sciences.' Routledge & Kegan Paul, London. 1953.
POWELL, H. J. 'Glass-making in England.' University Press, Cambridge. 1923.
SCHULZ, H. 'Die Geschichte der Glaserzeugung.' Akademische Verlagsgesellschaft, Leipzig. 1928.

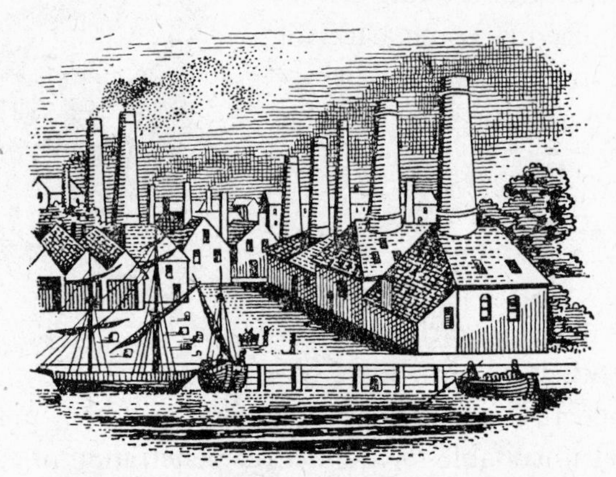

Fishergate Glass Works, York, c *1850, established by John Prince in 1794.*

13

PRECISION MECHANICS

MAURICE DAUMAS

PRECISION mechanics could not come into being until certain conditions were fulfilled. It is difficult to assess the order of importance of these conditions, as their influence was exercised in a rather complex manner, about which we still know very little. Up to now the historian has limited himself to mentioning the appearance of certain perfected instruments and new machinery. He has acknowledged that a certain technical evolution, which he has even incorrectly called revolution, occurred over a relatively short period. He has studied the industrial and social consequences of these changes. But the reasons for such changes, and the course of their development, have never been very thoroughly analysed.

There has always been a relationship between the needs and wishes of the user—the scientific research worker or engineer—and the limits of technical achievement. This relationship has itself been influenced by a number of factors, ranging from the general level of transformation techniques to the political situations within various states. These influences resemble pressures exerted upon several regions of a complex network, the object of the constant transformations being to maintain the internal equilibrium of the network as a whole The factors determining this equilibrium are still obscure, however, because their investigation would require the collaboration of specialists who have, as yet, had little occasion to meet each other.

The above remarks apply more or less strictly to technical progress as a whole, but they have a special importance in the history of precision mechanics. In this field, indeed, invention and the putting of invention into effect have been given expression only when there was some chance of a new object being attained by the users. Progress required the work of skilled craftsmen, the use of materials of the best quality, and costly instruments and machinery; in other words, it required relatively considerable human and monetary capital. If the capital thus tied up were not productive—that is to say, if there were no customers—the invention would languish for lack of means. In fact, customers were not numerous; they were not always prepared to use the new invention; and their financial state was variable.

On the other hand, the activities of the users stimulated invention by bringing new problems to the attention of those putting inventions to practical use. It was only by assessing the limits of the earlier products of the precision engineers that the user could ask them continually to exceed this limit.

Precision mechanics, which arose from clock-making, was first developed in workshops making scientific instruments (vol III, ch 23). The market for these articles was still very restricted in the eighteenth century, and the forces alluded to above must have been very closely balanced.

This is best explained by way of example. The invention of the compound sighting telescope at the beginning of the seventeenth century altered the manufacture of astronomical instruments only very slowly. The first such telescopes fitted to quadrants, for example, were more than a metre in length; the sizes of the instruments were not changed by this innovation. The problems of construction, and more particularly that of dividing the graduated limbs, were the same: the method of transversals used by Tycho Brahe was sufficient for satisfactory precision. After the invention of achromatic objectives (p 358), it was possible to shorten the sighting telescope, which then came into more general use. Observatory instruments remained large and their precision was increased; it was also possible to adapt the sighting telescope easily to instruments for geodesy and nautical astronomy. These were adopted by users because they were small and easy to handle; they were also more precise than instruments fitted with sights, because the technique of marking the scales had been improved. The vernier, the principle of which had been known for a century and a half, then came into use. Further, as large numbers of instruments were being manufactured, manual methods of division were no longer sufficient and dividing-machines were invented. With these it became possible to design new instruments and put them to practical use.

By comparing this process with that determining invention and improvements in other fields of mechanics, we can see what differences there were. If we confine ourselves to the steam-engine and to Watt's work, it is easy to see that the same factors applied, creating circumstances favourable to invention and to putting them to practical application; that is to say, causing progress. In this case, however, the pressure between the governing factors was not so acute; there was a greater opportunity for real and rapid progress.

Thus the precision mechanics industry was able to go ahead only under certain circumstances which it is not possible to analyse in detail here. An understanding of their nature, however, is sufficient to explain both the historical importance of the achievements of engineers in the eighteenth century and the manner in which these achievements stimulated an activity that has continually increased.

I. PROCESSES, TOOLS, AND MACHINES

Ever since the Alexandrian era there have always been instruments for special purposes with which it was possible to carry out operations more precisely than was feasible with common instruments, but this does not mean that the origin of precision techniques is to be found as far back as that. For clarity, it may be agreed that these techniques constituted a special field from the time when craftsmen devised and used special methods and, in particular, special tools. These tools consisted of machines which replaced manual work by mechanical work. The manual skill of expert workers was no longer used directly in making instruments, but for the construction of machines with which a craftsman of ordinary ability could execute work previously done by experts.

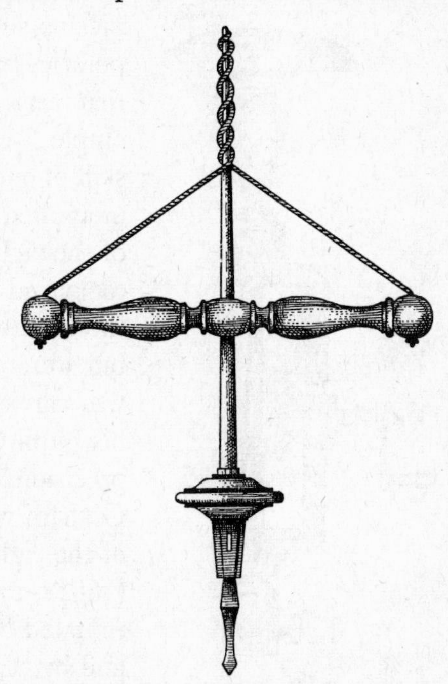

FIGURE 207—*Strap drill.*

Hand tools. The methods used by precision manufacturers up to this period were borrowed from the ancient guilds, such as those of locksmiths, sand-moulders, and tool-makers: they were allowed by the rules of the guilds to use tools of all the metal-workers. From the time that good steel began to be manufactured, namely the end of the seventeenth century, the form of these tools has not varied fundamentally. Some still used are just as they were two or three centuries ago.

Although for a long time only the strap drill (figure 207) was known, the drill with crank and bevel gearing (figure 208) came into use as early as the second half of the eighteenth century. Chisels, gouges, drills, dies, vices, and in general all hand tools used in the workshop, have hardly changed at all since then. They were adopted by instrument-makers who worked in steel, cast iron, brass, or copper. Apart from these, they do not appear to have had any special tools, except for an occasional device invented for executing a special job; some such devices have been abandoned and others adopted. An example of the latter is the machine for cutting helical teeth on wheels (figure 209).

Mathematical and engraving instruments for dividing circles and rulers were also in use very early. In each workshop there was a round table, the surface of which was carefully trued and the centre accurately marked. Solidly constructed, this table was used for the assembly and graduation of quadrants and other sighting instruments.

Little by little, machinery borrowed directly from clock-makers, or based upon those they used, was added to these standard tools. The art of the clock-maker developed only after the inventions of seventeenth-century scientists and technicians such as Huygens, Hooke, and their contemporaries (vol III, ch 24). All masterpieces made before that period, Burgi's astronomical computers for example, were individual works due to the exceptional skill of one man: they had no influence on the progress of applied mechanics as a whole. From the beginning of the eighteenth century this was no longer so. New tools and special methods of working were devised; these were not only soon adopted by all clock-makers, but were used in all workshops where precision work was carried out. Thomas Tompion (1639–1713) and his pupil George Graham (1673–1751) exemplify how precision mechanics derived from clock-making. Graham was the first great English instrument-maker of the eighteenth century; he trained Jonathan Sisson (1694?–1749) and John Bird (1709–76), and he was imitated by all the instrument-makers of that period and by their immediate successors.

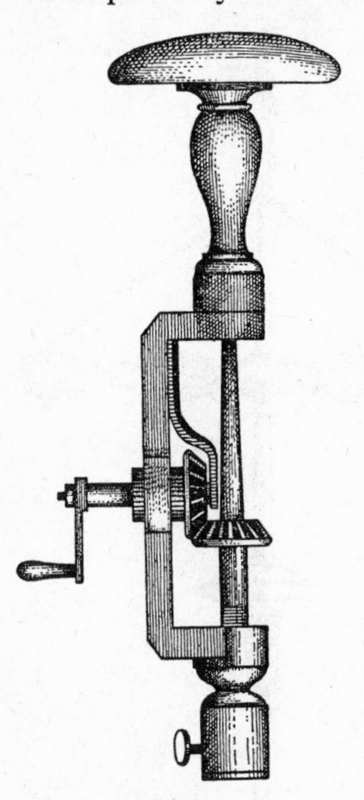

FIGURE 208—*Hand-brace with bevel gearing.*

The lathe. The first machine available to engineers, as regards both date and importance, was the lathe. This machine, which goes back to some unknown period, did not achieve popularity until the sixteenth and seventeenth centuries; it became really useful in the second half of the latter century (vol III, pp 335–6). Opticians used it for cutting lenses for astronomical telescopes, modifying a relatively rough technique for their special purposes. They gave their lathe a stronger frame in order to ensure its stability, but it was still constructed of wood, and was thus unsuitable for metal-work. It was the clock-makers who invented the first precision lathes.

Arbors and the cylindrical parts of clocks were turned on small iron lathes. These consisted mainly of an iron bar, square in section, on which were a fixed headstock at one end, and a second, loose headstock sliding the whole length of the bar (figure 210). A cylindrical opening was made in the top of each headstock, and through this a pointed rod passed to secure the work. Headstocks and centres were tightly fixed by screws. The bracket for the tool was carried by a sliding support. The part to be turned, placed between the centres, was rotated by a bow.

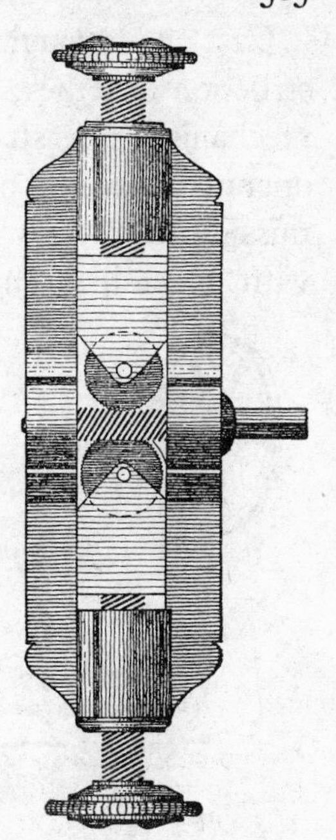
FIGURE 209—*Stock and die for cutting helical teeth on wheels.*

Large lathes were used by turners of fancy work and by cabinet-makers. Their frames were of wood and they had one or two headstocks according to whether the work was turned on the face plate or between centres: these headstocks were of iron. The main part was the mandrel, on which the part to be turned was fixed. A cord passed around the mandrel: one end of the string was fixed to the end of a flexible pole, and the other end was attached to a treadle under the table (vol III, figures 218, 220). Such a pole-lathe had an alternating rotary motion. For big jobs, turners used a lathe driven by a hemp or gut cord passing round a pulley. The driving-wheel was large; it was fixed to the ground and operated by an assistant who turned the handle. This kind of lathe employed continuous rotation.

From the end of the seventeenth century the pole-lathe was adopted by many amateurs who set up workshops adjoining their chemical and physical laboratories and their cabinets of curiosities. Wood, horn, and ivory were the chief materials worked. Then the working of metals became fashionable, and important improvements were made in the design of lathes. Engineers constructed them not only for wealthy and exacting amateurs but for craftsmen who manufactured for customers.

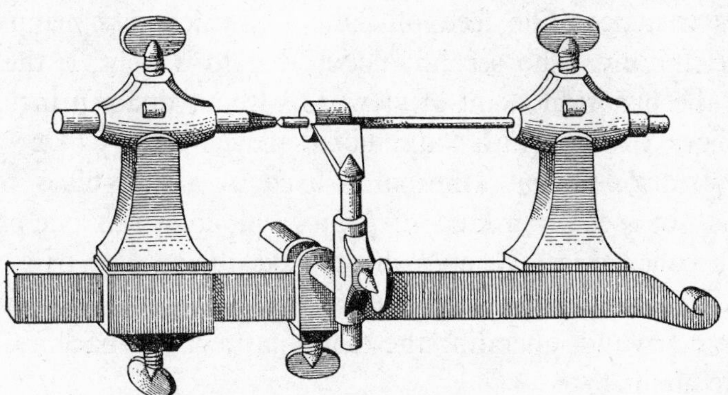
FIGURE 210—*Clock-maker's lathe.*

Cast and wrought iron, steel, and brass gradually replaced wood in the construction of lathes; this gave them greater strength and stability. The driving mechanism consisted of a heavy wheel placed on a bracket above the lathe and operated by a cord connecting a crank on the wheel to a treadle below; the transmission from the wheel to the shaft of the lathe was made by grooved pulleys with an endless cord (figure 211). Devices were added not only to regulate the tension of the cord according to the dampness of the air, but to vary the speed of rotation of the lathe as required without altering the foot-movement. A lathe constructed by the Saxon engineer Merklein, about 1775, had a screw system of great precision for this purpose.

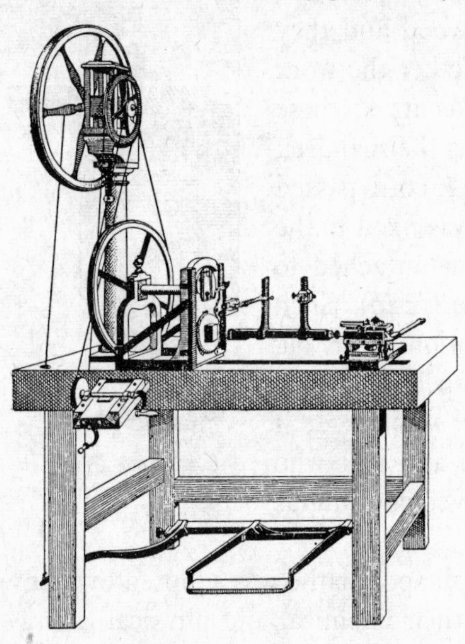

FIGURE 211—*Rotary lathe with treadle and flywheel.*

The greatest improvement was made to the tool, which until then was held in the hand. Its handle was usually bent; it was used as a lever, the bend resting on the tool-holder. The latter was only a support and it did not guide or regulate the feed. Towards the beginning of the eighteenth century, however, clock-makers began to use mechanically guided tools. Antoine Thiout (1692-1767) and Fardoïl, in France, invented machines for cutting fusees (vol III, p 656) in which the part to be turned moved in front of the fixed tool, or conversely the tool moved in front of the part. In the first model, the fusee was given the shape of a cone by inclined guides in the form of very flat isosceles triangles. The feed of the tool, which was manual, was later effected mechanically. The second model, due to Thiout, is the most interesting from the historical point of view, as without doubt it incorporated the first tool-holder carriage with longitudinal movement [1] to be constructed. It is of very simple design. The tool is fixed by a slide-block to a flat bar; movement is obtained by a kind of pantograph in which one of the bars is fitted with a collar threaded internally to take the gearing of a worm screw (figure 212). Here we have one of the earliest examples, if not the earliest, of the use of a screw drive for operating the tool of a precision machine. This device dates back to about 1750.

Jacques de Vaucanson (1709–82) was the first to adapt these methods to machinery for working on a larger scale. He devised a lathe and a drill each fitted with a tool-holder carriage moved by a threaded screw [2]: these must have been made between 1768 and 1780. He redesigned the iron frame of a shaping lathe and made it larger. He copied the idea of the lead-screw and carriage for the tool in machines for turning fusees and for guilloching.[1] His lathe measured 140 cm in length. The carriage was moved by a lead-screw placed parallel to the line of the headstock centres; it moved along a prismatic bench, a device which was used

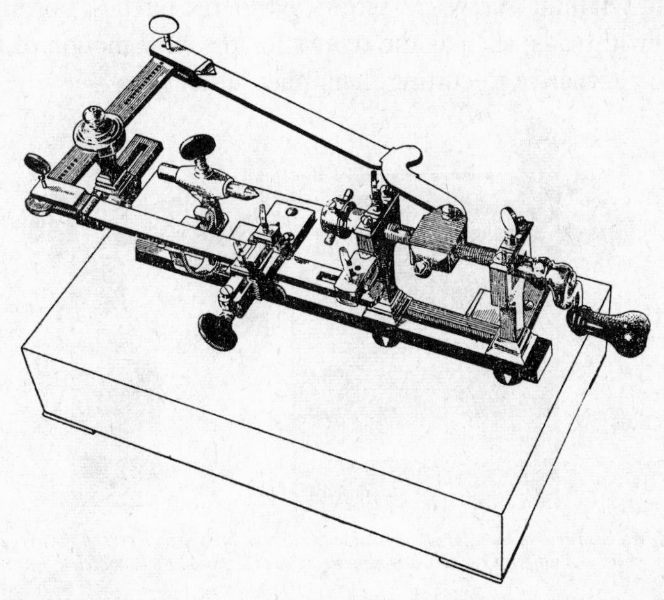

FIGURE 212—*Thiout's lathe for cutting screw-threads on spindles for clocks and watches.*

later on all machine tools. The advance of the tool was also controlled by a screw (plate 23 A).

Vaucanson's drill is even more interesting. It is a horizontal drill in which the carriage is guided by a horizontal prismatic bench; the tool-holder moves along a vertical bench similar to the horizontal one (plate 22 A). The movements are controlled by threaded guide-rods, the cranks of which rotate in front of graduated dials. There is as yet no vernier: this was used only by instrument-makers of the next generation, in the first half of the nineteenth century.

Henry Gambey (1787–1847) constructed for his own use an improved lathe, the tool of which was controlled by micrometer screws and tilted by a toothed sector with helical gearing and vernier graduation.

Screw cutting. All these working methods were adopted by precision-instrument

[1] A guilloche is an ornament in the form of interlaced bands.

makers during the last quarter of the eighteenth century, but it is not possible to find out to whom the credit for any of these adaptations is due. However, a few examples will enable us to understand how the first special engineering tools were developed.

One of the most essential operations in the construction of instruments for the measurement of angles is the cutting of an accurately threaded screw. Several methods were used to do this. With stocks and dies it was possible to obtain only levelling- and retaining-screws, or screws with large pitches. For finer and more accurate screw threads, such as the screws for the slow motion of microscopes, there was no alternative to cutting them on a lathe.

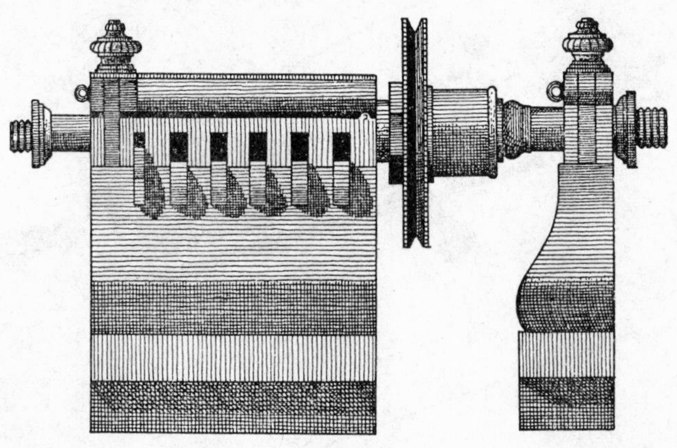

FIGURE 213—*Keyed headstock of lathe for screw-cutting. The 'keys' are the six levers on the left. The first is locked. A different thread corresponding to each is cut on the mandrel.*

With a lathe it was possible to work in several ways. The usual process was to use a headstock with a threaded chuck in which a guide-screw rotated; at the extremity of this screw was fixed, along the same axis, the rod to be threaded, supported by a second headstock. When rotating, the rod moved backwards and forwards in front of the tool according to the pitch of the guide-screw selected. In the second half of the eighteenth century lathes were fitted with keyed headstocks, which made it possible to change the pitch easily. These keys consisted of levers, integral with the headstock, each of which engaged independently in the thread of a guide-screw of a given pitch (figure 213); five or six threads of different pitch could therefore be cut on the same spindle.

For precision work, or for cutting lead-screws, the following procedure was adopted (figure 214). On a rectangular sheet of paper transverse lines were drawn, the spacing and angle of inclination of which corresponded to the thread to be traced. The paper was wound around the rod to be made into a screw and the threads were traced by following the line with a sharp file; the cutting was done first with a triangular file and finally with a steel chaser having teeth spaced to correspond with the pitch of the screw to be made.

Such methods took a long time, and the quality of the result depended entirely upon the skill of the operator. To overcome these difficulties the great English engineer, Jesse Ramsden (1735–1800), in 1770 invented two screw-cutting lathes which were certainly the first machines of this type ever constructed and which gave satisfactory results [3].

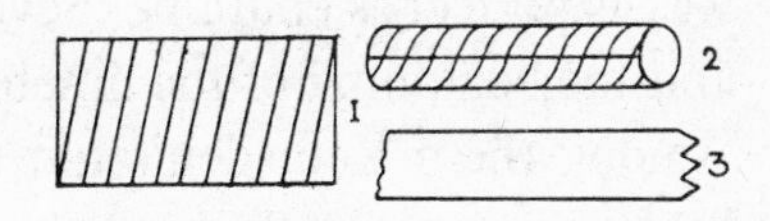

FIGURE 214—*Screw cutting by means of file. (1) Track of thread cut; (2) paper wound on the rod to be threaded; (3) metal comb.*

In the first of these machines the guide-screw and the rod to be threaded are placed parallel to each other (figure 215). The latter is set in motion by a crank; its motion is transmitted to the lead-screw through toothed gearing-wheels, the number of teeth being a function of the ratio between the pitch of the guide-screw and that of the screw to be cut. The lead-screw has a threaded collar which drives the tool-holder. The guiding is effected by a bar of triangular section placed parallel to the lead-screw. The tool is fitted with a diamond for cutting hard steel.

Ramsden's second screw-cutting lathe is of a more elaborate design (figure 216). The lead-screw guides the tool by means of a chuck-plate with helical teeth into which it engages. At the centre of this chuck-plate there is a grooved pulley, and the guide-bench of the tool-holder is placed more or less at a tangent to this. After being pushed back to the end of the bench the tool-holder is drawn towards the centre of the chuck-plate by a small cord which winds around the pulley when the machine is working. The rod to be threaded is placed parallel to the guide-bench. It is rotated by the driving crank of the lead-screw by means of gearing which includes an angle pinion, the two pieces in this instance not being parallel. When we consider the construction of these two machines in the light of the means available to the engineers of those days, and of other contemporary inventions, we must form a very high opinion of Ramsden's technical ability and understanding. In research and in the design of tools intended to reduce the personal factor in the making of accurate parts, the personal factor itself played a considerable part.

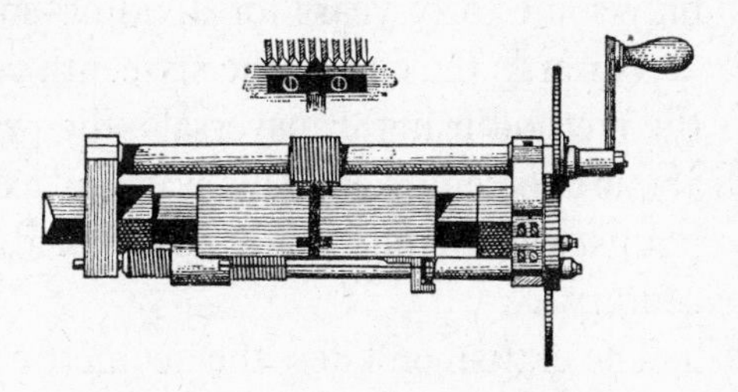

FIGURE 215—*Ramsden's screw-cutting machine with lead-screw (detail above).*

Ten or fifteen years after Ramsden, the French engineer Jean Fortin (1750–1831) had his own method for screw-cutting. Unfortunately no description of this has been handed down to us. We only know that Fortin proceeded in stages; from an original screw he cut another more uniform, then with this a third which was as perfect as could be. Several engineers at the end of the eighteenth century and the beginning of the nineteenth became past-masters of the art of threading. Among them Ramsden's old craftsman, Samuel Rhee, was reputed to be the best.

Towards the end of the century the engineering industry began to have screw-cutting lathes at its disposal, thanks to Maudslay. In 1795, the Frenchman, Senot, constructed a screw-cutting lathe for working large parts which does not appear to have been known to his contemporaries. In 1797, Maudslay designed a lathe which was widely adopted in the trade; its history is part of that of machine tools and is considered elsewhere (p 424). It is worth mentioning, however, that it is not impossible that Maudslay knew of Ramsden's lathes. The latter was an instrument-maker with an international reputation; he was a Fellow of the Royal Society; and his workshop was of very great repute. Further, the description of his lathes was published. The great English engineers who in the nineteenth century invented the principal machine tools for the engineering industry were no doubt influenced by his work.

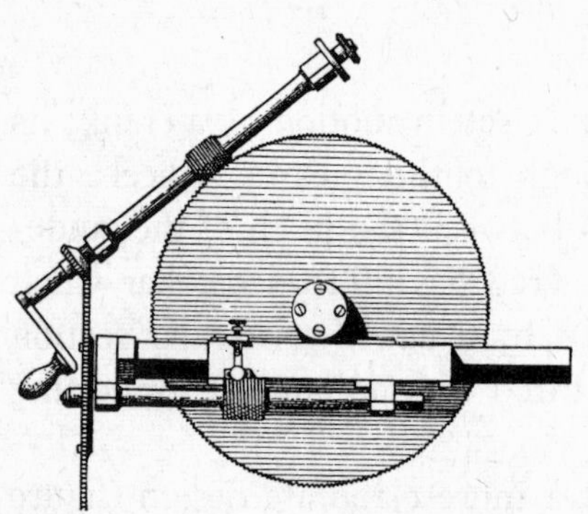

FIGURE 216—*Ramsden's screw-cutting lathe with lead-screw and toothed plate. This made it possible to make long screws from a small original.*

Division of limbs. From about 1760 precision workers had to solve another problem, that of mechanically dividing the graduated limbs of instruments and rules. For centuries previously, methods had evolved very slowly, but it took only some forty years for dividing-engines to be adopted in all workshops.

Towards the end of the sixteenth century Tycho Brahe had brought into use the method using transversals, the principle of which had then been known for about two centuries. This was replaced gradually by the traditional dividing by points, which was finally abandoned only towards the end of the seventeenth century.

The craftsmen knew the geometrical processes for dividing by means of compasses. The method with transversals consisted in tracing parallel lines cut perpendicularly by the division marks of the rule (figure 217); to obtain the tenth of these divisions a transversal was drawn, that is, a diagonal of the rectangle bounded by the first and eleventh lines and the two neighbouring dividing marks. The tenths of a unit were found by intersection of the transversal and each of the ten parallels. The reading was made by moving a pointer in front of the scale cutting all the parallels at right angles. It was thus possible to find one-hundredth of an inch or a tenth of a line (on the old measuring system 1 line = $\frac{1}{12}$-in).

On circular limbs the transversals were concentric circles. With seven concentric circles angles of ten minutes could be read. When achromatic reading telescopes were adopted and the mechanical parts of instruments were improved, sighting was made more precise and the instrument-makers had to revise their method of dividing. It was no longer sufficient to trace rectilinear transversals and equidistant arcs of circumference on the limbs. The transversals themselves had to be circular arcs passing through the centre of the instrument (figure 218). Concentric circles no longer had to be equidistant; their radii were determined by dividing into six equal parts the circular arcs serving as transversals. The geometrical methods enabling this lay-out to be effected strictly were perfected in the first few years of the eighteenth century.

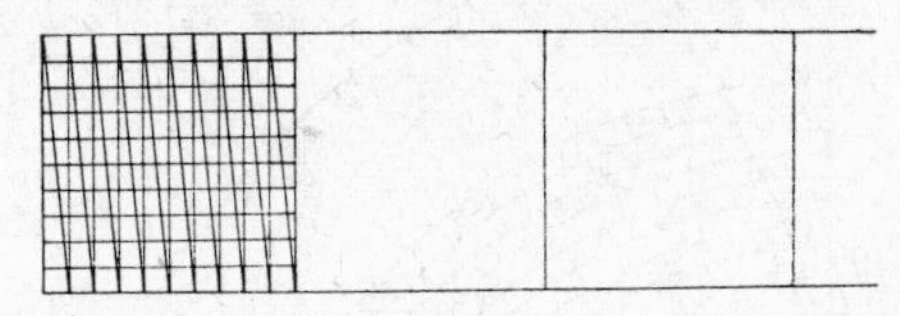

FIGURE 217—*Method of division by transversals.*

For a long time one great difficulty still remained in the principal operation, the division of an arc into 90 degrees. The only strictly accurate division which can be done with a compass is the bisection of an arc, but it was not possible to go very far with this alone; consequently various devices were invented.

First, an arc of 90° must be accurately measured on the limb to be graduated, whether this is a circle, semicircle, or quadrant. The geometrical method was to begin by striking an arc of 60° from the zero point: this was done with the dividers, since the chord of 60° is equal to the radius of the circle. Bisecting the arc gave the 30° point, and by setting off an arc of 30°, again with the dividers, beyond the 60° point, 90° was found. Bisection of these three arcs gave 15°, 45°, and 75° respectively. For the rest, the worker used a table for finding the opening of the compass corresponding to one-third of each of the chords, and then to one-fifth of the latter. When the limb was thus divided into degrees, the subdivision into ten-second intervals was made by the method of transversals mentioned above.

When limbs had to be more accurately graduated, the instrument-makers invented processes for determining a 90° arc by double sighting using a plumb-line. However, the difficulty of dividing the arc itself remained unsolved. In 1725

George Graham (p 382) devised a method using a duplicate scale with 96 units for 90 sexagesimal degrees. This enabled him to mark accurately, by repeated bisection, sections of 3 such units (instead of 5° sections, each divided into degrees); the units were in turn subdivided into 8 by bisection. A table gave the equivalence between these units and their subdivisions, and the sexagesimal degrees and seconds. Following Graham, his pupil John Bird further perfected the geometric operations required for this method.

The construction of the first machines for dividing did not do away immediately with the necessity of using a compass for large instruments. With the machines of Ramsden and his contemporaries it was possible to divide mechanically only the limbs of small instruments such as sextants and geodesic circles. The large mural circles in astronomical observatories still had to be divided by hand. It was only in the first quarter of the nineteenth century that J. G. Repsold (1771–1830) and H. Gambey (p 394) discovered how to construct machines for dividing the limbs of large instruments. Consequently the instrument-makers of the end of the eighteenth century used Bird's method, or invented ones of their own.

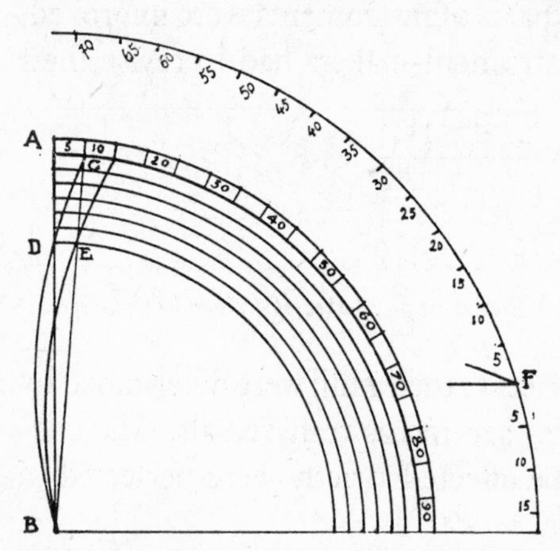

FIGURE 218—*Division of a limb by transversals. The outer curve is the geometric locus of the centres of all the arcs of the circles forming the transversals of the graduation. See p 389.*

Dividing-engines. These delicate operations were of no pecuniary interest to the instrument-maker unless they were entrusted to a specialized craftsman who executed a series of them, or unless they were included in the construction of a large instrument for which he could command remuneration. Consequently, almost throughout the eighteenth century it was only the English workshops which had a clientele abundant enough for these manufactures to be carried out satisfactorily. Besides those of Graham, Sisson, and Bird the workshops of the Adams and the Dollonds had undisputed supremacy in the whole of the market for precision instruments, because they employed numerous specialized craftsmen, each for a given operation.

Meanwhile the progress in the optical qualities of telescopes, the improvement in manufacturing materials such as brass, steel, and bronze, and above all the ever-increasing demand of users—navigators, geodesists, and surveyors—necessitated the search for new graduation processes. Geometrical methods had attained their ultimate perfection; for this reason the first tentative steps were taken towards the construction of dividing-engines.

Clock-makers had already solved the problem some time previously for their own purposes. The machines they had been using since early in the eighteenth century to cut toothed wheels and pinions consisted of a division-plate on which concentric circles were traced, each having a certain number of equidistant points incised upon them. The divisions of these circles, which had been traced by geo-

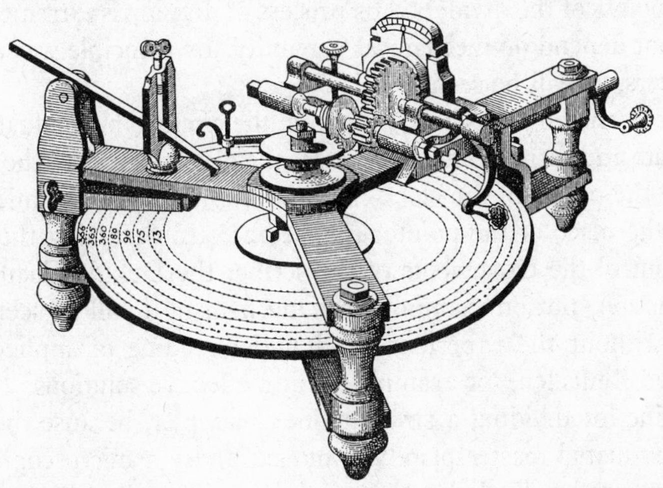

FIGURE 219—*Machine, with division-plate, for cutting clock-wheels. Cf figure 238.*

metrical methods, corresponded to the usual divisions of the wheels and pinions in clock-making. From the plate on which they had been engraved they could be reproduced at will. The disk to be cut was fixed above the division-plate and parallel to it. It was marked by a cutter moved by a crank; a pointer following the graduations on the plate, mark by mark, and moved after each cut, made it possible to turn the disk through the arc corresponding to one tooth (figure 219).

The first attempt by instrument-makers consisted in trying to adapt the clock-maker's machine for dividing scales. That of the English clock-maker Henry Hindley, made in 1739, does not seem to have led very far. Although the attempt is of some historical interest, it is probable that the technical means available at the time did not enable Hindley to obtain very satisfactory results.

A little later, in 1765, the Duc de Chaulnes (1714–69), a French academician, had two machines constructed, one for circles, the other for straight lines [4]. He used the principle of the clock-maker's division-plate, on the edge of which he cut helical teeth. This is the first example of drive by tangent screw being applied to this type of machine, but the threading of a screw with strictly constant pitch was not then practicable. For a long time to come all instrument-makers came up against this obstacle, and had to find a device for turning the dividing-plate.

The Duc de Chaulnes established empirically the correspondence between the number of turns of the crank and the angle of rotation of his plate. On the latter he traced a division by the ordinary method, but instead of using dividers he used two microscopes of his own invention, the cross-hairs of which took the place of the points of the dividers. His process of division is extremely ingenious, but it does not depend on mechanical ingenuity. Its principle was used later by other engineers, as will be seen.

A master copy having thus been prepared, the circle to be graduated was fixed above the plate and turned under a scriber; the division lines of the master were used as were the points of the clock-maker's division-plate, the microscope this time taking the place of the pointer (figure 220). In designing the mechanism serving to control the movements of the scriber the Duc de Chaulnes showed some imagination, but on examining the mechanism it will be seen that its inventor was without the experience and understanding of applied mechanics which enabled Ramsden, for example, to find effective solutions.

The machine for dividing a straight line is simpler, because the problem is simpler. A graduated master-plate was moved under a microscope at the same time as the rule to be divided was moved under a scriber. The displacement was obtained by a plate with helical teeth engaging on one side with a worm screw turned by a crank, and on the other with a toothed rack on a carriage bearing the master-plate and the rule.

The Duc de Chaulnes's tests were described and published. They drew the attention of engineers to the usefulness of adopting the tangent-screw drive and position-finding by a microscope. Ramsden was the first to use these two methods, and constructed the first dividing-engine suitable for use on an industrial scale (plate 1) [5]. His research lasted nearly fifteen years: it was during the period 1760–73 that he invented the two screw-cutting lathes mentioned above. But his enterprise could not have succeeded without progress made by the founders and turners.

One of the principal parts of the dividing-engine for circles (vol III, figure 378) was a bronze wheel, cast in one piece. This wheel, having a diameter of 110 cm, was reinforced by ten spokes, an inner ring, and ribs. Placed horizontally on three rollers, it could revolve around a vertical axle consisting of a steel shaft turned with great precision. The creation of this unit involved the co-operation of several craftsmen, each of them excelling in his own craft.

The edge of the wheel had helical teeth cut with the aid of a hardened steel worm-screw, the threads of which were sharpened to a keen edge. The operation was effected in discontinuous fractions, corresponding to 9 out of 10 teeth of the wheel, so as to distribute throughout the circumference the error arising in the cutting of the sharp screw. The wheel had 2160 teeth, each corresponding to an angular distance of 10 minutes. Ramsden reckoned that the precision of his tooth-cutting was about 2½ seconds per tooth, or 10 minutes for the whole circumference.

The other special features of the machine are the tangent screw, which turns

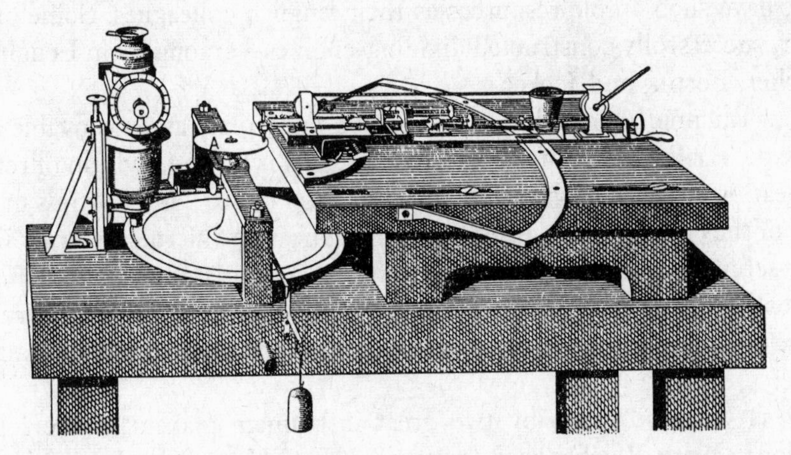

FIGURE 220—*The Duc de Chaulnes's dividing-machine fitted with dividing plate and microscope.* A *is the disk to be divided; the scriber control mechanism is at the right.*

the toothed wheel, and its method of operation. For the latter, Ramsden invented a mechanism comprising a spring drum round which a string was wound. Drawn by a foot-operated treadle, the string turned the tangent screw; the spring drum returned cord and treadle to the starting position. At each touch of the treadle the plate of the machine turned through a given angle, always the same, carrying the scale to be divided under the scriber. By a special appliance the feed could be regulated and limited to the extent of the travel of the treadle. The mechanism permitted the obtaining of automatic feeds of up to 10 seconds.

In the construction of the machine for dividing a straight line Ramsden used a screw of strictly constant pitch. This screw engaged throughout virtually the whole length of the rectilinear toothed rack of the carriage bearing the rule to be divided. In the former machine only a few threads of the tangent screw engaged with the toothed wheel, so that its irregularities had less effect. It was for the making of this important screw that Ramsden constructed his second screw-cutting lathe (figure 216). The movement of the carriage was obtained by a mechanism similar to that of the dividing-engine for circles.

Ramsden's machines aroused keen interest. The Board of Longitude in London entered into an agreement with the inventor for their application and for the publication of their description. A number of engineers of the day, among them Edward Troughton (1753–1835), constructed several examples.

From that moment the main difficulties in making dividing-engines seemed to have been overcome by all good engineers. In France several first-class engineers acquired a high reputation though unfortunately they did not, for numerous reasons, have such ample resources as their English colleagues. Some of them, however, successfully constructed dividing-engines—among them Lenoir, Mégnié, Richer, Fortin, and Jecker.

That of Étienne Lenoir (1744–1832) had a fixed plate and a movable alidade carrying the scriber round its centre. Lenoir used it for the division of reflection and repeating circles, which we shall describe later (p 401). On Fortin's machines the feed of the circular plate, or of the carriage bearing the rules, was obtained by a worm-screw operated by a crank. A buffer and graduated disk mechanism enabled this feed to be controlled accurately to a given interval; in its return movement the crank did not turn the worm. Jecker imitated but simplified Ramsden's machine.

Progress was also made by two great instrument-makers of the following generation: Georg Reichenbach (1772–1826) and Henry Gambey (1787–1847). The former constructed a machine the plate of which measured 135 cm in diameter. It was a little larger than that of Ramsden, but constructed on the same lines; it was stationary. Two superimposed alidades revolved around the centre; they could be set with a given difference. Reichenbach first traced twenty divisions corresponding to an angle of 18° between the alidades. Then he traced the intermediate divisions.

This method is based on the principle used by the Duc de Chaulnes in his method of position-finding by microscope. Gambey took it up in his turn for the construction of a machine the precision of which was better than any that had preceded it; he used it also for the graduation of the great 2-metre mural circle constructed in 1840 for the Paris Observatory [6].

The division of this great circle was a masterpiece of precision. Gambey operated as follows. The circle was placed horizontally, and the points of its vertical axis were supported by conical bearings. Four microscopes suitably contrived served first of all to mark two orthogonal diameters, and then a certain number of intermediate divisions on the circumference. In order to mark out the teeth on the circle he worked with a sharp-pitch screw by the Ramsden method, progressing by limited portions of arc in such a way as to distribute the error of tooth-cutting over the whole of the circumference. After having calculated the average error of pitch in each space, Gambey made a rectifying plate which he fixed on the pin of the tangent screw. In this way he was able by means of a crank to advance his large circle by strictly constant angles.

The division of the circle was effected with the aid of a specially constructed dividing-engine [7]. The platform for this machine had itself been toothed by an original rectification process. Two circular limbs had been superimposed and fastened to each other by screws and a first common cutting of teeth effected; the position of one of the limbs was then modified in relation to the other and the thread of the tangent screw was passed through the teeth again. This operation being repeated systematically a certain number of times, the teeth of the two limbs were corrected reciprocally, and Gambey obtained a perfectly regular pitch.

Gambey also tried to eliminate two other sources of error. The first concerned the imperfection of the centring of the circle to be divided on the machine; the second the magnification of errors arising from the fact that the circle to be divided was of a larger diameter than that of the machine. He conceived a deformable parallelogram, driven by a rectifying plate, which automatically corrected the position of the scriber for each division, causing practically all the mechanical faults to disappear. This correcting device was used after him by other instrument-makers.

We cannot give details of all the precautions that Gambey took in carrying out his operations. We will give as examples compensation for the inertia of mobile parts by judiciously placed counterweights, and remote control of the scriber in order to eliminate the effects of the body-heat of the operator. These demonstrate Gambey's sense of mechanical precision. His great mural circle, which was executed about 1840, remained in use until 1920.

Dilatometers and comparators. Clock-makers were the first to try to measure the thermal expansion of metals. The earliest instruments served to study the expansion of brass and steel rods intended for making pendulums. In 1726 John Harrison invented his bimetallic gridiron, designed to cancel by compensation the effects of variations of temperature on the length of the pendulum.

About the same time, Graham conceived the first precision dilatometer. This instrument was composed essentially of two fixed end-pieces between which was placed the metal rod to be examined; one of the end-pieces was pierced by a threaded hole, in which a micrometer screw was inserted. The desired constant temperature having been established, the screw was turned until its extremity touched the extremity of the rod. The displacement of the screw was read on a dial whose divisions indicated the thermal elongation of the rod. The experiment was repeated at a higher temperature, when a different setting of the screw was necessary to make contact with the rod. A little later, in 1754, Smeaton described a dilatometer of his own invention (figure 221) which is merely an improvement on that of Graham [8]. One of the end-pieces is hinged and moves as a result of the thrust due to thermal expansion. The elongation of the rod is then amplified

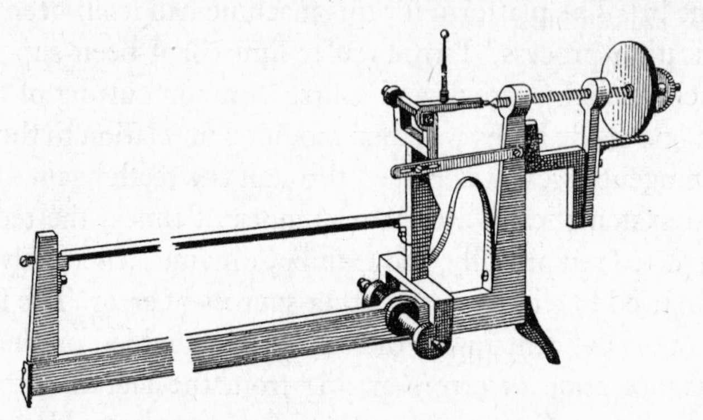

FIGURE 221—*Smeaton's dilatometer, 1754.*

and the movement of the reference point is measured by the rotation of a micrometer screw fitted with a dial and bearing on a stop carried by the end-piece.

About 1760 Berthoud made a constant-temperature enclosure in which he suspended metal rods to be studied. One extremity of these was fixed; the other rested on one arm of a small bent lever, the other arm of which carried a toothed sector engaging with a pinion, on the shaft of which was placed a pointer. A counterweight, the cord of which passed over a grooved wheel, brought the pointer back during cooling. This device for amplifying small movements has been used in nearly all instruments, both dilatometers and comparators, constructed subsequently. A common form of these instruments was the Musschenbroek dilatometer, made simply for physical laboratories and not used industrially.

Lavoisier used the same appliance, on a large scale, for the expansion measurements carried out with Laplace in 1781 [9]. The rod to be examined was placed in a large tank containing water heated to a given temperature. One of its extremities rested against a fixed glass stud, and the other on the arm of a lever bearing a sighting telescope. The inclination of the telescope was measured by means of a graduated levelling-rod placed 200 metres away. The degree of precision was of the order of 0·003 cm.

About 1784 Ramsden constructed a dilatometer for William Roy, in charge of geodesical triangulations in Kent (p 607), which in certain respects recalls that of Lavoisier and Laplace [10]. The rod to be examined, placed in a tank, rests on rollers; one of its extremities rests on a fixed stud, the other on a hinged spring. The observation is made according to a principle quite different from that described above. Ramsden used two microscopes, each placed at an extremity of the apparatus. The body of one of the microscopes being divided, the objective followed the displacement of the free end of the rod being examined, and this displacement was measured by a micrometer fitted to the eyepiece. The precision was of the order of 0·0014 in.

In 1792 Edward Troughton constructed a comparator accurate to 0·001 in. This instrument is nothing else than a beam compass, the points of which were moved by micrometer screws.

In France several comparators were constructed by Fortin and by Lenoir for the *Commission des Poids et Mesures*. Fortin's comparator was designed to measure the dimensions of cylindrical standards of the kilogram [11]. It consisted of a carriage which rested against the cylinder to be measured and was fitted with a feeler which moved in front of a graduated scale a pointer whose position was read through a microscope. The apparatus was accurate to 0·00008 in.

Under the direction of J. C. de Borda (1733–99) and Lavoisier, Lenoir made rules for measuring the bases of triangulations. These rules were of platinum; each had at one end a small graduated slide which moved in a guide in front of a vernier. Lavoisier had some years previously used a rule made on the same principle by Lenel. The thermal examination of the rules was made by transforming each of them into bimetallic thermometers; a copper foil, of about the same length as the rule, was fixed on each platinum rod at one of its extremities; and a vernier graduation was engraved on the other end in order to read the differences in the variation of the two lengths. Lenoir also made an original thrust comparator, with which the reading was made with the aid of a vernier. Later he designed another thrust and bent lever comparator; the unequal arms of the lever increased the precision of the reading [12]. Several examples of this apparatus, which was accurate to 0·00008 in, were made subsequently.

Afterwards, lever comparators and microscope comparators were used simultaneously for a long time. Gambey used a microscope for reading on the vernier the position of a sliding rule on his comparator, which was constructed on the principle of externally measuring calipers; he obtained an accuracy of 0·001 mm. He also constructed a lever apparatus. Brunner, about 1850, constructed a dual lever comparator the precision of which was about 0·001 mm. Subsequently he constructed very precise microscope comparators for the *Commission des Poids et Mesures.*

II. THE INSTRUMENTS MANUFACTURED

Astronomical instruments. We shall speak here only of the mechanical parts of these instruments and their general arrangement. Thanks to the improvement in methods, the construction of large instruments made considerable progress in the period between the middle of the eighteenth century and the middle of the nineteenth. Telescopes, which since 1755 had been fitted with achromatic objectives, continued to be used as transit instruments, meridian or equatorial telescopes, or for equipping circles or quadrants serving to determine the position of the stars. But what characterizes the period up to about 1820 is the favour that large reflecting telescopes found with astronomers.

It was not until the second quarter of the eighteenth century that the reflecting telescope began to be commonly made. Scarlett (d 1743) in England, and Paris and Passemant (1702–69) in France, were those who spread its manufacture. The instruments that came from these workshops consisted of small brass cylinders 16 inches in length, usually mounted on a folding tripod. From this period the orientation of the tube was controlled by toothed sectors engaging with a cranked pinion. The adjustment of the small mirror was effected by a knob turning a threaded rod.

These telescopes were drawing-room pieces. The first observatory telescopes were constructed by James Short (1710–68). This Scottish astronomer and instrument-maker confined himself to Gregorian telescopes, some of them being of large dimensions, up to 12 ft in length. He must have made a special study of the mechanical design. For controlling the different movements he used long mahogany handles with Cardan joints, a device fitted at this time to all instruments above a certain size. Short made the tubes of his instruments of mahogany with a polygonal section. At about the same time Dom Noël, custodian of the royal collection of physical apparatus in Paris, constructed large telescopes of the Cassegrain type; the largest had a focal length of 24 ft.

It was with Sir William Herschel (1738–1822) that the reflecting telescope became a true instrument of astronomical research. From 1785 to 1789 he devoted himself to the construction of a 40-ft instrument, called a 'front view telescope' on account of the principle on which it had been designed [13]. The main difficulty consisted in the casting and polishing of the mirror, but the mechanical equipment also demanded quite new methods. A wooden frame supporting the tube, which measured 12 metres in length and 147 cm in width, was mounted on a platform revolving on rollers.

Herschel's discoveries aroused great interest in this type of telescope. Several examples were constructed in the years that followed. In France, Carochez made one in 1800. But the success of the big refracting telescopes began soon afterwards, and for a time engaged the attention of instrument-makers and astronomers. On account of their dimensions, the mechanical problems posed by their installation were very difficult to solve; their cost was very high. It was only towards 1850 that large reflecting telescopes were built again. Lord Rosse's 52-ft telescope, constructed in Ireland in 1845, amazed his contemporaries. Léon Foucault revived this tradition in France at the same time.

The German optician Fraunhofer and his French colleague Lerebours (1762–1840) were the first to succeed in constructing large lenses for astronomical purposes when, about 1815–20, the manufacture of flint-glass became relatively straightforward (ch 12). The progress of the optician's art led to correspondingly great progress in the mechanical art. During the first half of the nineteenth century the dimensions of refractors grew steadily. The construction of stands for them, and the making of driving devices, developed rapidly. Among the problems most difficult to solve were those relating to the setting and adjustment of transit telescopes and meridian circles. The outline which has been given above of the improvement of the working resources available to engineers enables us to understand how the solutions devised could be progressively improved. Instrument-makers like Ramsden and Troughton were the first to seek entirely new appliances. They adopted the truncated-cone shape both for the telescope bodies and for the transverse arms supporting them. The mechanical strength of two frusta of a cone joined by their bases led them to introduce this structure into the construction of numerous instruments. They used a metal frame, having the shape of a long cage with four or six pillars, to hold meridian or equatorial telescopes. They abandoned the old toothed sectors and replaced them by circular plates with helical teeth engaging with tangential screws. These devices had first been used for small instruments like sextants or microscopes, but the improvement in materials and tools permitted them to be successfully used for large astronomical instruments.

Later, Reichenbach, Repsold, Airy, and Gambey used and improved these devices still further. Great progress was made in the casting of metal parts. Up to the end of the eighteenth century large parts had consisted of metal bars joined by screws. John Bird brought the manufacture of quadrants to the highest point of perfection that it could at that time attain, by determining the most suitable shape of the different elements and the best manner of assembling them.

The cage-like frame with metal pillars was abandoned for meridian instruments, and replaced by solid masonry columns, but great ingenuity and skill had then to be devoted to the supporting parts. In order to avoid bending the supports, and to reduce the strain on the driving gears, the large parts were counterpoised. It was during this period that the constructional principles of the large modern instruments were worked out.

Geodesy. The construction of instruments for geodesy and nautical astronomy developed much more rapidly than that of the larger astronomical instruments. After the end of the seventeenth century, Hadley's quadrant and octant were added to the standard instruments which had been in use for several centuries (vol III, ch 20). Whereas the quadrant was adopted fairly quickly by geodesists, sailors remained faithful to the old instruments up to the middle of the eighteenth century. Octants with sights, several types of which were invented about 1730–2, came into use only towards the middle of the century.

The octant consists of a sector of forty-five degrees; a moving alidade carries a small mirror situated in the centre of the instrument. On one arm is a sighting telescope and on the other a second fixed mirror. The height of a star is measured by noting the position of the alidade when the image of the star, reflected from the pivoted to the fixed mirror and thence into the telescope, coincides with the horizon, seen through an unsilvered portion of the fixed mirror. To permit direct reading, 30 minute divisions on the limb are numbered as degrees (vol III, figure 342).

New problems were set by the manufacture of these instruments, which are not, however, more complicated in their principle than the traditional quadrants and circles. The most difficult to solve were the optician's. In particular the manufacture of perfectly plane mirrors presented serious difficulties even at the end of the eighteenth century.

Iron, brass, and wood were for long used in combination in the making of the bodies of octants and quadrants. Much effort was devoted to the alidade and to the method of fixing it, and to the engraving of the divisions. For long, a brass plate carrying the graduations was fixed to the wooden or iron limb. In the end it was seen that this combination of materials impaired the precision of the measurements, particularly on account of the differences in expansion. Towards 1760 these instruments, the radius of which attained 40 to 50 cm, were cast in one piece. The length of the radius was reduced and that of the arc extended. The 60° sector was divided into 120 degrees and the instrument assumed the name of sextant (plate 22 B). With the addition of a vernier and an adjusting-screw it rapidly assumed the form in which it is used by sailors in our own times.

All these little manufacturing problems were relatively simple, and had already been solved in other connexions. It is, however, interesting to note that the invention of the sextant led to their systematic study with a view to finding large-scale manufacturing processes; all the workshops adopted the best available solutions, which quickly became standard ones. It has already been mentioned that it was the industrial manufacture of sextants that gave the incentive to the invention of dividing-engines.

The quadrant remained the favourite instrument of geodesists up to about 1780. In 1752 the German astronomical geometer J. T. Mayer (1723–62) thought of using a small circle and repeating the measurement of the same angle several times without reverting to zero between each measurement. The error due to the defects of the instrument was thus divided by the number of observations. About 1772 the navigator and astronomer J. C. de Borda (1733–99) took up Mayer's principle, which had remained unused, and slightly modified the apparatus of the German astronomer. He invented the instrument known as the Borda circle [14]. This instrument (figure 222) was made by the French engineer Lenoir. About ten years later the same engineer thought out the dual-telescope repeating circle for terrestrial observations.

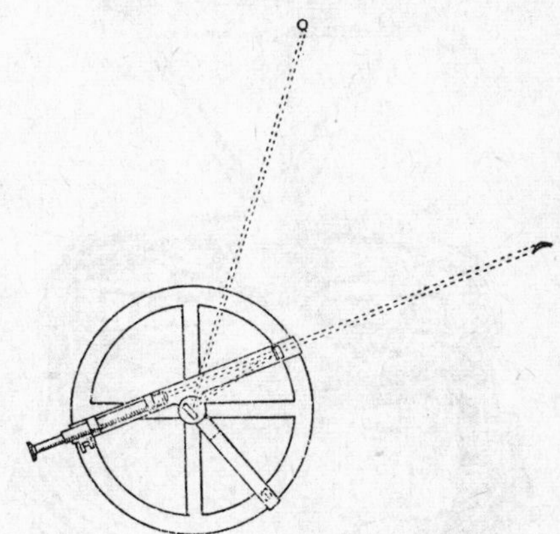

FIGURE 222—*Borda's reflection circle, constructed by Lenoir.* (*See figure 329.*)

The reflection circle was quickly adopted because Lenoir (1744–1832) knew how to manufacture it perfectly. The art of the engineer was here applied to the turning of the axis of the alidade, and its seating in the alidade and in the centre of the circle [15]. The circle itself was cast in one piece. The division of the graduated limb was done by machine. Numerous other details of design were executed with excellent judgement.

The repeating circle is of a much more complicated design. It is borne on a conical column resting on a plate fitted with clamping screws, alidade, and vernier, and can be orientated in every azimuth. The circle is fixed at its centre to a cylindrical axis perpendicular to its plane. This axis has at its other extremity a counterweight balancing the whole equipment; at its centre it passes through another axis, the extremities of which, turning on pivots, rest on two branches of a vertical brace surmounting the column. This shaft, turning on its pivots, enables the circle to take any inclination from horizontal to vertical. The circle has two telescopes which move independently of each other. The limb is graduated into 4000 degrees, and reading is effected by four microscopes opposite four verniers.

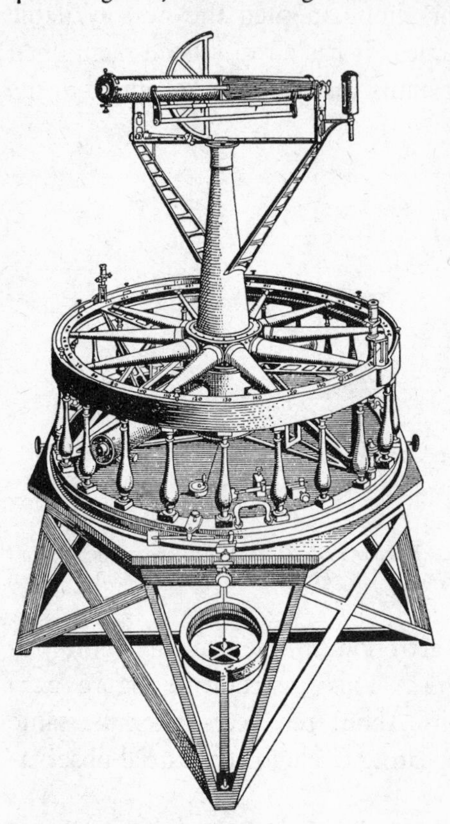

FIGURE 223—*Ramsden's first large theodolite, 1784.*

The invention and execution of these two instruments were notable events in the history of precision mechanics. Lenoir's repeating circle is in fact one of the first modern instruments for geodesy. It gave much better results than other instruments known at the time. Following the linking up of the triangulations of France and England (p 604), it enabled measurements to be made which were as accurate as those effected with Ramsden's theodolite, one of the masterpieces of the great English engineer. It was this instrument that was adopted for Mechain and Delambre's operations; the best instrument-makers of the time, Fortin, Reichenbach, and later Gambey, were inspired by its principle to construct other triangulation instruments.

The first theodolite had been described by Leonard Digges about the middle of the sixteenth century (vol III, p 541), but the instrument was not much used until towards the end of the eighteenth century, following the magnificent work of Ramsden, who between 1784 and 1790 built two large theodolites which were used for the triangulation of Great Britain [16]. These instruments are interesting because we see in them the best design of the time.

All the parts subject to mechanical stress are frusta of cones (figure 223). The cradle of the telescope consists of two parallel circles; the stability of the brace on which the cradle-shaft rests is ensured by two perforated struts. The reading is made by means of two microscopes on the zenith circles and four microscopes on the azimuth circle. The circles are operated by tangential screws. This instrument enabled bearings to be taken at a distance of 10 miles with a precision of about one second.

No theodolite of such large dimensions was subsequently constructed, but the best engineers of the nineteenth century made numerous models of similar type. The telescope with its zenith circle generally rests, through a brace, on a brass column fixed on an azimuth disk; the latter is provided with clamping-screws. These are Ramsden's solutions adapted to smaller instruments.

The instruments used by geometers and surveyors for measuring angles benefited from the optical and mechanical improvements made during this period in instruments for geodesy. Among these we shall mention only the graphometer, in which the telescope was substituted fairly late for the sighted alidade. This substitution involved a more accurate division of the semicircular limb with a vernier, and the use of the tangential screw for the two movements.

Physical apparatus. The improvement of physical instruments and the increase in their number and diversity were the consequence of many factors. We shall ignore here all the demonstration instruments with which the physical laboratories of the day were equipped: conceived during the first quarter of the eighteenth century to illustrate the laws of Newtonian physics, they were reproduced for more than a century without any mechanical improvement or any great practical advantage.

This was not so, however, as regards observational instruments, all of which received the improvements made possible by the progress of technology. Turning, adjusting, division of scales, the introduction of verniers and micrometer screws gave each of them a modern construction in the period approximately from 1780 to 1840; this is true also of barometers, thermometers, hygrometers, and microscopes, and, later, of polarimeters and the numerous optical instruments which appeared, pneumatic pumps, and electrical machines.

The increase in number and improvement in design and construction of these appliances are facts whose importance must not be underestimated. Two examples will enable us to understand how laboratory research was linked with the techniques of instrument-making from the middle of the eighteenth century.

The first is that of the construction of precision balances. The art of the scale-maker is an old one. Relatively sensitive and precise balances were manufactured very early to meet the needs of goldsmiths and money changers. In the laboratory, the assayers were the first to need good balances. Physicists used hydrostatic balances to ascertain the density of solids. But these adaptations were made without any fundamental transformation of the balance itself. The proportions of the parts were reduced to make assay balances in which the beam, with a shaft passing through its centre, rested on bearings at the end of a vertical rod. Such balances were, however, articles of ironwork rather than fruits of mechanical theory.

The method of suspension was improved, but only very slowly. The pivots of the beam were better cut, and the bearings on which the pivots rested were provided with a hard steel bushing. The true knife-edge bearing, however, was not in current use until the beginning of the nineteenth century. The suspension wires of the scale pans were lengthened to lower the centre of gravity of the system, and began to be made of brass to eliminate the influence of variations in the humidity of the atmosphere. An indicator moving in front of a scale was fixed in the middle of the balance beam. Finally, placed under a protective glass cover, the balance was fitted with a device to check the movement of the pans [17]. Such a balance was made by the clockmaker Gallonde for the chemist Rouelle about 1760 (figure 224).

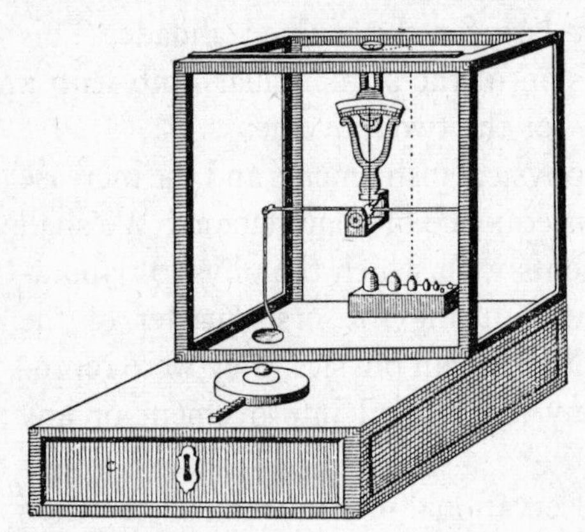

FIGURE 224—*Assayer's balance, constructed by Gallonde about 1760.*

Some years later the structure of the balance was profoundly modified and all the problems of sensitivity and accuracy were carefully studied. The first precision balance, apparently, was the one constructed by John Harrison (1693–1776) for Cavendish about 1770–5 [18]. Harrison tried to ensure the rigidity of the beam by giving it a triangular section, and adjusted the position of the centre of gravity by means of threaded rods, fixed one at each end of the beam, carrying movable nuts. For the first time there appeared a knife-edge of triangular section, and a device for raising the beam clear of it while at rest.

Several of these designs were used at the same time by the mechanical engineer Mégnié (1751 ?–1807), who made the first two precision balances for Lavoisier. Mégnié understood the need to make the central knife-edge of the beam rest on a hard steel plate placed at the top of a rigid column. The beam was raised when the balance was not in use by a cranked lever placed inside the column; this system is neater and more finished than Harrison's [19].

Two other large precision balances, one made by Ramsden about 1787 (figure 225), the other by Fortin in 1788, served as models for more than twenty years.

Ramsden made the beam in the form of two frusta of cones united at their bases, a principle widely used, as already stated, for the construction of all parts where rigidity was essential [20]. The knife-edge, whose section was diamond-shaped, rested on agate plates supported by a brass frame. The support for this frame consists of four small brass columns fixed firmly on the base.

About 1797 Troughton constructed a balance inspired by that of Ramsden [21], but great differences can be seen, which should have made Troughton's instrument superior. Although we again find the beam to be formed of two frusta of cones united at their bases, the devices for supporting the knife-edge and balance pans are designed differently. Moreover, the base of the apparatus no longer consists of a vertical cage but of a brass column of large diameter (figure 226). The advantages of this design are easily understood.

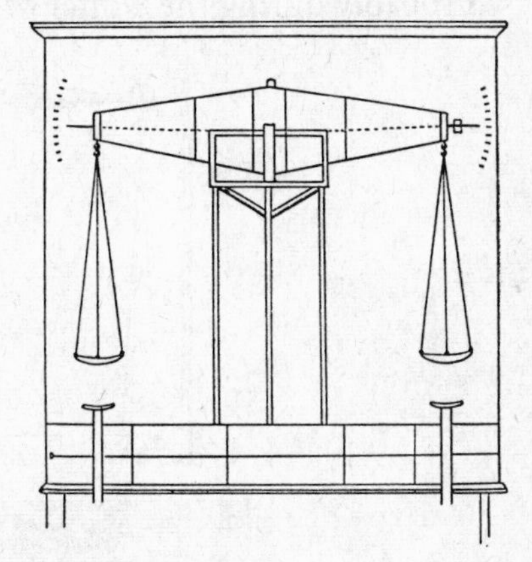

FIGURE 225—*Ramsden's precision balance, c 1787.*

In Fortin's balance, 1788, the beam is made of a strong steel blade turned on edge [22] (figure 227); the hardened steel knife-edge rests on less hard steel bushes so that the edge is not worn down. The beam is supported on a strong brass column. For thirty years Fortin remained faithful to this kind of beam and suspension. He used various devices for lifting the beam and releasing the knife-edge while at rest, each simpler and more precise in operation than the previous one. Like his colleagues, he used a long pointer to give more precise readings, which were made with a microscope. Curiously enough, the balance-makers apparently soon abandoned the microscope, and it does not reappear again until later. Fortin constructed many balances. The first was ordered by Lavoisier, others by the *Commission des Poids et Mesures.* An excellent scale-maker at the Paris Mint, Fourché, also built some balances inspired by those of Fortin.

All the precision balances at the end of the eighteenth century were designed for weighing quantities of the order of a kilogram with an accuracy of about a milligram. In general they had long beams and large pans suspended by metal attachments. To meet government requirements, scale-makers like Parent continued to make large precision balances, but for laboratories the dimensions of the balances were reduced after the Swedish chemist J. J. Berzelius (1779–1848) had shown that it was more convenient to work with small quantities.

Gambey and the engineers of his generation gave precision balances their modern appearance about 1840–50 [23]. The beam was from that period made of brass; it was in the form of a flattened lozenge turned on edge. Finally, in a balance made by Collot in 1855, we see small fractional weights or riders placed on the balance beam by a hook manipulated from outside the case by a long rod with a milled head. This device remained in use for a very long time and only recently disappeared from modern balances.

A second example of the part precision mechanics played in the construction of laboratory apparatus is provided by instruments of quite another kind constructed for Lavoisier, though not all of them can be discussed here. It is sufficient to mention only the history of the two large pneumatic bell-jars which he called 'gasometers'.

Probably during the winter of 1781–2, Lavoisier had a first pneumatic apparatus of this kind made to a fairly simple design [24]. Above a water-tank made of tin is suspended a similar, but slightly smaller tank, which can be inserted upside-down in the first. The suspension is by a cord carrying a counter-weight and passing over a pulley. Nozzles and cocks were fitted to let gases in or out. This device did not represent any particular mechanical invention, but soon afterwards Lavoisier felt the need to turn it into a measuring device. It was easy to add differential barometers (virtually manometers) and thermometers for determining the physical state of the enclosed gas.

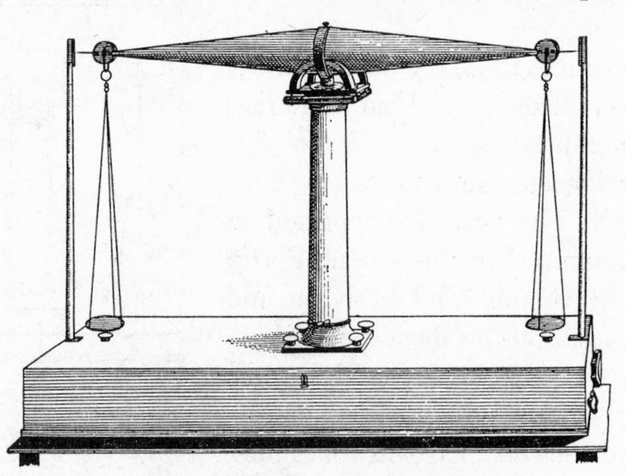

FIGURE 226—*Troughton's precision balance*, c *1797*.

It was also necessary, however, to modify the system of suspension. Meusnier, an engineer officer and member of the Académie des Sciences, who collaborated with Lavoisier in studying the industrial preparation of hydrogen, invented the first device for this purpose. The tank was suspended at the end of a balance beam by chains which would not stretch, or at least were considered not to do so. The idea for the balance beam was undoubtedly borrowed from early steam-engines of the Newcomen type. Each arm of the balance ended in an arc of a circle on which the suspension chain was supported, as in fire pumps of the day. One of the arms supported the pneumatic tank, the other a pan on which weights were placed to balance the weight of the tank. In addition, however, it was necessary to compensate for the variation in the upthrust on the suspended tank, which depended on the extent to which it was immersed. Meusnier succeeded in doing this by means of a parallelogram, whose shape would be altered by means of a screw; by adjusting the latter it was possible to vary as desired the position of the centre of gravity of the system (figure 228). In 1783 Mégnié constructed two devices based on this principle.

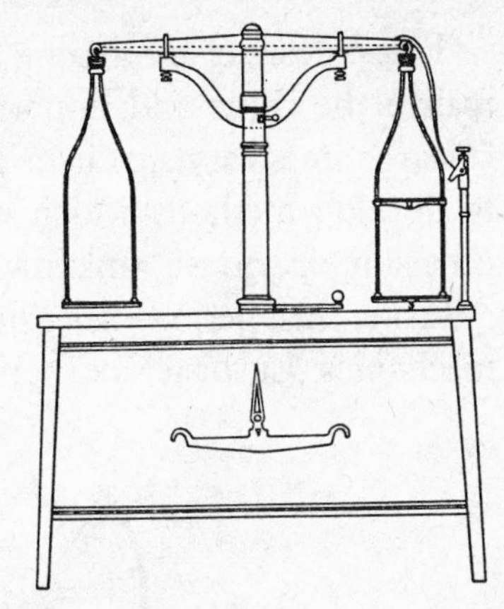

FIGURE 227—*Precision balance constructed by Fortin between 1788 and 1800.*

Two years later Lavoisier ordered from the same engineer two other 'gasometers', which were completed in 1787. It is particularly interesting to compare them with the preceding ones. The rectangular tanks were replaced by cylindrical tanks with convex bottoms. This form did not give satisfaction, however, because during use the upper bell revolved and it was difficult to remove the gaseous residues that accumulated in the top of it. Apart from this, all the other innovations seem to have been very judiciously designed. The balance beam terminated by two arcs of a circle was retained; it was made of brass and neither of its arms was cut, which certainly ensured much greater precision of the readings. Compensation for changes in upthrust was effected by means of a loaded brass ball sliding on a metal bar fixed to the middle of the balance beam, and perpendicular to it. On one side of the bar was a rack, and the ball had a toothed pinion which could be turned with the aid of a rod fitted with a milled head. The ball could thus be moved with precision. Attention was also given to the rollers on which the axis of the beam rested; the idea was borrowed from the clock-makers, who used it at that time for the construction of the most delicate movements. This structural detail, which gave the apparatus exceptional sensitivity, makes it an excellent precision instrument (figure 229).

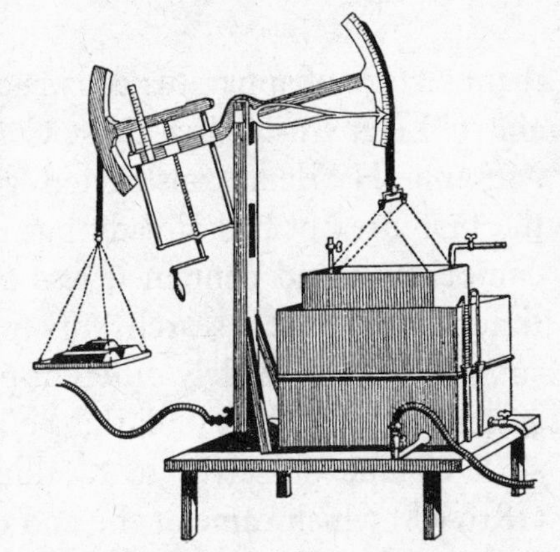

FIGURE 228—*Lavoisier's first 'gasometer' devised by Meusnier and built by Mégnié.*

These designs are among the first, if not the first, in which it is possible to realize the value and importance of the engineer's contribution to laboratory research. It is very characteristic that it came just when engineers were beginning to develop methods which enabled them to give their work a sensitivity and precision previously unknown.

From this period, scientific research was increasingly linked with applied mechanics. Lavoisier's experiments on the composition of water gave rise to the

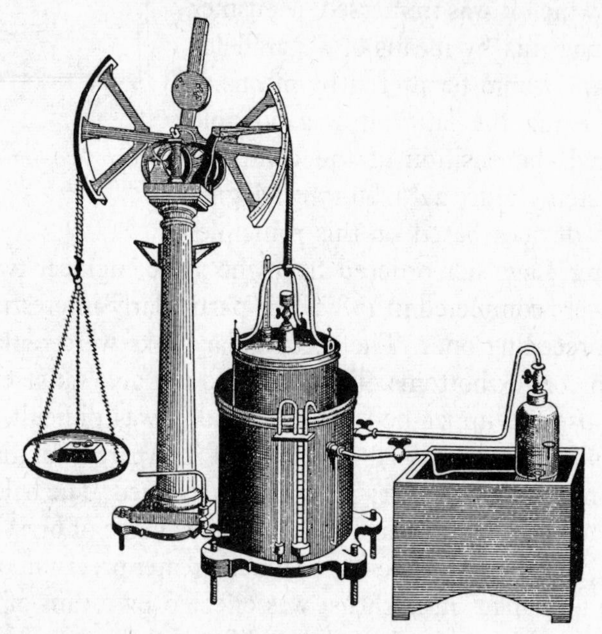

FIGURE 229—*Lavoisier's second 'gasometer', constructed by Mégnié, 1787.*

manufacture of apparatus constructed on the same principles as those described above. Lefebvre-Gineau at the Collège de France and Van Marum at the Teylers Museum, Haarlem, constructed 'gasometers' in subsequent years. The result of the first attempt had already borne fruit; the new types of apparatus were less cumbersome and contained less finical structures than those of Lavoisier. As time went by, the research worker had to appeal constantly to the engineer, and submit the most widely different problems to him. It is impossible here even to summarize the history of this collaboration. Having emphasized the point, we shall confine ourselves to recalling very briefly the work of Léon Foucault (1819–68) which came at the end of the period with which we are dealing.

Foucault carried out two experiments of historical importance, namely the physical demonstration of the rotation of the Earth by the pendulum and gyroscope and the measurement of the speed of light by the rotating mirror method. The success of these experiments is due chiefly to the mastery with which Gustave Froment (1815–65) constructed the apparatus designed by Foucault. Froment, who was a student at the École Polytechnique in Paris, was one of the best of the French precision engineers who worked in the middle of the nineteenth century. Almost all the French physicists of that time owed their practical achievements to his feeling for applied mechanics and his constructive skill. From 1840, in association with Dumoulin, he won a high reputation for his firm. He was the first, from 1844, to use an electric motor for driving his dividing-engines. He did not make scientific instruments only: among his achievements of great historical importance should be mentioned telegraphic equipment with a dial (1843) and the Hughes telegraphic equipment (1856).

These two examples show the extent of the application of precision engineering at this time: until then, although it fulfilled many needs, it still had only a relatively limited field of application. Engineering achievements at the beginning of the nineteenth century represented only a relatively low degree of precision: it cannot be considered, for example, that the boring of the cylinders of steam-engines then showed a very high degree of precision. Several decades later this was no longer so. The perfection of mechanisms and the industrial use of electricity, in telegraphy for example, were creating new and rapidly expanding fields.

Chronometers. Innovations in the mechanism of clocks and watches resulting from the use of the pendulum and spiral spring led clock-makers and mechanics to devote much effort to the construction of chronometers that could be used at sea. This research was of great interest in view of the difficulties, indeed the impossibility, confronting a navigator in plotting his exact position at sea if he did not know the time at the zero meridian. Since the different astronomical methods of measuring longitude gave only inadequate results, the solution consisted in finding means of constructing very accurate clocks whose working was not disturbed by the motion of the ship.

Huygens thought of making the end of the pendulum travel in a cycloidally curved path to ensure the isochronism of its oscillations, while to compensate for the motion of the sea he suggested various modes of suspension of the pendulum. The majority of clock-makers who studied the problem at this time, or later, attempted to use double balance wheels, copied from Hooke, with the idea that the irregularity of one would be offset by that of the other. Henry Sully (1680–1728) was perhaps one of the last to attempt to apply such solutions, but when his clocks were tried out at sea they did not give good results. At the same time, many other investigations were carried out; among them, for example, that of a Frenchman, de Rivaz, who used circular balance wheels fixed at the centre of a flexible steel beam stretched between two supports.

The most interesting of unsuccessful experiments was that of Pierre Leroy (1717–85), who devoted himself to the problem between 1748 and 1766 [25]. At the beginning of this period, Leroy invented a new escapement which he used in the construction of his two chronometers. Very ingenious in design, but very difficult to construct, this escapement was not used by any other clock-maker, but its principle—that of the escapement leaving the balance wheel free during the greater part of its movement—is the one used later in marine chronometers [26].

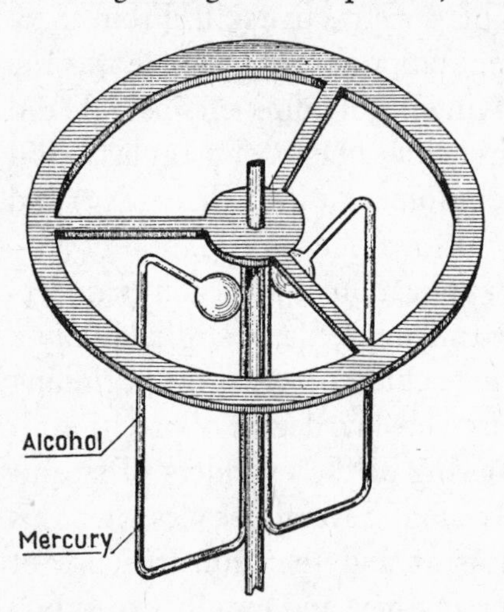

FIGURE 230—*Leroy's balance wheel with alcohol-mercury thermal compensation.*

Leroy also thought of thermal compensation for the balance wheel. For this purpose he used what were in effect two thin curved thermometers, each containing mercury and alcohol, fixed on either side of the staff of the balance wheel so that the mercury was pushed towards the staff when the temperature rose (figure 230). Finally, he obtained isochronism of the oscillations by using two spiral springs, wound in opposite directions, for the attachment of which he applied a principle which has since been known as the Leroy rule for points of attachment.

Tried out at sea during three successive voyages between 1767 and 1772, Leroy's two chronometers gave excellent results, comparable with those obtained by the English clock-maker Harrison some years earlier with his best marine watch. However, at this time Leroy had a long dispute with his rival, Ferdinand Berthoud (1727–1807), and decided to retire from the field: except for this incident his work would have had a wider result. In the event, it remained merely an episode without a sequel in the history of chronometry. Although Leroy was the first to expound clearly the principles on which marine chronometers were later constructed, none of the actual solutions which he used was adopted.

The English clock-maker John Harrison (1693–1776) was undoubtedly the first maker of a timepiece that could be used satisfactorily at sea [27]. As early as 1728 he had submitted the plans for a marine clock to Graham, who had encouraged him and advanced him £200 for further experiment. In 1735 he completed his first marine chronometer: this was tested at sea and gave results which were sufficiently good for further financial help to be granted to its maker. Harrison then began clock No 2, which he did not submit for trial, announcing that he had

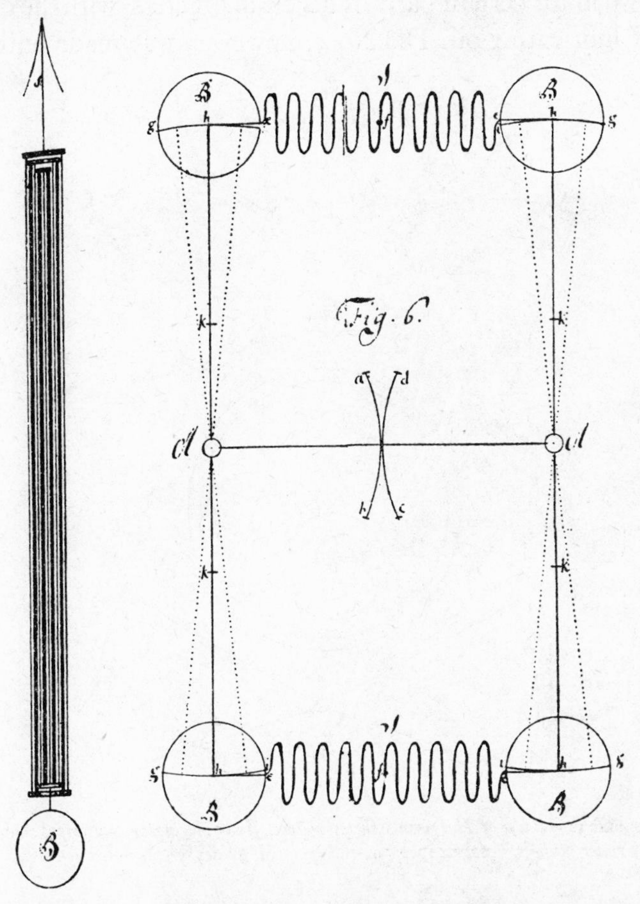

FIGURE 231—*Parts of Harrison's chronometers, according to an original manuscript, showing gridiron pendulum and rectilinear compensator.*

begun to construct, by a different principle, his clock No 3, which was completed in 1757. Finally clock No 4 was completed in 1759 [28]: only this last one was tested at sea. The responsible authorities in England (the Board of Longitude) demanded numerous trials, and caused the clock-maker Larcum Kendall (1721–95) to make a replica of Harrison's No 4; when tested this gave results as satisfactory as those of the original. It was not until 1772, however, that Harrison received the whole of the award of £20 000 which the Board of Longitude had offered since 1714 for the first marine chronometer capable of enabling longitude to be determined at sea with an accuracy of half a degree (vol III, pp 557, 672).

Throughout his work Harrison's mastery as a mechanic can clearly be seen. The son of a carpenter, he began by manufacturing wooden clocks: for a long time he used wood for certain parts of his chronometers, with the object of avoiding the use of lubricating oil. His No 4, however, was made entirely of metal.

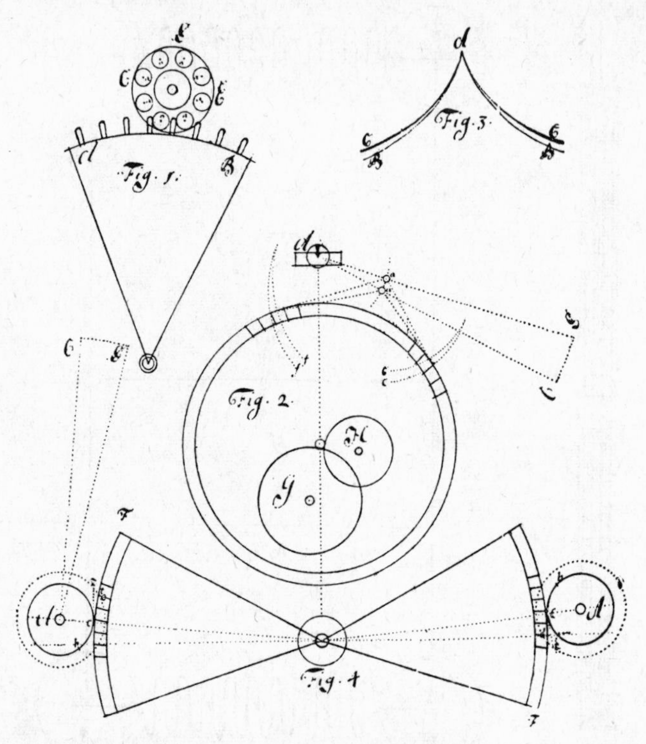

FIGURE 232—*Parts of Harrison's chronometers, from original manuscript, showing roller pinions, bevel escapement, and cycloidal guides for the balance wheels.*

In his first two clocks he used a double rectilinear balance mounted on counterpoised shafts and guided by cycloids (figure 231). On the first there is a bimetallic compensating device for thermal variations. Harrison made long investigations to perfect this device, still called the Harrison grid. The three grids of clock No 1 have the effect of displacing steel stops, and so causing the tension of the spiral springs on the balance wheels to vary. This system was simplified for clock No 2.

The modifications made in the construction of clocks Nos 3 and 4 are numerous. The most important are the abandonment of the rectilinear balances in favour of balance wheels, and the replacement of the grid by a bimetallic strip. The latter device ensured thermal compensation of the oscillations of the spiral spring in a simpler and more elegant manner.

Harrison also invented a special 'grasshopper' escapement (figure 232 and vol III, figure 411), and an original device to ensure the isochronism of the two balance wheels. He used roller bearings to eliminate friction and the need for lubrication. He introduced certain complications in his mechanism, such as a remontoir to keep the driving force to the escapement practically constant and a spring to maintain the movement during the winding of the clock.

Most of these inventions appear in John Harrison's fourth and last design, chronometer No 4, but this again is entirely different from the one that preceded it. Its dimensions are considerably reduced, and approximate to those of a watch. He abandoned the principle of a double balance wheel and the use of rollers; he remained faithful to the cycloidal correction of the movement of the balance; and he invented a new escapement with diamond palettes. Tested over long distances, including two voyages to Jamaica, chronometer No 4 consistently showed variations that involved errors in the calculation of longitudes less than the maximum of half a degree stipulated by the Board of Longitude for its full award.

Harrison had already obtained remarkable results when the Swiss clock-maker Ferdinand Berthoud began his investigations, which were conducted mainly from 1760 to 1768. Berthoud, indeed, made more rapid progress than his English contemporary. He was already a skilled clock-maker when he began to devote himself to the problem of marine chronometers, and unlike Harrison he did not have to complete his training while working. He proceeded more directly to good mechanical design. He devoted less thought and reflection to his work than Harrison did, but his work was guided by wider experience in the practice of clock-making. As with Harrison and Pierre Leroy, Berthoud's work shows outstanding practical ability.

The range of parts constructed by Berthoud is large [29], but the complete clocks made during these researches numbered only seven or eight. His clock No 1 was made in 1760, followed in 1763 by clock No 2. These two instruments are bulky, though No 2 was notably smaller than the first. In these clocks Berthoud put two circular balance wheels oscillating in opposite directions and connected with one another by means of a toothed wheel. Their axes rested on roller bearings. A bimetallic gridiron, already widely used by clock-makers since its invention by Harrison, compensated for variations in temperature by variations in the length of the spiral. The escapement was made more complicated in clock No 2, in which Berthoud introduced an equalizing remontoir. It should be noted that he at first used a spring barrel fitted with a fusee as the source of motive power; this device has been retained until the present time for the construction of marine chronometers, but Berthoud himself temporarily abandoned it almost at once. In a marine watch, also made in 1763 (watch No 3), Berthoud used a bimetallic strip for thermal compensation and a single balance wheel.

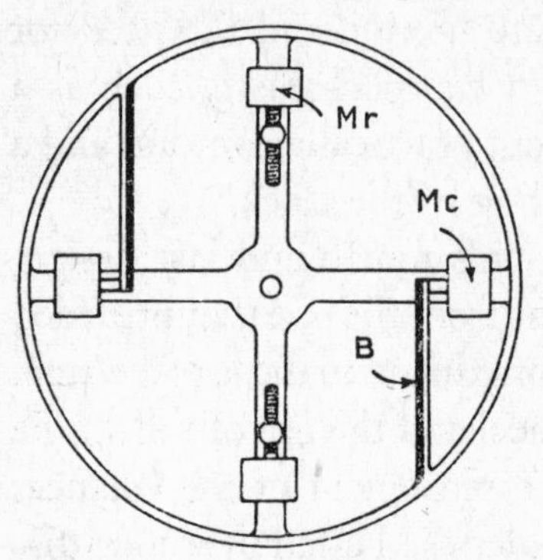

FIGURE 233—*Berthoud's compensated balance wheel.* (MR) *Adjustable slider;* (MC) *slider attached to bimetallic strip* B.

Retaining the single balance wheel suspended by a wire and guided by rollers, he returned to the gridiron method of compensation for the construction of his subsequent clocks, of which Nos 6 and 8 (1767) ensured his success. In this series the motive power derived from weights placed on a vertical metal plate which descended the length of three brass columns. An escapement with ruby cylinders replaced the escapements previously used, and all the parts were relatively compact. The mechanism was above the gridiron and the whole occupied the top part of the clock, which was enclosed in a long glass cylinder; the three brass columns guiding the descent of the weight took up almost the whole height of this cylinder. The horizontal dial covered the glass box. Clocks 6 and 8 were tested at sea in 1768 and 1769, and showed variations in their working of the order of from 5 to 20 seconds a day.

We know of only five chronometers made by John Harrison, who did not reach his goal until a fairly advanced age. Berthoud, on the contrary, was able to continue working for thirty years and it was he who gave the marine chronometer practically its modern form. Abandoning the roller suspension of the balance wheel, he adopted a pivot suspension. He came back to compensation by bimetallic strips, eliminating the cumbersome gridiron, and used a balance wheel compensated by means of four small weights. Two of these weights were fixed and the two others were carried by a bimetallic strip which moved towards or away from the arbor according to variations in temperature (figure 233). Finally, Berthoud returned almost definitively to the spring drive.

His nephew, Pierre-Louis Berthoud (1754–1813) succeeded him in his work as marine clock-maker, and began to industrialize the construction of chronometers in France. The four apprentices allowed him by the government—Motel, Gannery, Jacob, and Dumas—in their turn, with Breguet, made similar productions during the first half of the nineteenth century.

During the same period, several English clock-makers fulfilled the same function: Thomas Mudge (1715–94), John Arnold (1736–99), and Thomas Earnshaw (1749–1829). They endeavoured to simplify the construction of chronometers and to devise more efficient parts. The efforts of the two latter were devoted chiefly to constructing compensated balance wheels and detent escapements. They each invented a type of free escapement, in which they made various modifications. Earnshaw's model was finally adopted in view of the simplicity of its design and the regularity of its functioning (figure 234). Arnold, for his part, studied and recommended a particular form of helical spring to ensure the isochronism of the oscillations. His work paved the way for that of Edouard Phillips, who in 1861 published his researches on the terminal coils of spiral springs. This famous paper by the French mathematician, and later the discoveries of the Swiss Ch.-E. Guillaume, enabled marine chronometers to be given the only two improvements that clockmakers at the beginning of the nineteenth century had left for their successors to discover. The perfection of the marine chronometer was in the main established by the intelligence and skill of a relatively few men working between approximately 1730 and 1820.

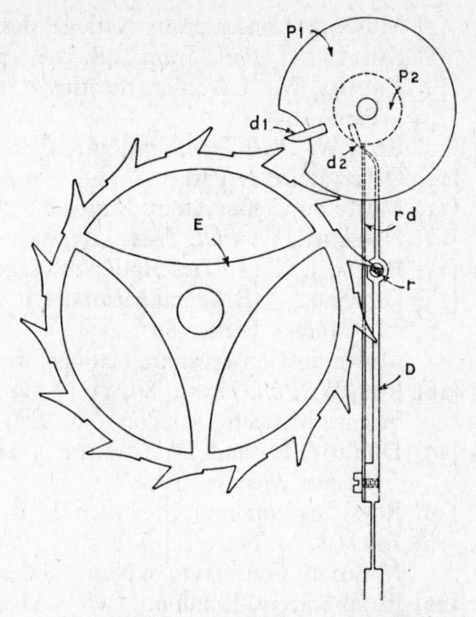

FIGURE 234—*Earnshaw's free detent escapement.* (P1) *Notched plate carrying the impulse lever* d1; (P2) *plate bearing the axle of the balance wheel and the pawl* d2; (E) *escapement wheel, of which one tooth engages with the catch* r *of the detent* D; (rd) *detent spring.*

REFERENCES

[1] Musée du Conservatoire National des Arts et Métiers, Paris, No. 1234.
[2] *Idem.*, Nos 12, 16.
[3] RAMSDEN, J. 'Description d'une machine pour diviser les instruments de mathématiques' (French trans. by J. J. LE F. DE LALANDE). Paris. 1790.
[4] CHAULNES, DUC DE. 'Nouvelle méthode pour diviser les instruments de mathématiques.' Paris. 1768.
Musée du Conservatoire National des Arts et Métiers, Paris, No. 832.
[5] RAMSDEN, J. 'Description of an Engine for Dividing Mathematical Instruments.' London. 1777.
[6] SÉGUIER, BARON A. DE. "Note . . . sur la machine à diviser les cercles de Gambey et sa méthode pour diviser le grand mural de l'Observatoire de Paris." *C.R. Acad. Sci., Paris*, **68**, 207, 1869.

[7] Musée du Conservatoire National des Arts et Métiers, Paris, No. 8323.
[8] SMEATON, J. *Phil. Trans.*, **48**, 598, 1755.
[9] DAUMAS, M. 'Lavoisier, théoricien et expérimentateur', p. 154. Presses Universitaires, Paris. 1955.
[10] ROY, W. *Phil. Trans.*, **75**, 461, 1785.
[11] Observatoire de Paris.
[12] Musée du Conservatoire National des Art et Métiers, Paris, No. 3335.
[13] HERSCHEL, W. *Phil. Trans.*, **85**, 347, 1795.
[14] BORDA, J. C. DE. 'Description et usage du cercle de réflexion.' Paris. 1816.
[15] DELAMBRE, J. B. J. and MÉCHAIN, P. F. A. 'Base du système métrique décimal', Vol. 2, pp. 160–9. Paris. 1807.
Musée du Conservatoire National des Arts et Métiers, Paris, No. 8604.
[16] ROY, W. *Phil. Trans.*, **80**, 111, 1790.
Science Museum, London, No. 1876–1203.
[17] DIDEROT, D. and D'ALEMBERT, J. LE R. (Eds). 'Encyclopédie', Vol. 2, p. 247. Article: Balance. Geneva. 1772.
[18] Royal Institution of Great Britain, London.
[19] DAUMAS, M. See ref. [9], p. 136.
Musée du Conservatoire National des Arts et Métiers, Paris, Nos 19.885, 19.886.
[20] Royal Society, London.
[21] EVELYN, SIR GEORGE (SHUCKBURGH). *Phil. Trans.*, **88**, Pt I, 135, 1798.
[22] Musée du Conservatoire National des Arts et Métiers, Paris, No. 19.889.
[23] CONSERVATOIRE NATIONAL DES ARTS ET MÉTIERS, PARIS. 'Catalogue du Musée, Section K: Poids et mesures.' Paris. 1941.
[24] DAUMAS, M. See ref. [9], pp. 143–50.
[25] DITISHEIM, P. *et al.* 'Pierre Le Roy et la chronométrie.' Tardy, Paris. 1940.
[26] Musée du Conservatoire National des Arts et Métiers, Paris, No. 1395.
[27] GOULD, R. T. *Mariner's Mirror*, **21**, 115, 1935.
LLOYD, H. A. *Suisse horlog.*, **68**, No. 3, 35, No. 4, 21, 1953.
[28] National Maritime Museum, Greenwich, London.
[29] Musée du Conservatoire National des Arts et Métiers, Paris, Nos 165, 166, 1386–93, 8802, 11.057.

BIBLIOGRAPHY

BERGERON, L. E. [pseudonym of L. G. I. SALIVET]. 'Manuel du Tourneur' (2nd ed., 3 vols). Paris. 1816.
BRITTEN, F. J. 'Old Clocks and Watches and their Makers' (ed. by F. W. BRITTEN, 6th ed.). Spon, London. 1933.
CONSERVATOIRE NATIONAL DES ARTS ET MÉTIERS, PARIS. 'Catalogue du Musée, Section B: Mécanique.' Paris. 1956.
Idem. 'Catalogue du Musée, Section JB: Horlogerie.' Paris. 1948.
DAUMAS, M. 'Les instruments scientifiques aux XVIIe et XVIIIe siècles.' Presses Universitaires, Paris. 1953.
'Encyclopédie Méthodique: Arts et Métiers.' Paris. 1784–91.
GOULD, R. T. 'The Marine Chronometer: its History and Development.' Potter, London. 1925.
REPSOLD, J. 'Zur Geschichte der astronomischen Messwerkzeuge von 1830 bis um 1900' (2 vols). Reinicke, Leipzig. 1914.

14

MACHINE-TOOLS

K. R. GILBERT

MACHINE-TOOLS are fundamental to industrial civilization, for without them the machines used in many manufacturing processes, and the engines to drive them, could not be built. Machine-tools make it possible to work metal objects of great size and to shape metals with an accuracy unattainable by hand. Moreover, the high speed of working with machine-tools makes commercially practicable processes which, even if mechanically possible, cannot be performed economically by hand. In the case of wood-working, where the necessity for great accuracy does not arise, the advantage of using machinery comes mainly from the high speeds attainable and the great saving of labour that may be effected.

The invention and development of machine-tools was an essential part of the industrial revolution. The steam-engine, the railway, and textile and other manufacturing machinery required machine-tools for their progress; and it was this demand that stimulated the great progress in the invention of machine-tools that took place in the period under review. In 1775 the machine-tools at the disposal of industry had scarcely advanced beyond those available in the Middle Ages: by 1850 the majority of modern machine-tools had been invented.

The credit for this remarkable progress belongs largely to a group of British engineers, though towards the end of the period the leadership moved to the United States. The employer–employee relationship that existed at one time or another between members of the British 'school' of inventors, was undoubtedly partly responsible for the speed of the advance. One inventive mind was stimulated by contact with another, and experience became cumulative. In figure 235 the connexions of the British machine-tool inventors with each other are set out diagrammatically.

An eighteenth-century turner's workshop is depicted in plate 28, which is reproduced from a volume of Diderot and d'Alembert's *Encyclopédie*, published in 1772. The pole-lathe shown at the back of the workshop was the typical lathe of the time, and had been used since the thirteenth century. A cord attached at the top to a springy pole passed once or twice round the lathe-mandrel, or round the work held between fixed centres, and was tied at the bottom to a treadle. On depressing the treadle, the mandrel was caused to rotate; and the cutting-tool, supported by a rest, was applied to the work by a turner. On releasing the treadle, the pole returned to the starting-position; during this time the work rotated in the reverse direction, and the tool had to be withdrawn. The process was then repeated. This intermittent method of working made it almost impossible to turn an accurate cylinder. The use of a crank and fly-wheel to give continuous rotation had been known since the sixteenth century, but lathes work-

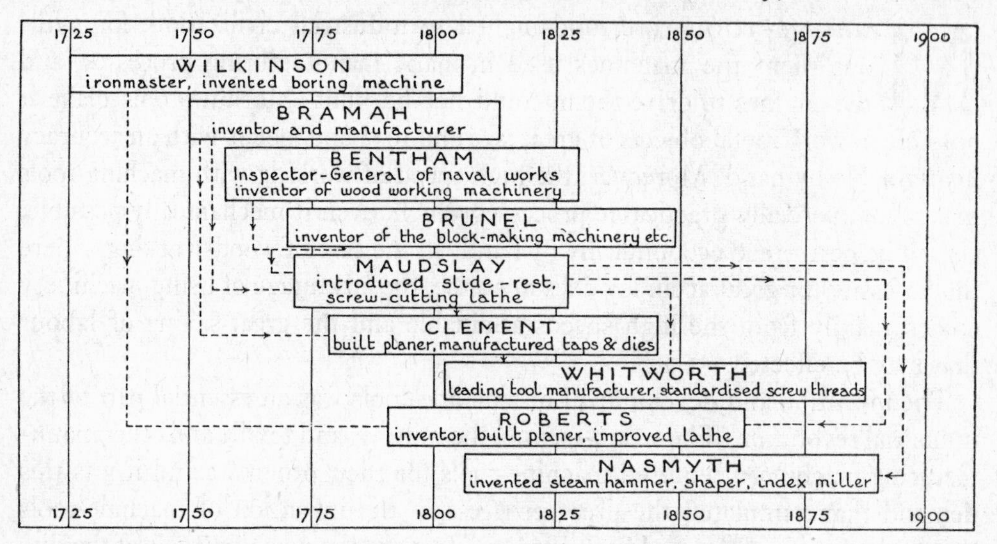

FIGURE 235—*Some important machine-tool builders of the eighteenth and nineteenth centuries. The dotted lines represent employer–employee relationships.*

ing on that principle were not so commonly used. When greater power and speed were required, the great wheel shown in the foreground was used. This provided continuous rotation, but the control of the tool, and hence the accuracy of the work done, depended entirely on the skill of the turner. These lathes were constructed of wood, and metal was used only for the centres and for some of the fastenings. The head-stock and tail-stock were often secured in the lathe-bed by wooden wedges. It must not be supposed, however, that the invention of the modern machine-tools led to the complete supersession of the earlier tools. Indeed, primitive machines like the pole-lathe and tilt-hammer still exist in use in out-of-the-way places.

Some lathes were provided with a number of guide-screws of different pitch, cut on an extension of the mandrel. It could be arranged for the mandrel to slide along horizontally under the control of one of these screws, by engaging the screw with a bearing having a threaded surface of the same pitch. A chasing-tool held against a cylindrical rod rotated in a chuck on the front of the mandrel would then reproduce the thread. A long screw could be cut in a series of short lengths. Screws were also hand-cut by the means of a screw-plate or by a die held in a die-stock: two die-stocks are shown hanging on the wall in plate 28. Screws were originated, however, by the laborious process of filing a marked cylinder (figures 213, 214).

Matthew Boulton (1728–1809), who employed between seven and eight hundred workers in his Soho factory at Birmingham, wrote in 1770: 'I have two

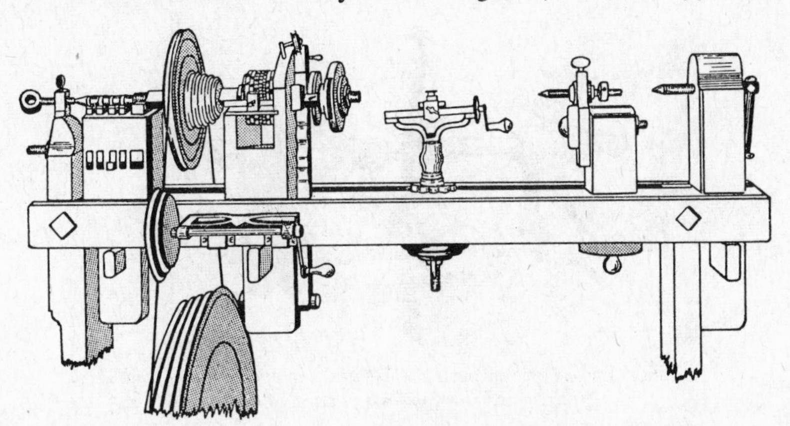

FIGURE 236—*Lathe for ornamental turning, late seventeenth century. To the left of the pulley are guide screws for the traversing-mandrel method of screw-cutting, and to the right are the rosettes for ornamental turning.* (*Cf figure 213*.)

water mills employed in rolling, pollishing, grinding & turning various sorts of Laths.' To this list of machine-tools of the period should be added the tilt-hammer. A heavy hammer was pivoted at a point about a quarter of its length from the tail, which was depressed by the action of cams set on a shaft rotated by a water-wheel. When the tail became disengaged from one of the cams, the hammer-head fell: the rotation of the wheel thus caused the hammer to deliver a succession of heavy blows. A variation was to make the cam lift the hammer at the heavy end.

This picture of the meagre equipment of the time requires qualification in two respects. There were two specialized fields in which more advanced machine-tools were used, namely ornamental turning and clock-making (see ch 13).

The interest of wealthy amateur turners led in the seventeenth and eighteenth centuries to the development of ingenious lathe accessories with which complicated patterns and shapes could be cut. One type of chuck, for example, was constructed so as to carry the work in an elliptical path. The lathe illustrated in figure 236 is a late seventeenth-century example of a lathe for ornamental turning. The mandrel can be made to oscillate laterally under the control of the rosettes to the right of the pulley, enabling patterns to be cut on the face of an object rotated in the chuck. The slide-rest with which the lathe is equipped is probably an eighteenth-century addition. This lathe is constructed partly of wood, but in the eighteenth century the use of metal throughout led to improved rigidity and accuracy, and some highly decorated and elaborate lathes were built.

Clock-makers in the first half of the eighteenth century invented several screw-

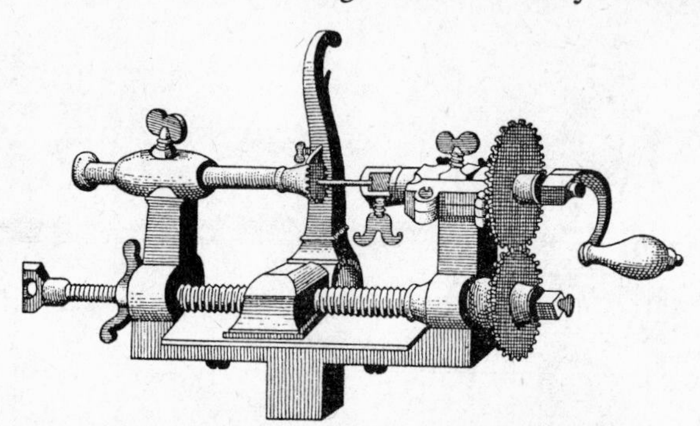

FIGURE 237—*Fusee-engine, 1741, showing the application of lead-screw and change-wheels to screw cutting.*

cutting machines for making fusees; the latter is a clock-part in the shape of a hyperboloid on which a screw-like groove is cut. The eighteenth-century tool shown in plate 27B is typical of a common type of fusee-engine. The cutter is constrained to move parallel to the screw being cut—in this illustration an ordinary screw and not a fusee—and is made to traverse as a result of its linkage with a nut threaded on the lead-screw on the mandrel. The pitch of the resulting screw depends on the leverage employed in the linkage, which may be varied by moving the fulcrum. A machine described by Antoine Thiout (1692–1767) in 1741 had a separate lead-screw, connected with the headstock-spindle by means of gear-wheels, the ratio of which determined the pitch of the thread cut (figure 237).

Robert Hooke (1635–1703) in 1671 invented a machine for cutting clock-wheels which employed a rotary file or milling-cutter to cut the teeth; these were then filed to shape by hand. In some later machines the cutter was shaped to cut the teeth in their final form. The teeth were correctly spaced by means of a divided plate, and the cutter was geared up to the handle so that it could be driven at speed. A machine of this kind, dated 1789, is shown in figure 238. In some machines the axis of the cutter could be inclined so as to cut skew teeth. That a large variety of hand-tools and some machine-tools was available to clock-makers in the eighteenth century is shown by the illustrated catalogue issued by John Wyke (1720–87), a Lancashire clock-tool manufacturer.

In 1765 James Watt (1736–1819) made his great invention of the separate condenser (p 182), but for lack of capital the construction of a large-scale steam-engine, embodying his idea, took years to accomplish. Even when this financial problem was solved, it was still necessary to overcome the great difficulty of boring an accurate cylinder. The close fitting of the piston in the cylinder, which did not so greatly matter in the Newcomen engine, was essential to the proper

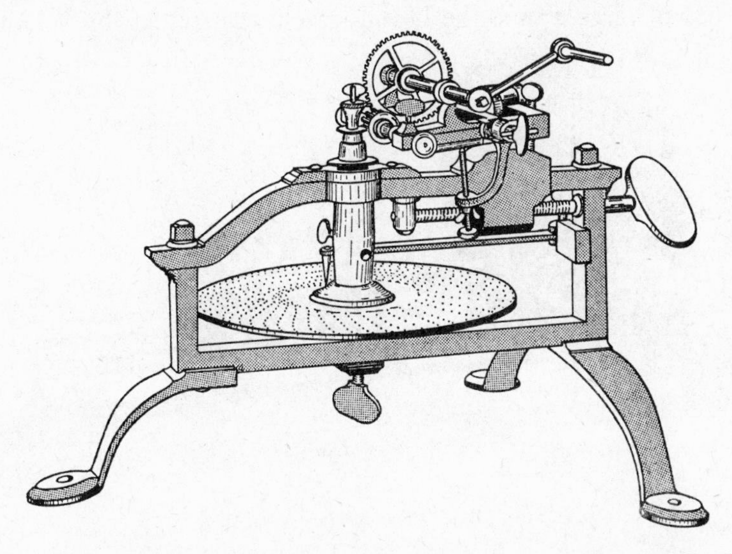

FIGURE 238—*Machine for cutting clock-wheels, 1789. The teeth are cut by a rotary cutter in the wheel blank which is mounted above the divided plate.* (*Cf figure 219.*)

working of Watt's. For want of an accurate boring-machine, the cylinder of his first engine was made of tin and hammered to shape against a hard-wood block; the gaps between piston and cylinder were sealed as far as possible with felt, paper, oiled rags, and the like. John Smeaton (1724–92), who had himself built a boring-machine in 1769, considered Watt's engine too difficult to build. The difficulty in boring a large cylinder was that the long, heavy boring-tool tended to sag and wander from the true, as it worked through the cylinder.

In 1775, however, the ironmaster John Wilkinson (1728–1808) built at Bersham a new type of boring-mill on which large cylinders could be bored with sufficient accuracy. Plate 27 A reproduces a model of this mill constructed with the guidance of contemporary records: the only part of the original mill still in existence is a boring-bar 15 ft long. In front of the water-wheel on the right are the remains of a boring-mill of the Smeaton type. Here the cylinder was mounted on a truck which could be moved along rails, and was fed over a rotating cutter-head. The weight of the cutter caused it to cut mainly on the lower part of the cylinder, and it received no guidance other than that given by the rough-casting. An attempt was made to correct this disadvantage by taking four cuts and turning the cylinder through 90° after each cut. Smeaton's apparatus, a model of which is reproduced in figure 239, was very similar to a machine for boring cannon described by Biringuccio as early as 1540 (vol III, p 367).

On the left of plate 27 A is the boring-machine invented by Wilkinson. The

FIGURE 239—*Model of Smeaton-type boring-mill*, c *1770*.

large driving-wheel is keyed to the squared end of the boring-bar, which is supported in a bearing at each end. The cylinder, shown sectioned in the model, is securely fixed in a cradle. Mounted on the bar, and rotating with it, is the cutter-head, which is fed forward through the cylinder by means of a rod passing down the centre of the hollow bar and attached to the head through a longitudinal slot. The other end of the rod is prevented from rotating by a cross-bar resting on two wooden beams, and attached to a rack. The feed is given by a weighted lever acting through a pinion engaging with the rack. The success of the machine was due to the rigidity obtained by supporting the boring-bar at both ends and by securing the cylinder. It made possible the successful development of Watt's engine, and for twenty years all his cylinders were cast and bored by Wilkinson. The following tribute from Boulton, written in 1776, incidentally shows the contemporary notion of the accuracy that might be attained: 'Wilkinson hath bored us several cylinders almost without Error; that of 50 inches diam^r for Bentley & Co. doth not err the thickness of an old shilling in no part....'

Wilkinson's invention was an isolated one and his only other connexion with the machine-tool builders, to be mentioned later, was that his executors for a time engaged Richard Roberts (p 428) as a pattern-maker.

The next advance arose from the necessity of devising an economical method of manufacturing Bramah's patent lock. Joseph Bramah (1748–1814), the son of a Yorkshire farmer, was an ingenious man responsible for many inventions, including the hydraulic press, an improved water-closet (figure 285), a wood-planing machine, and a machine for numbering bank-notes. In 1784 he patented a very successful lock which he exhibited in his shop-window in Piccadilly with the notice, 'The artist who can make an instrument that will pick or open this lock shall receive two hundred guineas the moment it is produced.' Although many attempts were made, the money was not won until 1851, when a mechanic succeeded in opening the lock after fifty-one working hours. This is sufficient proof of the excellence of the lock, but it was a complicated mechanism which could be satisfactorily and economically manufactured only by a well designed series of machine-tools.

To help in building these tools Bramah engaged Henry Maudslay (1771–1831), an eighteen-year-old blacksmith employed at Woolwich Arsenal, who a year later became his superintendent. John Farey, writing some fifty years later, described Bramah's factory thus:

> The secret workshops . . . contained several curious machines, for forming parts of the locks, with a systematic perfection for workmanship, which was at that time unknown in similar mechanical arts. These machines had been constructed by the late Mr Maudslay, with his own hands, whilst he was Bramah's chief workman. . . . The machines before mentioned were adapted for cutting the grooves in the barrel, and the notches in the steel plates . . . the notches in the keys, and in the steel sliders, were cut by other machines, which had micrometer screws so as to ensure that the notches in each key should tally with the unlocking notches of the sliders. . . .

Bramah used milling-cutters mounted on the spindle of a lathe, while the part to be machined was held in an indexing-bush in a quick-grip vice mounted on the lathe-bed. These tools have been preserved in the Science Museum, London, together with a machine for sawing slots in the lock-barrels, and a spring-winding machine. This latter machine is made on the lines of a screw-cutting lathe, having a saddle that travels the entire length of the bed and is drawn along by a lead-screw. The lead-screw is driven from the headstock by change-gears which permit the relative speeds of headstock-rotation and saddle-travel to be varied, so that springs of different pitch can be made. Instead of a cutting-tool, however, the saddle carries a reel of wire which is wound on to an arbor held between centres. This machine is a forerunner of Maudslay's screw-cutting lathe, reproduced in plate 25 A.

In 1797, having been refused an increase in his wages, Maudslay left Bramah and set up in business on his own account. His firm prospered, and held a leading position throughout the nineteenth century. He was joined in 1804 by Joshua Field, formerly a draughtsman at the Portsmouth dockyard. Field was later taken into partnership and the firm continued under the well known name of Maudslay, Sons and Field. Maudslay's influence exerted through his pupils and workmen is as important as his more direct contributions to engineering. His central relationship to other important inventors is shown in figure 235.

Most machine-tools that act by cutting require the work or the tool, or both, to move in a straight line or a circle. Thus when a cylinder is generated on a lathe the tool moves in a straight line parallel to the axis of the rotating work; in the boring-mill, the rotating tool travels in a straight line through the stationary work. In the milling-machine the work moves in a straight line at right angles to the axis of the rotating tool. The rectilinear motion of a moving part of a machine-tool results from its control by two intersecting planes. Thus the cutting of a true cylinder on a lathe is brought about by ensuring the proper movement of the tool by means of the slide-rest, which is guided by two plane surfaces. The accuracy of the product of a machine-tool is therefore determined by the accuracy of its plane guiding-surfaces.

Another essential element of machine-tool construction is the screw, since it translates a rotary motion into a linear one. Thus, in the lathe the motion of the tool may be linked with the rotation of the work by means of the lead-screw. Screws are used for the correct setting and adjustment of the movable parts of machine-tools. The screw is also an essential component of the micrometer. The precision with which such screws are made is obviously unnecessary for screws used merely as fasteners.

The outstanding features of Maudslay's engineering practice were the production of accurate plane surfaces; the use of the slide-rest; the adoption of all-metal construction; and the production of accurate screws. According to Nasmyth:

The importance of having such Standard Planes caused him [Maudslay] to have many of them placed on the benches beside his workmen, by the means of which they might at once conveniently test their work. Three of each were made at a time, so that by the mutual rubbing of each on each the projecting surfaces were effaced. When the surfaces approached very near to the true plane, the still projecting minute points were carefully reduced by hard steel scrapers, until at last the standard plane surface was secured.

When placed over each other they would float upon the thin stratum of air between them until dislodged by time and pressure. When they adhered closely to each other, they could only be separated by sliding each off each. This art of producing absolutely plane surfaces is, I believe, a very old mechanical 'dodge'. But, as employed by Maudslay's men, it greatly contributed to the improvement of the work turned out. It was used for the surfaces of slide valves, or wherever absolute true plane surfaces were essential to the attainment of the best results, not only in the machinery turned out, but in educating the taste of his men towards first class workmanship.

The reason for making three surfaces coincide is that, with two only, one might be convex and the other concave, but if a third surface can be made to coincide with the first two, all three must be plane.

The earliest known illustration of a slide-rest occurs in a German manuscript of *c* 1480, the *Mittelalterliche Hausbuch* of Waldburg. It is not shown fitted on a lathe, but in isolation and without explanation. In the eighteenth century slide-rests were used on ornamental turning-lathes. About 1745 Jacques de Vaucanson (p 384) made a lathe able to turn work up to 1 metre in length; its slide-rest has two 90° V-grooves underneath and slides on two bars of square section running the length of the lathe. Yet Nasmyth, writing the appendix to Buchanan's book on mill-work in 1841, attributed the invention of the slide-rest to Maudslay. It was evidently regarded as an innovation by the practical engineers of his time.

The use of a lead-screw for screw-cutting on the lathe is found, as has been mentioned, in the fusee-engine. The idea occurs in a crude form as early as 1569 in the work of Besson (vol III, figure 217). Indeed, a screw-cutting machine with two lead-screws and complete with change-wheels was devised by Leonardo da Vinci in the fifteenth century (vol II, figure 598), but without practical consequences, since his drawing of it remained unpublished for four centuries. The screw-cutting lathe in a form similar to Maudslay's was made by Senot, a Frenchman, in 1795, and by David Wilkinson, an American, in 1798. Although the claim that Maudslay was sole inventor of the screw-cutting lathe with slide-rest, lead-screw, and change-gears cannot be sustained, he may be credited with the practical and successful introduction of these devices to engineering.

Maudslay's original screw-cutting lathe no longer possesses its gear-wheels; these would have been fixed on the three spindles on the right (plate 25 A), thus linking the lead-screw with the head-stock. The slide-rest, driven by the lead-screw, travels on two triangular bars. This lathe is notable for being made entirely of metal and marks the abandonment of wood in the construction of metal-working machines. The machine-tools Maudslay built for Bramah had wooden frames, but the exclusive use of metal in subsequent machine-tools greatly improved their rigidity and accuracy. Thereafter the use of metal throughout, for building even the largest machine-tools, became universal.

Maudslay gave much attention to the initial formation of accurate screw-threads. In the method finally adopted a hard-wood cylinder was rotated in a suitable holder against a crescent-shaped knife held obliquely to its axis. The knife in cutting into the cylinder caused it to traverse, thus generating a screw which could be copied in steel. Using an accurately made screw Maudslay was able to make a bench micrometer accurate to 0·0001 in, which served him as a workshop standard. He also effected improvements in the system of taps and dies, and standardized the pitches and diameters of the screws used in his workshop. He introduced the practice of making castings with rounded internal edges, recognizing that sharp angles were a source of weakness.

Maudslay became a leading builder of table engines—a type of stationary engine used as a power-unit in factories—and of marine engines, but his first important order was for the construction of a complete plant of machine-tools known as the Portsmouth block-making machinery.

At the end of the eighteenth century, Sir Samuel Bentham (1757–1831) was Inspector-General of Naval Works. After education as a naval apprentice at the Woolwich Arsenal, and a period at sea, he had been sent on a tour of northern European ports and had eventually taken service in Russia as a military and naval engineer and constructor. In 1791 he returned to England and the service of the Admiralty, to whom he proposed the introduction of labour-saving machinery in the dockyards. He made a study of the problem of wood-working by machinery and embodied his conclusions in his comprehensive patent of 1793. This patent included planing-machines with rotary cutters 'to cut on several sides of the wood at once'; the preparation of dovetail joints by means of conical cutters; and veneer-cutting, mortising, and moulding machines.

Bentham was particularly concerned with organizing the manufacture of pulley-blocks, of which 100 000 were required by the Admiralty each year. These were costly, as they were made by hand apart from the initial roughing out of the shells by a circular saw and the turning of the sheaves on the lathe. In 1801 Bentham was approached by Brunel with a scheme for their manufacture which he recognized as superior to his own. With characteristic lack of self-interest Bentham recommended to the Admiralty the adoption of Brunel's proposals.

Sir Marc Isambard Brunel (1769–1849) was born in Normandy and served as a naval officer until the French Revolution, when, because of his royalist sympathies, he became a refugee, first in the United States and then in England.

He made several inventions, but his best-known achievement in later years was the building of the first Thames tunnel (pp 449, 463, plate 32 A). He was the father of I. K. Brunel, the ship-builder, bridge-builder, and railway-engineer.

The block-making machinery designed by Brunel was constructed by Maudslay, who doubtless contributed to the design of the machinery. The project is of historic interest because it constituted one of the earliest examples of the use of machine-tools for mass-production. The plant was in full operation in Portsmouth by 1808, with a yearly output of 130 000 blocks. With this machinery ten unskilled men did the work of 110 skilled men, and it was estimated that for a capital outlay of £54 000 the Admiralty made a saving of £17 000 per annum. Brunel's reward was one year's saving. When first built, the Portsmouth block-machinery was one of the mechanical marvels of the time, with the fortunate result that a very full contemporary description of it was published in Rees's 'Cyclopaedia'. So well were the machines designed and built that several of them continued in use for 145 years, and examples of the more interesting of them have been preserved.

The blocks were made in three size-ranges, so that machines for certain processes were made in two or three sizes. There were altogether forty-three machines, and these carried out all the processes, except the final fitting and polishing, necessary to convert the raw material into finished pulley-blocks. They were driven through overhead shafting by a 30-hp steam-engine. The first stage in the preparation of the shells was to saw elm logs into convenient lengths by means of a reciprocating or circular saw. The latter machine was so contrived that the saw could be taken round the log and so could cut timber of almost its own diameter. The blocks of wood were then cut roughly to shape on circular-saw benches. Next, a block was placed in a boring-machine which simultaneously bored two holes at right-angles, one for the sheave-pin and the other to start the mortise for the sheave. The act of clamping the block in the boring-machine made indentations which served to fix its position correctly in subsequent machines. The block was placed in a mortising-machine which cut a slot for the sheave, and transferred to a shaping-engine which formed the outer surfaces. Grooves to hold rope were then cut in the surfaces by means of a scoring-machine. The rotating cutters of this last machine were carried in a swinging frame guided by a template, so that the cutters scored the required grooves without the exercise of any skill on the part of the operator.

The machine illustrated in plate 26 A could cut mortises in two blocks at a time. The shaft, rotating at 400 rpm, imparted a reciprocating motion to the chisels, which carried projecting tongues to clear the chips of wood. A ratchet, actuated by a cam on the shaft, engaged a toothed wheel on the lead-screw which caused the block-holder to advance after each cut. At a predetermined point the process was finished by automatically disengaging the ratchet. This machine is the earliest mortising-machine and the ancestor of the slotter or vertical shaper.

The machine reproduced in plate 26 B formed the surfaces of ten blocks at a time. A cutter, guided by a former, was moved across the face of the blocks as they revolved in the drum in which they were mounted. The simultaneous indexing of all the blocks about their centres was effected through bevel-and-worm gearing mounted on radial shafts actuated by a central crown-wheel. The blocks were turned through 90°, the other former was selected, and the blocks were faced in their new position. The procedure was continued until the four sides had been shaped.

In the manufacture of the sheave a slice of lignum vitae was rounded and bored on the rounding-machine, by means of a crown-saw and a drill running coaxially. The sheave was then grooved and faced on a special lathe which had a power-driven cross-slide. Finally, three recesses for the metal bush were cut in the sheave on a milling-machine designed for the purpose. There were in addition machines for turning and burnishing the pins.

The most eminent of the engineers who at one time or another worked for Maudslay were Roberts, Nasmyth, and Whitworth. Richard Roberts (1789–1864) was born at the village of Carreghofa in central Wales. As a youth he worked in a quarry, but at the age of twenty he found employment at Wilkinson's Bradley ironworks. After various jobs he was employed for two years as a turner and fitter by Maudslay, and then in 1814 set up on his own at Manchester, his first equipment consisting of a hand-lathe and a drilling-machine.

In 1817 he designed and built the lathe illustrated in plate 24 C; this has the new feature of the back-geared headstock. For direct driving the four-speed cone-pulley is connected with the spur-wheel keyed to the headstock-mandrel, but for slow-speed running they are disconnected. The countershaft is then engaged so that the pulley drives the headstock through the two pairs of gears. Another feature of this lathe is the self-acting carriage, which is traversed by a long screw driven from the mandrel through a variable-speed gear and a bevel-wheel reversing and disengaging gear. The ordinary slide-rest of the period was a self-contained appliance, clamped to the bed where required, and able, without being reset, to turn work only of the length commanded by its short screw. In this lathe the lead-screw is provided not for screw-cutting but to facilitate ordinary turning. The feed-gear consists of a divided plate with seven rings of pin-teeth which engage with a pinion sliding on the tail-end of the mandrel. Either of the two bevel wheels, mounted loosely on the lead-screw, may be connected with it by a clutch actuated by levers and a rod running the whole length of the bed and passing through the carriage; a stop placed upon this rod causes the carriage to disengage the clutch when it reaches the end of the required traverse. In the same year Roberts designed a planing-machine, to be described later.

In 1821 Roberts advertised himself as a maker of screws, division-plates, and bevel-, spur-, and worm-gears up to 30 inches in diameter. These gears were cut by milling-cutters, as was noted in his diary by Field, who visited Roberts in the course of a tour through the provinces: 'he has good lathes, screw engines, cutting engines; with the latter machine he does a good deal of work in cutting wheels for the cotton spinners both in brass & iron. His machine has the wheel held as in a lathe but not turned, being held centrally by ring on a arbor, his cutters are made of steel plate turned to the shape of the tooth. . . .'

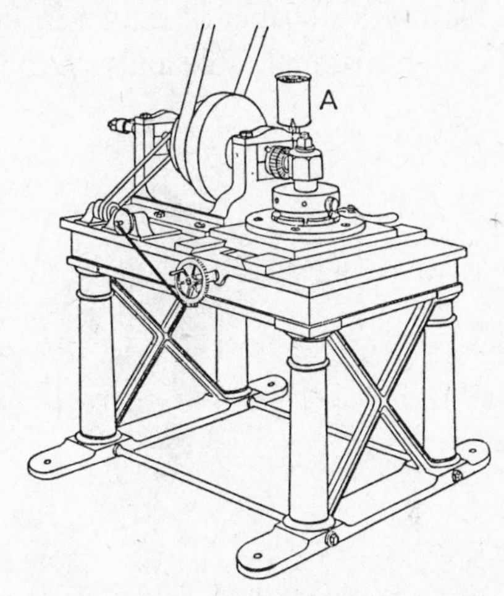

FIGURE 240—*Nasmyth's self-acting nut-milling machine, 1829.* A, *water drip. The drawing is by the inventor.*

Roberts was a most versatile inventor, but his greatest achievement was to devise the mechanism to render the spinning-mule self-acting (figure 159, p 289). His machine-tool inventions included a punching-machine for punching holes at exact intervals in steel plate. This was produced in 1847 in response to a request from the constructors of the Menai Straits railway-bridge (vol V, ch 21). Roberts's business ability unhappily did not match his mechanical ingenuity and he died in poverty, unlike the other eminent machine-tool inventors mentioned in this chapter who, it is pleasant to record, were financially successful.

James Nasmyth (1808–90) was born in Edinburgh, the son of a painter, landscape-gardener, and engineer. He had a high-school education and used the opportunity afforded by his father's workshop to make model steam-engines. At the age of twenty-one his interest in the mechanical arts led him to apply for employment at Maudslay's. He was Maudslay's personal assistant for two years.

In 1829 Nasmyth built the milling-machine depicted in figure 240, in which the cutter is shown machining the face of a hexagonal nut. Water was used for cooling, as indicated at A in the drawing. The columns are typical of machines of the time, but the classical style was soon to give place to more utilitarian designs.

When Maudslay died in 1831, Nasmyth left the firm in order to open his own workshop, first in Edinburgh and then at Patricroft, Manchester. In 1836 he invented the shaper. This was the machine which is used under that name today; it is quite distinct from Brunel's shaping-engine. An early example of Nasmyth's shaper is shown in figure 241. In this machine the work is secured on a horizontal table and is cut by a tool, clamped to a horizontal ram, which is

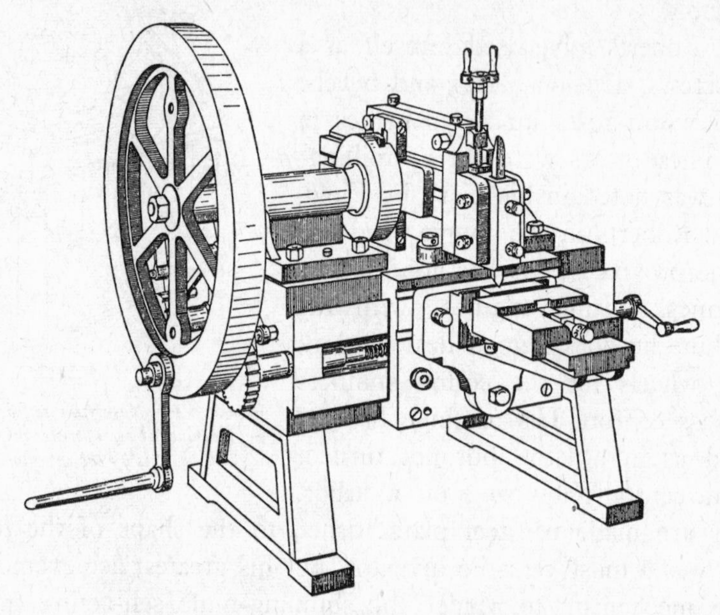

FIGURE 241—*Nasmyth's shaper, c 1850, invented in 1836. The cutter reciprocates horizontally to produce surfaces formed of straight-line elements.*

given reciprocating motion. The work-table slides on guides on the front of the main casting and is traversed by an internal screw driven either by hand or automatically by a pawl-feed motion rocked by an eccentric on the main shaft. The shaper is suitable for planing small surfaces, cutting key-ways, or producing any surface that can be formed of straight-line elements. In Nasmyth's shaper the driving-shaft ends in a disk carrying a crank-pin, to the other end of which is fitted a block sliding in a vertical slot in the ram. Whitworth subsequently improved the shaper by inventing a crank mechanism which causes the ram to make a quick return, so that a higher proportion of the working time is usefully employed in cutting.

Nasmyth's most celebrated invention is the steam-hammer. A photograph, taken in 1856, of a large steam-hammer with the inventor is reproduced in plates 24 A and 24 B. The tilt-hammer suffers from the limitation that it can be raised only a comparatively short distance. This distance and, consequently, the impact of the hammer are reduced by the thickness of the work on the anvil. Moreover, the force of the blow cannot be controlled. The designer of the engines of the steamship *Great Britain* had proposed a paddle-shaft 30 inches in diameter—though in the event the ship was built with a screw-shaft—but, finding that no one could undertake such a forging, he applied in 1839 to Nasmyth, who immediately devised his steam-hammer. The two standards that form guides for the hammer-head also support an overhead cylinder, the piston of which is connected with the hammer-head by a rod passing through the bottom of the cylinder. Steam is admitted by a valve to the cylinder in order to raise the hammer-head to the required height. The hammer falls when the steam is allowed to escape. The hammer was later made double-acting by admitting steam above the piston, so that a more powerful blow could be obtained. The description of Nasmyth's hammer in the catalogue of the Great Exhibition of 1851 states: 'This steam hammer is capable of adjustment of power in a degree highly remarkable. While it is possible to obtain enormous impulsive force by its means, it can be so graduated as to descend with power only sufficient to break an egg shell.' The steam-hammer greatly increased the size of forging possible.

Sir Joseph Whitworth (1803–87) was the son of a schoolmaster. At the age of fourteen he entered his uncle's cotton-mill to learn the business, but, being more interested in machinery than in commerce, he soon left in order to work as a mechanic with a firm of Manchester machinists. At the age of twenty-two he went to London and obtained employment with Maudslay and later with Clement (p 434). The method of making true metal plane surfaces three at a time (pp 424–5) by hand-scraping is generally supposed to have been devised by Whitworth while working at Maudslay's, but this claim is inconsistent with Nasmyth's statement, quoted earlier, that it was 'an old dodge'. Holtzapffel (1806–47), writing in 1846, attributed to Whitworth what he regarded as the essential feature of the method, namely the substitution of scraping for grinding. This does not, however, dispose of the contradiction, because Nasmyth mentioned scraping but did not refer to Whitworth.

In 1833 Whitworth rented a workshop at Manchester and displayed the sign 'Joseph Whitworth, Tool Maker from London'. The engineers who have been discussed up to this point built machine-tools primarily in order to be able to make other machines, but Whitworth built them for sale to other manufacturers. At the 1851 Exhibition he was the outstanding machine-tool maker. One, two, or even three machine-tools were exhibited by each of twenty other firms, but

Whitworth had twenty-three exhibits, including lathes and machines for planing, shaping, slotting, drilling (both plain and radial), punching and shearing, nut-shaping, screwing, wheel-cutting, and dividing. He also showed screwing-apparatus, a measuring-machine, a set of stepped gauges, and a set of internal and external cylindrical gauges. At the International Exhibition of 1862 Whit-

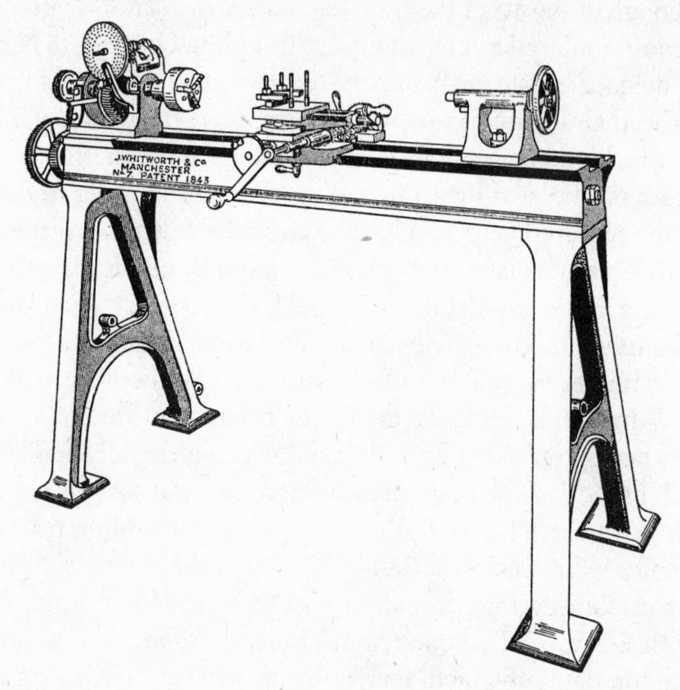

FIGURE 242—*Whitworth's lathe, 1843. Note the hollow-box construction of the bed.* (*Cf plate 25 A.*)

worth maintained his lead, for, although more than sixty firms then exhibited, his firm occupied a quarter of the total space allotted to machine-tools.

Whitworth described several improvements to machine-tools in his patent of 1839. Among them were the split nut by which the lead-screw of a lathe could be engaged at will to make the saddle traverse, and the mechanism by which the cross-feed could be actuated by the lead-screw. The lathe shown in figure 242 was built in 1843 and was in use until 1951. It exemplifies the hollow-box design of lathe-bed, introduced by Whitworth. This design makes the machine much more rigid, weight for weight, than the earlier triangular-bar construction, besides protecting the lead-screw from damage and dirt. The lead-screw passes through the split nut, which forms part of the carriage, and causes the carriage to traverse. If the split nut is disengaged, the carriage stops, and cross-feed motion is obtained through the meshing of a pinion with the lead-screw. If the cross-feed is thrown out of gear, the handle at the front, which is connected with the pinion, may be used to give rapid traverse to the carriage. In this case the lead-screw is being used as a rack.

Whitworth was responsible for bringing about the standardization of screw-threads. He collected and compared screws from as many workshops as possible throughout England and in 1841 proposed, in a paper to the Institution of Civil Engineers, the use of a constant angle (55°) between the sides of the threads, and a specification for the number of threads to the inch for the various screw-diameters. The Whitworth thread remained standard in engineering until 1948.

Whitworth also gave much attention to accurate measurement and considered end-measurement to be more satisfactory than measurement between lines. In 1834 he made a measuring machine capable of comparing yard standards to an accuracy of one-millionth of an inch. For detecting the exact point of contact he introduced the gravity- or feeling-piece. A movement of a millionth of an inch was sufficient to make a feeling-piece stand or fall. For ordinary workshop use he made measuring machines of smaller sensitivity.

Speaking in 1856, Whitworth said: 'Thirty years ago the cost of labour for facing a surface of cast iron, by hand, was twelve shillings per square foot; the same work is now done by the planing machine at a cost for labour of less than one penny per square foot, and this, as you know, is one of the most important operations in mechanics. It is, therefore, well adapted to illustrate what our progress has been.'

The invention of the planing machine for metal has been attributed to several engineers. Matthew Murray, a steam-engine manufacturer of Leeds, who died in 1826, was an important rival of Boulton and Watt. According to one of his workmen, March, who joined him in 1814 and who later became a tool manufacturer, Murray invented a planing machine for planing D-valve surfaces. March said: 'I recollect it very distinctly, and even the sort of framework on which it stood. The machine was not patented, and like many inventions in those days, it was kept as much a secret as possible, being locked up in a small room by itself, to which the ordinary workmen could not obtain access. The year in which I remember it being in use was, so far as I am aware, long before any planing machine of a similar kind had been invented.' James Fox of Derby, a manufacturer of lathes and of textile-machinery, is said to have built a planer in 1814.

The earliest planing machine still in existence (plate 25B) was made by Richard Roberts in 1817. The marks on the bed show that it was itself made without the assistance of a planer. The work is secured to a table which moves to and fro on a straight bed under a tool capable of being traversed, so that, by the two motions, plane surfaces are produced as the tool makes successive cuts. The table is moved by means of chains wound on a drum rotated by hand. The tool can be raised or lowered by means of a screw. The tool-clamp is hinged and spring-loaded, so that, although it is firm during the cutting stroke, it is free to move on the return stroke, thus avoiding damage to the tool and to the work.

The best known early planing machine was that made in 1825 by Joseph Clement (1779–1844), who set up on his own after working as a chief draughtsman, first for Bramah and then for Maudslay. Clement did much work on the problem of accurate screw-cutting, manufactured taps and dies, and introduced the tap with a small squared shank which would fall through the threaded hole instead of having to be screwed out. The table of his planing machine ran on rollers, and the machine was bedded on a massive foundation of masonry. The machine was driven by hand and had two cutters, one for each direction of travel of the bed. For ten years this machine was the only planer capable of taking large work—up to 6 ft square. Clement charged 18*s* a square foot. At this rate the machine could earn £20 per day, if fully employed, and it was his chief source of income.

Whitworth's planing machine (figure 243), made in 1842 under patents dating from 1835, was power-driven and self-acting. A lead-screw in the middle of the bed of the machine, driven by fast and loose pulleys and with a three-bevel wheel reversing arrangement, transmitted motion to the V-guided table. The cross-slide is supported on, and actuated by, two vertical screws connected by bevel-gears and to a shaft, which is hand-operated. The swivelling tool-box is on a screw on the cross-slide and is fed across the work by a ratchet and pulley. The latter is actuated by a band from a rocking pulley on the same shaft as a pinion moved by a rack-rod on the bed. This rod is moved to and fro by the table coming against stops. By means of guide pulleys, the band also reverses the tool-holder at the end of each stroke, thus cutting in both directions. In 1851 Whitworth exhibited a similar planer, and also a planer of conventional type to plane one way only, with a quick-return motion.

Work that may be done on the shaper, planer, or lathe may often be done more advantageously by milling, provided that there is sufficient repetition to justify the trouble of making a milling-cutter of suitable shape and size. The advantages of the milling process are, first, that the use of a large number of cutting edges permits high-speed machining without excessive heating, and, secondly, that special shapes can be obtained in a single operation by the use of formed cutters. The difficulty of making milling-cutters and keeping them sharp restricted their use in the early days of machine-tools.

As has already been noted, rotary cutters were first used for cutting clock-wheels, and were used for special purposes by Bramah, Brunel, Roberts, and

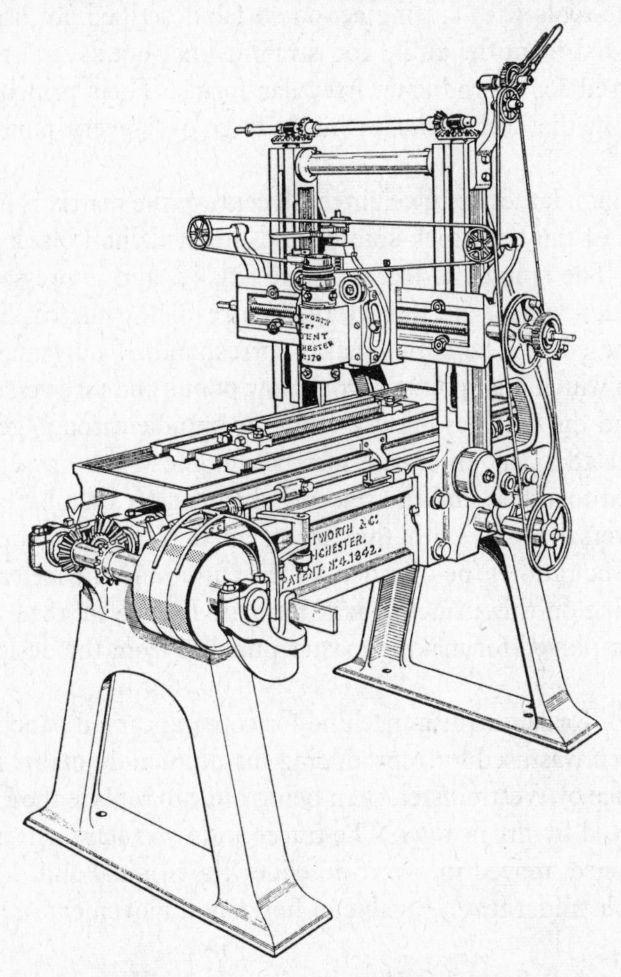

FIGURE 243—*Whitworth's self-acting power-driven planing machine, 1842. The tool is reversed after each traverse of the bed, so as to cut both ways.*

Nasmyth. The development of the milling machine for normal workshop use took place in America. Eli Whitney (1765–1825) in 1818 made a small milling machine which had a power-driven table moving horizontally below the cutter-spindle and at right-angles to it. The first milling machine manufactured for sale was designed in 1848 by Frederick Webster Howe (1822–91) for the Robbins &

Lawrence Company of Windsor, Vermont. A back view of this machine is reproduced in figure 244. The spindle, shown with a cutter in place, is driven by a cone-pulley and back-gears. The table is traversed by rack and pinion through bevel and worm gearing which can be engaged at will.

The machine-tools with cutting action so far described are used for cutting out forms derived from the circle and straight line, but several machines have also been devised for reproducing irregular forms. Their principle is that the cutter is linked with a feeler which is made to go over every point of the object to be copied.

In the medallion lathes of the eighteenth century the matrix is held in a chuck at the rear end of the headstock-spindle and the medallion blank is mounted at the front end. The spindle is free to move axially, and is pressed by a spring against the feeler which, starting at the centre of the matrix, is very slowly traversed to the edge. The cutter makes corresponding movements and cuts a reverse copy in which high points become low points and vice versa. The motion of the feeler and the cutter is derived from the spindle through gearing.

Hulot, about 1800, mounted the matrix and the blank on separate parallel spindles, geared together, and the tracer and the cutter on a bar pivoted at one end on a universal joint. With this arrangement a positive copy was made, diminished in the ratio of the distances of the cutter and the feeler from the fulcrum. A machine on this principle was built in France in 1824 for the Royal Mint; it was employed for making master punches from the designers' original medallions.

In 1845 T. B. Jordan made a machine for copying carved panels of wood and soft stone, which was used for reproducing furniture and notably in the decoration of the Palace of Westminster, then being built to replace the Houses of Parliament destroyed by fire in 1834. The tracer and two rotary cutters, for making two copies at once, moved in a vertical slide; the original and the blanks were placed on a table underneath, capable of horizontal movement in two directions at right-angles.

Between 1804 and 1819, when in retirement, James Watt improved on Hulot's principle by placing a pivoted arm between the bar and the universal joint, with the result that it was possible to under-cut and to copy objects in the round. He also used rotating cutters. Watt made two such sculpturing machines, for reducing and for copying to the same size, but they were neither patented nor generally known. A similar machine was independently invented by Benjamin Cheverton in 1826. In 1818 Thomas Blanchard of Worcester, Massachusetts, made a copying-lathe of considerable economic importance, for turning gun-stocks.

The invention of wood-working machinery, which removed the hard work from sawing and offered the possibility of high-speed working in other processes, was stimulated by the advent of the steam-engine. Reciprocating saws driven by water-wheels had, however, been used from the Middle Ages. The circular saw was probably invented in the third quarter of the eighteenth century by Walter Taylor (1734–1803) of Southampton, who had a contract for making pulley-blocks for the Royal Navy. The band-saw was patented in 1808 by William Newberry, but it was not a practical invention at the time because a steel band which would run for long without snapping could not then be made. The band-saw was successfully re-invented in the United States by Lemuel Hedge in 1849 and in France by Perin in 1855.

Bentham's comprehensive patent for wood-working machinery has already been noted. The mortising machine originates from Bentham and the block-making factory at Portsmouth. His proposals for using rotary cutters came to fruition later in the United States, in J. A. Fay's tenoning machine of 1840 and Andrew Gear's vertical-spindle moulding machine of 1853.

Bramah in 1802 made a rotary wood-planing machine for Woolwich Arsenal, and this was in use for fifty years. The wood to be planed was placed on carriages which ran on rails 40 ft long. The carriages were moved backwards and forwards by an endless chain which derived its motion from a hydraulic engine. Above the carriage was fixed the planing disk—carrying twenty-eight gouges for rough cutting and two planing-irons—which was rotated at 90 rpm by a steam-engine. In 1827 Malcolm Muir, another former employee of Maudslay, invented a machine for making flooring-boards. Planks were fed into it by an endless chain fitted with catch-hooks at intervals, and were treated by a succession of planes and circular saws which reduced them to the required dimensions and formed the tongues and grooves. This machine was improved in 1836 by John McDowall by using rotary cutters for tonguing and grooving, and by substituting for the chain-feed—which had a tendency to tear the wood—pairs of rollers under pressure at each end of the machine to feed the boards through the cutters.

In a letter written in 1785 Thomas Jefferson, then American minister to France, described as follows a visit he had paid to a gunsmith named Le Blanc:

> An improvement is made here in the construction of muskets, which it may be interesting to Congress to know, should they at any time propose to procure any. It consists in the making every part of them so exactly alike, that what belongs to any one, may be used for every other musket in the magazine. The government here has examined and approved the method, and is establishing a large manufactory for the purpose of putting it into execution. As yet, the inventor has only completed the lock of the musket on this

plan. He will proceed immediately to have the barrel, stock, and other parts, executed in the same way. Supposing it might be useful to the United States, I went to the workman. He presented me the parts of fifty locks taken to pieces, and arranged in compartments. I put several together myself, taking pieces at hazard as they came to hand, and they fitted in the most perfect manner. The advantages of this when arms need repair are evident. He effects it by tools of his own contrivance, which, at the same time, abridge the work, so that he thinks he shall be able to furnish the musket two livres cheaper than the common price.

The system of manufacture thus described is known as the interchangeable system.

In the United States interchangeable manufacture began with a contract given in 1798 to Eli Whitney, the inventor of the saw-gin for cotton. He spent two years in constructing his plant, with which he manufactured 10 000 muskets. He aimed 'to make the same parts of different guns, as the locks, for example, as much like each other as the successive impressions of a copper-plate engraving'. In 1812 he had a contract for a further 15 000 muskets. He cannot have been aware of Le Blanc's project, for he wrote that 'this establishment was commenced and has been carried on upon a plan which is unknown in Europe, and the great leading object of which is to substitute correct and effective operations of machinery for that skill of the artist which is acquired only by long practice and experience, a species of skill which is not possessed in this country to any considerable extent'. Thus the United States, with but few skilled gunsmiths to resist, perhaps, the mechanization of their craft, was a favourable ground for the introduction of the new system of manufacture, which became known in Europe as the 'American' system. The system was economical because the manufacture could be broken down into a number of operations, each of which was carried out on a special machine designed for the job. The military advantage of interchangeable gun-parts needs no emphasis.

The interchangeable system was later used for the manufacture of sewing-machines, typewriters, bicycles, motor-cars, and similar machines made in large quantities and built up chiefly from accurately fitting metal components. The system depends on the use of jigs for holding the work and guiding the tools in such operations as the drilling of accurately located holes; on accurate machine-tools; and on gauges for frequent checking during the process of manufacture.

In 1799 Simeon North began the manufacture of 1500 pistols and in 1813 he obtained a contract to make 20 000 more, the components of which were to be interchangeable. The interchangeable system was also used from 1828 onwards for the manufacture of the Hubbard rotary-gear pump. In 1835 Samuel Colt patented his revolver, but commercial success came to him only in 1846, with the Mexican war. In 1853 he built an armoury at Hartford, Connecticut, containing 1400 machine-tools. His superintendent, Elisha K. Root, devised the system of tools, jigs, fixtures, and gauges. The latter's designs included a drop-hammer and a horizontal turret-lathe. This plant probably represents the limit

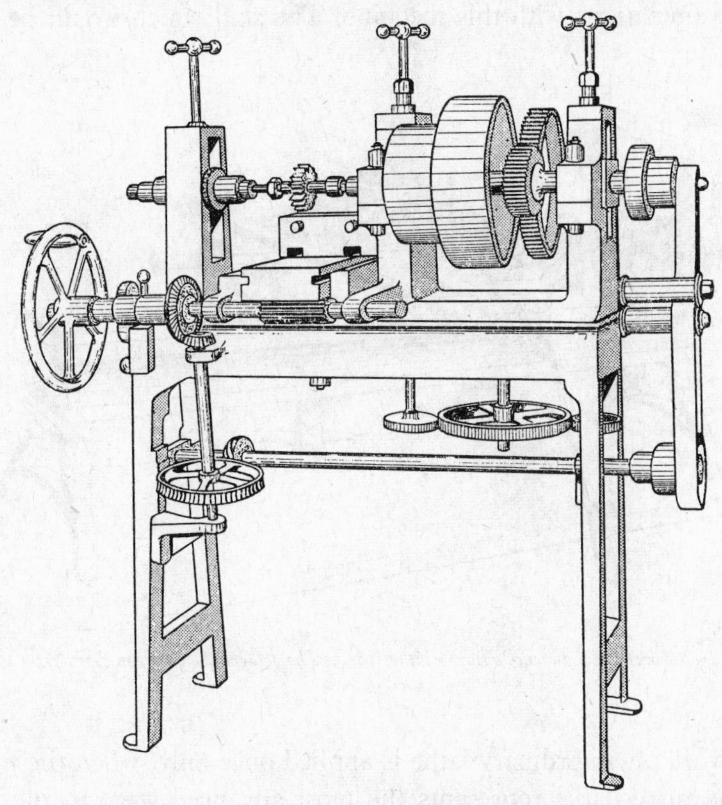

FIGURE 244—*Howe's milling machine, 1848. This was the first milling machine manufactured for sale. The cutter is not original.*

of achievement reached in large-scale precision manufacture by the middle of the nineteenth century.

One of the most influential firms in the gun business was that of Robbins & Lawrence of Windsor, Vermont, whose milling machine, designed by their superintendent, F. W. Howe, has already been mentioned (figure 244). Richard S. Lawrence, F. W. Howe, and Henry D. Stone were responsible for the modern type of turret-lathe with the vertical turret. Figure 245 shows such a lathe, made in 1855 and called at the time a screw-milling machine, because it was used for making screws. The turret-lathe was probably first made in the previous decade, both with the horizontal drum type of turret and with the vertical turret as illustrated. The turret is advanced on a slide by moving the horizontal handle to bring up in turn each of the eight tool-holders, each fitted with a tool, to the work in the head-stock. The turret is indexed by hand between operations. There is also a cross-slide with a tool-holder. It is thus possible to carry out nine predetermined operations with this machine. The skill which would be necessary

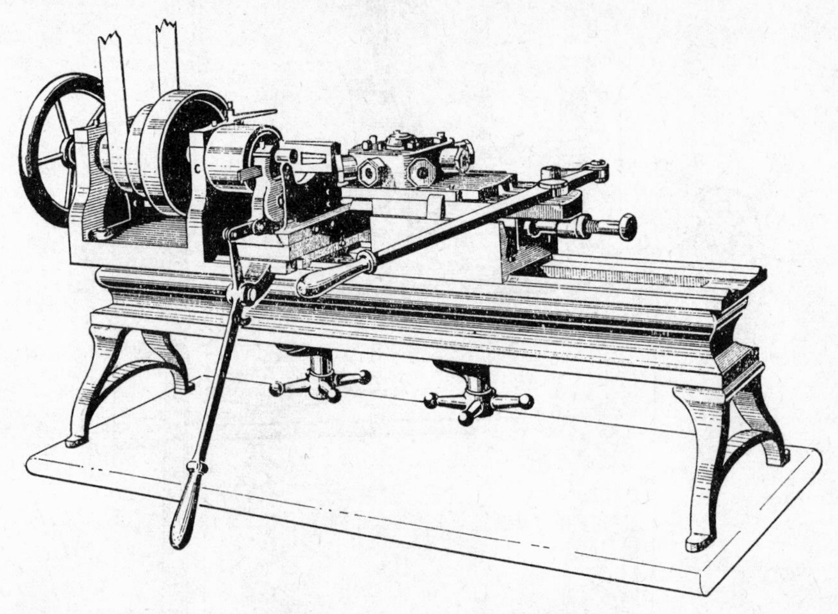

FIGURE 245—*Robbins and Lawrence's turret-lathe, 1855. The octagonal turret can carry eight tools to be used in turn.*

to do this work on an ordinary lathe is applied once only, when the machine is set up. The turret-lathe represents the most advanced stage in the evolution of the lathe in the period now under review. At the 1851 Exhibition Robbins & Lawrence showed six American army rifles, interchangeably manufactured, which attracted much attention.

In 1853 a Royal Small Arms Commission was set up under the chairmanship of James Nasmyth to advise on the manufacture of small arms, which were at that time assembled centrally from crude parts made in scattered workshops. It was resolved to introduce the American system into England. Some members of the commission visited the United States and as a result the Royal Small Arms Factory at Enfield was re-equipped. Blanchard lathes were purchased for making the gun-stocks; and for the manufacture of the metal parts of the rifle Robbins & Lawrence were given a contract for 150 machine-tools and the requisite jigs, fixtures, and gauges. The machine-tools included 57 plain milling machines, a number of universal milling machines, four- and six-spindle drilling machines, and screw-milling machines or turret-lathes. By 1857 a thousand rifles a week were being made with this machinery. Although the American system had thus been introduced into Britain, turret-lathes and milling machines do not appear in Clark's full account of the machinery exhibited in 1862. It appears, however, that steam-hammers, planers, shapers, slotters, screwing machines, punching machines, drilling machines, and radial drilling machines were obtainable in fair variety.

The smaller machine-tools were often driven by hand or foot, and even quite large machines (cf plate 28) were sometimes built for manual drive. Large machines, and workshops with several machines, were driven by water-power if available, but more usually, from about 1800 onwards, by steam-power. The power was transmitted from the steam-engine to the machines by belts and overhead shafting.

By the middle of the nineteenth century the majority of the machine-tools now in use, with the notable exceptions of automatic lathes, screw machines, and gear-cutting, broaching, and grinding machines, had been brought into existence, though not always in their modern form.

BIBLIOGRAPHY

BALE, M. P. 'Wood-working Machinery: its Rise, Progress and Construction' (3rd ed. rev.). Lockwood, London. 1914.

BUCHANAN, R. 'Practical Essays on Millwork and other Machinery' (3 vols, 3rd ed. rev., with additions by T. TELFORD and G. RENNIE). London. 1841.

CLARK, D. K. 'The Exhibited Machinery of 1862: a Cyclopaedia of the Machinery represented at the International Exhibition.' London. [1864.]

DICKINSON, H. W. "Joseph Bramah and his Inventions." *Trans. Newcomen Soc.*, **22**, 169–86, 1941–2.

Idem. "Richard Roberts: his Life and Inventions." *Ibid.*, **25**, 123–37, 1945–7.

FORWARD, E. A. "The Early History of the Cylinder Boring Machine." *Ibid.*, **5**, 24–38, 1924–5.

HUBBARD, G. "The Development of Machine Tools in New England", *Amer. Mach., N.Y.*, 1923–4.

NASMYTH, J. 'An Autobiography' (ed. by S. SMILES). London. 1883.

REES, A. 'The Cyclopaedia; a Universal Dictionary of Arts, Sciences and Literature', Article: 'Machinery for Manufacturing Ships' Blocks.' London. 1819.

ROE, J. W. 'English and American Tool Builders.' Yale University Press, New Haven. 1916.

SMILES, S. 'Industrial Biography: Iron Workers and Tool Makers' (2nd ed.). London. 1879.

15

BUILDING AND CIVIL ENGINEERING CONSTRUCTION

S. B. HAMILTON

I. ORGANIZATION AND TECHNICAL TRAINING

In the periods covered in the earlier volumes of this work no clear distinction can usually be drawn between the work of the military engineer, the civil engineer, and the architect. The same man might well serve at different times in all three capacities; Leonardo da Vinci is well known to have done, but so did many of less outstanding ingenuity and versatility.

In the latter part of the seventeenth century, however, at least in France, a tendency to specialize developed. Employment in any of the three capacities was practically a state monopoly. In 1661 Jean Baptiste Colbert (1619–83) became chief minister to Louis XIV at a time when public buildings, the improvement of communications, and the erection of fortifications were all matters of great importance. In 1664 Colbert took to himself the title of *Surintendant des Bâtiments*; he had a staff of architects, most of whom were already working on the Louvre or some other royal building. In 1666 he persuaded the king to found the Académie des Sciences, and in 1671 the Académie de l'Architecture. In 1672 Sébastien le Prêtre, Seigneur de Vauban (1633–1707), who had revolutionized the arts both of attacking and of building fortifications, was placed at the head of a formally constituted *Corps du Génie*—a body of military engineers whom he had organized and trained for such work. In 1715 the roads and bridges of France were placed under the care of a *Directeur-Général des Ponts et Chaussées*, and in 1716 a staff of engineers was embodied to work under his direction. The weakness of this organization at first was that it had no regular subordinate cadre. In 1744 it was given a small staff of draughtsmen and a registry of maps and plans. In 1747 this was enlarged to become the École des Ponts et Chaussées, the regular training-centre for surveyors and engineers under the direction of Jean Rodolphe Perronet (1708–94). In 1763 Perronet became also the *Premier Ingénieur* of the *Corps des Ingénieurs des Ponts et Chaussées*, which by then included a trained staff of all grades [1].

There was very little science applied to construction by architects, by builders, or by engineers in the early part of the eighteenth century. Henri Gautier's *Traité des Chemins* (1715) and *Traité des Ponts* (1716) are almost entirely descriptive. Gautier stated the customary proportions between the supporting pier, the arch-ring, and the span of a masonry bridge, but gave no reason for them other than tradition. Bernard Forest de Belidor (1693–1761) in *La Science des Ingénieurs* (1729) gave simple rules based on statics for checking the stability of retaining-walls and arches, and for calculating the strength of beams. He also summarized much practical information. His theory was simple and was used to reinforce, rather than to derive, practical rules. In his four-volume *Architecture Hydraulique* (1737–53) he gave full descriptions, with drawings accurate in detail, of work as it was carried out on marine structures, canals, bridges, and pumping installations, together with the plant used for various purposes.

At the École des Ponts et Chaussées there were no regular lectures, but notes were made and circulated; and there appears to have been opportunity for informal discussion between young men in training and experienced engineers, and between practical men and scholars. Some of the engineers contributed papers to be read at the Académie des Sciences, and several wrote books. Examples of their work will be considered later.

In England after the Great Fire of 1666 the rebuilding of St Paul's Cathedral and the London churches, and work on the royal palaces at Greenwich, Hampton Court, and elsewhere, was placed in the hands of Sir Christopher Wren (1632–1723), who thus attained a unique position; but in England there was never anything approaching a crown monopoly of building, still less of public works. Architecture as a profession was recognized, even in 1768, only by the inclusion of four architects at the foundation of the Royal Academy in that year.

In 1771 a group of men who were frequently called upon to prepare surveys, or to give evidence before parliamentary committees on schemes for the building of canals, docks, harbours, and the like, formed themselves into a Society of Engineers, and began to refer to themselves as civil engineers. John Smeaton (1724–92) was the recognized leader of the profession at the time. He was never the president of the society, although its surviving lineal descendant is known as 'The Smeatonian'. The Institution of Civil Engineers was founded in 1818. In 1791 a number of London architects formed an association. As with the Society of Engineers, the Associated Architects were members of a club rather than of a professional institution. The British Institute of Architects was founded in 1834; it became the Royal Institute of British Architects in 1866.

It may be said that a recognized division between military engineering and architecture—including civil engineering—took place in France in the 1670s.

The division between architecture and civil engineering began in 1715, and was practically complete soon after the middle of the eighteenth century. In England there had long been men carrying out works of drainage and river-improvement who would not have claimed to be architects in any sense, but not until 1771 did they band together as members of a common calling. Although after that time bridges and other works of an engineering character were sometimes constructed by men calling themselves architects, the practice was obsolescent.

The École des Ponts et Chaussées was, with other special schools, merged at the Revolution into a comprehensive École des Travaux Publiques. In 1795 this became the École Polytechnique, and the specialist schools, to which its courses served as an introduction, were refounded. Three innovations were made in the running of these schools, which were to serve as a precedent for technical education everywhere in the future: entrance to be by competitive examination; lectures to large classes to be given by leading scientists appointed as whole-time teachers; and practical work to be done by students in chemical and physical laboratories. The revived École des Ponts et Chaussées came under the direction of Gaspard François Prony (1755–1839), formerly closely associated with Perronet in the design and construction of some of his finer bridges. Prony wrote textbooks on mechanics and hydraulics, but the work of greatest influence in this respect was by C. L. M. Navier (1785–1836), who brought the theory of construction right up to date for students in his *Leçons sur l'application de la mécanique* (1826).

In Britain, means of instruction lagged far behind those available in France. Both John Rennie (1761–1821) and Thomas Telford (1757–1834), who, after Smeaton's death, were the most notable British civil engineers, learned French in order to be able to read Belidor and French writers on chemistry. Rennie, whose career began as a millwright, attended classes at Edinburgh University under Joseph Black in chemistry, and under John Robison in mechanical philosophy, although he did not take a degree course. Telford, who began his career as a stone-mason, made a collection of technical books, which on his death formed the foundation of the library of the Institution of Civil Engineers, of which Telford was the founder-president. There were, however, a few English books likely to be useful to a civil engineer. There was J. T. Desaguliers's 'Experimental Philosophy' (two volumes, 1734 and 1744). William Emerson's 'Fluxions' (1743) included the first explanation in English of La Hire's smooth voussoir theory of the arch. John Muller's 'Treatise concerning the Practical Part of Fortification' (1755) formed the basis of his instruction to army cadets at Woolwich Academy. His book was by no means restricted to its subject title: it included discussion of retaining-walls and arches, and of the strength and other properties of constructional materials, based in the main on Belidor. There was also a 'Treatise on Inland Navigation' (1763) by Charles Valency, which consisted of translations from Belidor and several Italian engineers, with illustrations copied from Belidor. The first English textbook on 'The Principles of Bridges', by Charles Hutton, followed La Hire and Emerson. It first appeared in 1772, and was reissued in 1801 and 1812.

In 1760 John Anderson (1726–96) was appointed to the chair of natural philosophy at Glasgow University, and from then until his death gave lectures which he invited artisans to attend in their working clothes. His work was continued at Glasgow, and later in London, by George Birkbeck. So began the Mechanics' Institutes (vol V, ch 32), many of which by the end of the nineteenth century had become famous technical colleges.

The essential engineering theory developed by the French engineers and savants in the eighteenth century was embodied by Thomas Young (1773–1829) in his 'Lectures on Natural Philosophy' (two volumes, 1807), but Young was heavy reading, and was certainly not read by many practising engineers. His ideas did, however, become known through the textbooks written by Thomas Tredgold, and through articles in the 'Encyclopaedia Britannica' by Young himself and by John Robison.

Some lectures on architecture and on engineering were delivered at University College, London, from its foundation in 1828, and at King's College, London, from its foundation in 1829. A Regius professor of engineering was appointed at Glasgow University in 1840. From 1855 that chair was held by John McQuorn Rankine (1820–72), whose subsequent comprehensive textbooks provided the English-reading student for the first time with something equivalent to the works that had long been available only in French.

Generally speaking, neither architects nor engineers placed much value on a university training for their juniors. The young man aspiring to practise either profession was articled to a practitioner already established. He paid a fee and drew no salary, usually picking up what he could from salaried assistants to whom he made himself useful. His progress depended largely on using initiative, keeping his eyes and ears open, and studying in his spare time. In an office handling important and interesting work the keen and industrious pupil could learn much, and by the end of his pupilage prove himself worthy of regular employment. If his connexions were good and his funds adequate, he could buy a partnership or open an office of his own. On the continent of Europe, towards the middle of the nineteenth century, training usually began in a polytechnic school where both theory and design were taught. The young engineer had usually acquired no actual experience of commercial or professional practice when his training ended, and in that respect he was behind his British counterpart, although his technical instruction was far more advanced. By the 1850s German designers and builders of structures and even of machinery had overcome their later start, and in many fields were competing successfully with the British and French [2].

II. MATERIALS

For the walls of buildings in towns the favoured materials were dressed masonry (ashlar) or brickwork. Since the Great Fire of 1666, buildings in London had been required to have incombustible walls and roof-coverings, and most of the provincial towns had followed the example of the metropolis. The practice in small country towns and villages depended on the locality. Where building-stone could be quarried near at hand, stone building was traditional: in well wooded parts of the country hardwood framing with daub-and-wattle infilling persisted into the eighteenth century. However, widespread clearing for agriculture, felling of timber in some areas for ship-building and building, and, in a few areas, conversion of forest to coppice for charcoal-burning, had reduced or hindered the regrowth of stands of tall, straight trees. Much of the vast quantity of timber needed for the rebuilding of London came as softwood from the Baltic, and once established the trade continued. Where neither stone nor hardwood was readily available, brick became the common material for walls, since more or less suitable clay was to be found in most parts of the country that were not well provided with stone. To most low-lying parts of the country coal for brick-making could be brought by the rivers, of which the navigable lengths were markedly extended during the earlier part of the eighteenth century; these waterways were augmented by canals during the last quarter of the century (ch 18). In Holland, Flanders, and north Italy building in brickwork had a much longer history. In France, as in England, the choice of stone, timber, or brick depended largely upon the local facilities.

Carved stonework is expensive, and when ornament was to be repeated it was often considerably more economical to use clay moulded to shape before burning. The Italians had long produced such work under the name of terracotta. About the middle of the eighteenth century attempts were made to popularize this material in England. The most successful makers were Coade and Sealy of Lambeth. They began in 1769 with John Bacon as designer. He also, and independently, designed statuary in stone and in bronze. Coade stone was resistant to weather and to fire, and was pleasing in colour: it won the approval of many architects and owners of buildings just at the time when large areas were being opened up for residential building in the West End of London, and its popularity continued into the Regency period. The basic material was kaolin (china-clay). The superiority of Coade's products to that of most competitors gave colour to the legend that the makers possessed a trade secret which died with the closure of the business about 1840. It seems more probable that good design and carefully controlled mixing and firing were the real foundations of its reputation [3].

The popularity of Coade stone and other such products waned with the hard times following the Napoleonic wars. For mural decoration John Nash (1752–1835), for instance, covered walls of brickwork with stucco, a mixture of lime and sand which relied for its appearance and permanence on a covering of paint. For garden ornaments and statues cast iron and pre-cast concrete were cheaper than Coade stone, which they tended to replace in just the same way as Coade stone and lead had replaced the more expensive carved natural stone. For massive features such as columns, as at Carlton House Terrace and Buckingham Palace, Nash used cast iron painted to look like stone.

Cements, mortars, and plasters. The commonest substance for use as the active ingredient of mortar is lime; but lime made by calcining natural limestones is not always pure, and its adhesive property may be improved or spoilt according to the nature of the impurity. For use as a plaster-finish a pure lime was preferred, the purest coming from marble. Realization of this fact led to the destruction of much ancient statuary by medieval lime-burners and their successors. For adhesion, however, some of the darker limes were to be preferred, and some of them had the property of setting in damp places, even under water, situations in which a purer lime remained soft or became leached out altogether. This hydraulic property of certain limes, as L. J. Vicat (1786–1861) named it, was known and utilizied by the ancient Roman builders. They also knew that a volcanic earth called pozzolana when added to non-hydraulic lime could form a mixture having powerful hydraulic properties. Finely powdered clay tiles and the iron-scale from a blacksmith's forge had a similar property, as did a substance used in Holland known as trass, which resembled pozzolana.

When John Smeaton was commissioned to build the third Eddystone lighthouse (figures 263 and 264), he realized the importance of using a strongly hydraulic lime to joint the masonry, in addition to dove-tailing and dowelling the stones together. He collected samples of lime from many parts of the country, tested them for strength, and submitted them to chemical analysis. He thus discovered that this property of setting under water was always found in a lime made from a limestone that contained an appreciable proportion of clay. This discovery formed the basis of a number of 'natural' and 'artificial' cements. The natural cements were made from minerals in which calcareous and argillaceous constituents were present in roughly suitable proportions to make, when calcined and finely ground, an 'eminently hydraulic' lime. The best known of these was the so-called Roman cement, which was supposed to make mortar or concrete as hard as the best specimens surviving from the Roman occupation. It was made from nodules or *septaria* found in the London clay at Harwich and at Sheppey. It was patented by James Parker in 1796 (Brit. Pat. No 2120/1796).

The artificial cements were made by mixing together chalk or limestone and clay or mud in proportions that had to be empirically determined, because the chemical reactions involved in the setting and hardening of cement were then unknown; they are in fact highly complicated. Important pioneer work on this subject was done in France by L. J. Vicat [4]. The London clay and the chalk of the North Downs occur together in north Kent, and thus cement-works there were conveniently situated both for the unloading of coal brought by sea and for the transport of the product to London by river-barges. This important industry made Kent its home in the late eighteenth century, and it is still conducted there on a very large scale. The early work, including some of his own, was well described by Sir Charles Pasley (1780–1861), first director (1812–41) of the establishment of field-instruction at Chatham, in his book on 'Limes, Calcareous Cements, Mortars etc.' (1838). The most famous of the artificial cements was Portland cement, so named by its patentee Joseph Aspdin (1779–1855) on the optimistic assumption that the dull, grey artificial stone, or concrete, made with this cement would be an acceptable substitute for Portland stone [5]. Aspdin was a stone-mason, bricklayer, or builder in Wakefield, who in 1824 took out a patent (No. 5022) for his product. His son William, with a partner, opened works on the Thames in 1843; in 1851, with another partner, he set up a works at Gateshead. To obtain what came to be known, and is still made, as Portland cement, the calcination of the mixed chalk and clay must be taken to a sintering temperature, but of this no hint appears in Aspdin's patent specification. Aspdin may deliberately or accidentally have obtained the hard-burnt clinker and found it better than the low-temperature product he first made; he did not, however, take out a further patent, probably preferring, if he really made the discovery, to rely on secrecy. One of his rivals, L. C. Johnson (1811–1911), stated much later that it was he who had made the discovery: that what he had at one time thrown away as over-burnt and spoiled clinker, proved, when he made the experiment of grinding it fine and using it as cement, much superior in strength to the hitherto normal lightly-burnt material. However that may be, about 1850 the advantage of high-temperature calcination was generally understood by makers and users of cement, and this became the common practice. The kilns were shaped either like bottles or like truncated cones (figure 246): one dating from 1856 measured 36 ft high, 17 ft in diameter at the base, and 2 ft 9 inches in diameter at the top: it is reported to have held enough cement to fill eighty barrels. The cement-barrel, if it was the same as that used into the twentieth century for export, held 400 lb. Portland cement was thus entirely British in invention and development.

FIGURE 246—*Original kiln in the works erected by William Aspdin at Northfleet, Kent.*

The production of a fairly consistent quality of cement gave considerable impetus to the use of concrete as a structural material. The use of hydraulic-lime concrete in bridge-foundations by French engineers has already been noted (vol III, p 425). George Semple (*c* 1700–*c* 1782) mixed roach lime (fortunately hydraulic) with gravel from his excavations to form a concrete for the foundations of the Essex bridge over the Liffey in Dublin in place of the more usual grillage [6]. George Dance the younger (1741–1825) and Sir John Soane (1753–1837) made occasional use of lime-concrete in foundations. Sir Robert Smirke (1781–1867) made it a practice to use it in his larger works—such as the Penitentiary, the Customs House, and the General Post Office in London—in the form of a thick layer or raft spread evenly over the whole site. Sir Marc Isambard Brunel (1769–1849) used Roman cement in the mortar for the Thames tunnel (1826–43) (p 463); but in the concrete filling that he dumped in the bed of the Thames to stop the break-through in 1828 he used Aspdin's cement. For repairs to a defective portion of the wall at Victoria Docks, London (1850–5), Portland cement concrete was used. The first really large-scale use of Portland cement however, was in the main drainage of London, by Sir Joseph Bazalgette (p 510); 70 000 tons were used, and 15 000 tests were made during the course of the work (1858–75) [7].

A material widely used instead of lime as the basis of a plaster for walls and ceilings was made by driving off part, but not the whole, of the water combined with calcium sulphate in the mineral gypsum. Beds of this material were worked in the Middle Ages at Montmartre and it was widely used in Paris—hence the name plaster of Paris. An early reference to gypsum plaster occurs in the mid-thirteenth century, when Henry III gave orders for its use in some work at

Nottingham Castle [8]. The alabaster of the Nottingham neighbourhood is a fine form of gypsum, and the waste and inferior grades of this material came to be burnt for plaster. Gypsum is also found, and since the Middle Ages has been worked, in Dorset, Yorkshire, and many other districts.

The main use of gypsum plaster was to give a smooth, clean finish, but both in France and in England it was used structurally in floors. In Paris in the 1840s fire-resisting ceilings were constructed by supporting plaster of Paris by means of wrought iron bars and joists, between and around which it was poured as shown in figure 247. The woodwork of the floor above the ceiling was thus protected from attack by fire in the room below. In the neighbourhood of Nottingham gypsum plaster was poured over a mat of reeds supported on floor-joists. The top of the plaster was smoothed to form the surface of the floor, which required no boards.

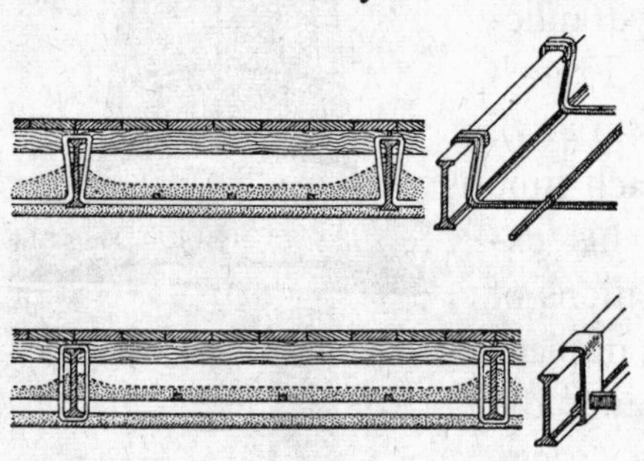

FIGURE 247—*French method of constructing iron floors.* c *1840.*

Ironwork. Iron as a structural material first became important during our period, and in two forms: wrought or malleable iron, a form of the metal in which impurities were few and incidental and made no marked change in its characteristic qualities, and cast iron, in which carbon was present to the extent of from 2 to 5 per cent. Part of the carbon in cast iron forms a carbide of iron, which adds considerably to the hardness and compressive strength of the material, and part exists as plate-like deposits of graphite which, by dividing one crystal of the metal from another, introduce planes of weakness that leave the metal brittle and of low tensile strength. Wrought iron when heated to redness becomes malleable, and can be hammered or rolled into shape. Cast iron melts at a temperature (about 1200° C) lower than the melting-point of wrought iron (1500 to 1600° C) and when fused can be run into moulds. It expands slightly on solidifying and thus reproduces the details of the mould.

In the late Middle Ages, and to a greater extent thereafter, fastenings of wrought iron were used to make or strengthen the joints of large and important structural frameworks of timber, such as roof trusses, but the metal was expensive. Bars forged to link together were used for such structural members as the chains round the bases of masonry domes.

Improvements in the availability of wrought iron in the eighteenth century made little difference in England to the direct use made of it by the builder or the structural engineer. In France, however, some bold experiments were made in the structural use of wrought iron, both to bind masonry together and give it tensile strength where needed, and to form the members of roof frameworks.

The burial of ironwork in masonry had one serious drawback: masonry is not entirely impervious to air and moisture, particularly at joints, and access of damp air to ironwork leads to the formation of rust. Rust occupies a much greater volume than the metal from which it is formed, and thus tends to force apart the masonry in which the iron is embedded. The consequent open joints or cracks are liable to let in more water and air, and the rate of corrosion is accelerated, with progressive expansion, extension of the damage, and the appearance of unsightly stains. These risks, added to the high price of iron, defeated the medieval builders who used the metal to tie together some of the slender masonry in early experimental Gothic work.

FIGURE 248—*Perronet's bridge across the Seine at Neuilly. 1768–74.*

At the Great Exhibition held in 1851 in Hyde Park, London, a large beam of brickwork, reinforced with hoop-iron laid in the horizontal mortar-joints, was displayed carrying an impressive load. Sir Marc Isambard Brunel had indeed been experimenting with this combination since 1832. The plaster ceilings with embedded iron rods, as constructed in Paris about this time, might almost be regarded as a primitive reinforced concrete; but the regular use of iron as a reinforcement, to relieve masonry of tensile stresses against which its resistance is weak, had to await the development of a concrete that could be made practically impervious to water and so retain its alkaline reaction, which inhibits corrosion. Such concrete became possible with the general introduction of Portland cement in the latter half of the nineteenth century.

Cast iron was used for cannon from the mid-sixteenth century: for fire-backs in the seventeenth. In 1684 Rannequin, at the famous waterworks at Marly-la-Machine, used cast iron for pipes and pump-barrels; so did George Sorocold in 1704 in water-works at London Bridge. Smeaton used it in gearing and other millwork in the 1750s. Late in the eighteenth century cast iron became of importance as a material for structures. It assumed great prominence in the first half of the nineteenth century, and then slowly faded out of the picture as its place was taken by other materials. In its manufacture, properties, and uses it is, as previously noted, a vastly different material from wrought iron.

III. ENGINEERING CONSTRUCTION

Bridges. The century under review was one of great expansion of trade and manufacture, for which existing means of communication and transport were inadequate. A great extension and improvement of the highway system, first in France, then in Britain, and later in western Europe and North America, called for bridges in places where previously fords and ferries had been acceptable. Navigable rivers came to be supplemented in Britain, as already in Italy, the Netherlands, and France, by canals. Increase in shipping, both in gross capacity

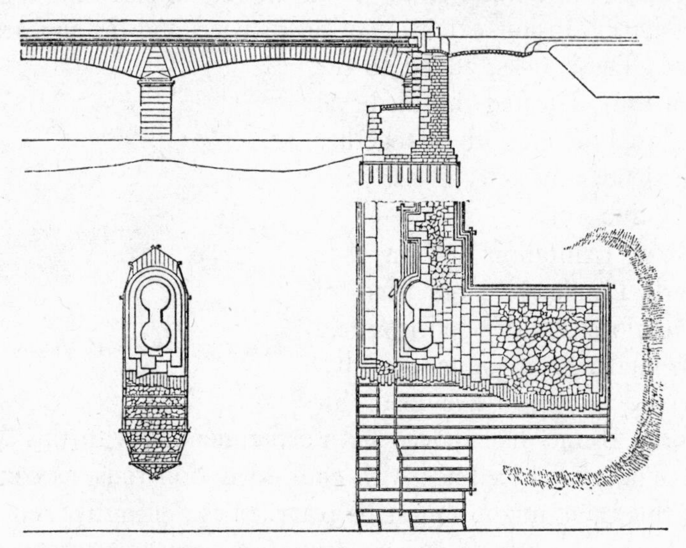

FIGURE 249—*Perronet's bridge at Ste-Maxence.* (Above) *elevation;* (below) *plan.*

and in the size of vessels, called for improved harbour facilities and justified expenditure on breakwaters, docks, and quays on an unprecedented scale. Towards the end of the period, railways, hitherto ancillary to canals, came first to rival and then to supersede them. All these developments called for construction that had to be planned, financed, and organized.

Bridge-building continued along the lines described in volume III, but with a tendency to lighter and bolder construction. The power of steam, first developed for the drainage of mines, was also available for the drainage of deep excavations, and before the end of the eighteenth century James Watt's rotative engines could be used to drive machinery, including winding- and hauling-gear. A steam-engine could be used to wind up the hammer to drive piles, or a direct steam-hammer (p 430) could be used. Without steam-power even the vast numbers of men recruited to build the railways could not have carried out the work so expeditiously, and some of it would have been impossible.

In France, from 1750 until the Revolution, many masonry bridges of advanced design and excellent workmanship were built by the engineers of the *Ponts et Chaussées* under Perronet's leadership. In comparison with the works of his predecessors, Perronet's bridges are characterized by flatter arches, shallower arch rings, and thinner piers. In these respects his work came to be regarded as bordering on the reasonably safe limit in masonry construction. The bridge across the Seine at Neuilly is shown in figure 248 as an example. Perronet was satisfied with an arch-ring of a thickness equal to about 1/24th of the span, a rise of crown above

FIGURE 250—*The centres for the bridge at Neuilly. 1768–74.*

springing at the Pont Ste-Maxence across the Oise a few miles north of Senlis of only 1/12th, and a pier-thickness of 1/10th of the span (figure 249).

Perronet's arch-centres were built up as shown in figure 250. They comprised in effect a multiple-ribbed timber arch to carry the thrust to the abutments or piers of permanent construction. The radial members were made in two pieces, halved so that when bolted together they embraced the arch-members and held them firmly in place. These centres were not well contrived to take any marked unevenness in loading, and were somewhat flexible. To strike the centre the bolts and fastenings were removed, and ropes were attached to the lower ends of the radial members. A sideways pull on the latter by winches on the banks, or in moored barges, caused the whole centre to collapse into the river.

An improved method of centring was devised by Robert Mylne (1734–1811). Mylne was the descendant of a line of masons to the Scottish crown. After qualifying as a master of his trade he studied in Rome for four years, returning in 1759 just in time to prepare the winning design for Blackfriars bridge, London, in competition with the leading practitioners. The award was undoubtedly deserved, but nevertheless aroused bitter jealousy and recrimination. Mylne's centring, shown in figure 251, embodied multiple wedges, which could be driven back when it was desired to lower the centre. Striking could be suspended if the consequent movement of the masonry aroused suspicion of weakness, whereas in Perronet's arrangement the first movement of the centre sealed its fate: there was no drawing back. The inclination of some of the members and the overall depth of the frame made Mylne's arrangement much more rigid than Perronet's, although it used less timber.

FIGURE 251—*Mylne's bridge over the Thames at Blackfriars, London. 1760–9. In the lower figure the centring is in position.*

At the outer face, the exposed voussoirs of the Blackfriars bridge were so cut as to butt against the masonry of the spandrel walls. Inside, an inverted arch was built to transmit the thrust from one span to the next. The junction between the main and the inverted arches was somewhat crude and weak, but the intention was sound. The elliptical form of the arch at Blackfriars bridge was a novelty in British bridge-building. The largest of the nine spans was 100 ft. The bases of the piers were in caissons, the bottoms of which rested on piles.

The *Ponts et Chaussées* had developed the form of contract under which a single contractor tendered a lump sum for the whole work on a bridge to a strict specification and bill of quantities, as is still customary in public works. The general contractor had not yet emerged in Britain, and Mylne had to let masonry, carpentry, smith-work, ballast-work, and so forth to different contractors. He drew 5 per cent on their bills. The bridge was opened to traffic in 1769, and only in 1869 was it replaced by the present wrought iron, arched bridge.

Before Blackfriars bridge was finished Mylne had been appointed surveyor to St Paul's Cathedral and to Canterbury Cathedral, and had designed the Jamaica bridge at Glasgow. In 1770 he became engineer to the New River Company. He also reported on harbours, canals, and water-works in various parts of the country. He was a founder-member of the Associated Architects, London, from 1791, and designed some country houses. He was the last British architect of note to be at the same time an eminent civil engineer.

John Rennie (1761–1821) graduated to bridge-building from millwrighting. He adopted and improved upon Mylne's form of bridge centring, and also the combined inverted arch and springing between adjacent spans. His most famous masonry bridges were Waterloo bridge, London—completed in 1817—(figures 252, 253 B) and the present London Bridge (figure 253 A), which in 1831 took the place of the medieval bridge. The foundations of these bridges were on piles, and were built within coffer-dams. Rennie distrusted the caisson: he preferred to see

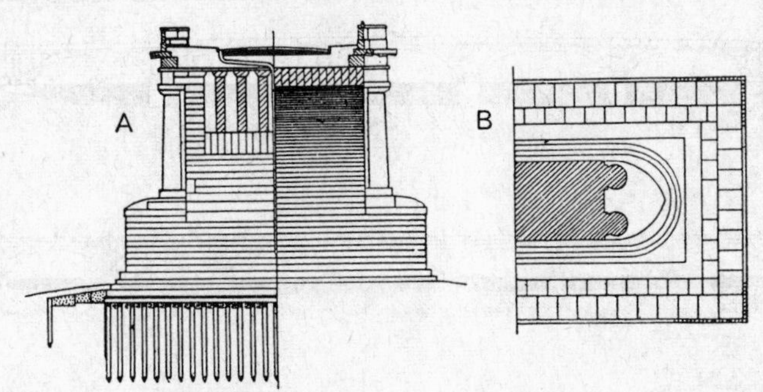

FIGURE 252—*Rennie's Waterloo bridge.* (A) *Cross-section of pier and arch;* (B) *plan through pier.*

the bottom upon which his work would rest. He built harbours, canals, and a variety of buildings, and simultaneously with Thomas Telford (p 444) developed in Britain the system whereby one main contractor undertook the responsibility for the work of all trades employed on one engineering project, however large or complex.

The first important structural use of cast iron was in the bridge that crosses the Severn at Ironbridge, near Coalbrookdale (plate 30 A). The credit for instigating this venture has usually been given to John Wilkinson, the famous iron-master of Bersham. It is true that Wilkinson in 1775 took some of the original shares, but he sold them to Abraham Darby III (1750–91) long before the actual bridge was even designed. Credit for the design has likewise been given to T. F. Pritchard, a Shrewsbury architect. Pritchard did, in fact, produce a design for an iron bridge, but not that to which the actual bridge was built. The design, casting, and erection of the bridge were undertaken and completed by Darby, who also bore more than half the expense of the venture [9]. The bridge, of which an artist's impression is shown in plate 30 A, is nearly semi-circular. The span is 100 ft 6 in, and the rise 45 ft. There are five main ribs 12 in by $6\frac{1}{2}$ inches in section, virtually hinged at the springing and at the crown; there are also lighter incomplete ribs and connecting members. The castings for the main ribs were 70 ft long. They were cast in open sand direct from a blast-furnace, which had to be built for the purpose; the remains of the furnace, though probably altered and now partly buried in a spoil-tip, still exist (p 117, tailpiece). The parts of the bridge were so arranged as either to pass through, or to mortise into, one another, and were secured by wedges. No bolts or rivets were used. The procedure for erection was rehearsed on a wooden model, now in the Science Museum, London, for which in 1788 the Society of Arts awarded a gold medal. The main rib-castings are said to have been brought to the site by water, secured

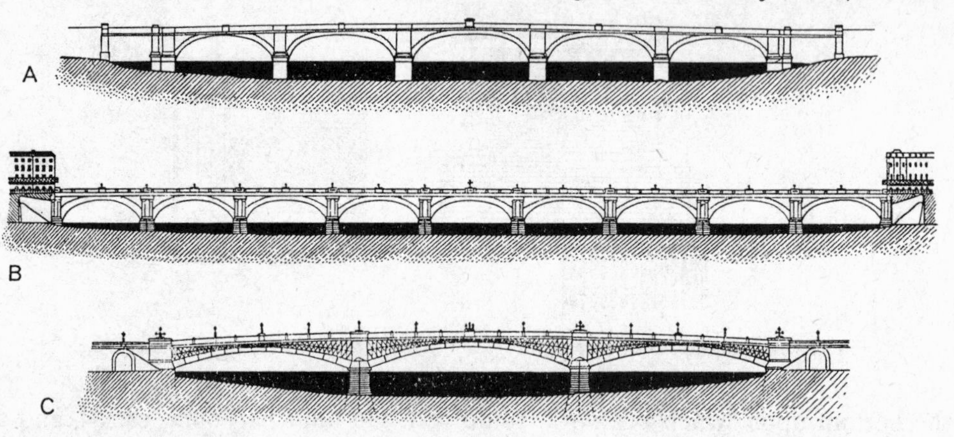

FIGURE 253—*Rennie's bridges over the Thames:* (A) *London, 1824–31;* (B) *Waterloo, 1811–17;* (C) *Southwark, 1814–19.*

in position at the foot, and hoisted up by ropes, both halves simultaneously, and joined together at the crown. The total weight of iron work, including deck, is stated by Telford to have been 378 tons. The arrangement of the secondary members shows, as would be expected for that date, no clear appreciation of their specific functions.

The abutment on the left-hand (east) side of the river is against a solid bank, and the approach for traffic is across a masonry arch. That on the right-hand (west) side is on lower ground, probably alluvial, and started to move towards the river soon after the bridge was completed. The masonry and earth-filling behind the main abutment pier were removed and wooden approach spans erected. Within forty years these were showing signs of decay, and were replaced by cast iron arch-spans which still remain, although they have been repaired. There has been some recent movement of the eastern abutment, causing cracks in the masonry which have had to be grouted. However, the bridge still stands after 180 years: a notable example of a pioneer venture and a monument to the courage and structural sense of Abraham Darby and his associates. It has been scheduled as an ancient monument, and is now used by foot traffic only.

In 1787 Thomas Telford became surveyor to the county of Shropshire, and as such assumed responsibility for the care and, where needed, the provision of bridges. Some of these he built in stone, but his curiosity was naturally aroused by the iron bridge at Coalbrookdale. When the old stone bridge of several arches at Buildwas on the Severn, a few miles above Coalbrookdale, was swept away by flood in 1795, he decided to replace it by one of iron arch construction, of the form shown in figure 254. The span was 130 ft, but the bridge weighed only 173 tons, showing a considerable economy on the Coalbrookdale design. The sup-

FIGURE 254—*Telford's iron bridge at Buildwas. 1795.*

port of the deck from the ribs by vertical members braced together was also an improvement, but the attempt to combine two different depths of rib was not. They behaved differently under both load and changes of temperature, cracked, and had to be repaired with fish-plates. When the plating was tightly fitted the rib cracked at some other place, until in the end the bridge had to be left alone, loosely held with fish-plates, to find its own adjustment. It lasted, however, until 1906.

A more manageable design than the solid arch rib for longer spans was the type erected in 1796 over the river Wear to connect Sunderland and Monkwearmouth. The span was 236 ft, the rise 34 ft; and the construction was of six segmental ribs each virtually consisting of 125 open-work cast iron voussoirs and wrought iron straps (figure 255 and plate 29). The builders were Walker's, the iron-founders of Rotherham, in association with Rowland Burdon—M.P. for Sunderland—who took out a patent for this type of construction (B.P. No 2066, 1795). It has often been stated that the design was due to Tom Paine, the revolutionary, who, on a mission from the United States of America, spent some time at Walker's negotiating for an iron bridge to be made by them and exported. Paine did take out a British Patent (No 1667, 1788), but he was in no sense an engineer, and the crude construction described in his patent bears little resemblance to that of the Sunderland bridge. Part of a small-span bridge to Paine's design was erected for exhibition at St Pancras, but this was broken up when he dropped his project and went to take part in the French Revolution.

In 1798 Telford, in association with James Douglas, proposed to replace Old London Bridge by a cast iron arch construction with 600 ft in a single span. It was estimated to require 6500 tons of cast iron; the abutments were to consist of 432 000 cu ft of granite and 20 000 cu ft of brickwork. How, or even whether, this vast weight could have been supported by any foundation-technique then available is conjectural. Fortunately for Telford the project was turned down, but it led to a most interesting theoretical discussion, to which reference will be made later (p 484 and tailpiece).

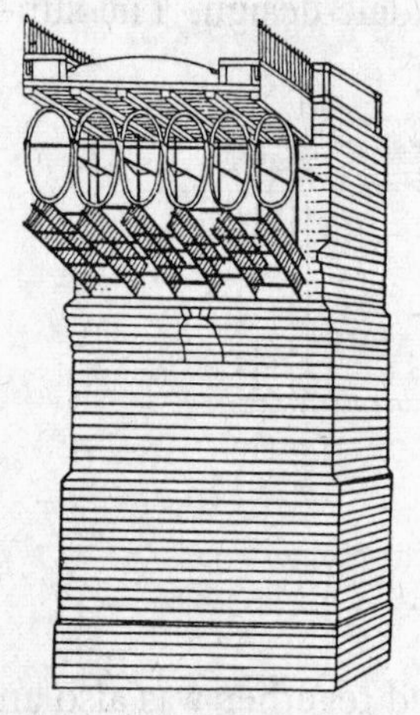

FIGURE 255—*Burdon's iron bridge over the Wear at Sunderland, showing construction. 1796.*

After a lull, caused by the wars with France, the construction of iron bridges was resumed. The general type comprised a number of parallel segmental arch ribs, with a lattice-work, or grid, of bars above to support the deck, cast either with the rib or separately, according to the size of the bridge. Cross-bracing between the parallel systems ensured stability. It was presumably realized that the rings above the ribs of the Coalbrookdale and Sunderland bridges were not an efficient device to carry a vertical load, for they were not repeated. Telford built a number of such bridges; so did John Rennie, the greatest being Southwark bridge, London, erected between 1814 and 1819, with a central span of 240 ft and two rather shorter side-spans (figure 253 C). The segmental iron ribs were of I-section, 6 to 8 ft deep and 2¾ in thick, with flanges 4 in wide. Thirteen castings, end to end, fixed to one another with taper-keys, formed each arch: they acted rather like the voussoirs of a masonry arch. The ironwork was cast by Walker's of Rotherham and weighed about 5800 tons. The bridge was replaced in 1922 by the present Southwark bridge, which is of steel arch construction.

The suspension bridge naturally attracted the attention of American bridge-builders, for at this time they had poor facilities for making large castings and forgings and yet rapidly growing centres of population were in many places separated by wide rivers. The suspension bridge with a stiffened deck seems to have been contrived by Judge James Finley (*c* 1762–1828) of Pennsylvania, who built a number of them in the first decade of the nineteenth century, and obtained a patent in 1808. One, of which the towers still stand and carry the bridge as rebuilt in 1909, had a span of 244 ft.

While Southwark bridge was still under construction several suspension bridges were erected in the south of Scotland, where winter floods were liable to undermine the masonry piers of arches. The greatest of these, of 300-ft span, was completed in 1820 by Captain Samuel Brown, and crossed the Tweed at Kelso. It had twelve chains consisting of iron links 2 inches in diameter and 15 ft long, with an eye-bar at each end bolted to flat links. The piers and abutments were built on rock clear of flood-level. In 1817 Brown took out a patent for flat wrought iron links. Telford had been experimenting with links consisting of bundles of small rods welded together at the ends, but on learning of Brown's links he adopted them for the chains of his famous bridge, of 580 ft span, to carry the Holyhead road across the Menai Straits.

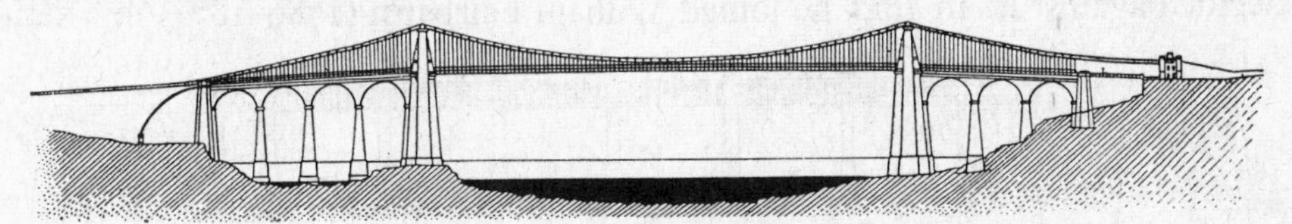

FIGURE 256—*Telford's Menai bridge, 1826.*

Work on the bridge over the Menai Straits began in 1820 and finished in 1826 (figure 256). The deck was of timber and unstiffened: it was wrecked in 1839 by a storm. A heavier timber deck lasted till 1893, when Sir Benjamin Baker reconstructed it in steel. This in turn was replaced in 1940, when the chains also were renewed in high-tensile steel; indeed, except for the towers and abutments, the present structure is a new bridge.

In 1834 Joseph Chailey, a French engineer, built a suspension bridge over the river Sarine at Fribourg, Switzerland, with a span of 870 ft; the deck was suspended by cables each comprising 1000 wires bound together with wire wrapping. It lasted 90 years.

Famous among the American pioneers in this field was Charles Ellet, who made his cables on the French system of bundles of small wires. In 1848 he broke what was then the record for length with a bridge of 1010-ft span across the river Ohio at Wheeling, West Virginia. In 1854 this bridge was seriously damaged by a tornado. Ellet's towers remained, and the rest of the bridge was rebuilt by John August Roebling, who later achieved fame by his own record-breaking activities in building long-span suspension bridges of wire cable. In 1956 the Wheeling bridge was again under repair. Ellet's towers and anchorages, and Roebling's cables and suspenders, were to be retained, but the deck was to be entirely renewed.

Although some suspension bridges were still giving good service in the 1840s, many had collapsed through the buffeting effect of winds, or even through oscillations built up by the impact of marching troops or droves of cattle. Brown had built many, and had quite a number of failures, including his bridge of 449-ft span across the Tweed at Berwick; this he completed in 1820, but it was blown down only six months later. In 1830 he had even built one to carry the Stockton and Darlington railway across the Tees, only to find that the train sank down and raised before and behind it a wave in the deck, which racked the bridge to pieces in a few years. By the use of stiffening girders, which, however, sacrificed some of the lightness that was the outstanding merit of this type of bridge, such a defect could be mitigated, but for railway work Robert Stephenson decided against it. In 1845 he joined William Fairbairn (1789–1874) in a series

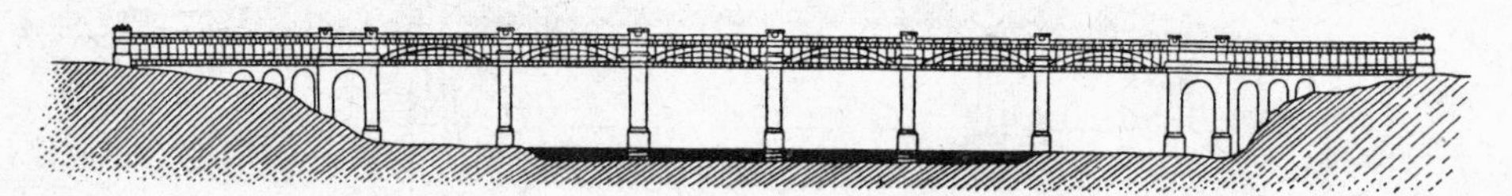

FIGURE 257—*Robert Stephenson's high-level bridge, Newcastle upon Tyne. 1846–9.*

of experiments on wrought iron girders, to determine the best form these could take for a long-span bridge, in particular for the bridge that would carry the Chester and Holyhead railway across the Menai Straits within sight of Telford's road-bridge.

Wrought iron plates and angles, riveted together, were in general use for steam-boilers at this time. There seemed no reason why this technique should not be used to build up bridge-girders of considerable size once a suitable form was decided upon. Experiments were made on tubes, and eventually it was decided to build rectangular tubes through which the trains would pass, the tops and bottoms of the tubes being themselves cellular. The test specimens worked up to a model of one-sixth of the full size before the design was made final. This bridge, however, must be regarded as the first of the next period, rather than as the last of that covered by this volume, and accordingly its construction will be described in volume V.

Although wrought iron eventually replaced cast iron as the approved material for railway-bridges before itself being superseded by mild steel, many bridges were built of cast iron in the 1840s, and some of these are still in service. There were, however, failures, and in 1848 a royal commission was appointed, which reported in 1849 upon 'The Application of Iron to Railway Structures'. Much evidence was collected, and experiments were carried out by Eaton Hodgkinson and others, but the conclusions favoured conservative design, and, in the case of cast iron, recommended adhering to the arch and beam forms of construction. There was indeed as yet no developed theory of structures upon which the design of framed girders could be based, and the commission advised against their use. This did not, however, deter the more adventurous from experimenting with these and other forms. Neuville, a Belgian engineer, had in 1846 erected a bridge with an open frame comprising horizontal top and bottom booms, joined by diagonal members set at 60° so as to form in elevation a chain of equilateral triangles. In 1848 Captain James Warren and W. T. Manzoni took out a British Patent (No 12242 of 1848) for such a construction assembled either from separate members, or from castings in which the top boom and two dia-

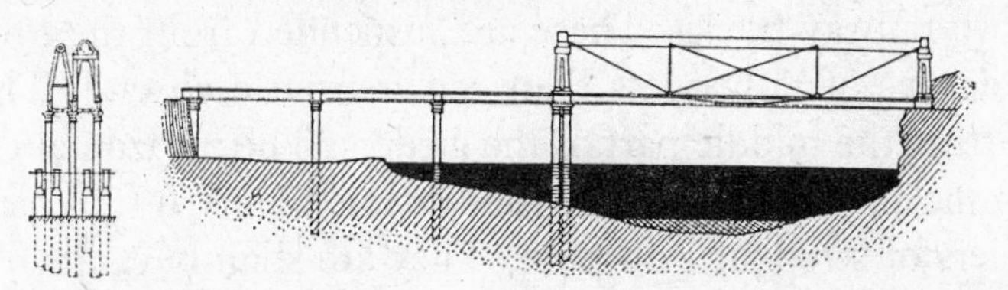

FIGURE 258—*Section and elevation of I. K. Brunel's bridge across the Wye at Chepstow, 1849–52.*

gonal members of one bay formed a triangular unit and the bottom boom in each bay was a wrought iron rod threaded to take nuts at both ends. Such girders became known as Warren girders in England, and as Neuville girders on the continent.

The most notable cast iron[1] railway-bridge is Robert Stephenson's high-level bridge at Newcastle upon Tyne, erected in 1849 (figure 257). It consists of six spans, and the distance between the centres of the piers is 139 ft. Each span takes the form of a tied arch, the railway being carried just above the crown level; there is a roadway, and there was later a tramway, at the level of the tie. This bridge still carries main-line and road traffic, now far heavier than that for which it was originally intended. The piles in the foundations were driven by means of a Nasmyth steam-hammer (p 431), which delivered one blow a second as against the one blow every few minutes previously possible.

Isambard Kingdom Brunel (1806–59), the builder of the Great Western railway, nicknamed the 'Commission on the Application of Iron to Railway Structures' the 'Commission for Stopping Further Improvement in Bridge Building'. He built many bridges in wrought iron, masonry, and timber, of which perhaps the most original was his bridge across the Wye at Chepstow (figure 258). Con-

[1] Some wrought iron was also used in this bridge: for instance, for the suspension rods concealed within the vertical cast iron members.

siderable head-room had to be left for navigation, and, as the river is subject at times to a 40-ft tidal range, ample precautions were needed against scour. He therefore made his main span across the normal river-bed 300 ft long.

The use of compressed-air caissons to permit foundations to be sunk through water-logged ground had been introduced in 1830 by Sir Thomas Cochrane, and they were used in 1851 by Cubitt and Wright to sink the cylinder-piers for Rochester bridge across the Medway to a depth of 61 ft. Brunel used the method at Chepstow in 1852 to sink the cylinders that form the piers of the bridge, six of them carrying the cast iron tower (figure 258) at the west end of the main span. The tower at the east end of this span is of masonry, built on the rock of the natural cliff. The deck is carried by four wrought iron girders, one on each side of each of the two railway tracks. These are suspended from the towers by link-chains, at distances of rather less than 100 ft from each end. The chains are continued to truss the middle part of the girders. The horizontal component of the tension in the chain is resisted by tubular top booms, 9 ft in diameter, made like huge boilers of wrought iron plate. They are slightly cambered and intermediately supported at two points. In some ways the Chepstow bridge served as a trial run for the design and methods of construction Brunel employed in the greater bridge over the Tamar at Saltash.

Tunnels. Tunnelling has long been an important branch of engineering construction, having previously been a regular practice in mining. Even before the Christian era lakes in the craters of volcanoes were drained by Roman engineers, who cut tunnels through solid lava. Medieval fortresses are known to have been reduced by tunnelling under corner towers, and then setting fire to the shoring that held up the roof. The Languedoc canal, built between 1661 and 1681, included tunnels in its course; there was a summit-tunnel over 500 ft in length cut through solid rock. Brindley adopted the same expedient in his eighteenth-century English canals. Tunnelling in rock was arduous; but the rock-face and roof, at least in small tunnels, were usually self-supporting. When a tunnel was driven through soft, wet ground, precautions to avoid collapse were imperative but sometimes extremely difficult to execute. The Tronquoy tunnel on the St-Quentin canal in France is said to have been 'the first in which a system of timbering and arching for supporting loose and soft ground had to be devised for a wide tunnel' [10].

There are several ways of tunnelling. In one, for instance, work is begun at the top: a narrow heading is driven forward from the face for a predetermined distance. A heavy timber is then drawn forward at a level just above the roof of the finished tunnel-lining. Its forward end is supported by a short post which bears on a short sill on the bottom of the heading; its rear end is wedged up from the section of roof last completed. If necessary, short boards can be driven above and at right-angles to the main timber. Other main timbers or 'bars' are placed in the same manner, until the whole roof is supported. The gaps above the completed lining, out of which the bars have been drawn forward, are packed and filled. The new lengths of arched roof and sides are built, and, if the bottom requires it, inverted arches or 'inverts' as well. Then another length of heading can be driven and the bars moved forward again, one at a time.

In tunnelling under a river there is the added risk that a break-through may flood the workings. Such a catastrophe brought an end to the attempt by Richard Trevithick (1771–1833) to drive a tunnel-heading about 3 ft wide by 5 ft high under the Thames with timber shoring; the disaster happened after he had cut his way for nearly 1000 ft. The feat of first tunnelling beneath the Thames was finally achieved by Sir Marc Isambard Brunel, father of Isambard Kingdom Brunel, who served him as resident engineer. Brunel made use of a shield that provided working-space for twelve men side by side at each of three levels, working on a rectangular face 38 ft wide by 22 ft 6 in deep (figure 259). Each group of three working-spaces, one above another, was within a cast iron frame, with a flat top and foot each hinged to the body; and there were two intermediate platforms. Large screw-jacks at head and foot bore against the completed masonry and held the edges of the shield tightly against the working face. Small screw-jacks bore against the verticals of the shield and held boards against the face, except where it was actually being cut.

FIGURE 259—*A portion of the shield used by Brunel to drive the Thames tunnel. 1826–43.*

The tunnel started from a vertical shaft 50 ft in diameter at the Rotherhithe end, and dipped slightly, on a slope of 2 ft 3 inches in 300 ft, towards the middle, where the base of the excavation was 76 ft below high-water level. The shield was placed in position on 1 January 1826, and at first worked in London clay, but within a month the workings had been carried forward into water-bearing sand and gravel not disclosed in the survey. This seriously impeded progress. As the shield worked forward 18 in at a time it was followed by a double-arched tunnel of masonry, built with Roman cement. In May 1827, and again in January 1828, the river broke in. The holes in the river-bed were attacked from a diving-bell above, plugged with Portland-cement concrete, and filled in with bags of clay; but after the second flooding the face was blocked off, and work was suspended for seven years.

After resumption of work with a heavier shield there were three more serious floodings, but at last, on 26 May 1843, the tunnel was completed and opened to foot-traffic (plate 32 A) [11]. It was ultimately taken over for the railway line that connects Whitechapel and New Cross, and is still used by the electric trains of London Transport.

IV. MARINE WORKS

Harbours were required for two purposes: to shelter ships caught in stormy weather off a lee shore, and to provide ports for the landing and embarkation of cargo and passengers. In the days of sail it was very important that there should be harbours of refuge where ships making a landfall could find shelter until the wind changed. Such harbours might also be ports, but not necessarily so: some were needed in localities where there was little or no trade. If a harbour, natural or artificial, were available, however, it would nearly always be used by, or give rise to, a local fishing industry. On a rocky, deeply indented shore some shelter could generally be found in bays partially enclosed by capes and islands, and often only a short breakwater was needed to augment existing natural protection. A port was a more complicated matter. Vessels might have to shelter there in large numbers and for long periods. Quays in still water were preferable for ships and essential for lighters. Early ports, therefore, were nearly always situated within the mouths of rivers, or even some distance upstream, where facilities were available for settlement and for land- or river-transport to other populated areas.

A breakwater, as the name implies, is intended to resist the force of the waves, so that comparatively calm water will be available for anchorage on its lee side. Resistance can be provided in one or other of two forms: a solid mass against which the waves beat and rebound ineffectively; or a long slope up which they run until their energy is dissipated in friction by rolling shingle up and down and by the interference of flow and return. In Nature these take the forms of rocky cliff and storm-beach respectively.

The force of waves depends largely on the 'fetch', that is, the direct distance from land over which the surface of the water has been exposed to a steady wind. On an ocean coast this distance may be immense, and waves of enormous height may have to be resisted. The most important 'fetch' is that of the prevailing wind. In the neighbourhood of Cape Horn waves in the Pacific Ocean have been reputed to reach a height of 50 ft with a distance from crest to crest of 600 to 1000 ft. Only vast masses of the hardest natural rock can withstand their onslaught, and only at the cost of continual erosion by the battery of stones hurled at them by the immense waves. The greatest fragments stand in the steepest

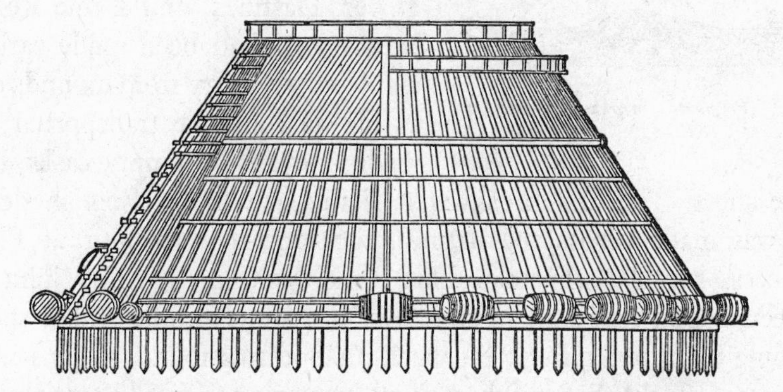

FIGURE 260—*One of Cessart's cones for Cherbourg harbour breakwater. 1780.*

heaps; the smaller are stable only on less steep slopes. Artificial breakwaters can be made to stand only on the same principles.

The port of Cherbourg is an artificial harbour, needing protection from up-Channel storms. An attempt was made by Louis de Cessart (1719–1806) to construct a breakwater of giant caissons of timber, like huge inverted tubs, floated into position by casks, and sunk by filling with rock. There was to be an open channel around both ends, but behind the breakwater the French fleet operating in the English Channel could take refuge, protected from foul weather by the breakwater, and from English privateers by the coastal defence batteries that were to be erected on it. Work was begun in 1780. The caissons (figure 260) were 70 ft high, and tapered in diameter from 150 ft at the base to 60 ft at the top. 45 000 cu ft of timber were required to build each one. They were towed into position by rowing-boats, then submerged by loading with stones and connected by a bank of stone [12].

The cost in labour and money was immense, and in 1788, when 18 cones had been placed, orders were issued to discontinue the work. The cones broke up and the stones were spilled on the sea-bed. They stood at a slope of 1 in 3 in deep water, but between high and low water the bank was dragged down by the waves to a slope of 1 in 10, and would stand no steeper however much material was added. When a stable profile had apparently been achieved, forts were built on a bed of blocks that weighed 3 or 4 tons each, but in 1812, and again in 1824, they were destroyed by storms. Eventually Vicat produced a hydraulic lime by the use of which a concrete causeway was built on top of the bank, faced and capped with coarse masonry from low-tide level to 3 metres above high-tide level. This work was successfully completed in 1850.

Nothing nearly so ambitious had been attempted off the English coast. At Dover, Hastings, and Lyme Regis small breakwaters had been made early in the eighteenth century from mounds of stones as big as could be transported on rafts made buoyant by empty casks, but their lives were short. The first breakwater of any size on the English side of the Channel was made across the natural, rock-enclosed harbour at Plymouth, leaving access round both ends. This work was undertaken by John Rennie. It had been hoped that a great mound of limestone rubble would stand with sides sloping at about 1 in 3; but such a slope was found to be stable only in deep water. Blocks that weighed about 10 tons each would stand at a slope of about 1 in 5. In the end the whole bank, when stabilized, assumed the profile shown in figure 261, similar to that finally assumed by the breakwater at Cherbourg. The mass of the interior was of smaller stones. Finally, the top was paved with granite blocks set in cement. Although a stable shape would be reached, individual stones would be dragged down the slope or thrown over the crest were such a finish omitted: consequently a good deal of replenishment of surface stones would be needed after storms. This work was begun in 1812 and finished in 1841.

FIGURE 261 — *Plymouth breakwater (section). 1812–41.*

There are, or have been, many small ports along the coasts of Kent and Sussex, but the current in the English Channel carries a considerable drift of solid matter in suspension, consisting of silt or gravel derived from the gradual erosion of coastal cliffs. Most of these ports have become choked with this matter, and their deterioration has in some cases been hastened by man. The river Rother was at one time tidal far inland, and the incoming waters flooded a wide area behind the town of Rye. On the ebb, the accumulation of water, rushing through the narrow channel beside the town, kept the course clear. Sluices and dikes designed to keep the tide from drowning the flats made it possible to reclaim valuable land for agriculture, but they robbed the port of its scouring current.

Similarly, the construction of flood-gates at Stonar to divert the storm-water that formerly scoured the bed of the Stour at Sandwich led to the silting-up of that port.

Ramsgate is an entirely artificial port, and has to be artificially kept clear. A harbour of refuge is needed on this part of the coast for shipping caught in the Roads by a northerly gale, against which the Goodwin Sands afford no protection. Labelye, and later Smeaton, were consulted regarding the harbour works undertaken at various times, and the work was eventually completed by Smeaton. The outer basin, nearly enclosed by two curved arms projecting from the coast, was rapidly choking with silt when Smeaton reported upon it in 1774. A quarter of a million cu yds had already settled, and the removal of 70 cu yds daily by two barges, each manned by ten men, was failing sadly to cope with the accumulation. The successful scheme was to enclose an inner basin of about 42 acres, let this fill with water at high tide, and discharge its contents at low tide through one or other of six sluices (figure 262). In the path of the current a barge was manœuvred so that the rush of water under and around it would scour a wide channel. At this state of tide the current passing the entrance to the harbour carried away the washings.

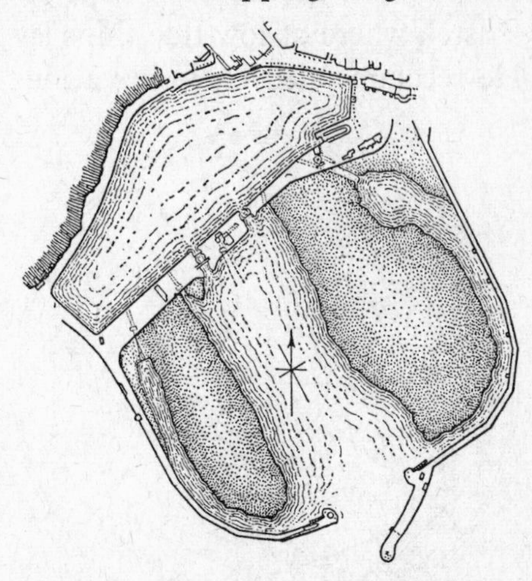

FIGURE 262—*Ramsgate harbour*, c *1800. Inner and outer basins are separated by a wall through which pass two gated channels and six sluice-ducts. Water released by the sluices at low tide scours the navigable channels between which are mud-banks on which vessels lie aground.*

Until the closing years of the eighteenth century little had been done to provide docks within which vessels could ride at any state of tide. Anchored in the rivers, vessels settled at low tide on mud-banks. With the riverside open to everyone, petty thieving was rife, and on the Thames robbery on a large scale was carried out by organized gangs. The Thames Police were instituted in 1798, but their task was practically impossible until enclosed docks were built. On the Surrey side, the Howland Great Dock was completed in 1700 by John Wells for the whaling-fleet. The first on the north side, opened in 1802, were the West India Docks, constructed in Poplar by William Jessop, a pupil of Smeaton. These were followed in 1808 by the East India Docks. The London Docks in Wapping—nearer the City—were constructed between 1801 and 1805 by John

Rennie, who introduced cast iron columns and roofs for dock warehouses, and steam-operated cranes on the quayside for loading and unloading the ships.

The first dock in Liverpool, on the site of what had been the original Pool, was built by William Steers between 1710 and 1715. In 1826 it was filled in and the Customs House built over it. Smeaton was consulted about the port of Bristol, where at low tide ships lay right in the heart of the city on river mud. He recommended enclosing a long bend of the river between lock-gates and cutting a by-pass for the river Avon. This work was eventually carried out between 1803 and 1808 by William Jessop. Rennie was consulted in 1799 about the Clyde at Glasgow, where various schemes had been suggested and some river-training works constructed. Rennie recommended docks at Broomielaw, and a dredged channel thence to the sea. The dredged channel was eventually completed, but the dock scheme was not.

FIGURE 263—*The fifteenth course of masonry in Smeaton's Eddystone lighthouse, 1759.*

For the guidance of ships at night, whether they are making a port or avoiding a dangerous coast or reef, lighthouses are essential. Generally they are on headlands or islands; but occasionally one is needed on some isolated rock that lies too near for safety to a shipping lane or the approach to a harbour. Such was the Eddystone rock, lying about fifteen miles south-west of Plymouth. Twice before our period, lighthouses, built mainly of timber, had been built on the rock, but the first was destroyed by the exceptionally severe gales that swept along the south-west coast of England in November 1703, spreading havoc and desolation, and the second by fire in 1755.

Smeaton was asked to design and superintend the construction of the third Eddystone lighthouse. He realized that the structure must have sufficient mass to resist very heavy buffeting by storms straight off the Atlantic, and as no means could have been devised to transport single blocks of sufficient mass, he had every stone cut to dove-tail with its neighbour so that, when grouted in with a strong hydraulic mortar, every course would act virtually as a solid disk of stone (figure 263). The lower courses consisted partly of the solid rock itself. The stones of each course were also drilled and pegged to those of the course above and below by oak pegs or trenails, giving further solidity to the structure. This method, aided by the tree-like profile Smeaton gave to the tower, proved successful (figure 264). Smeaton's lighthouse tower had to be replaced in 1882, but not through any fault in the structure itself. Even by choosing the highest part of the rock for his foundation, Smeaton had had great difficulty in excavating for the lower courses in the open, because of the few hours a day during which work was possible even in fine weather. That highest part was slightly overhanging, and as erosion below proceeded with the years, fears were felt for the safety of the tower. Another has since been built alongside, using a coffer-dam and techniques not developed in Smeaton's day. Smeaton's pioneer effort has been re-erected on Plymouth Hoe as a fitting memorial to his enterprise and courage.

FIGURE 264 — *Smeaton's Eddystone lighthouse, 1759. Partially in section.*

V. BUILDINGS

The pages of a history of technology do not provide the ideal setting for a discussion of aesthetics, but as building, particularly in the period under review, cannot be considered without reference to architecture, and as architecture was regarded as a fine art, some reference must be made to the aesthetic attitude of those whose buildings are characteristic of their day.

The construction of the great churches, which the thought of medieval architecture immediately calls to mind, was essentially functional. The master-mason designed, constructed, and lived with his building. Whether the structural designs, growing ever bolder from the tenth to the fifteenth century, were coaxed out of the designer by the demand of the ecclesiastical patron for more daylight and more coloured glass, or whether the patron merely seized the opportunity presented to him by the designer, driven by his own desire for ever neater and more economical structural forms, could be argued indefinitely. No doubt each tendency reinforced the other, but there is nothing to suggest that either party was driven or pursued by any theory as to what would be beautiful.

With the Renaissance all this was changed. The building façade, developed by Greek architects, had been formalized by the Romans, codified by Vitruvius, and brought to perfection by designers of buildings in the high Renaissance, particularly by Andrea Palladio (1518–80). Beauty was thought to be inherent in certain geometrical forms and proportions, as it was in the harmony of musical notes the vibration-periods of which were in appropriate numerical ratio. Beauty was supposedly intrinsic in any architectural composition that embodied the rules. By the time Palladio published his great work [13], Italian architects were already tiring of the restraints imposed by these rules, but their influence persisted in France for another century. They actually became dominant in English architecture in the eighteenth century, largely through the influence of Richard Boyle, third Earl of Burlington (1695–1753), who sponsored an English translation of Palladio (1715) and acted as patron to a number of promising young men

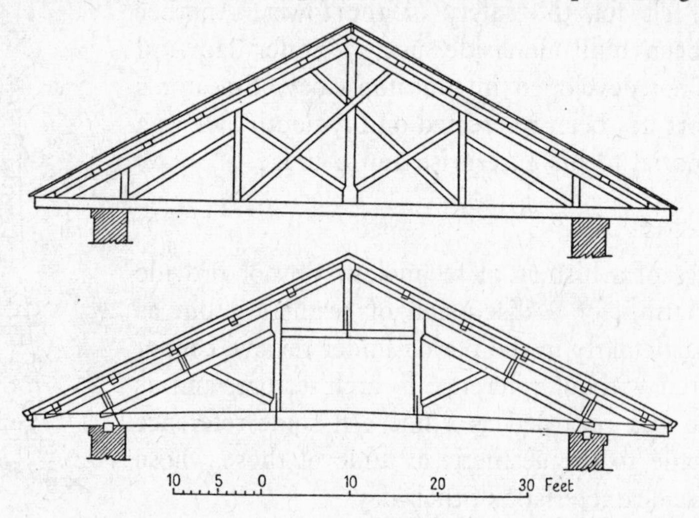

FIGURE 265—*Roof of St Paul's Church, Covent Garden.* (Above) *1636;* (below) *1796.*

such as Colin Campbell, William Kent, and Henry Flitcroft. He sent them to study, as he had done himself, in Italy, and set the fashion in England for public buildings and gentlemen's country houses in the Palladian style (plate 30 B). John Wood (1707–64) and his son of the same name (1727–82) replanned Bath in that style. It was not long before the rules were reduced to copy-book presentation by authors such as Michael Hoare (who wrote under the pseudonym of William Halfpenny) and Batty Langley, 'carpenter and architect'. With the aid of these books an ambitious craftsman could even set himself up as an architect, or at least build correctly to architect's drawings incompletely detailed.

Buildings designed in accordance with Palladio's rules were dignified, but they lacked variety or originality. Both architects and patrons tired of them in time, and in Britain early in the nineteenth century, and much sooner on the continent, movements were set on foot to adopt alternatives. Such movements involved the repudiation of the theory that beauty was intrinsic in objects: beauty was believed to be in the eye of the beholder. Objects which aroused certain associations were beautiful to those in whose minds these associations were emotionally powerful and pleasant. If certain things were widely acclaimed as objects of beauty, that was because a common outlook and culture disposed people to find the same associations pleasant. If, then, one admired Gothic buildings one need not be written down a savage; nor was it monstrous to repudiate Palladio and go back

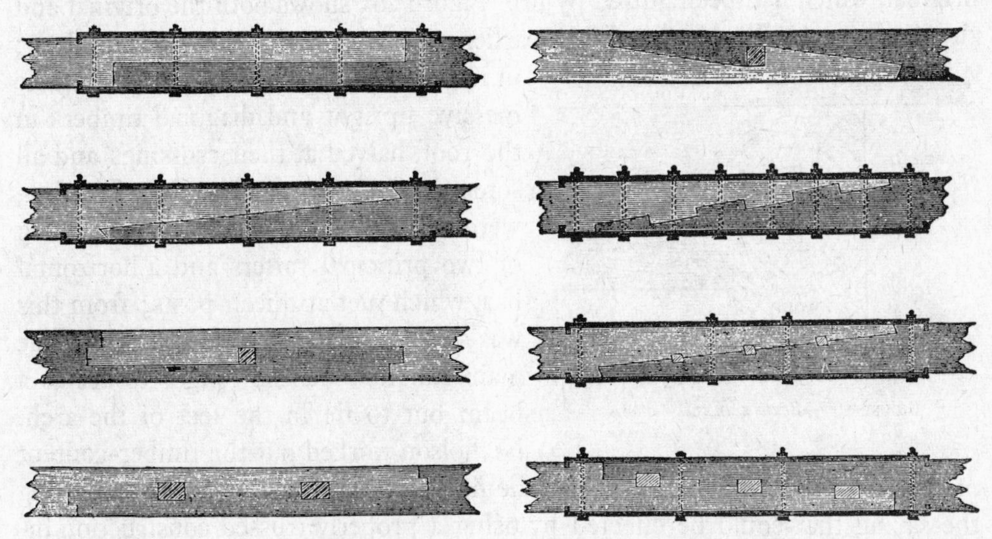

FIGURE 266—*Scarfed joints in timber ties.*

for inspiration to the original classic Greeks, who knew nothing of Palladio's rules.

The Renaissance, however, had done its work only too well, separating those who built into gentlemen and players. The architect was a scholar—a man of the drawing-board. The master-craftsman still directed the actual work of building, and the training of apprentices in his own trade, but he was no longer permitted to design. Unless he thoroughly assimilated the copy-book and took to speculative building in the growing towns, as naturally many did, he must be content to operate as a contractor. Details of construction were often left to the master-craftsman; in carpentry, for instance, the general use of sawn softwood in place of axe-dressed hardwood led to considerable modification of traditional practice. Medieval joists and purlins were often square in section, and even if oblong were often laid with the broad side flat. Galileo (1638) showed that the strength of a beam was proportional to its breadth and to the square of its depth, but Joseph Moxon (1627–1700), writing in 1677 [14], seems not to have known this fact: indeed, as a practical rule it probably diffused from the work of Wren and Robert Hooke, each of whom was both scientist and architect.

A striking example of the changed ideas in carpentry appears in Peter Nicholson's 'Carpenter's and Joiner's Assistant' (1810) in which he compares the roof of Inigo Jones's church of St Paul, Covent Garden (1631–8), with Hardwick's roof-work in the apparent replica of that building erected in 1796 to replace the original, which had been gutted by fire. Figure 265 shows both the original and the replacement. The purlins in the earlier work were 12 in wide by 10 in deep; in the latter 6½ in wide by 9 in deep. The massive upright and diagonal timbers in the roof, halved at their crossings and all somewhat indeterminate in their function, were replaced by a neat arch consisting of two principal rafters and a horizontal bar, which met at queen-posts; from this was suspended the tie-beam, of which the main function was no longer to act as a beam but to tie in the feet of the arch. Nicholson worked out the timber-content of the two roofs (the old 298 cu ft, the new 198 cu ft), thereby demonstrating the saving that could be effected by using a properly trussed construction instead of a vague assembly of props and struts. It may be noted that Wren used trusses in the roof-work of St Paul's Cathedral and his other buildings. He may well have been the first English architect to make a clear, functional approach to the design of a timber roof-truss.

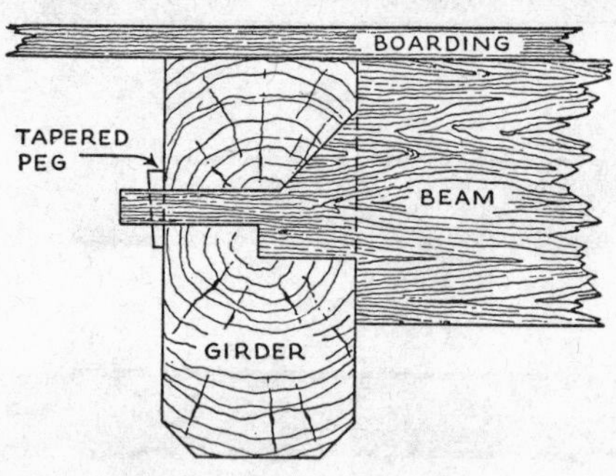

FIGURE 267—*Beam with tusk-tenon.*

The difficulty in designing a timber framework has always been to provide joints through which a pull could be transmitted. Except in such great roofs as those of Notre-Dame, Paris, and Rheims Cathedral [15] the medieval carpenter tried to avoid them, as he had to depend on mortised joints and wooden pegs or trenails. The eighteenth-century architect could afford to make freer use of smith's work. The tie-beam came to be hung from the foot of the king- or queen-post, no longer regarded as a post but as a means of suspension, by a forged strap secured by gib and cotter. With improved saws and bolts, a scarfed joint in a long tie-member became practicable (figure 266). No substantial improvement was made until the introduction in the twentieth century of toothed-ring connectors, so clamped by bolts as to bite into the flanks of the timbers that they joined, laid side by side. Meanwhile mortising, halving, and other devices, though they could be used to make sound joints, drastically reduced the useful load-bearing section of the wood. Moxon realized that a mortise-hole was less deleterious to the strength of a beam if it were made half-way down than if it removed material from near the top or bottom. This recognition led to the development

FIGURE 268—*The House of the Royal Society of Arts, designed by Robert Adam, 1772–4.*

of the tusk-tenon (figure 267) to join, for instance, a heavily loaded trimmer or secondary beam to a main girder, a problem frequently encountered in building the large floors of eighteenth-century mansions.

Except for improved jointing and the more economical use of wood, the altered style of building made little change in the structural design of domestic buildings: the emphasis was rather on appearance and finish. The use of smooth plaster on interior wall-surfaces and ceilings spread from large and important houses to much humbler dwellings, at least in towns; and the improvements in joinery and the use of sash-windows (vol III, p 267) also became general. Even in gentlemen's town houses and other buildings of importance, however, heavy classic features in solid masonry were less commonly adopted after the Napoleonic wars: the desire

FIGURE 269—*Regent Street, Piccadilly, designed by Nash, c 1820.*

for elegance was undiminished, but money was scarcer. Surface decoration of exteriors was shallower than before. In this movement Robert Adam (1728–92) took an active lead (figure 268), and, as already mentioned, John Nash (p 447) often substituted cast iron for carved masonry in columns, and a smooth rendering of mortar or stucco for large surfaces of masonry (figure 269).

Reference has already been made to the use of wrought iron in the last quarter of the eighteenth century by certain Parisian architects, both in roof-work and as armature embedded in masonry. As armature to masonry Claude Perrault (1613–88) between 1667 and 1670 reinforced flat architraves and vaults at the Louvre. In 1779 J. G. Soufflot (1713–81) planned an iron frame of 15 ft 8 in span to carry a mansard roof, a coved ceiling, and a skylight 17 ft wide. It covered a hall and stairs leading from a public entrance to a gallery. The roof was completed in 1781, but disappeared when the hall was rebuilt about 1805. The framework consisted of wrought iron bars with forged ends pinned together. Soufflot also buried a framework of wrought iron bars in the masonry of the churches of Ste-Geneviève and St-Sulpice, Paris, in an attempt to break away from the dependence of masonry-work solely on thrust and weight for stability [16] (figure 270).

Iron has an advantage over woodwork in the roof—for instance, in theatres—in that it is incombustible. It is not, however, as was sometimes claimed for it, fire-proof, for if strongly heated iron loses its strength, and the structure collapses. Combined, however, with slabs made of hollow earthenware pots embedded in plaster, a roof or floor supported by iron beams offers a high degree of resistance to fire. Pots suitable for this purpose were introduced in 1785 in Paris by St-Fart, an architect who specialized in hospitals (figure 271). Soon these pots were being made also in London, where Sir John Soane used them in vaults in the Bank of England (1792). They were commended in a report of a committee of the Associated Architects on the prevention of fires (1791). William Strutt (1756–1830), a prominent mill-owner of Derby and Belper, adopted them in parts of the 'fire-proof' mills he was building at this period [17].

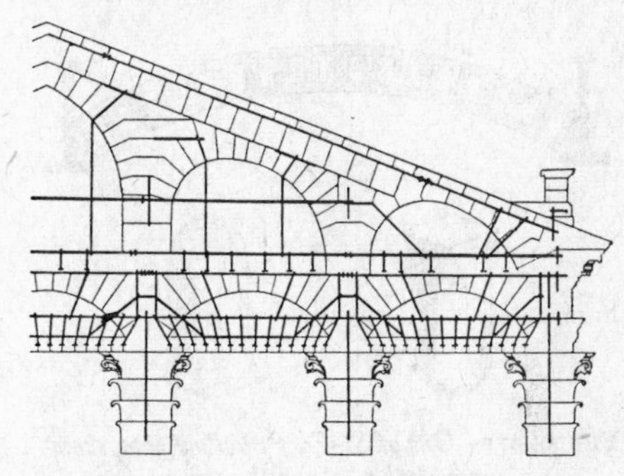

FIGURE 270—*Wrought iron armature to masonry by Soufflot at Ste-Geneviève (later the Panthéon Français).*

Until Strutt turned his mind to this problem of improving the fire-resistance of factories, the typical multi-storey mill building had solid wood-plank floors, carried by heavy beams that stretched from wall to wall. If the span was great or the loading heavy the span of each beam was divided by wooden posts jammed in between the floor below and the beam above. Heavy timbers did not easily catch fire; they tended to char and smoulder, but with naked lights everywhere a fire among inflammable goods could only too easily be started and get out of hand before the primitive fire-fighting appliances of the time could make any impression on it. In that way many valuable mills had been destroyed and lives lost. Strutt's first modification was to substitute brick arches for the wooden floor between beams (figure 272). A hardwood skewback was fixed on each side of the beam, and given some fire-protection by sheet iron on the exposed face. The underside of the beam was plastered. The supporting columns were of cast iron, spigoted into the beam. Subsequent developments were to replace the wooden beams by cast iron, and to improve the shape of the iron beam [18]. In end-spans of floors at Belper, and in the roof, Strutt used—for the sake of lightness—arches of hollow pots in place of solid bricks. Cast iron played an important role in developing the theory of construction, as its use and some failures drew attention to the lack of knowledge of the behaviour of this material under load, and of the most economical shape in which to make the castings. Up to the middle of the nineteenth century cast iron was widely used in the construction of bridges and buildings other than factories. By that time, however, the riveting together of wrought iron plates, as practised by the boiler-maker, was finding other uses, particularly in ship-building. The *Great Britain*, of the unprecedented length of 320 ft, which had in 1845 made her first Atlantic voyage to New York in fourteen days, was built of wrought iron, a fact that gave great encouragement to the use of this material in other ships and also for bridges and beams. A wrought iron beam need be only half the weight of a cast iron one of the same load-carrying capacity, and thus although the material was, weight for weight, twice as expensive, the net cost was about the same. The reduction in dead-load was therefore an advantage that cost nothing.

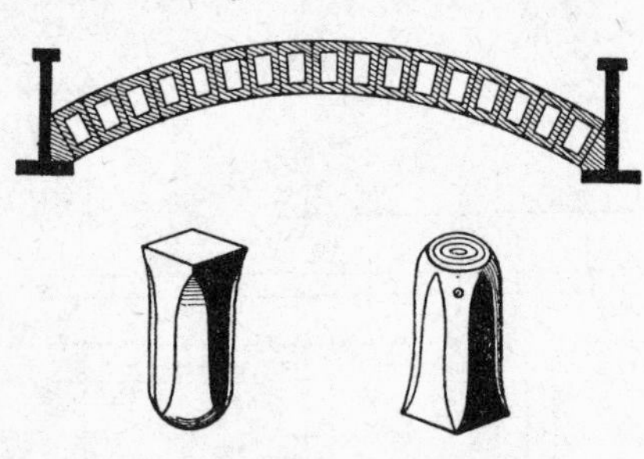

FIGURE 271—*One of St-Fart's hollow pots, showing assembly into arch. 1785.*

The extended use of wrought iron had brought into use machines for shearing plates to the size required, and for punching holes (p 429) in them. Rolled bars of T- and angle-section were available about 1820, and small ⌶-section beams, useful for light work, were produced in Paris from 1847. Heavy ⌶-section beams were not easily produced, as wrought iron was practically hand-made from blooms that weighed less than 2 cwt each. Though several blooms could be hammered together before rolling, the heavy work involved made the process more expensive than the riveting together of plates and angles. Heavy rolled ⌶-section beams had to await the invention of mild steel, cast in massive ingots, in the 1860s.

One of the most remarkable buildings erected at the end of our period was the Crystal Palace, which in 1851 housed the Great Exhibition in Hyde Park, London. The idea of using a vast greenhouse to cover the whole exhibition occurred to Joseph Paxton (1801–65), a man of affairs and initiative, who, as head gardener on the Duke of Devonshire's immense estate at Chatsworth, had already experimented in buildings of iron and glass on a considerable scale. When the scheme was accepted, Paxton immediately engaged the services of Fox, Henderson and

Company, who worked out the design in detail and organized the production and delivery, within a period of months, of parts containing 3500 tons of cast iron, together with large quantities of wrought iron, glass, timber, paint, and other materials. No single foundry could deal with so large an order, so the work was split between three midland firms. All girders and other parts were to be made to

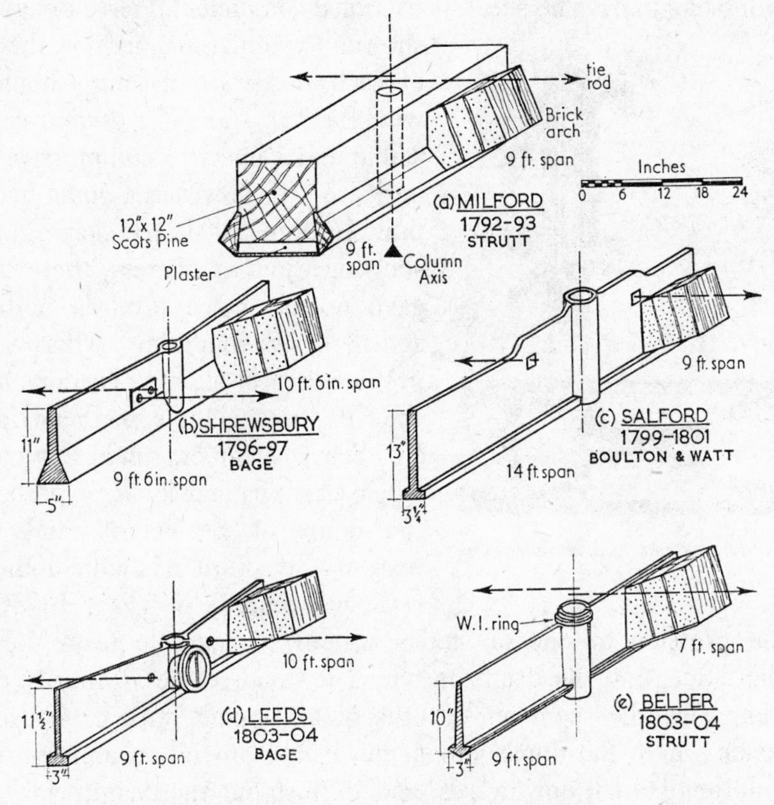

FIGURE 272—*Evolution of beam design for 'fireproof' mill buildings, 1792–1803.*

strict measurements, so that, without any fitting at the site, they should go together (figure 273). To ensure this, each girder as it arrived at the site was lifted by crane from the lorry and dropped into a frame, built to serve as a gauge, and also provided with hydraulic jacks to apply a proof-load. Testing for fit and strength took only four minutes a beam.

VI. THEORY

It will be clear from the notes on theory in the chapter (16) on bridges in volume III that up to 1750 the builders of bridges had at their disposal very little scientific knowledge. Galileo had shown geometrically that the moment of resistance of a beam rectangular in cross-section was proportional to its breadth, to the square of its depth, and to the resistance of the material to direct tension. La Hire had shown how the loading should vary across the span of an arch if the whole of the material were to be in compression and the force across any joint between voussoirs to have no shear or frictional component. Pierre Bouguer had shown in a similar manner how the weight of each course of masonry should vary with the curvature if a dome were to be stable and subject to compressive forces only [19]. If, however, a dome had been built to some arbitrary shape, and was showing signs of distress, these theories gave no assistance towards finding its actual stress-condition. This was the problem set by Pope Benedict XIV in 1742 to three notable mathematicians—Le Seur, Jacquier, and Boscovitch—when alarming cracks were observed in the dome of St Peter's, and in the masonry structure below the dome.

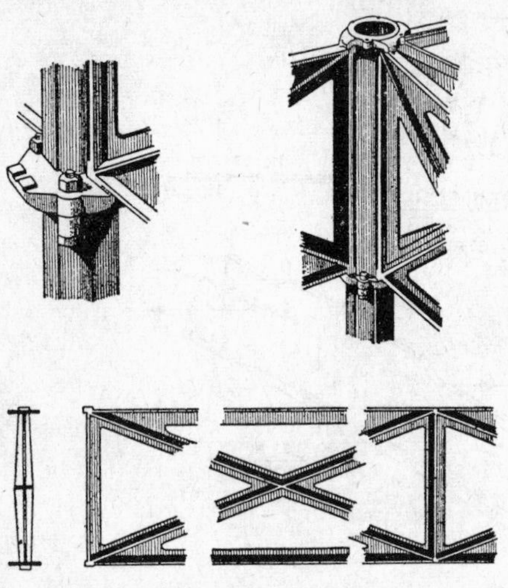

FIGURE 273—*Typical girder used in building the Crystal Palace, 1851.*

They reported in 1743. In order to reduce the problem to one of statics and of manageable form they considered the dome, and the drum on which it stood, to be arbitrarily divided into portions like the segments or liths of an orange, with a virtual hinge on the inside where the dome joined the drum. On this assumption liths of dome would tend to fall downwards, and to push out the drum, which would therefore tilt about the outer edge of its base (figure 274). The work done by a lith of dome would be the product of its weight by the amount its centre of gravity was lowered. This was partly balanced by the work done on the section of drum, which was the product of its weight by the amount its centre of gravity was raised by the tilting. The difference must be made good by the work done in stretching the retaining-chain which encircled the dome where it joined the drum. This was reckoned to be the product of (*a*) the amount by which the chain was lengthened and (*b*) the force exerted in stretching the chain. If the chain were unstressed when the tilting began, the average force resisted would be half that at the finish. The calculation showed that if stability depended on the chain the situation was serious, for the chain would have to resist three times the force which would break it, even if it were as strong as the iron wire the strength of which had been tested and recorded in 1729 by Pieter Van Musschenbroek [20]. The strength of a heavy forged and welded chain was, on the contrary, likely to be, area for area, much less than that of a fine drawn wire. No account was taken in the calculation of the energy absorbed in shear-resistance, friction, and the crushing of masonry in the movement, but the fact that a virtual work calculation was undertaken is of some interest. Further developments in that direction, combined with the studies of the elastic behaviour of materials by members of the Académie des Sciences and the *Ponts et Chaussées* were in due course to lead to powerful techniques of stress-analysis and structural design. Meanwhile the tendency was—with some plausibility—to blame earthquakes, thunderbolts, defects in workmanship, and flaws in design for the incipient failure of St Peter's. There was, however, no disagreement about the need to supply additional chains and to replace damaged masonry. These measures proved effective.

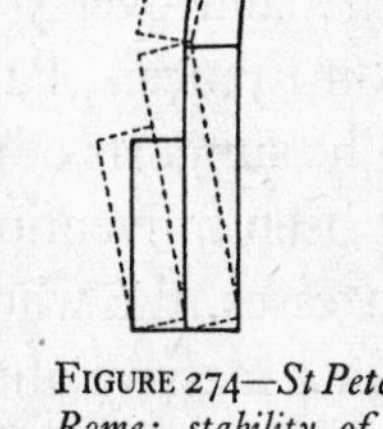

FIGURE 274—*St Peter's, Rome: stability of the dome. 1743.*

An important step in the study of the elastic behaviour of materials was undertaken by Leonhard Euler (1707–83), a Swiss mathematician. His interest lay not so much in the study of the actual materials as in that of curves into which they were bent, which could be mathematically defined. These included the curves into which laths or laminae would be bent under the action of given forces. In 1757 he derived an expression for the critical load under which a long, flexible column would become unstable. In later theory Euler's work proved of fundamental importance, but long, flexible columns were of no practical interest in the 1750s, and Euler was ignored.

Charles-Augustin de Coulomb (1736–1806) came much nearer than any predecessor to providing engineers with a working theory of the strength of materials, in a paper he presented in 1773 to the Académie des Sciences 'on the application of the rules of maxima and minima to some problems of statics relative to architecture' [21]. In forty pages he covered the theory of beams as still taught in modern textbooks, including that of shearing-forces, based on the laws of static equilibrium which he stated clearly at the outset: he developed the wedge theory of earth-pressure on retaining-walls, as still used, and the treatment of the arch. This was not a set of smooth voussoirs liable to slide one on another, but a body liable to crack, and so rotate and fold up piecemeal about virtual hinges, the position of which could be found by a method he described. At the time, however, Coulomb's work, like Euler's, appeared to be too mathematical and indigestible, and was not widely noted. Coulomb himself became interested in other things, and did not develop his work to show how it could be applied to practical examples. It was, however, studied by Gauthey (see below), Prony, and others at the *Ponts et Chaussées*, and in the fullness of time was embodied by C. L. M. Navier in his 'Lectures on the Application of Mechanics' [22], which formed the basis of instruction on the subjects of strength of materials and theory of structures to students of that famous school.

Closely contemporary with Coulomb was Emiland Marie Gauthey (1732–1806), like him an officer in the *Ponts et Chaussées*, and a writer on the theory of construction. Although of much less fundamental importance, his work was more immediately influential than that of Coulomb, because he became involved in the controversy over the dome of Ste-Geneviève—later to become the Panthéon Français, Paris.

The supports of the domes of St Peter's in Rome, and of St Paul's in London, had been conventional. In each case the dome was carried on a drum backed by buttresses, the whole carried on four great arches bearing upon and thrusting against massive abutment-towers or bastions within the body of the church at the four corners of the crossing. In the reconstruction of Ste-Geneviève, begun in 1757, the architect, Soufflot, decided to try a new scheme. He would support the great arches beneath the dome on four clusters of columns sufficient to take the vertical load. The horizontal thrust he would transfer to the main walls of the building, and so avoid the obstruction by bastions in the body of the church. In channels within the joints of the masonry he proposed, where necessary, to bury cages of wrought iron bars, linked together to form virtually a system of open-framed girders. When they realized his intention, traditionally-minded architects were scandalized and prophesied disaster. Gauthey, however, when consulted by Soufflot, approved of his scheme. Gauthey also designed and built a testing machine with a wooden frame and an iron lever 7 ft long, to apply a leverage of 24 to 1 to the specimen under test (figure 275). On this machine Gauthey tested many specimens of the selected stone to make sure that the columns would safely carry their load. So far as is known this was the first time that a testing machine had been used to provide information required in the design and erection of an actual building. Soufflot had a similar machine made, but with an iron frame; so did the *Ponts et Chaussées*. Finally Jean Rondelet (1734–1829), who worked under Soufflot and completed the rebuilding of Ste-Geneviève after Soufflot's death, improved the machine by providing a knife-edge instead of a bolt at the fulcrum, and a screw-jack to apply the load, so that the weigh-beam could be kept level while the specimen under observation was compressed [23].

Within a few years of the completion of the work ominous cracks appeared both in the dome and in the columns that carried its weight. The battle of pamphlets that had raged in 1770, and had been checked only by Gauthey's arguments backed by the results of the tests, broke out anew in the 1790s. The building itself appeared to have taken sides with Soufflot's enemies. All manner of pro-

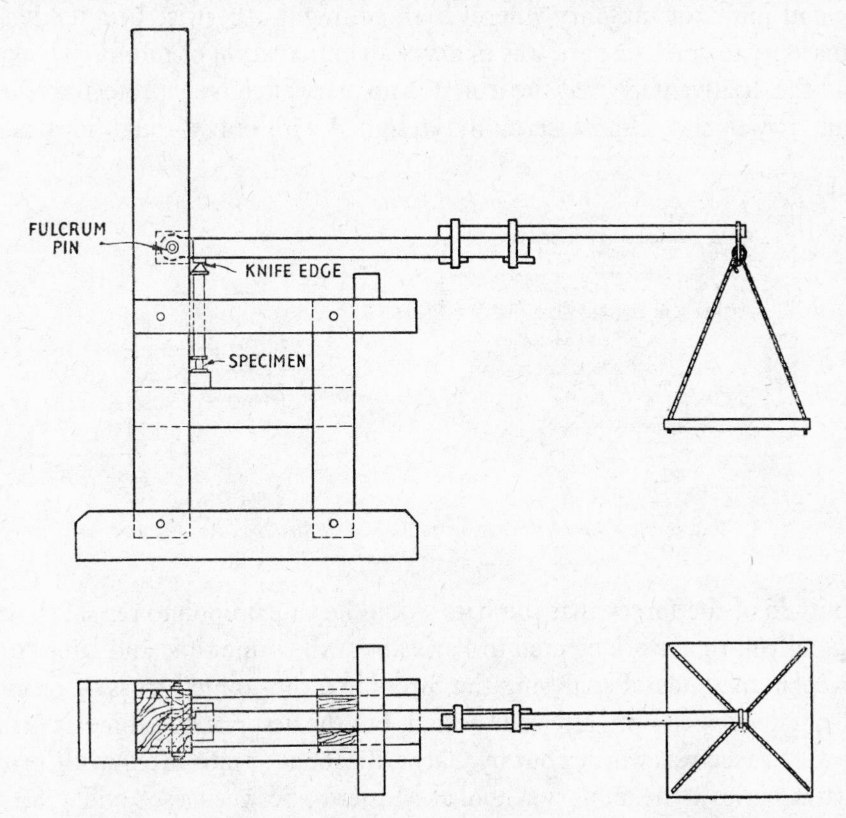

FIGURE 275—*Gauthey's testing machine, 1770.* (Above) *elevation;* (below) *plan.*

posals were made: for erecting great additional columns and buttresses inside the building, and even for pulling down the dome and replacing it by a much shallower and lighter construction. Gauthey again came to the rescue with fresh calculations, which showed that the average loading of the piers below the dome was only 28 tons to the sq ft, which was not excessive for the stone used. In erecting the piers, however, a hard stone had been used for the facing, and a softer stone for the hearting. This threw a greater share of the load on the harder, less compressible stone; and to make matters worse the masons had worked the beds to a taper, showing hardly any thickness of joint at the face but allowing a thicker bed of mortar behind. Naturally the overloaded edges of the stone had cracked and spalled. In the end, Rondelet added about 2 ft of additional stonework to two of the sides of the triangular piers, and bound them into the original masonry by means of wrought iron bars (figure 276).

This use by Soufflot of iron bars embedded in mortar, in grooves cut into the beds and joints of masonry wherever there might otherwise be a tendency for the masonry to crack or part, was in a way an anticipation of reinforced concrete. It had the disadvantage that the iron was not very effectively protected from corrosion. It was also, almost certainly, designed with only a rough idea as to the

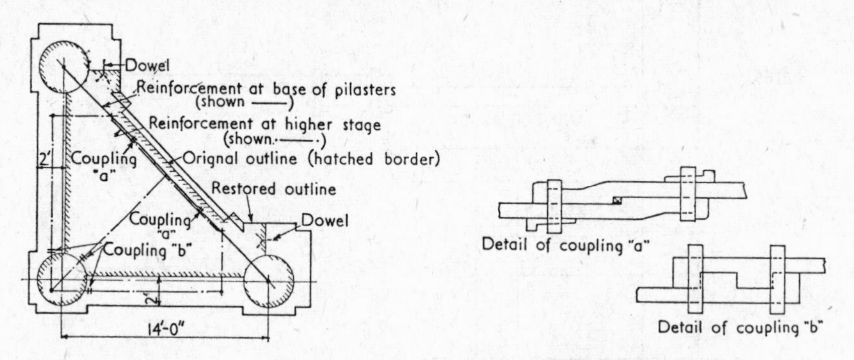

FIGURE 276—*Rondelet's additions to the piers of Ste-Geneviève. 1806–10.*

magnitude of the forces that the bars would be called upon to resist; so was the wrought iron roof-work erected in Paris about the same time and later [16].

Graphic methods of analysing the forces in a pin-jointed truss or framework were not developed until after our period, but the descriptive geometry on which they were based was worked out by Gaspard Monge (1746–1818) while professor of mathematics at the military school at Mezières, between 1768 and 1780. Later he taught at the École de Marine. When in 1794 the school was founded in Paris that in 1795 became the École Polytechnique, to give basic scientific training to cadets of all services, both military and civil, it was Monge who was called in to organize it.

Between Robert Hooke (1635–1702) and Thomas Young (1773–1829) no English scientist contributed anything of importance to the theory of construction. All overlooked Hooke's justly famous law *ut tensio sic vis*: the distortion in any material is proportional to the force that produces it. Some of the French students of the subject, notably Coulomb, had assumed such a law as a useful working hypothesis, but none appeared to be aware of the carefully conducted experiments by which Hooke had established it. The subject had also been confused by failure to distinguish between the effect of low stresses, which produce small elastic distortions in accordance with Hooke's law, and the effect of high stresses, which, in ductile materials, produce large plastic deformations. The behaviour of all materials, whether ductile or brittle, deviates markedly from Hooke's law at loadings far below the ultimate. Most tests made until well into the nineteenth century had been tests to destruction, and consequently had thrown no light on the importance of elastic movement within the range of normal working loads. Euler had introduced into his equations a term, constant for any given material, relating load and distortion, but it remained for Young to define the 'elastic modulus'[1] in a way that made it potentially useful as a means of calculating actual deflections. The word potentially is used advisedly, for Young's writings were obscure and difficult to read. They did not receive the attention which, had he expressed himself more intelligibly, their topical importance would have ensured. Young was a man of great learning, but unfortunately he never even began to realize the limits of comprehension of ordinary minds. His lectures were unintelligible to his audiences, and in printed form were, and still are, difficult reading. He was called upon to give lectures on natural philosophy at the Royal Institution. The appointment was cancelled after the second year, but Young had gone to immense trouble to prepare his lectures and decided to publish them. They appeared in two volumes in 1807 [24].

On the subject of materials of construction Young extended the work of Euler, and of Coulomb, whom he greatly admired. He introduced into beam theory the term 'neutral axis' for the trace, on the cross-section of a beam, of the neutral layer, the substance of which is neither stretched nor compressed. As he dealt with none but 'prismatic' sections he did not define its position in general terms, but he did show how its position was changed when an end-wise load was added to the normal transverse load on a beam. Euler, as has been noted, had given an equation for the load under which a long, straight, slender column would collapse through becoming elastically unstable. He had assumed a perfectly central load, and had been surprised to find that in theory no deflection was produced at all under a gradually increasing load until the load reached the critical value, when sudden collapse occurred.

Young considered the cases of a column slightly bent, and of a column eccentrically loaded. He showed that, with either of these, deflection increased more rapidly as the load increased. His equations for these two cases were rediscovered in the twentieth century, and put forward as new [25].

[1] Young's own elastic modulus was a weight equivalent to what we now know as 'Young's modulus' multiplied by the area of cross section of the material. His 'height of the modulus' was our Young's modulus divided by the density of the material.

Young's work was studied by John Robison, who was the author of an influential textbook on practical mechanics. Some of Young's ideas found their way, presumably by way of Robison, into the textbooks of Thomas Tredgold, which were widely read by engineers of the period.

The scheme put forward by Telford and Douglas (p 458) to replace Old London Bridge by an arch of cast iron in a single span of 600 ft was referred to a select committee of the House of Commons on the improvement of the Port of London, and discussed in their third report (1799 and 1800). The committee called as expert witnesses an imposing selection of mathematicians, including the Astronomer Royal, and engineers, among them Rennie, Jessop, and John Sothern of Soho, Birmingham. A list of questions was drawn up, mainly about the distribution of load through such a vast assembly of castings. Would it act as one solid object? Would the bulk of the weight be thrown on the lowest rib? How should the parts be joined? Could it crack up piecemeal? And so on. Young followed their deliberations, although he was not summoned to take part. He summed up in these words: 'It would be difficult to find greater discordance in the most heterodox professions of faith, or in the most capricious variations of taste, than is exhibited in the responses of our most celebrated professors on almost every point submitted for their consideration.' In the article on bridges that he wrote for the 'Encyclopaedia Britannica', Young attempted to answer the questions himself. The article was highly technical, and is too long to summarize here. The important features are that Young visualized the problem as one of elastic movements no less than of strength. Only Robison and John Sothern had shown any appreciation of this aspect of the problem in the evidence before the committee. Where witnesses had usually been content to make vague general statements, Young backed up nearly every answer by calculations. None had been able to give a reliable figure for the strength of cast iron; indeed, the first test-figure published was probably that obtained by George Rennie in 1818 [26]. Not to be defeated on such a point, however, Young made a simple test for himself. He filed a small prism of cast iron $\frac{1}{8}$ in $\times \frac{1}{8}$ in $\times \frac{1}{4}$ in long, placed it in a vice, and measured the force needed to crush it. Allowing for friction, he calculated this to be about a ton, or 64 tons to the square inch, a very fair result for such an extemporized test.

The proposal for London Bridge was in the event turned down, but strangely enough nothing was said about the abutment foundations, although these might have proved the most difficult part of the undertaking, since any appreciable settlement could easily have been disastrous to the bridge.

In none of his investigations had Young encountered the problem of the most economical shape in which to make a cast iron beam, having regard to the fact that the metal was at least five or six times as strong in compression as in tension. The problem was raised, however, when it came to be considered that a good way to improve the fire-resistance of mill buildings was to carry the floors on brick arches springing from cast iron beams (p 475). The early beams were nearly rectangular in section; but proof-tests soon showed that extra metal, provided at the lower edge to give a better support to the skewback of the arch, also increased the strength of the beam in much greater proportion than it added to the weight.

William Fairbairn adopted an inverted T-section with advantage: then, finding that Eaton Hodgkinson (1789–1861) was already making experiments on similar lines with small specimens, Fairbairn invited him to join forces, and to make use of his foundry and plant for a comprehensive series of tests. By this means Hodgkinson was able to discover the most economical section, and to devise a formula for calculating the strength of a cast iron beam. The load W, which it would carry concentrated at mid-span, was proportional to the area of the tension flange A, the depth of the beam d, and, inversely, to the span L. Expressing W in tons, and all dimensions in inches, Hodgkinson calculated [27] that for the most economical section:

$$W = 26Ad/L.$$

It was found, however, that a large beam of Hodgkinson's ideal section had so much metal concentrated in the bottom flange that the thinner parts elsewhere tended to cool more quickly, and high internal stresses might in consequence be set up in the metal. In practice, therefore, full theoretical economy was not usually attempted.

Hodgkinson continued his investigations to include the strength of columns. Unlike masonry columns, metal columns were not infrequently long and thin, and the tendency to instability—quite apart from the risk of crushing—to which Euler had drawn attention was found to be no longer negligible. Hodgkinson tried to fit his results to a formula for the collapse load, P, of the form

$$P = cd^n/L^m,$$

where c, m, and n were constants and d was the diameter. In Euler's case, where L was great compared with d, n was 4, and m was 2, but both these constants were too high for Hodgkinson's test-results. Eventually he found that no pair of constants fitted all cases, and that the best approximation to the collapse load was obtained by taking the harmonic mean between the crushing load and Euler's critical load. If the beam was very short, this coincided with the crushing load; if very long, with Euler's load. Between the extremes, the curve fitted fairly well the lower limit of the scatter of points of failure loads, plotted for intermediate values of L/d. Hodgkinson's final formula, modified by Lewis Gordon and later by William Rankine, entered the textbooks as the Gordon–Rankine formula for columns and was widely used throughout the nineteenth century.

Towards the middle of the nineteenth century, as already noted in the section on bridges (p 460), an alternative to the use of cast iron for beams arose in the form of built-up plate-girders of wrought iron. The top flange had to be stiff to resist compression: the bottom flange, which resisted tension, was less complicated. The function of the vertical 'web' plate or plates, other than that of holding the flanges in place, was not immediately recognized, but experiments on forms suitable for the Britannia bridge showed that this, too, required a certain amount of stiffening if it were not to buckle or fold into a wavy and unstable form. In these experiments, indeed, the design of plate-girders, and a theory of the way they functioned, were evolved. The investigation was made jointly by George Stephenson, William Fairbairn, and Eaton Hodgkinson.

In 1850 W. Bindon Blood and W. T. Doyne submitted to the Institution of Civil Engineers a short paper on the calculation of the forces in these web-members; and in 1851 W. H. Bow published in Edinburgh a 'Treatise on Bracing'. That type of bridge-truss had, however, made considerably more progress in the United States, where bridges with timbers for compression-members, and wrought iron rods for at least some of the tension-members, were in common use as highway bridges. Many ingenious arrangements of bracing were tried, and some became standard practice in certain districts. The early examples were entirely empirical, but in 1847 Squire Whipple brought out 'A Work Upon Bridge Building', and in 1851 Herman Haupt 'The General Theory of Bridge Construction'. Both American and British authors resolved the forces in the members meeting at each joint as a separate system of forces in equilibrium. Graphical methods, which simplified both the problem and its solution, were not developed until the 1860s. The pioneer of graphic statics was Carl Culmann, who between 1849 and 1851 visited both England and North America: he was particularly interested at that time in the work of Squire Whipple.

REFERENCES

[1] HAMILTON, S. B. *Trans. Newcomen Soc.*, **22**, 149, 1941–2.
[2] *Idem. Struct. Engr*, **32**, no. 12, 315, 1954.
[3] *Idem. Archit. Rev., Lond.*, **116**, 295, 1954.
[4] VICAT, L. J. 'Recherches expérimentales sur les chaux de Construction.' Paris. 1818.
[5] GOODING, P. and HALSTEAD, P. E. 'Proceedings of the third International Symposium on the Chemistry of Cement, London, 1952', pp. 1–29. Cement and Concrete Association, London. 1955.
[6] SEMPLE, G. 'On Building in Water.' Dublin. 1776.
[7] *Min. Proc. Instn civ. Engrs*, **25**, 66, 1865–6.
[8] SALZMAN, L. F. 'Building in England down to 1540', pp. 155 f. Clarendon Press, Oxford. 1952.
[9] RAISTRICK, A. 'The Darbys; a Dynasty of Ironfounders.' Longmans, London. 1953.
[10] KIRBY, R. S. and LAURSON, P. G. 'The Early Years of Modern Civil Engineering', p. 167. Yale University Press, New Haven. 1932.
[11] BEAMISH, R. 'Memoir of the Life of Sir Marc Isambard Brunel.' London. 1862.
[12] CRESY, E. 'An Encyclopaedia of Civil Engineering', pp. 227 f. London. 1847.
[13] PALLADIO, ANDREA. 'I quattro Libri dell'Architettura' (4 vols). Venice. 1570.
[14] MOXON, JOSEPH. 'Mechanick Exercises.' London. 1677.
[15] CHOISY, F. A. 'Histoire de l'architecture', Vol. 2, pp. 327 f. Paris. 1899.
[16] RONDELET, J. 'Traité théorique et pratique de l'art de bâtir', Vol. 2, p. 151. Paris. 1812.
ECK, C. L. G. 'Traité de construction en poteries et fer à l'usage des bâtiments civils, industriels et militaires.' Paris. 1836.
[17] HAMILTON, S. B. 'The Structural Fire Protection of Buildings. A Historical Note'. H.M. Stationery Office, London. (In the press.)
[18] JOHNSON, H. R. and SKEMPTON, A. W. *Trans. Newcomen Soc.*, **30**, 1956. (In the press.)
[19] BOUGUER, P. *Hist. Acad. R. Sci.*, 149–66, 1734.
[20] MUSSCHENBROEK, P. VAN. *Physicae Experimentales et Geometricae*. Leiden. 1729.
WOLF, A. 'History of Science, Technology and Philosophy in the Eighteenth Century', pp. 517 f. Allen & Unwin, London. 1938.
[21] COULOMB, C. A. "Essai sur une application des règles de maximis et minimis à quelques problèmes de statique, relatifs à l'architecture." *Mém. Acad. Sci. Sav. étrang.*, **7**, 343–82, 1776.
[22] NAVIER, C. L. M. 'Leçons sur l'application de la méchanique.' Paris. 1826.
[23] RONDELET, J. See ref. [16], Vol. 3, pp. 72 f. 1805.
GIBBONS, C. H. *Trans. Newcomen Soc.*, **15**, 169, 1934–5.
[24] YOUNG, T. 'Lectures in Natural Philosophy' (2 vols). London. 1807.
[25] HAMILTON, S. B. *Min. Proc. Instn civ. Engrs*, **1**, Pt III, 379 f., 1952.
[26] RENNIE, G. "Account of Experiments on the Strength of Materials." A letter to Dr. Thomas Young published in *Phil. Trans.*, [**108**], 118–36, 1818, in which a new testing machine was described capable of applying a load of about 11 tons.
HAMILTON, S. B. *Trans. Newcomen Soc.*, **21**, 143, 1940–1.
[27] HODGKINSON, E. *Mem. Manchr lit. phil. Soc., Manchester*, second series, **5**, 407, 1831.

BIBLIOGRAPHY

CRESY, E. 'An Encyclopaedia of Civil Engineering.' London. 1847.
GWILT, J. 'An Encyclopaedia of Architecture.' London. 1842.
HANN, J., MOSELEY, H., HOSKING, W., *et al.* 'Bridges.' London. 1843.

SMILES, S. 'Lives of the Engineers, with an Account of their Principal Works' (3 vols). London. 1861–2. See also: SKEMPTON, A. W. "The Engineers of the English River Navigations, 1620–1760." *Trans. Newcomen Soc.*, **29**, 1953–5. (In the press.)

Modern works:

HAMILTON, S. B. "The Historical Development of Structural Theory." *Min. Proc. Instn civ. Engrs*, **1**, Pt III, 374–419, 1952.

KIRBY, R. S. and LAURSON, P. G. 'The Early Years of Modern Civil Engineering.' Yale University Press, New Haven. 1932.

STRAUB, H. 'Die Geschichte der Bauingenieurkunst.' Birkhäuser, Basel. 1949.

Idem. 'A History of Civil Engineering' (Eng. trans. by E. ROCKWELL). Hill, London. 1952.

TIMOSHENKO, S. P. 'History of Strength of Materials.' McGraw Hill, New York. 1953.

WOLF, A. 'A History of Science, Technology and Philosophy in the Eighteenth Century.' Allen & Unwin, London. 1938.

Telford's plan for a new London Bridge embodying a single 600-ft span of cast iron. This project was never started.

16

PART I

SANITARY ENGINEERING: WATER-SUPPLY

J. KENNARD

THE period from 1750 to 1850 saw the development of modern water-supply in Britain. The influx of population to the towns from rural areas, the rapid growth of manufacture, and the introduction of railways entailed large demands for a continuous supply of clean water, not only for domestic use but for industry.

Before 1800 no reliable estimates of population were possible. The first census was undertaken in 1801, following an abortive attempt in 1753. The growth of population in England, Wales, and Scotland during the next half-century is shown in the following table:

Year	*Total*
1801	10 500 956
1811	11 970 120
1821	14 091 757
1831	16 261 183
1841	18 534 332
1851	20 816 351

The population of cities grew remarkably quickly. That of Glasgow, for instance, increased four-fold between 1801 and 1851, and the demand for water increased from 6 500 000 gallons a day in 1838 to 14 000 000 gallons a day a little over a decade later.

To meet such demands, numerous joint stock companies were constituted by private enterprise throughout Britain, under special powers conferred by private Acts of Parliament; over a hundred of these Acts were passed in the nineteenth century. Generally the companies were very successful financially. In a number of towns, however, with the encouragement of Parliament, several companies competed with each other in providing supplies. Towards the middle of the nineteenth century amalgamations were taking place, and in some cases the local authorities acquired the undertakings of the companies, especially when it was felt that the latter did not have the resources or the initiative to undertake the large works that were then considered to be necessary. In the case of Edinburgh the reverse took place: the municipality handed over its supply to a company in 1819, for the sum of £30 000.

In 1840 a Select Committee of the House of Commons was appointed to inquire into the supply of water to large towns and populous districts in England and Wales. Reference was made to the many shortcomings and the deficient supplies, sometimes polluted: out of fifty towns considered, the supply of water was regarded as good in only six. The Committee's recommendations resulted in the passing of the Waterworks Clauses Act of 1847 and the Public Health Act of 1848, which became the foundation of modern water-law in Britain. They provided that water-supplies were to be 'pure, safe, and constant', and of such a pressure as to reach the highest house within the area of supply. The Acts further dealt with the provision of compensation for loss and damage to property in developing resources, constructing works, and laying pipes, and with the method of charging for water on the basis of the ratable value of the property for domestic purposes, and by gallonage for industry. The principal object was to standardize, as far as possible, the powers of undertakings authorized to supply water, and to avoid the necessity for setting out the powers and duties in detail in each individual private Act.

The development of canal systems during the first phase of the industrial revolution, and the construction of large reservoirs for the purpose of supplying them with water, provided much valuable information and experience which were in turn applied to the construction of similar works for water-supply. Nevertheless, it was soon realized that the essential basic data necessary to enable proper consideration to be given to the hydrological aspect of reservoir-design depended on reliable records of rainfall, evaporation, and absorption-losses, and of dry-weather flows of streams and rivers. J. F. Bateman, when designing the early water-works for Manchester, deplored the rule-of-thumb and guesswork methods then in use, as did other engineers of that time, and they persuaded undertakings to set up rain-gauges on several gathering-grounds under consideration.

The first known rainfall records for the British Isles were kept by Richard Townley at Towneley, near Burnley, from 1677 to 1703. By 1788 there were ten such records, but the recording of rainfall was regarded as nothing more than a hobby of scientists and clergymen. It was not until 1825 that serious recording was started by James Glaisher; it was continued by G. J. Symons from 1860 onwards. Symons energetically recruited observers, and by the end of the century there were over 3000 of them. In 1919 the recording of rainfall became a national service undertaken by the Meteorological Office of the Air Ministry.

The importance of geology to the water-engineer was realized when James Hutton published his 'Theory of the Earth' in 1795. In 1815 William Smith published his famous 'Delineations of the Strata', with the first geological map; three years later he produced a geological atlas. Meanwhile, in 1807, the Geo-

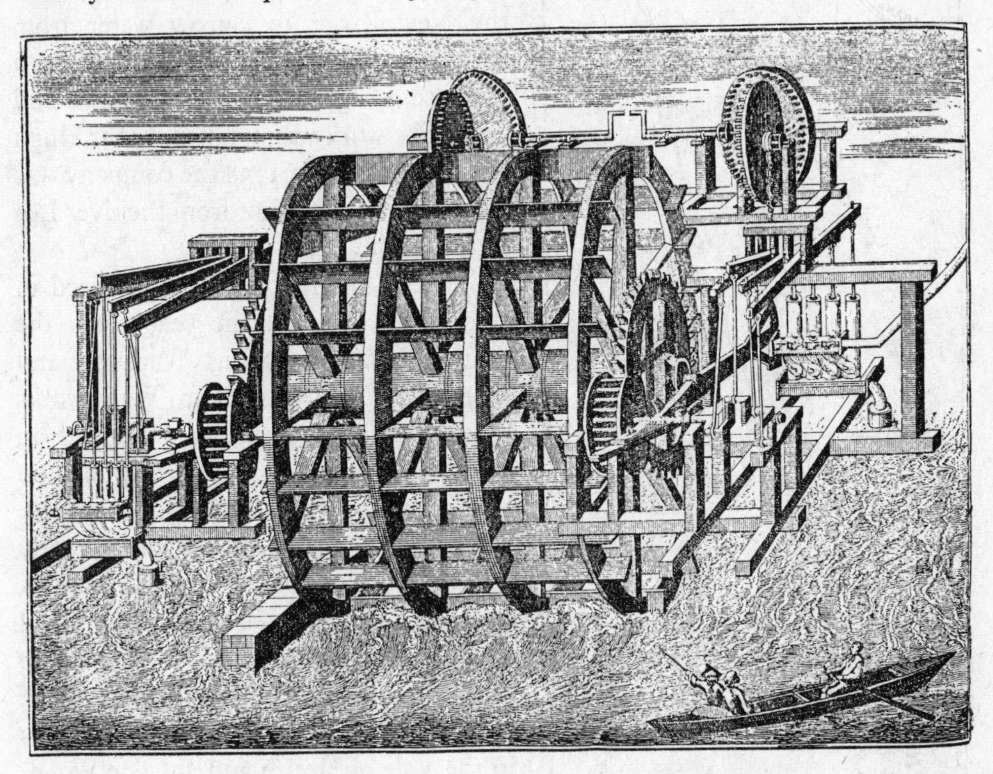

FIGURE 277—*Water-wheel and pumps at London Bridge water-works. 1749.*

logical Society was founded, and this society in 1835 established the Geological Survey of Great Britain, the first organization of its kind in the world. A few years later saw the introduction of ordnance survey maps on a scale of 6 in to a mile.

No history of water-supply in this period would be complete without a brief description of that to the City of London. The first company to be established was the London Bridge waterworks in 1581; by means of pumps driven by water-wheels, water was raised from the Thames at London Bridge (figure 277). The works when fully established are stated to have been capable of furnishing a supply of nearly 4 m gallons a day, but the great fall of water occasioned by their operation endangered navigation through the bridge; an Act was therefore passed in 1822 for their removal, and for the transfer of the undertaking to the New River Company. In 1613 this company had constructed an aqueduct known as the New River, to convey water from springs in Hertfordshire to London, a distance of 38 miles (figures 278 and 279). The work was initiated by Sir Hugh Myddleton, and in 1738 the company was allowed to divert water from the river Lea into the aqueduct.

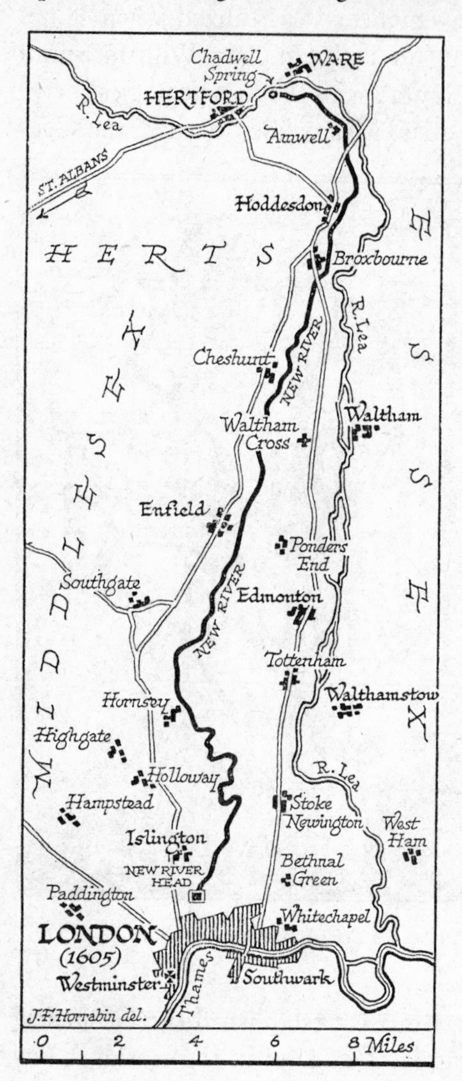

FIGURE 278—*Map of the New River cut.*

The Shadwell Company originated in works set up about the year 1669, the area supplied including Wapping and Stepney. The West Ham Waterworks originated in 1743, and was situated on an arm of the Lea at Bow; it supplied an area including Mile End and Stratford. Both these companies were subsequently acquired by the London Dock Company.

In 1692 the City leased its Hampstead Heath undertaking to certain lessees to form the Hampstead Water Company, which subsequently constructed reservoirs in the Vale of Health and at Cane Wood. These supplied an area starting from below Hampstead and reaching to Camden Town. In 1833 a well was sunk at the bottom of Hampstead Heath, followed a few years later by a second well at Kentish Town.

The excavation of a shallow well generally required little skill. With a plumb-bob to check verticality, a method of removing the excavated material, and the provision of a suitable lining to hold up the sides and to exclude pollution as much as possible, very little else was necessary. Brickwork was commonly used for the lining, but in wet ground the addition of puddled clay behind the brickwork was relied upon. In more recent times concrete and cast iron linings were developed. In a vain attempt to obtain further water a boring was made from the bottom of the Kentish Town well, but it was abandoned in 1855 after reaching a depth of 1302 ft.

In the case of deep boreholes sunk from the bottom of a shallow well the principal method of boring consisted of pounding the strata into small fragments and dust, and removing the debris as sand or mud. The boring-tool, which varied according to the nature of the work to be done, was attached to steel or wooden rods, and a vertical reciprocating motion was given to the tool, thus breaking up the material at the bottom of the hole. It was also given a circular motion in order to ensure that it did not strike the same point at each stroke. The tool was removed from time to time, to enable the debris to be removed by baling and flushing, and further rods were added.

FIGURE 279—*Water-carrier selling New River water.*

The York Buildings Waterworks Company, incorporated by Act of Parliament in 1691, owned works situated near the bottom of Villiers Street, Strand, which enabled water to be taken from the Thames. The water was raised to a cistern by means of a horse-driven engine, and delivered to Piccadilly, Kensington Gardens, Whitehall, and intervening streets. This company was the first in London to make use of steam for pumping, and about the year 1712 Thomas Savery erected for it a machine for 'raising water by fire'. The need to undertake expensive alterations to meet the increasing competition of other companies resulted in a financial loss, and in 1818 the undertaking was acquired by the New River Company.

The Chelsea Waterworks Company was established in 1723, and two ponds in Green Park were converted into reservoirs. The water was obtained from a canal extending from Pimlico to the river-bank at Chelsea, where water-wheels were used to raise the water. The first attempts to purify river-water supplies were made at Chelsea, but increase in pollution of the river caused the company, in common with others affected by the Metropolis Water Act of 1852, to move its intake beyond the tidal waters. This Act also required all water to be filtered unless drawn from wells, and all reservoirs within 5 miles of St Paul's to be covered.

The Lambeth Waterworks Company was incorporated by Act of Parliament in 1785 for supplying Lambeth and adjacent areas. Considerable works were established to meet increasing demands, and in 1848 the company procured purer sources of supply by moving its intake to Surbiton, where filter-beds (p 501) were constructed.

The East London Waterworks Company was established in 1807, and in the following year acquired the undertakings of the Shadwell Waterworks Company and the West Ham waterworks from the London Dock Company. Intake-works and reservoirs were constructed at Old Ford, but in 1829 the company decided to move its intake to Lee Bridge, which became the centre of the distribution system. By the end of the century this was the second most powerful station in the metropolitan area.

The Kent Waterworks Company was established in 1809, and obtained water from the river Ravensbourne for the supply of Deptford, Lee, Greenwich, Lewisham, and Rotherhithe. After developing a deep well at Deptford in 1856 the company abandoned the use of river-water, and the area was supplied entirely from wells. In 1811 the Grand Junction Waterworks Company was incorporated, and from 1820 drew water from the Thames at Chelsea, but subsequently the intake was removed to Kew Bridge. In 1845 the Southwark and Vauxhall Company was incorporated to amalgamate the Southwark and the Vauxhall companies, whose principal works comprised an intake at Battersea, which was subsequently moved to Hampton.

The following table gives the amount of water supplied by the nine Metropolitan companies in existence in 1848–9 (figure 281):

Company	*Total number of tenements supplied*	*Average daily supply (million gallons)*
New River	83 206	15·5
East London	56 673	9·0
Southwark and Vauxhall	34 864	6·0
West Middlesex	24 480	3·3
Lambeth	23 396	3·1
Chelsea	20 996	3·9
Grand Junction	14 058	3·5
Kent	9 632	1·1
Hampstead	4 490	0·4
Total	271 795	45·8

By the middle of the nineteenth century, almost every house in London, except the very poorest, had a cistern filled at stated times. Figure 280 shows the method of supply to houses in Piccadilly at the beginning of the nineteenth century.

Where geological conditions were favourable in gravel areas it was quite usual to sink shallow wells, from which supplies of water were obtained for individual houses and industries, and also to rely upon springs issuing at the junction of pervious strata with impervious clay. The spread of pollution, however, caused many of these supplies to be abandoned, and eventually purer, deep-seated sources were tapped by sinking boreholes.

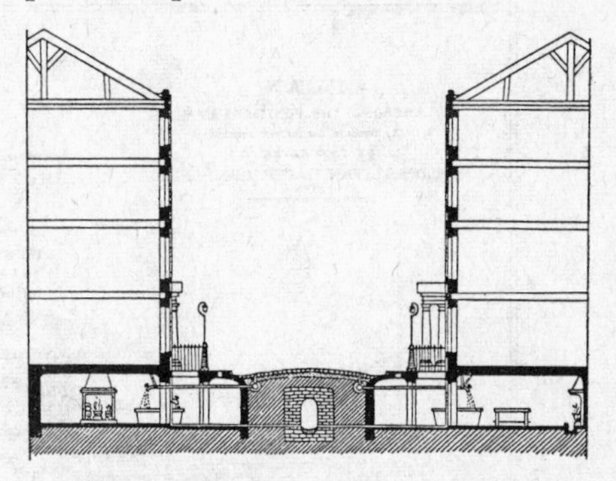

FIGURE 280—*The water-supply in Piccadilly, London, at the beginning of the nineteenth century, showing the distribution of water within each house. It also shows water from the roof drained into the main sewer running beneath the centre of the road.*

As the lower reaches of rivers in many parts of the country were rapidly becoming polluted, and the demand for water increased beyond the capacity of wells and boreholes, attention was directed to the purer head-waters. This generally necessitated the construction of dams to form storage- or impounding-reservoirs, in order to augment the natural flow in time of drought.

A number of nineteenth-century Acts authorizing local undertakings to construct reservoirs and take water from a river were free of restriction as to the rate of abstraction, but in others it was the practice to protect the interests of such riparian proprietors as mill- and factory-owners. The practice of providing compensation-water steadily developed, and when water-wheels were in common use for driving mills the compensation-water which had to be discharged into the river was fixed at high rates of flow. Failure by the water-undertakings to fulfil their obligations involved substantial penalties. In more recent times, as the nature of the use of rivers altered, lower rates of compensation-water were sanctioned by Parliament.

A notable example of an early waterworks-dam is the Belmont dam in the Pennines, constructed about 1827 by the Great and Little Bolton Waterworks Company. The company obtained powers to take water from springs that flowed into the Belmont brook, but in order to provide compensation-water for the mills lower down, on the river Eagley, a reservoir was necessary. The dam was built of clay, to a height of 65 ft above the stream bed, and in 1843 it was raised by 16 ft. It is still in use, although extensive repairs were carried out in 1925–6.

The success of this reservoir, and the benefits obtained by the mills owing to the evening-out of the flow of the river, led other mill-owners to construct for their own benefit the Turton and Entwistle reservoir, also near Bolton. The embankment was planned to be 128 ft high, but was completed to only 108 ft. These examples furnished reliable information for calculating the yield of reservoirs in such districts, and the data so obtained were used for the design of larger schemes, such as the Longdendale works for Manchester.

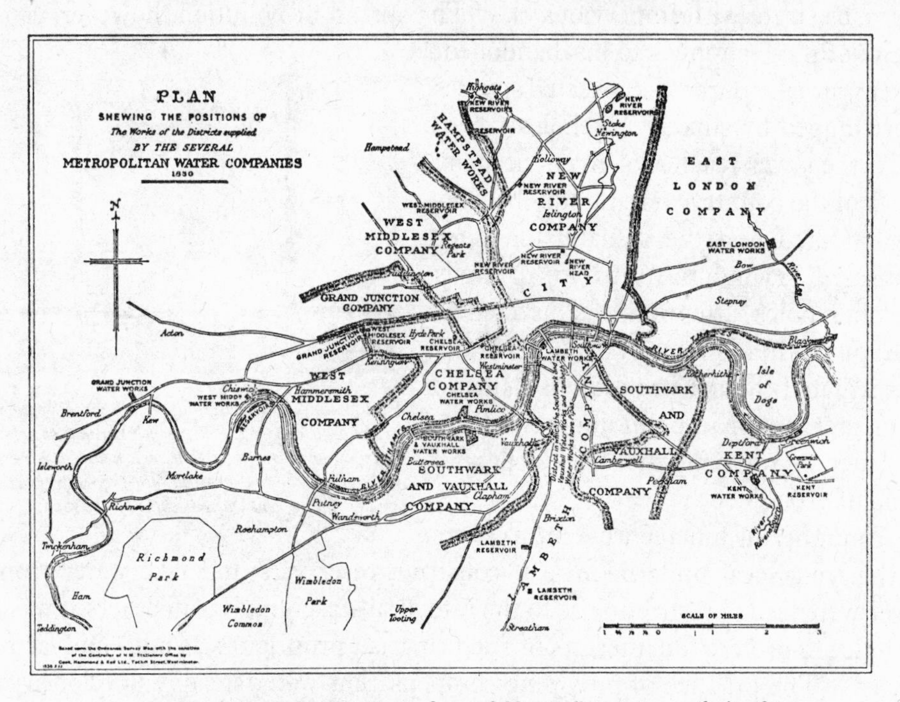

FIGURE 281—*Plan showing positions of several Metropolitan water-works in 1850.*

In 1848 Manchester Corporation obtained parliamentary powers to utilize the Longdendale Valley, about 10 miles east of the city. Five embankments were constructed forming reservoirs; two, at a low level, were used solely for storing compensation-water. The scheme was begun in 1848, and water was sent to the city in 1851. The yield of these works is 19 m gallons a day, but even by 1879 this was considered to be insufficient, and Manchester put on foot the construction of the Thirlmere scheme, to take water from the Lake District through an aqueduct 96 miles long.

The Longdendale scheme was the first important supply-scheme in Great Britain based upon impounded water. Considering the limited information and experience available at that time, the fact that such works are still in satisfactory use reflects great credit on the engineers, J. F. Bateman and G. H. Hill. These two men were also responsible for the Loch Katrine scheme for Glasgow.

Embankments were generally constructed at that time by forming a central watertight core of puddled clay, flanked on each side with suitable filling-material. The face towards the water was covered with stone pitching, and the outer face with soil, sown with grass. To prevent water from passing under the dam through permeable strata, a trench was first dug down to a watertight foundation such as shale or solid rock, and then refilled with puddled clay. This mode of construction of earth-dams is still practised in Britain, but concrete has replaced the clay below ground. It was not unusual for landslips to occur during and after construction, but by the addition of more material the dams were usually made satisfactory.

An example of the serious consequences of failure is provided by a disaster that took place in 1864, when the Dale Dike reservoir for Sheffield was filled for the first time. Within a few hours, the embankment settled and allowed the water to overflow the top, and about a quarter of the dam was washed away. The consequent release of water resulted in the loss of 244 lives and a considerable amount of damage to property. The water company was required to pay £373 000 in compensation, and a special Act of Parliament was passed to enable it to raise the money.

The early earth-dams were mainly in the Pennines, where absence of sound rock near the surface generally precluded the construction of other types of dams, notwithstanding the invention of artificial Roman cement by Edgar Dobbs in 1810. This was followed in 1824 by Joseph Aspdin's patent for Portland cement (p 448). The first large masonry dam, the Vyrnwy dam in north Wales, for supplying Liverpool, was constructed during the years 1881–92. This dam is 1172 ft long and 161 ft high.

The development of water-supply on the European continent followed a pattern similar to that experienced in England, and in some instances British practice was introduced and British capital employed. In Belgium, it was only in the eighteenth century that local authorities took an active interest in the supply of water by establishing public wells, and not until the nineteenth century were underground catchments, surface-water dams, and distribution-systems developed. Denmark was always able to draw upon its underground resources, and although the first centralized supply, with pumping-arrangements and iron pipes, was not established until 1853, at Odense, other cities followed suit a few years later. In Finland the first water-works were established in Helsinki in 1876.

At the beginning of the nineteenth century the supply of water to Paris, which then had a population of slightly over 500 000, was obtained partly from springs but principally from the Seine. From 1786 the water was sold by water-carriers, who hawked the water obtained from public tanks known as *fontaines marchandes*, but from 1819 it was forbidden to fill the water-carts from these fountains. In 1821 experiments in filtration were commenced, and during 1834–41 an artesian well 547 metres in depth was sunk in the middle of the Place de Breteuil at Grenelle. Subsequently, in 1856, Eugène Belgrand (1810–78) initiated the system of dual supply which is in use at the present time, the supply for public services being obtained from the Seine and the Ourcq canal, and the domestic supply from distant springs.

Germany in 1770 already possessed about 140 central waterworks that provided an intermittent supply, but by 1867 over 140 large towns were using modern systems, chiefly municipally owned.

In the Netherlands drinking-water supplies developed rather late, and it was not until the beginning of the nineteenth century that water was obtained from a depth. The Amsterdam works came into being in 1853, with Dutch initiative but with the aid of English experts and money. In Switzerland, about the same time, central water-supply systems were being set up in the towns.

The dams built during the seventeenth, eighteenth, and nineteenth centuries in the vicinity of the Belgrade forest at Istanbul, as well as the viaducts built by Sinan (1489?–1587), indicated remarkable foresight on the part of the Turks. It is worth recording an ingenious method used by these pioneers to determine the suitability of drinking-water. Pieces of cotton-wool were weighed, moistened with different samples of water, and dried in the sun. The water was considered the best that left the weight of the piece of cotton the most nearly unchanged.

Examples of important early European dams include one constructed in France in 1843. This arched dam, the Zola-canal dam, was built in masonry and was 118 ft high. Some masonry dams for irrigation reservoirs were built in Spain in the sixteenth and eighteenth centuries. An example is the old Puentes dam, constructed in 1785–91 across the river Guadalentin. This dam failed in 1802, because of unsatisfactory foundations.

From the seventeenth century onwards, the sinking of deep wells was practised to obtain water from pervious underground sources, and quite frequently it was found that the water would rise to the surface and overflow. This type of well, known as an artesian well, was so called because the phenomenon was stated to have been first observed in Artois in 1126.

In the London area wells were driven down to the bed of water-saturated sand that underlies the London clay, but with the increasing number of wells this source of supply soon became exhausted. Subsequent wells were driven into the chalk, where the water was under pressure. The large amount of water abstracted from this source has had the effect of lowering the water-levels considerably. An example of such a well is one sunk in 1845 to a depth of 396 ft, at Trafalgar Square, to supply water to the fountains. The water-level then was 112 ft below the surface of the ground; by 1875 it was 141 ft, and in 1911 the well was abandoned when the water had fallen to 236 ft. The water is still falling and was 283 ft down in 1937.

The development of water-supply was naturally influenced to a considerable extent by the law relating to the ownership of the water abstracted. The law with regard to the question of ownership in underground water became definitely settled, so far as Britain is concerned, by the famous case of *Chasemore* v *Richards* in 1859. The defendants had sunk a well about a quarter of a mile from the river Wandle for the purpose of supplying water to Croydon, and in so doing abstracted water that formerly flowed through the ground into the river, thus decreasing the flow past the plaintiff's mill. It was held that unless the water is flowing in a known or defined channel, such as a mine-adit, the owner of the land has an unlimited right to abstract the water by means of a well, and is not liable for any injury to those above or below him. Subject to statutory control, this general rule of law obtains today.

The driving-power of pumps during the period we are now discussing was steam, and in about 1800 a number of steam-pumps, almost all designed by James Watt, were in use (p 181). The expiration of Watt's patent in 1800 led to further developments; in 1812 Trevithick produced the first high-pressure condensing pumping-engine, known as the Cornish engine (p 188). These engines were developed primarily for removing water from mine-workings in Cornwall and elsewhere, but some were used by water undertakings. The necessity for higher pumping-heads and for pumping against variable pressure caused the development of compound rotative beam-engines (p 191), and a number were built in 1848.

The hydraulic ram (vol V, ch 22) was invented and patented by a Frenchman, J. M. Montgolfier, in 1797, but did not come into general use until 1840. In 1868 John Blake of Accrington patented an improved type of ram capable of raising up to 100 000 gallons a day.

For the distribution of water, wooden mains up to 10 inches in diameter, and generally bored from elm trees, were in common use during the seventeenth and eighteenth centuries (figure 282); they were not prohibited in London until the passing of the Metropolis Paving Act of 1817. In some of the forested areas of Scandinavia and central Europe wooden pipes are still in use. Although cast iron pipes had earlier been used in small quantities at several places—for example, by the Chelsea Waterworks Company in 1746 and in Edinburgh in 1755—this date marks approximately the beginning of the use of cast iron pressure-pipes on a large scale. As long ago as the latter half of the seventeenth century, however, cast iron had been used for the mains of the Marly water-works installation at Versailles (figures 93 and 94). They comprised over 15 miles

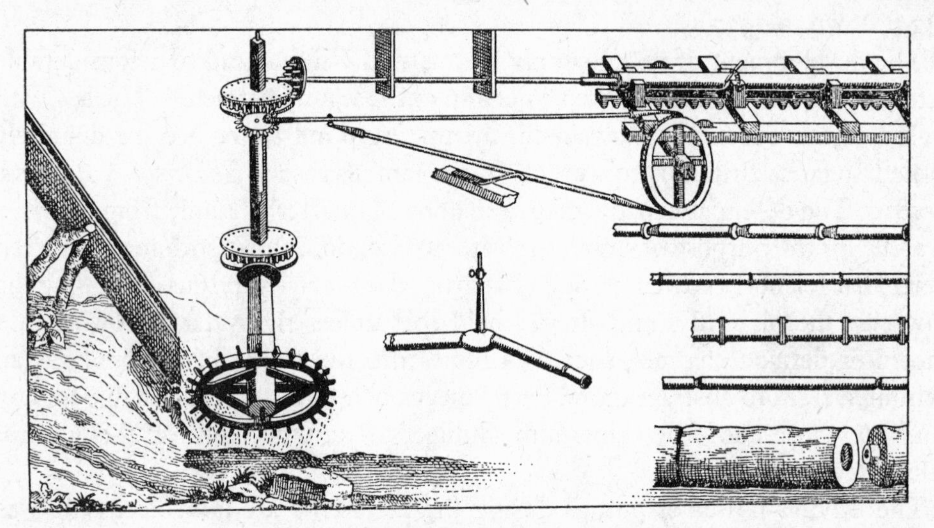

FIGURE 282—*The boring of wooden pipes, mid-eighteenth-century, showing use of water-wheel as source of power. Various methods of jointing are seen on the right.*

of piping, in lengths of about 1 metre only, having flanged joints. The diameter ranged from $1\frac{3}{4}$ to 20 in. The spigot-and-socket joint was invented by Thomas Simpson about 1785. Sandstone pipes had been tried in many towns, including Manchester (*c* 1812), but the stone was generally unable to withstand a pressure of more than 30–40 ft head of water and their use was discontinued. The West Middlesex Water Company experimented with stone pipes at the beginning of the nineteenth century, but experienced considerable leakage from them, and eventually substituted iron for wood. Until about 1850 all iron pipes were cast horizontally, but in 1846 D. Y. Stewart obtained a patent for producing vertically-cast iron pipes, and from that date the horizontal method became obsolescent. The longevity of cast iron is well known, and in Edinburgh a main of 7 to 9 in diameter, laid in 1790 to replace a wooden pipe, is still in use. In 1825, butt-welded steel tubes were introduced for distribution pipes.

Early forms of stop-valves in pipe-lines were generally very crude and inefficient, and as higher pressures were used the need for a better valve became apparent. Ball-valves were mentioned in 1748; before that the supply to cisterns had to be regulated by taps. In 1839 James Nasmyth (1808–90), at the request of the East London Water Company, produced a double-faced, wedge-form sluice-valve, and this forms the basis of valves employed today. Even earlier, in 1824, an old box-valve of peculiar design was fixed on the outlet end of a 15-in pipe-line controlling the flow from the Belmont reservoir (figure 283); it was discovered when repairs to the reservoir became necessary a hundred years later.

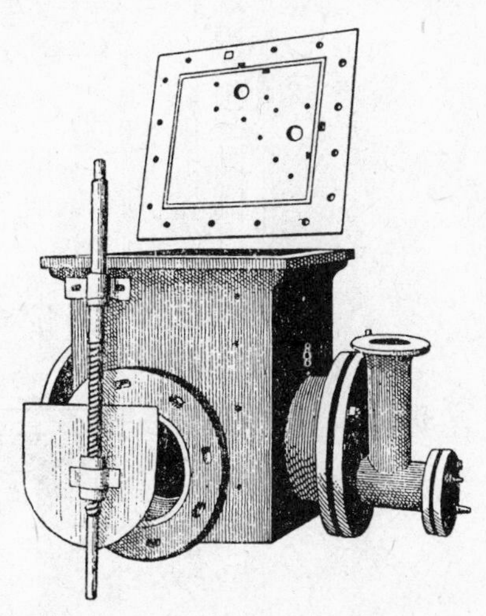

FIGURE 283—*Box-valve from the outlet end of a pipe in the Belmont reservoir. 1824.*

In 1797 Giovanni Venturi (1746–1822) postulated what is now termed the 'Venturi law', namely that in passing through converging pipes fluids under pressure gain speed and lose head, and vice versa for diverging pipes. Before 1800, it was possible to measure the rate of flow of water in open channels, but there were no means of metering flows in closed pipes. The first meter for this purpose was patented by Thomas Kennedy in 1852, and was at once used extensively by many water undertakings (figure 284). G. F. Deacon in 1873 invented a simple rising-disk meter that showed on a drum-chart the actual flow of water from hour to hour. This meter was devised to record the use and misuse of water, and is still employed. In 1887 the American engineer Clemens Herschel devised a simple instrument for the exact measurement of the flow of fluids, based on Venturi's law, and the Venturi principle is now very widely adopted for metering flows in pipes, tunnels, and channels.

The necessity for clear, clean water in the dyeing and bleaching trades prompted some Lancashire manufacturers to filter their water by passing it through beds of sand. In 1791 James Peacock (1738–1814) took out a patent for passing water upwards through beds of graded sand. Slow sand-filters were successfully constructed for treating water for public supply at Paisley in 1804, at Greenock in 1827, and at Chelsea in the same year. Later, such filters were built in many parts of Britain and elsewhere in Europe, and in the United States. Before such filters were introduced, the attempts to purify river-water consisted simply of allowing the impurities to settle in subsiding-reservoirs, but this was found to be inadequate. Water from upland reservoirs and from springs was generally considered to be naturally suitable, and was often supplied untreated in any way until after the introduction of chlorination in 1905. Early work on filters was concentrated on the clarification of turbid waters, and for a long time

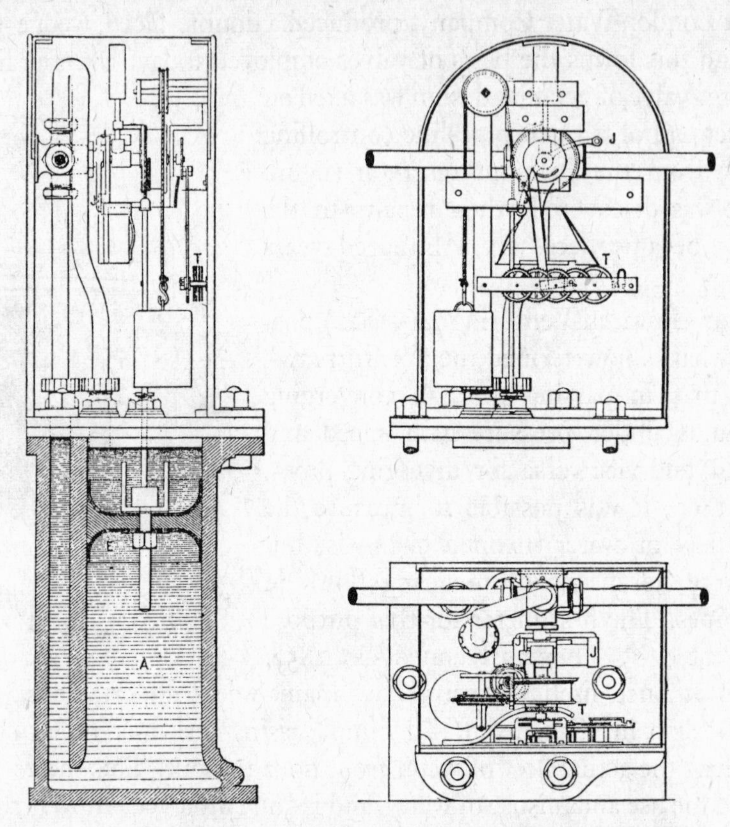

FIGURE 284—*Water-meter from the patent specification (1852) of Thomas Kennedy.* (Left) *Side view;* (top rlght) *back view;* (bottom right) *plan. This was the first meter for measuring flow in closed pipes. The quantity of water passing through the meter is recorded on the gauges at* T *by filling and emptying the chamber* A *by means of the piston* E. *The direction of movement of the piston is controlled by a valve operated by a hammer* J.

the production of a clear water was the sole test of efficiency. The action of filters was not understood until the development of the science of bacteriology. The slow sand-filter provides both a microscopic screen and an efficient biological instrument that is capable of removing bacteria from the water.

The filters designed by James Simpson for the Chelsea Water Company were the first to be built in London, and the form has not materially changed since then. Tunnels of loose bricks covered with tiles were laid on the floor; above this was placed a 2-ft layer of washed coarse gravel, and then a layer of washed fine sand. The bulk of the sediment was retained in the top 3 in of sand, which was removed, cleaned, and replaced from time to time. This bed was used till 1856, when the company's intake was moved to Surbiton. The first statutory provision for filtration was in the Lambeth Company's Act of 1834.

In 1849 and 1853–4 there were serious outbreaks of Asiatic cholera in London, which were traced by physicians to drinking-water derived from sources contaminated by excreted matter. The water from the Thames had become increasingly foul and these occurrences roused public feeling to a high pitch. The 1849 epidemic led to the passing of the Metropolis Water Act of 1852, which precluded the abstraction of water from the tidal reaches of the Thames, and made it compulsory for the water to be filtered. New sources of water were not to be tapped unless approved by an inspector of the Board of Trade.

The art of softening water was first developed in Great Britain. Although pioneer work had been done before the nineteenth century, it was not until 1841 that Thomas Clark (1801–67) was granted a patent for a 'New Method of Rendering Certain Waters Less Impure and Less Hard'. The varying action of water on soap had long been attributed to its hardness or softness, and in 1856 Clark formulated his famous scale of hardness, whereby one grain of lime or other soap-destroying ingredient in one gallon of water (or 1/70 000) corresponded to one degree of hardness. The first municipal water-softening plant in London was installed at Plumstead in 1854, but the idea of softening did not meet with great favour. In 1862, when the predecessors of the present East Surrey Water Company were constituted a water undertaking, the compulsory softening of water was first introduced in a private Act.

Sterilization of water was virtually unknown until the beginning of the twentieth century, but in 1897 Dr Sims Woodhead used calcium hypochlorite for the disinfection of water-mains at Maidstone following an outbreak of enteric fever.

BIBLIOGRAPHY

DICKINSON, H. W. 'Water Supply of Greater London.' Newcomen Society, London. 1954.
HOBBS, A. T. (Ed.). 'Manual of British Water Supply Practice' (2nd ed.). Heffer, Cambridge, for The Institution of Water Engineers, London. 1954.
ROBINS, F. W. 'The Story of Water Supply.' Oxford University Press, London. 1946.
WALTERS, R. C. S. 'The Nation's Water Supply.' Nicholson & Watson, London. 1936.

16

PART II
SANITARY ENGINEERING: SANITATION

J. RAWLINSON

It has been recognized from the earliest times that drainage, whether natural or artificial, is essential to the health and comfort of mankind. Surplus rainfall and the waste-products of humanity must be disposed of, and as populations have increased and centres of civilization have grown it has become necessary to augment or replace natural drainage systems by large and sometimes costly engineering works.

I. ANCIENT AND MEDIEVAL DRAINAGE SYSTEMS

There is evidence that at the palace of Minos at Knossos in Crete a drainage system existed before 1500 B.C., and that in many respects it was similar to the installations of much more recent times. Excavations have revealed that stone ducts and terracotta pipes conveyed rain-water from roofs and terraces to rain-spouts in the outer walls. A latrine on the ground floor was connected to a main drain, and provision was made for flushing it with rain-water. The drainage pipes were tapered so that the narrow end of one pipe fitted into the broader end of the next.

From remains that may still be seen it is apparent that sewers were to be found in ancient Greek cities. Ruins of houses have been discovered which show that they were equipped with closets of simple design. These were made so that they could be flushed with water, and sometimes were connected to a sewer in the street.

In the sixth century B.C. Rome possessed an extensive network of sewers draining the marshy ground lying between the hills on which the city was built. Small sewers collected the water and discharged it into a larger one known as the *cloaca maxima*, of which parts still exist. This sewer was probably built about 2500 years ago as an open drainage-channel and was roofed-in about 300 or 400 years later. Its dimensions were approximately 15 ft to the top of the arch, by about 15 ft wide. After the fall of the Roman Empire little progress was made in sanitation for some centuries.

In the Middle Ages the problem of drainage was more simply solved than it is today because it was the custom merely to throw all household refuse and human excreta into the street. By-laws issued by some town authorities forbidding this practice were ignored by the populace, since there was normally no alternative method of disposal (vol II, p 532).

In the records of Paris for the year 1412 a reference is made to 'the great drain'. This was apparently the brook of Ménilmontant, into which the drainage from the gutters in the streets was discharged. No improvement to this watercourse was made until 1740, when it was walled in; some time afterwards it was arched over. In 1513 the *coutume* (common law) in Paris decreed that every house should have its own privy, but as late as the eighteenth century it was still the prevalent custom to throw refuse into the street. A survey carried out in Madrid in 1773 disclosed that the royal palace did not contain even one privy.

II. STREET-CLEANSING

In the City of London there was considerable concern about the insanitary conditions of the streets. 'The plague had recurred from time to time in England since the Black Death in 1349. Kites and ravens were protected birds and they and the pigs which roamed about grew fat on the offal in the streets. Dogs were innumerable.' In the City itself instructions were issued from time to time to secure some degree of cleanliness, but usually these had little effect. Rubbish of all descriptions continued to be deposited in the streets, and the liquid from it, augmented in time of rainfall, ran down the central gutter into the nearest stream or ditch. After the fire of London in 1666 lay-stalls, or temporary dumping-places for rubbish, were set up in the streets, and orders were given for the refuse to be deposited there for later removal. Scavengers were appointed in each ward of the City; their duties were to supervise the cleansing of the streets. The holders of this office (Izaak Walton at one time held the position) were unpaid, and much of the work was done by rakers, who corresponded to the refuse-contractors of more recent days. As the City streets became increasingly built up, sites for lay-stalls became more difficult to find, and they were later replaced by fixed or movable boxes in which refuse was thrown. A charge was made for the removal of the rubbish by the rakers, who later became paid servants of the commissioners of sewers and afterwards of the City Corporation.

For the areas of the metropolis outside the City a number of Improvement Acts were passed during the eighteenth and early nineteenth centuries, which gave to vestries or special bodies of commissioners powers in regard to paving, cleansing, or lighting. Some of these powers required the householder to cleanse the pavement in front of his premises, and enabled the authorities to make arrangements with rakers for the sweeping of the carriage-way and the removal of dirt and rubbish. The Metropolitan Paving Act of 1817, known as Michael Angelo Taylor's Act,[1] codified these various Acts and remained the statute under which these works were carried out until the passing of the Metropolis Management Act, 1855. Among other things, the former Act required 'scavengers, rakers, or cleansers' to carry away at their own costs or charges the ordinary refuse, which they were empowered to retain. In those days, and even in more recent times, scavenging-contractors were willing to pay for the privilege of sweeping the streets and collecting the sweepings and household refuse, which they were able to sell at a profit.

Some authorities, such as the town council of Liverpool, took over the control of all cleansing operations and employed staff to carry out the work. The disposal of the refuse when it had been collected was a difficult problem. In many towns the contents of privies and domestic ash-pits were collected at the same time as the street-sweepings, and in Liverpool in 1866 it was estimated that the amount of refuse which had to be removed each month was as much as 64 000 tons. Some of the refuse was sold to farmers for use as a fertilizer, and sometimes markets could be found for other of the waste products, but there still remained a large quantity to be disposed of. This was done by sending it out to sea in barges and dumping it there; by burning it in specially built destructors; or by tipping it into disused chalk-pits or on waste land.

III. LAND-DRAINAGE AND SEWERAGE IN ENGLAND

In England complaints were frequently made in Parliament about the inadequacy of the land-drainage system, and from a very early date ordinances were issued to landowners to cleanse streams and ditches and to keep the banks in good order. In 1531 a 'Bill of Sewers' consolidated the earlier enactments and became the statute from which commissions responsible for drainage drew their authority.

The problem became intensified with the rapid increase in the population. The first census, taken in 1801, returned a figure of approximately 10 500 000 for Great Britain, but in 1851 this had risen to 20 800 000 (p 489). The rapid development of the urban areas, which was among the effects of the industrial revolution, resulted in great masses of country-bred workers being flung into a miserable existence amid unhealthy living conditions in overcrowded towns. In this insanitary environment disease inevitably flourished, and the finding of means to combat it became a progressively serious and urgent problem for the authorities.

[1] Michael Angelo Taylor (1757–1834) was a barrister of Lincoln's Inn, a Member of Parliament for many years, and a privy councillor.

IV. HOUSE-DRAINAGE

By 1800 the houses of the well-to-do usually contained at least one privy, but for the poorer classes a common privy serving a number of houses was the generally accepted standard. The wealthier residential areas were comparatively well scavenged and night-soil men emptied the privies every night. Even in the poorer districts collections were made at intervals, although these were usually very irregular. Compared with modern standards these arrangements do not seem very satisfactory, but in these matters England was at the time ahead of her neighbours. Smollett complained of the scarcity of privies in France and of their filthiness where they did exist.

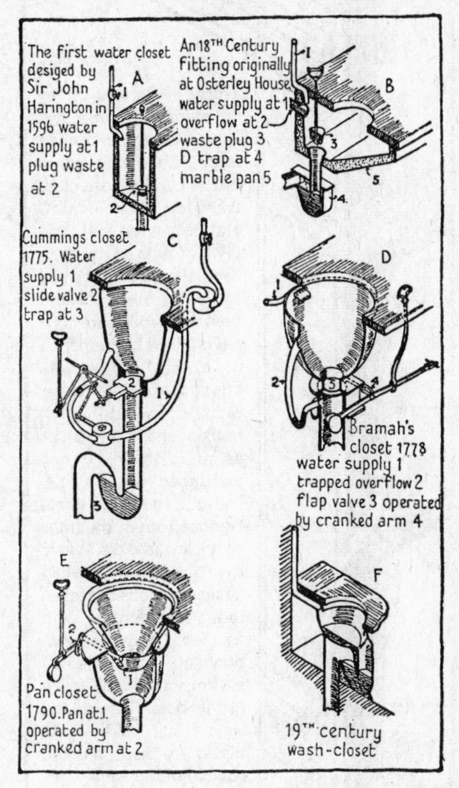

FIGURE 285—*The evolution of the water-closet.*

Collections of night-soil were still being made at the end of the century; in by-laws made in 1891 the London County Council prescribed that this should be done only between the hours of 4 a.m. and 10 a.m. from March to October and between 6 a.m. and 12 noon from November to February. This was to ensure that there was sufficient daylight to allow the work to be carried out efficiently, and to give as little offence as possible when the refuse was being transported through the streets.

By the end of the eighteenth century the water-closet in a very elementary form began to be introduced.[1] The apparatus was considered to be such an advance in sanitary arrangements that once one was installed in the house, then all difficulties of sewage-removal would at once be overcome. As, however, the closet was more often than not built into an enclosed cupboard and connected by an unventilated pipe direct to a cesspool it became a more virulent source of infection than even its forerunner had been. Foul gases were now conveyed directly into the house from the evil-smelling cesspool, usually built in the basement. In order to prevent the passage of these bad odours, traps containing a water-seal

[1] The valve water-closet was described, with figures, by Sir John Harington (1561–1612) in his book 'The Metamorphosis of Ajax', 1596.

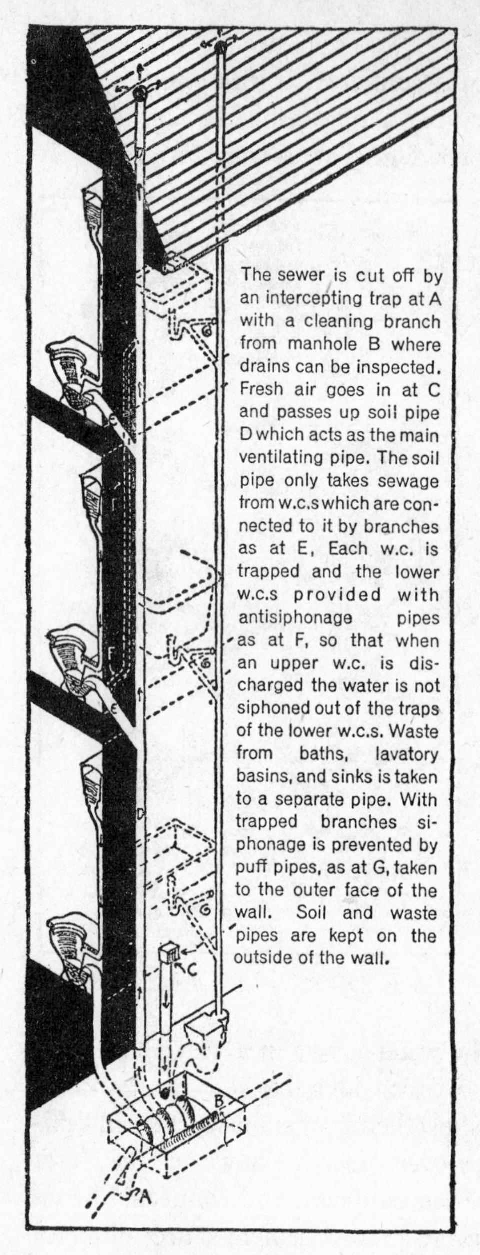

FIGURE 286—*The English two-pipe drainage system.*

were introduced. The first patent for this kind of trap was taken out by John Gaillait in 1782, for 'the invention of an entire new machine . . . a stink trap which will entirely prevent the very disagreeable smells from drains and sewers'.

Later developments and improvements in the design and construction of water-closets are shown in figure 285, but it was a long time before satisfactory methods of connecting them to the cesspool or sewer were brought into use. The two-pipe system of house-drainage shown in the diagram (figure 286), which effectively prevents all noxious odours from penetrating into the house, was coming into use in England at the close of the nineteenth century. This system requires separate pipes for the water-closet and bath- or lavatory-waste, but the contents of each pass eventually to the same drain.

Water-closets began to be installed in increasing numbers in the early 1800s, but drainage authorities frequently insisted that they should be connected to cesspools and not to the sewers. As the cesspools were seldom emptied, their contents frequently overflowed and the surrounding ground became sodden and stagnant. In spite of the veto imposed by the authorities, some cesspools were connected to the sewers in attempts to overcome the intolerable conditions. Even the sewers, however, were very often ineffective for this purpose. With their shallow gradients they retained for long periods the sewage which was discharged into them, with the result that it became putrescent and offensive. As improvements were made to the sewers, and in an endeavour to overcome the nuisance caused by the cesspools, it eventually became compulsory for all water-closets in the larger towns to be connected to the sewers.

Although this action produced beneficial results it also had the effect of greatly increasing the flow in the sewers, and as these usually discharged into the nearest river the pollution was transferred from the ground on which the houses stood to the river which flowed through their midst. A further problem was thus created which could be solved only by the execution of large-scale sewerage works.

FIGURE 287—*Deepening sewer under Fleet Street. 1845.*

In the latter half of the nineteenth century many large towns carried out extensive works for the better drainage of their areas. Liverpool obtained parliamentary powers in 1847, as a result of which the town council was designated the sole governing sanitary authority for the paving, sewerage, drainage, and sanitary improvement of the town. It at once proceeded to build a series of new sewers. Edinburgh constructed a trunk sewer in 1864, to which a number of the earlier sewers were connected.

V. DESCRIPTION OF DRAINAGE-WORKS IN LONDON

The drainage-works carried out in London between 1850 and 1900 may be regarded as typical of those executed in many other towns, and a short description of them will thus serve as an example of the schemes of sewerage that formed a feature of this period.

In 1843 the Poor Law Commissioners who had been appointed to investigate the sanitary conditions of the labouring population drew attention to the defective state of sewerage and drainage, and a commission was appointed to inquire into the means of improving the health of the people.

Some works to improve local drainage, such as the deepening of the sewer under Fleet Street, were carried out at this time (figure 287). Yet the banks of the Thames, in its wider reaches between Waterloo and Westminster bridges for instance, became covered with vast accumulations of foul and offensive mud which were exposed at low tide. Cholera epidemics in 1849 and 1853–4 (p 503), from which nearly 20 000 people died, emphasized the gravity of the problem caused by the pollution of the Thames, from which much of London's drinking-water was drawn. The accompanying illustration (figure 288) shows the Fleet river in 1844; the chutes discharging from the houses into the river may be clearly seen. Between 1848 and 1855 no fewer than six commissions were appointed, and numerous designs for improving the drainage were prepared and considered; but in spite of their efforts conditions became so intolerable that Parliament in 1855 decided to set up a new authority to deal with the problem. Under the Metropolis Local Management Act of 1855 the Metropolitan Board of Works was created. The Act provided that the Board 'shall make such sewers and works as they may think necessary for preventing all or any part of the sewage within the Metropolis from flowing into the Thames in or near the Metropolis . . .' Sir Joseph Bazalgette (1819–91) was appointed engineer to the Board, and within a year he put forward plans for complying with this order.

FIGURE 288—*The river Fleet in 1844, showing the chutes from the houses discharging directly into the stream.*

Up to this time the main sewers—which were the old water-courses and are now mostly bricked over—flowed to the Thames, mostly at right-angles to it. In order to prevent their contents flowing into and polluting the Thames, Bazalgette proposed to build large sewers running west to east, roughly parallel to the river, which would intercept the flow in these sewers and convey it to outfalls some distance down the river. There were to be three intercepting sewers on the north side of the river and two on the south, and the outfalls at Barking in Essex and Crossness in Kent were about 12 miles below London Bridge. Figure 289 shows a section of the low-level sewer on the north bank of the Thames. From Westminster bridge to Blackfriars bridge this sewer was incorporated in a new embankment, which served the triple purposes of providing a suitable route for the sewer, a wide roadway over it, and reclamation from the river of 37 acres of land which formerly consisted of evil-smelling mudbanks. The subway above the sewer was built to contain the services of public utility companies, in order to avoid disturbance of the road and footway when repairs and maintenance became necessary. Bazalgette's proposals entailed the construction of over 100 miles of large-diameter sewers, and of three pumping-stations to lift the sewage so that its flow to the outfalls could continue by gravity.

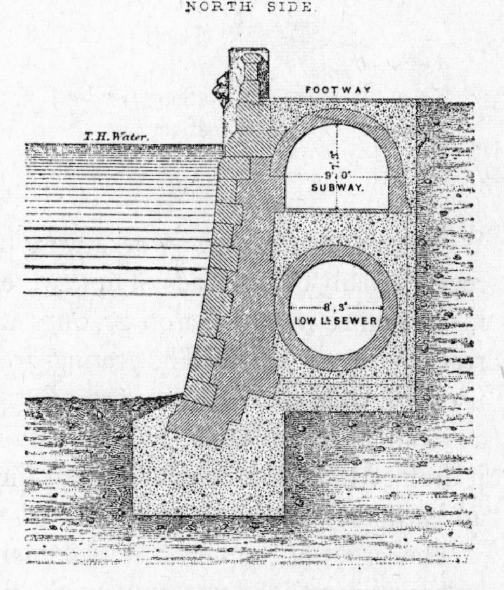

FIGURE 289—*Section of Thames Embankment, showing subway and low-level sewer.*

The design of the system of intercepting sewers provided for a daily flow of sewage to the outfalls of 5 cu ft or $31\frac{1}{4}$ gallons per head of the population, the population being taken as 2 300 000 on the north side of the Thames and 1 150 000 on the south side, a total of 3 450 000. In addition, rain-water amounting to 178 000 000 gallons a day on the north of the river and 108 000 000 gallons on the south side was allowed for. The latter quantities represent $\frac{1}{4}$-in and $\frac{1}{10}$-in of rainfall respectively, distributed over the 24 hours.

A disadvantage of the proposal was that in times of heavy rainfall the intercepting sewers would become surcharged, but provision was made for the excess storm-water—carrying with it a certain amount of diluted sewage—to flow over weirs into the old main-line sewers direct to the river. The points of intersection were so designed that the intercepting sewers, while carrying away to the outfalls any sewage coming down the old main-line sewers during dry weather, permitted any excessive flow due to rainfall to run away partly in the intercepting sewers and partly by short cuts down the old main-line sewers to the river.

All Bazalgette's plans had been carried out by 1875, and for many years few additions were made to the sewers in spite of the fact that the population and the discharge of sewage and rain-water were constantly increasing.

The effect of the new drainage system was remarkable. The condition of the Thames in the metropolitan area was considerably improved, and the unhealthy conditions, owing to defective drainage, previously suffered by many of those living on low-lying land near the river, were largely remedied.

Similar drainage-works were carried out at this time on the continent (figures 290, 291). In Paris a detailed survey of all the drains had been made in 1833, and a considerable amount of drainage-work was carried out, as the following table shows:

Year	*Total length of drains (of all kinds) in use*
1663	10 380 metres
1806	23 530 ,,
1832	40 330 ,,
1837	75 565 ,,
1863	350 000 ,,

While the new drainage-works were in progress, the opportunity was taken to regrade many of the roads. These were formerly concave in section, with a drain in the centre in which iron gratings were set at intervals to allow the water to reach the sewer below. The gratings frequently became blocked, and planks were used to enable pedestrians to cross the road; vehicles meanwhile travelled through a swamp of mud. During reconstruction the centre of the road was raised, so that it drained to gutters at each side; at the same time more headroom was provided and a sewer built beneath.

The larger of the new sewers contained sufficient room for a footpath on one or both sides of the water-channel, and in these, as well as in the smaller ones, provision was made for gas- and water-mains to be carried on brackets built into the sides or the floor (figure 290).

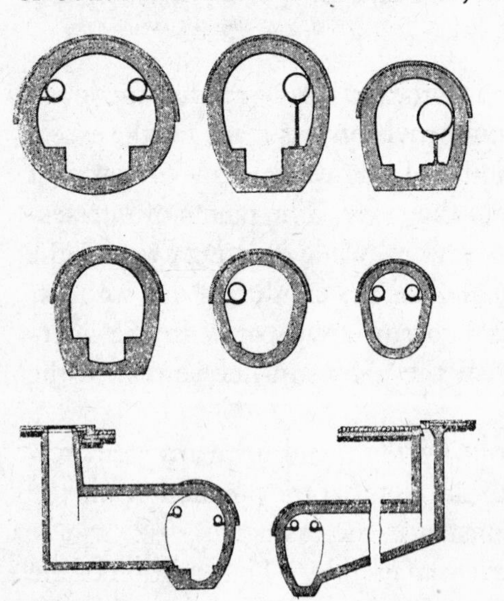

FIGURE 290—*Cross-sections of various drains in Paris.*

VI. TYPES AND SIZES OF SEWERS

Types, sizes, and shapes of sewers vary a great deal. The drainage from a dwelling-house normally passes through a stoneware pipe of small diameter, glazed to render it impervious, into a larger pipe or small brick-built sewer in the street. This in turn may connect with a larger sewer, the drainage flowing next into the main sewer and finally to the intercepting or outfall sewer. In the earlier days of their use stoneware pipes were unsatisfactory, not so much on account of defects in their manufacture as owing to the lack of knowledge and skill in methods of jointing and fixing them together. Today they are laid on a bed of concrete and benched up with the same material, a process which prevents fracture, and jointed with cement. Earlier, however, they were laid direct in the ground with no support, and the

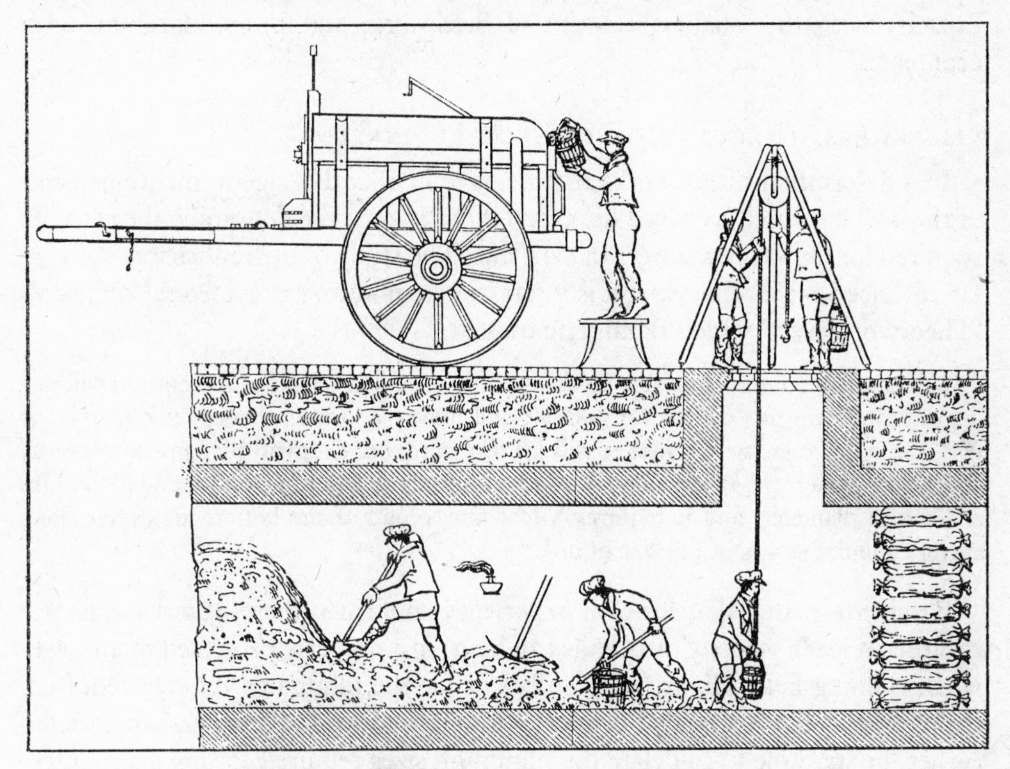

FIGURE 291—*Clearing drains in Paris, early nineteenth century.*

joints were made with clay. Frequently the joints broke apart and allowed the sewage to percolate into the surrounding ground. This gave rise to considerable controversy between those who recommended pipes—among whom Sir Edwin Chadwick (1800–90), the great English sanitary reformer, was a leading figure—and their opponents who preferred the larger brick sewers.

Brick sewers in Britain range from about 2 ft 6 in by 3 ft 9 in to about 12 ft or more in diameter. In Paris they are generally larger, the smallest being 5 ft 6 in high by 2 ft 3 in wide. For local drainage, where the flow is not constant, a sewer of oval section, with the narrow part at the bottom, is found to be more efficient than one circular in section. The reason is that in dry weather, when the flow is small, the former shape gives a greater depth of liquid and consequently greater velocity of flow and scouring-power. The broader section at the top gives greater room for the passage of storm-water, and for the workmen engaged in cleansing and maintenance. Intercepting and outfall sewers in which the flow is more constant are circular in section, a shape which combines the greatest strength and capacity with the smallest amount of brickwork, and is therefore the most economical.

VII. SEWERS: CALCULATION OF SIZES REQUIRED

In a description of his works that he gave in 1865 Bazalgette mentions some of the data on which he based his calculations in order to determine the capacity required for the various sewers in his plans. The study of hydraulics was not very far advanced at that time, and it is interesting to note an extract from Robinson's 'Theory of Rivers' which Bazalgette quoted:

> We learn from observation that a velocity of 3 inches per second at the bottom will just begin to work up fine clay fit for pottery, and however firm and compact it may be, it will tear up. A velocity of 6 inches will lift fine sand, 8 inches will lift sand as coarse as linseed, 12 inches will sweep along fine gravel, 24 inches will roll along rounded pebbles an inch in diameter, and it requires 3 feet per second at the bottom to sweep along shivery angular stones of the size of an egg.

Bazalgette stated that his own experience confirmed these observations. He regarded a mean velocity of 1½ miles an hour, in a properly protected main sewer when running half-full, as being sufficient for the minimum velocity required. By using this figure and the data regarding population and water-supply cited earlier, he was able to calculate the minimum sizes required for his main, intercepting, and outfall sewers.

London, Liverpool, and other populous cities situated on large estuaries have a combined system of drainage; that is, the same sewer conveys both sewage and rain-water. Some towns have been drained on the 'separate' system, which provides that rain-water is carried away separately to a stream or water-course, while the sewage is taken by a different system of sewers to the outfall or sewage-disposal works. The advantage of the separate system is that a smaller volume of material has to be purified and treated, a matter which will be dealt with later.

VIII. SEWERS: MAINTENANCE, CLEANSING, VENTILATION, AND REPAIRS

A well designed and well built brick sewer has a very long life. As it is below ground it is little subject to the effect of changes of temperature and to alternating wet and dry conditions. In the course of time the bottom, or invert as it is called, may become worn, but this can be repaired.

Inspection, cleansing, and maintenance of the sewers is carried out by gangs of men who regularly patrol them. In the older sewers, which, as has been stated, were frequently bricked-in streams, no alteration to the original gradients was made when they were enclosed, and consequently sand and grit are quickly deposited. This deposit is removed at suitable intervals while still maintaining the sewage-flow. It is shovelled up and placed in skeps, which are drawn up to the surface at the nearest man-hole, as in figure 291.

In order to carry out repairs to the sewer it is necessary to direct the flow into an adjoining sewer. This is achieved by using a sluice known as a penstock; it is a large iron flap or door which can completely close the sewer.

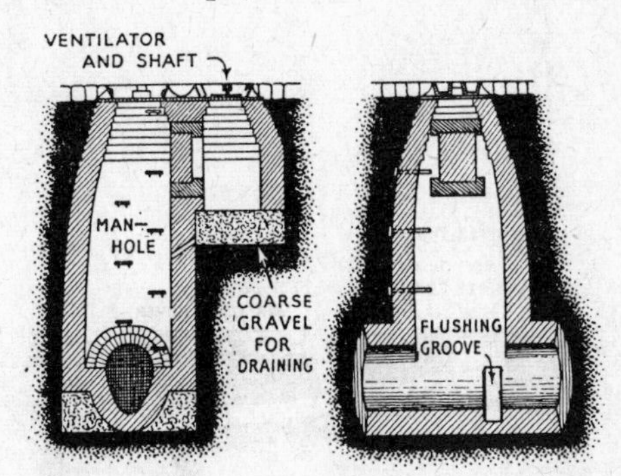

FIGURE 292—*Types of manholes and ventilating shafts on brick sewers, 1878. The covers over the manholes were airtight; those over the ventilating shafts were open and hinged so that the dirt collected at the bottom of them could be removed by scavengers.*

The safety of the men who work in sewers requires, among other things, that there should be adequate ventilation. To solve this problem without causing nuisance or annoyance has always been difficult. Sewers which took surface-water only were usually ventilated by gulleys at the sides of the streets, but this practice could no longer be tolerated when sewage was discharged into them. Until about 1830 none of these gullies contained traps, but in London during the following decade about 900 traps were formed in the surface-water gullies. The result was that, with the sewer-vents closed up, unpleasant emanations began to appear in other places. In 1852 the Board of Health proposed that openings should be made from the sewers to the centres of the roadways in order to reduce air- or gas-pressure in the sewers. The method of construction adopted in 1878 is shown in figure 292. In most towns this is still the current practice, and it has been found that the more ventilators there are the fewer are the complaints of nuisance caused by them.

In 1858 an experiment was made by Bazalgette and Colonel Haywood with a furnace built into the clock-tower of the Houses of Parliament; it was hoped that this would draw fetid air from the sewers and destroy it. It was not a success, as the radius within which the sewers were affected by the furnace was found to be very limited.

Another interesting system, devised at the end of the nineteenth century, was due to J. E. Webb: the details are shown in the illustration (figure 293). In addition to providing illumination for the streets, the gas-burners drew the air from the sewers and thus provided continuous ventilation. A number of these lamps were installed in Blackpool, where the cost at that time was stated to be £29 for installation and connexion to the gas-supply and sewer, with an annual maintenance cost of £16 10*s*. Other methods that have been tried include the fixing of pipe-ventilators to the sides of buildings, the use of the vent-pipes in the house-drainage system, the use of mechanically operated fans in conjunction with ventilating-shafts, and, on occasion, the draught created by neighbouring factory chimneys.

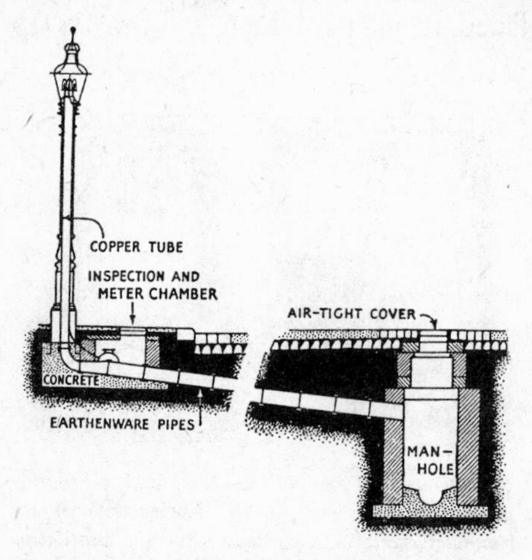

FIGURE 293—*Webb's sewer-ventilating lamp at Blackpool. The gases from the sewer pass up and through the lamp. Gas is burned at the top and the sewer gases are led through the hot zone and also burned.*

If the sewers are not ventilated there is a serious risk of explosions and of accidents to the sewermen, owing to the accumulation of explosive or injurious gases. In 1894 the London County Council obtained powers to prevent the discharge of improper substances into the sewers. Certain trade-wastes, although comparatively innocuous in themselves, may react with other wastes to produce poisonous gases. Gas from a leaking supply-pipe seeping into the sewer, and inflammable liquids, constitute additional hazards. The danger from all these causes is greatly reduced if there is sufficient ventilation.

It is interesting to record that, in spite of what might seem very adverse conditions, the health of the men who work and spend a great deal of their time in sewers is remarkably good; their sickness-rate compares well with that of other workers. There is a reference in Mayhew's 'London' to men called 'toshers', who in the early part of the nineteenth century used to search the sewers for metals, money, and valuables, referred to as 'tosh'. He writes:

It might be supposed that the sewer hunters would exhibit in their pallid faces the unmistakable evidence of their unhealthy employment. But this is far from the fact. Strange to say the sewer hunters are strong, robust and healthy men, generally florid in their complexion, while many of them know illness only by name. Some of the older men who head the gangs are between 60 and 80 years of age and have followed the employment during their whole lives. The men appear to have a fixed belief that the odour of the sewers contributes in a variety of ways to their general health.

The hazards already mentioned are not the only ones that sewer-workers are called upon to face. A sudden storm in a distant part of the drainage system may cause a rapid rise in the height of the water, and adequate means of warning must be installed to warn the men of this danger.

Sewer-men are also liable to attacks of leptospiral jaundice (Weil's disease, *Spirochaetosis icterohaemorrhagica*), which is due to the presence of rats and is contracted through abrasions in the skin. Precautionary instructions are issued to those likely to contract this disease, and the provision of special medical facilities has reduced the number of cases of infection.

IX. PUMPING-STATIONS AND PUMPING-PLANT

In a large town the sewage collected may have to travel considerable distances before it reaches the outfall. If the contours of the land are favourable it may flow for some part of the way by gravity, but it frequently happens that the sewage has to be lifted at intervals so that it may continue to flow on again by gravity. In London four pumping-stations were built and equipped with pumps for lifting the sewage to heights ranging from 14 to 41 ft. The plant in each case consisted of steam-driven double-acting beam engines driving ram or plunger pumps. At Abbey Mills pumping-station, on the north side of the river, eight engines each of 142 hp, and each with two boilers to provide steam, were installed. Their cylinders were 4 ft 6 inches in diameter with a stroke of 9 ft. Each engine worked two double-acting pumps having diameters of 3 ft 10½ in and a stroke of 4½ ft. The plant at this station was capable of lifting a maximum of 15 000 cu ft per minute of sewage and rain-water to a height of 36 ft.

The 'Illustrated London News' in 1865 referred to the pumping-machines at one of these stations as 'perhaps the finest specimens of engineering work in the country' and prophesied that 'they would exist for a very long time indeed, longer than anyone now living may hope to see'. The beam-engines of the station were in fact in service until 1952.

X. SEWAGE-DISPOSAL

Even when the sewage has been conveyed away from the town to the outfall on the river or sea the problem of its disposal still remains. Before the system of water-carriage came into being the night-soil from privies was sold for use as an agricultural fertilizer, and there were many advocates of the proposal that sewage should be allowed to flow on to the land so that its value should not be lost. In ancient Greece the disposal of sewage by land-irrigation was practised, and there is mention of the same procedure in use in Germany in the sixteenth century. Where the quantity of sewage was comparatively small, and where considerable areas of vacant land existed, this method was successfully employed in Britain. Thus at Salisbury the effluent from the pipe-sewers was allowed to flow over a number of fields in rotation, and at the time this was considered to be a satisfactory method of disposal.

The adoption of land-irrigation was considered by the Metropolitan Board of Works after complaints had been made of the nuisance caused in the region of the outfalls by the discharge of the whole of London's sewage into the Thames at that point. It was decided that the acquisition of sufficient land to enable the vast quantity of London sewage to be effectually filtered through the soil without nuisance to the local inhabitants would be attended with almost insurmountable difficulty, and that the cost would be prohibitive. As an alternative, the Board constructed works for the precipitation or chemical clarification of the sewage at both outfalls.

The chemical composition of sewage when it arrives at the disposal works is rather surprising. Nine hundred and ninety-nine parts out of every thousand are water. Only 0·1 per cent, or about 1·7 cu in per 1 cu ft, consists of impurities, and this amount can be divided again into inert solids, such as sand or grit, and organic material, such as faeces, fat, and vegetable matter, in roughly equal proportions. The organic matter may be in suspension or solution, and some of the solids are neither suspended nor dissolved but in a colloidal form. If left untreated the organic matter decomposes, taking up oxygen and releasing offensive gases in the process. When discharged into a river in sufficient quantity the sewage may denude the water of oxygen and render it incapable of supporting the life of fish and plants; it may also cause the formation of mud-banks and the silting up of the river.

In Germany and the United States of America, where sewage may be discharged into large rivers or lakes, it was customary to pass it through fine screens only, or in other words to give it merely the first stage of treatment. In Britain, however, with a much higher density of population in relation to the available rivers, it was found necessary to apply one or more further stages of purification. In the late nineteenth century this was carried out by chemical precipitation; by 1894 as many as 500 patents had been taken out for chemical precipitants.

One of these was known as the A.B.C. process, a name derived from the principal ingredients of the precipitant—alum, blood, and clay. This was a process carried out by the Native Guano Company. Aluminoferric, a substance containing aluminium and iron, was another common precipitant; lime also was widely used. At the London outfall-works a mixture of lime and ferrous sulphate was used for many years.

The method adopted was as follows. On entering the outfall-works the sewage flowed first through gratings or screens to remove the larger solids. It was then passed slowly through precipitation channels, where it received 4 grains of lime and 1 grain of ferrous sulphate for each gallon passed through the channels. After a channel had been in use for about 60 hours the flow through it was stopped and the contents were allowed 2 hours in which to settle. The liquid was then drawn off and discharged to the river as effluent. A deposit of wet sludge, about 4 ft in depth, remained; this was screened and pumped into sludge-settling channels where it was treated with 20 grains of lime and 10 grains of ferrous sulphate per gallon and again allowed to settle. The top liquid was then drawn off and pumped back into the outfall sewers; the sludge, which still contained about 93 per cent of water, was pumped to specially constructed ships which took it out to sea.

A disadvantage of this system was that as the precipitation channels were rectangular in shape the sludge lying at the bottom had to be pushed or swept to the outlet by men using squeegees. To overcome this drawback a very deep circular tank was used, first at Dortmund in Germany. Its lower part was shaped like a funnel and the sludge automatically slid down to the outlet, from which it was removed as necessary. Many attempts have been made to dry sewage and use it as manure, but its high water-content has made it very difficult to reduce it to a manageable commodity; up to 1900 comparatively little of it was used for agricultural purposes.

BIBLIOGRAPHY

BAZALGETTE, J. W. "The Main Drainage of London" (ed. by J. FORREST). *Min. Proc. Instn civ. Engrs*, **24**, 26, 1865.
BUER, M. C. 'Health, Wealth and Population, 1760–1815.' Routledge, London. 1926.
CHAMBERS'S ENCYCLOPAEDIA. Article: "Sanitation". Newnes, London. 1950.
DAWES, J. C. 'Public Cleansing.' H.M. Stationery Office, London. 1929.
EDINBURGH CITY COUNCIL. 'Main Drainage of the City of Edinburgh.' Edinburgh. 1955.
FINER, S. E. 'The Life and Times of Sir Edwin Chadwick.' Methuen, London. 1952.
JEPHSON, H. 'The Sanitary Evolution of London.' Unwin, London. 1907.
LIVERPOOL CITY COUNCIL. 'A Century of Progress.' 1947.
LONDON COUNTY COUNCIL. 'The Centenary of London's Main Drainage, 1855–1955.' Staples Press, London. 1955.

17

ROADS TO *c* 1900

R. J. FORBES

I. ROAD POLICY, 1600–1775

DURING the fifteenth and sixteenth centuries roads deteriorated rapidly. Those employed to make them or keep them in repair were ignorant farmers and uncouth forced labourers. The funds for repairs were scanty and new roads were rarely made. The oldest known technical document on road-building is a police ordinance of the Jülich-Berg (western Germany) district, of 1554. It states that timber, stones, and faggots found along the road could be used for repairs. It lays some stress on drainage by ditches, and specifies that the centre of the road should be well above the level of the ditches.

The pernicious use of bundles of faggots in building and repairing roads persisted up to the eighteenth century. Such fascines were used together with stones to fill pot-holes, but in central Europe even new roads were built on layers of fascines, which were believed to improve the drainage of the subsoil and to increase the carrying capacity of the road surface. However, more and more people voiced their doubts about the use of this material, and at Glatz (now Klodzko) the use of fascines was forbidden in 1767; in other parts of Germany fascine foundations were still laid as late as 1787. Fortunately, several factors were at work to improve road-building:

(*a*) a revival of interest in scientific road-building;
(*b*) the coming of wheeled traffic and an increase in travel;
(*c*) the growth of central authorities and their need of good roads; and
(*d*) the creation of administrative bodies dealing with roads and transport.

(*a*) The revival of interest in scientific road-building was part of the consequence of the renewed study of the documents and monuments of antiquity. Prominent Renaissance architects stressed the building of better roads. Thus Andreas Palladio (1518–80) put forward a well designed road-plan for cities (figure 294). His contemporary Vincenzo Scamozzi (1552–1616) considered that rural roads should be elevated well above the subsoil water-level on each side; that they should be straight and have an ample width; and that they should be constructed of durable materials. Other Italian authors, notably Castelli (1577–

1644), wrote much on the same lines; most of their ideas were inspired by Vitruvius. A more original contribution is the essay (*c* 1587) by Guido Toglietta describing the interaction of wheel, the 'destructor', and road, the 'resistor'. Toglietta describes the construction of cobble pavements, but favours a foundation of gravel carrying a road surface of stone, sand, and mortar, a type that would demand frequent repairs, though cheaper than the solid ancient Roman roads.

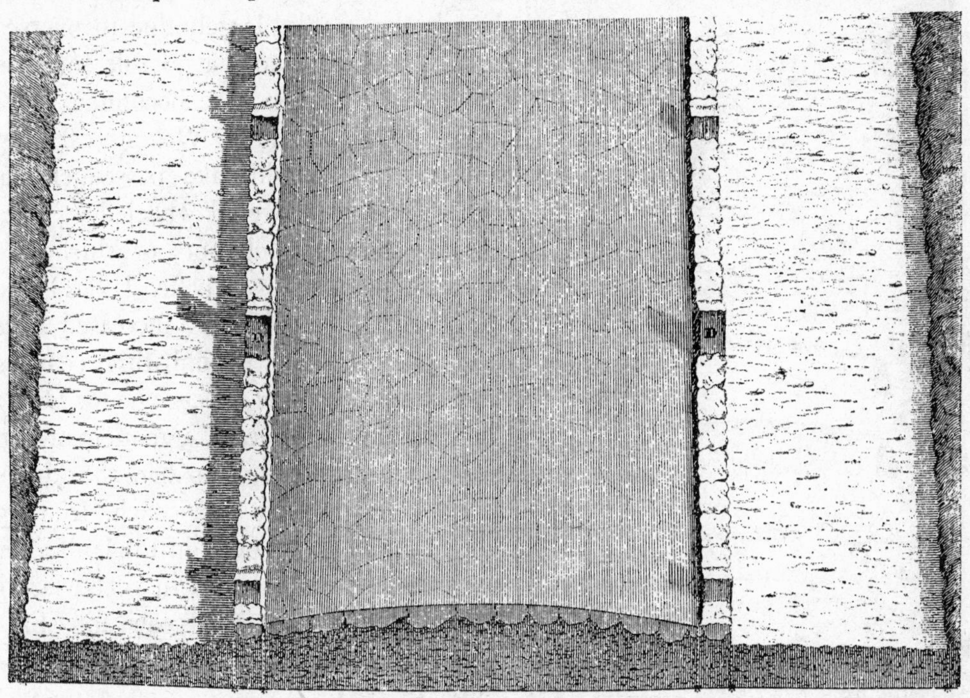

FIGURE 294—*Palladio's plan of a road. The centre, for pedestrians, was paved so that the edges of the stones met perfectly and the rain could run off. The sides, for carriages and cattle, were of sand and fine gravel. The stones along the edge were to help horsemen to mount, and the larger stones* (D) *marked the distance from Rome.*

These Roman roads stimulated engineers to invent new constructions. This started with the discovery by a Rheims lawyer, Nicolas Bergier (1567–1623), of remains of Roman roads in his garden. He studied them carefully and started to collect from ancient texts and archaeological reports data which he published in his *Histoire des grands chemins de l'Empire Romain* (plate 35) [1]. This book attracted the attention of many authorities who had for generations been plagued by merchants clamouring for better roads. The Duke of Sully, Henri IV's minister in charge of roads, was particularly interested (figures 295 and 296).

An important French handbook on road-building by Gautier (1660–1737) [2], engineer of the Corps des Ponts et Chaussées, proposed a road-body enclosed by stone walls and built from earth and hard-core, well rammed before traffic was admitted (plate 33 A). Like most French engineers of his day he paid great attention to good alignment, which was quite possible by that time since contemporary geodetical instruments were very accurate [3].

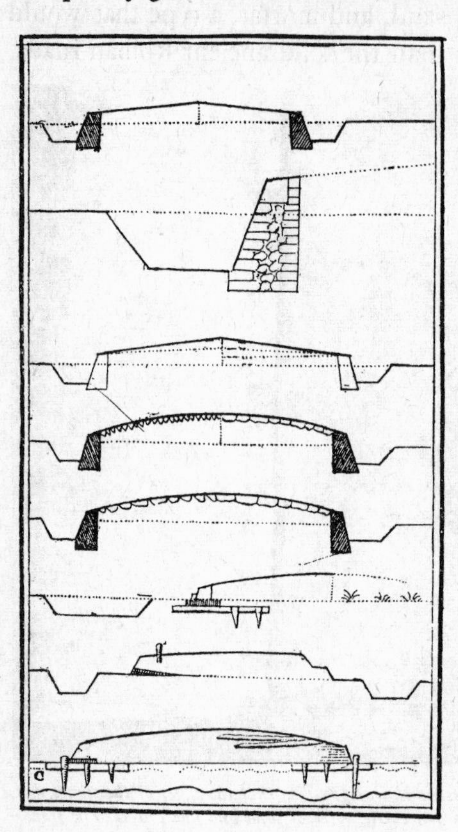

FIGURE 295—*Cross-sections of various eighteenth-century French roads.*

(*b*) The second powerful factor in the revival of road-building was the increase in wheeled traffic, largely due to oversea trade, which induced a notable increase in travel. Vehicles were becoming more suitable for travelling. Wagons carrying merchandise would take passengers as well. By 1500, covered wheeled vehicles called chares, cars, chariots, or whirlicotes were used, though only by ladies. The development of vehicles increased, but even in 1550 there were only three coaches in Paris, one for the queen, one for Diane de Poitiers, and one for a gentleman, too fat to ride a horse, who had the king's permission to drive in a coach. In 1555 the first coach was built in England after a continental model, and in 1556 Mary I obtained one. The state coach for Elizabeth I was imported from the Netherlands in 1564.

The early wheelwrights adopted wide-rimmed heavy wheels to minimize wear and tear from the very rough road surface. Iron tyres had been used by the Romans. In the Middle Ages it became customary to stud wheels with iron nails, in the belief that they gave a better grip on the road. The designs of the wheels were adjusted to suit the type of road surface (figure 297). The urge for rapid wheeled transport produced a host of pamphlets and books on wheel-design in the eighteenth century. Good road-building techniques were not yet forthcoming, and it was believed that better coach-construction, more wheels, and above all wider rims, would provide more comfortable travel and do less damage to the roads. During the seventeenth century coaches became so common that public services started in several towns.

The earliest steel springs bearing the body of the coach were C-shaped tempered steel strips. They were introduced about 1665. The heavy state coaches of the eighteenth century needed stronger springs. Elliptic steel springs came into use early in the nineteenth century. Then the new principle of eliminating the connecting-pole of front and rear axles and introducing cross-beds connecting the two axles with the body of the coach, discovered by Obadiah Elliot of Lambeth (1804), made more rational coach-design possible. By the eighteenth century two-wheeled vehicles such as the cabriolet or cab were introduced, and the wheels were fitted with brakes.

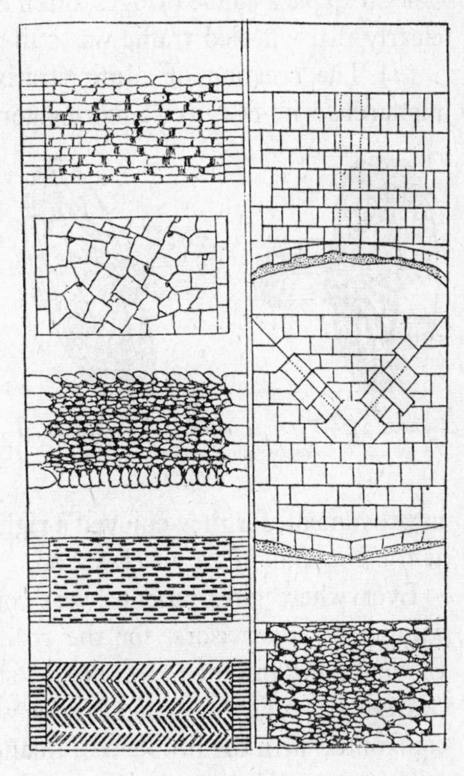

FIGURE 296—*Plans of various eighteenth-century road surfaces in Paris.*

There was as a result no longer any need to increase the width of wheels to lessen stresses on the road surfaces. Stage-wagons (plate 33 B) with 16-in tyres had been in use; in the reign of George II the average was 9 in, and they were very destructive of the poor roads. An attempt was made to limit them by legislation, and the designers started to build bevelled wheels so that no more than a rim-width of 3 inches actually touched the road.

In 1845 R. W. Thomson designed the first pneumatic tyre, but the state of the roads and the imperfect rubber produced in those days prevented the success of this happy solution of the wheel-impact problem. Thomas Hancock then introduced solid rubber tyres for carts (1847), and Thévenet (1865) adapted them to the early bicycle. By 1890 Thomson's invention was so completely forgotten that Dunlop's reintroduction of the pneumatic tyre was hailed as something novel (vol V, ch 31).

(*c*) The growth of central authorities also encouraged improved wheeled traffic, and was a third important factor in the renaissance of road-building. Travelling became increasingly fashionable, and this habit promoted the publication of good guides and maps (plate 34). In 1553 Robert Estienne published his famous *Guides des chemins de France*, and other countries rapidly followed suit.

Estienne's book revealed that although France already had a road-system of some 17 000 miles it was in a deplorable state. Even the 'royal' roads were paved for only a few miles beyond the towns. Traffic consisted mostly of pack- and saddle-horses, droves of cattle, pigs, and sheep, and a few wagons and carts. The steep pack-horse bridges, often built by rich and charitable persons, showed clearly that wheeled traffic was still a minor factor.

(*d*) The creation of administrative bodies for roads and transport by the monarchs who favoured a more vigorous road-building policy encountered much opposition. Guides, often working hand in hand with robbers, exacted money from the traveller to lead him by the most practicable way. The highway, sometimes hardly recognizable from the open field, was more a right of way from place to place than a surfaced road. Innkeepers considered that travelling was becoming too fast and that they would lose by good roads. Landlords set their faces against improvement, for they enjoyed a right to seize whatever fell upon the road, such as the contents of an upset wagon.

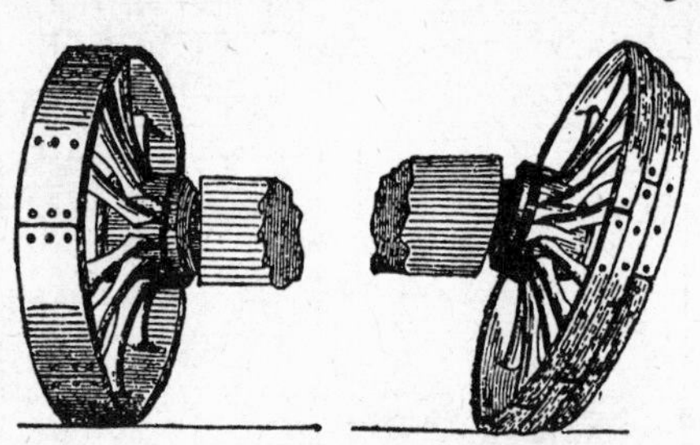

FIGURE 297—*Types of wheels;* (left) *cylindrical and* (right) *conical.*

Everywhere governments were confronted with a lack of expert labour and competent supervisors, for the roads often had to be rebuilt completely. In England, for instance, a series of statutes—all repealed and re-enacted by a codifying act of 1766—tried to cope with the difficult situation. The government, confronted with the problem of financing road-construction, wavered between a toll system and statutory labour. Queen Mary's Act of 1555, for example, laid the duty of financing the roads on the cities and parishes along them. Each parish was to appoint two surveyors and was subject to heavy penalties for neglect of the roads. This system, however, had already failed in the Middle Ages. The fact that there were so few properly paved roads proves the inability of the authorities to raise the necessary money and to enforce the four days of labour imposed by law upon each parishioner (1563), notwithstanding the heavy fines for default (1670). The surveyors obtained some legal backing from the Justices of the Peace (1654) and the extent of statutory labour and the fines were revised (1691), but it was all of little avail.

Statutory labour (plate 36 A) was universally disliked and could never be satisfactorily enforced. Efforts to supplement it by the proceeds of a rate were similarly a failure. The picture of the condition of the roads which John Ogilby draws in his 'Britannia' (1675), the first good English road-book, shows the menacing state of affairs. On the other hand, the government was greatly helped in its efforts to establish better roads by the union of the English and Scottish crowns (1603), and the establishment of the first parliament of Great Britain (1707). The seventeenth and eighteenth centuries saw a rapid growth of London and other ports, and a gradual rise of local distributive and manufacturing centres that heralded the industrial revolution.

The proper solution—the formation of a strong administrative and technical body to educate engineers and direct road-building, the fourth and final factor in the revival of road-building—was found in France. There the first organized system of trenched roads was initiated about 1720.

In France there was a complete absence of any authoritative planning in the days of Robert Estienne, who often had to indicate in his road-book that there were dangerous forests or robbers at two, three, or four miles from a particular spot. Henri IV made a brave attempt to cope with the situation. In 1599 he created the post of *Grand Voyer de France*, in order to centralize all road building and repairing activities: Sully was the first to hold it. In each province local lieutenants were nominated to deal with the situation (1604), and in 1607 the first highway code defined the duties of the Grand Voyer. The provincial Voyers were to inspect their own provinces and to report on the situation of the roads every year. The diverting of toll-money from road-repairing was strictly forbidden. The state helped the provinces in financing road-building by lending them money, to be repaid from the salt tax.

Unfortunately the post of Grand Voyer was suppressed by Louis XIII in 1621, but it was re-established in 1645. In 1661 Colbert was thoroughly impressed by the results: many roads had been repaired and new ones created, and the general state of the road-system allowed the creation of a service of state coaches in 1664. Colbert combined the functions of Grand Voyer and that of Comptroller-General of Finances, and in this dual capacity gave a further impetus to road-building. The administration of roads was entrusted to special commissioners, and royal grants were given for each new road-project. Many country roads were paved with stone setts, the so-called *pavés du roi*.

Towards the end of the reign of Louis XIV the wars demanded too much money and road-building suffered severely. The recovery under Louis XV was crowned by a very important step, namely the creation in 1716 of the *Corps des Ponts et Chaussées* (ch 15), a body of road and bridge experts and engineers formed to supervise public works. This was the first body of civil engineers in Europe maintained by a government, and it gave France the leadership in this field during the eighteenth century. Many accomplished engineers joined and led it. The early years of the *Corps* were not happy, but it was reorganized in 1726 and again in 1750 and 1754.

A training-school also was created, which was to become even more famous. Daniel Trudaine (1703–69), a French administrator, and Jean Perronet (1708–94), an engineer of Swiss origin, put into effect the royal decree of 1738 which established such a school. In February 1747 the *École des Ponts et Chausées* was opened, with Perronet as its first director. The school was directed by the department of home affairs, and fifty promising young scholars were selected to study at it; all the famous French engineers of the eighteenth century were trained there.

Both *Corps* and *École* had the steady support of the minister Turgot (1727–81). Decrees of 1705 and 1720 had ordered the roads to be laid out as avenues. In 1730 it was decided to call upon the population and to institute statutory labour, as there was not enough labour available for road-building; but even under such trained supervisors as were now available labour of this kind was bound to fail in the long run. Turgot soon realized that only paid labour would yield adequate results and in 1776 he abolished statutory labour. He was, however, forced to resign in 1777, and this unpopular form of labour was temporarily re-established; it was finally abolished in 1787, an example that, unfortunately, other countries did not follow until many years later.

By a decree of 6 February 1776 the *routes nationales* were defined and classified. The first-class roads were those leading from Paris to the principal cities; they were to be 42 m wide 'between the fences'. Second-class, 36-m, roads led from the principal cities in one province to those in another. Third-class, 30-m, roads connected the principal towns in one and the same province. Fourth-class, 24-m, roads connected smaller towns and villages. By then, France had some 25 000 miles of highways, half of which were being rebuilt or aligned. During the reign of Napoleon this system of national roads was revised; some roads were to be financed by the state, others by the provinces and towns. There was further legislation in 1836, 1851, and 1852.

During the French Revolution (1789–99) the roads were again neglected, but Napoleon was particularly interested in road-building for strategic purposes. Even in his day, however, ordinary road-traffic found it difficult to maintain an average of 15 miles a day, and the intrinsic cost of road-transport of goods was 8 to 12 times as high as at present.

II. ROAD-BUILDING, 1775–1830

In the meantime Pierre Trésaguet (1716–94) had developed a new system of road-construction which was to be introduced throughout France about 1775 (figure 298 B). Early in the eighteenth century the French road-makers had worked under the inspiration of Bergier and Gautier, who insisted on good drainage and a solid foundation (figure 298 A). A road trench was excavated, some 18 ft wide, and two or more layers of stones were laid flat, by hand, on the bottom of the excavation. On this foundation a layer of small stones was placed and rammed down, and the surface of the road was formed and completed with a finishing coat of stones broken smaller than those immediately beneath. The depth of the causeway, protected by large stones along the sides, was some 18 in at the middle and 12 in at the sides. The use of statutory labour working only in spring and autumn made roads of this thickness necessary in order that they might last through the intervals between repairs. With less depth they would have been cut through and totally destroyed by the deep ruts formed during the intervening months.

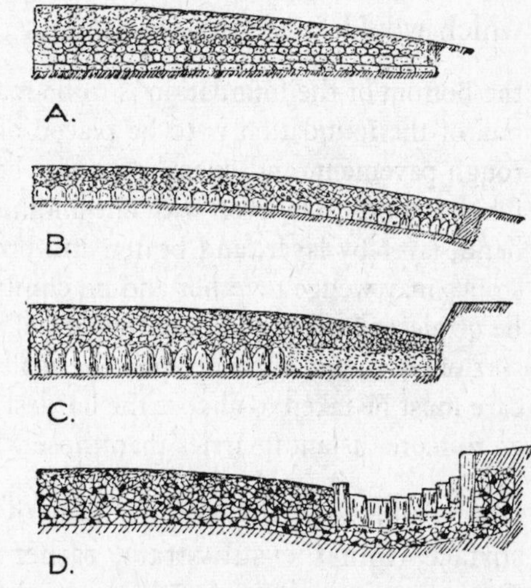

FIGURE 298—*Cross-sections of various roads.* (A) *French, previous to 1775.* (B) *Trésaguet (1764). The foundation layer, which was parallel to the road surface, was formed of large stones placed on edge and hammered in. The next layer was of smaller stones, also hammered in, and the surface, which was curved, was of small hard stones.* (C) *Telford (1824). A layer of large stones was placed edgeways on a level bed. Smaller stones were then added, to a depth of 7 in at the centre and sloping off to 3 in deep 15 ft away. The centre 4 ft were covered with small stones, well trodden down by horses. Finally the whole road was covered with 1 to 1½ in of good clean gravel.* (D) *McAdam (c 1820). No large stones were used, the only foundation being the well drained natural soil. A layer of hand-broken stones, about 1½ inches in diameter and none weighing more than 6 oz, was spread over and worked in. No binding material was used.*

Such stone highways had been built in other parts of Europe also. In the 1730s several German states issued ordinances prescribing such constructions. Swabia in 1737 demanded 12-m highways, the centre part, of 8 m, to be of a construction identical with the French one. Similar constructions were introduced in Hesse (1746), Treves (1753), Westphalia (1769), Weimar (1779), and Saxony (1781).

Trésaguet was not satisfied with this heavy construction. The foundation was often laid with little attention to the level of the subsoil water. Good drainage and proper selection of materials seemed essential to him. He thought that the hard-core and rubble employed were too uneven in quality, and he disapproved of a foundation that, by not running parallel to the road surface, became unnecessarily and wastefully deep in the middle of the road. He believed that he could reduce the depth of the road-bed to 9–10 in from side to side, which would lower the cost to less than one-half. He says:

the bottom of the foundation is to be made parallel to the surface of the road. The first bed of the foundation is to be placed on edge, and not on the flat, in the form of the rough pavement, and consolidated by beating with a large hammer, but it is necessary for the stones to be even with one another. The second bed is to be likewise arranged by hand, layer by layer, and beaten and broken coarsely with a large hammer, so that the stones may wedge together and no empty space remain. The last bed, 3 inches thick, to be of pieces broken to about the size of a small walnut with a hammer on one side of a sort of anvil, and thrown upon the road with a shovel to form a curved surface. Great care must be taken to choose the hardest stone for the last bed, even if it be necessary to go to more distant quarries than those which furnish the stone for the body of the road.

The object of the lower course of large stones was to separate the wearing-surface from the sub-strata, rather than to form a foundation for the road. Trésaguet stated that in Limoges such roads lasted for ten years when constantly maintained, and that they were then as good as when first constructed. His system allowed for proper drainage of the road surface without the excessive camber that made the older roads dangerous. His system was generally adopted by the French road-engineers, and the method spread to central Europe, Switzerland, and Sweden; it was later imitated by Telford (figure 298 C), and it inspired McAdam (figure 298 D).

The rise of absolute monarchy and of economic nationalism in eighteenth-century Europe promoted road-building in other countries as well. In Germany political dissension and the division of the country into many states, each too limited financially to execute a good road-building plan and all jealous of their own rights, were the principal arresting factors. Thus even in 1816 Prussia could claim only 500 miles of good roads.

The rulers of Austria were active road-builders during the eighteenth century [4]. Charles VI (1711–40) started by having a *chaussée* built from Vienna to Trieste and another from Karlstadt to Fiume. Road-building then stopped for some time because of the wars, but it was resumed by Maria Theresa about 1760 and continued under Joseph II (1780–90), to be resumed again in Napoleonic times. The impetus came from France. The earlier roads were built by military engineers, but the state slowly built up a central administrative body of road-commissions directing the work in each of the states under Habsburg rule.

In Russia road-building was now begun. From 1720 to 1746 over 450 miles of road were built to connect St Petersburg (Leningrad) with Moscow, and in 1781 the great Siberian highway from Moscow to Perm, Tobolsk, and Irkutsk was started. The first macadam road-surface (p 532) was laid on the highway connecting Tsarskoe Selo (residence of the Czars) and Gatchine during the reign of Paul (1797).

In the Low Countries road-building was stimulated by the Austrian authorities. In the north, brick roads were often made, for the Dutch cities had already long been paved with the 'clincards'[1] that John Evelyn admired. However, organized road-building did not start in this part of Europe before the time of Napoleon.

Farther north, road-building was sporadically attempted in Scandinavia, but at that period sea-traffic was dominant, and the use of canals postponed the developments of roads until well into the nineteenth century. Little, too, was done in Italy [5], then politically divided, though several popes concerned themselves with the maintenance of the old Roman road-system, even establishing a tax to pay for such roads in the Papal States. In the Balkans and Spain road-building did not start until much later.

The Alpine roads regained their importance by the end of the eighteenth century (plate 36B). The Roman roads over the Alps had been totally neglected, but the passes with their sharp ascents and descents remained important trade-routes. The passes were used fairly continuously for foot-passengers and for pack-animals. A few monasteries and cities occasionally undertook their repair. The monastery on the St Bernard, founded in 962, yearly fed and lodged 20 000–22 000 pilgrims; that on the St Gotthard, founded in 1331, roughly half as many. Driving over the Alps was impossible. The building of highways under such conditions was too much for the earlier generations of road-engineers.

In 1591 the Duke Charles Emanuel of Savoy made a mule-trail through the Tenda Pass; this was later (1782) extended into a carriage road. Then the Emperor Joseph II made the road through the Arlberg Pass (1782–5), but it had to be repaired again in 1793. The Mönchberg Pass had been made negotiable for carts and wagons by Sigismund, archbishop of Salzburg (1765–7). However, Napoleon was the first to make proper Alpine highways. Swiss engineers like Lucas Voch understood their task but funds were lacking. After the conquest of the country by Napoleon centralization set in. The Swiss engineer Guisan, inspector of roads and bridges, had effective plans for the improvement of the roads. The Montgenèvre–Mont Cenis road was taken in hand by the end of 1797,

[1] Dutch *klinker*, *klinckaerd*, a hard type of brick.

and was reconstructed between 1803 and 1810. The Simplon road was built by Nicolas Céard (1747–1821) between Brigue and Domodossola, a stretch of 48 miles on which two brigades of French engineers worked. This reconstruction period lasted until 1830. After some thirty years another two decades of building began, to be stopped by the advent of the Alpine railways (1880); the roads again received attention when the motor-car came to these regions about 1907.

III. THE COACHING AGE, TELFORD, AND McADAM

The second half of the eighteenth century thus saw a general improvement in the highway system, though it failed to meet the demands of the rapidly increasing traffic. In Great Britain there was no central educational system for engineers, and the civil engineers trained their pupils on the road itself. The industrial revolution called for cheap and rapid transport of goods. Scotland was well served by a system of military roads built by General Wade after the rebellion of 1715 (figure 299), but in England the state of the roads found many critics. In 1749 John Shapleigh, in his 'Highways . . . a treatise showing the hardship and inconvenience of presenting or indicting parishes', pointed out the difficulties of bringing negligent surveyors and other officials to book. A cartoon of the period depicts a sailor with a wooden leg beside a stage-coach. Asked whether he wants a lift, he replies: 'No, I am in a hurry!' Arthur Young in his 'Six Months' Tour' (1770) speaks of the 'infernal' Wigan road. The costs of carriage weighed heavily on prices, and it was not exceptional for timber to take a year to reach the coast. By contrast, a German visitor like Moritz (1782) found the roads around London incomparably good.

By the time the earlier British road-statutes had been given embodiment in the Road Act of 1766 (p 524), the system of turnpikes was generally accepted, and trusts were allowed to levy tolls provided the yield was partly devoted to the maintenance of the road. The first turnpike, on the Great North Road, was authorized during Charles II's reign (1663). There were seventy-one Turnpike Acts between 1720 and 1730. By 1829, 3783 turnpike trusts had been established, covering some 20 000 miles of highways. These turnpikes were not always erected with discrimination; they were the bane of travellers and their evasion by roundabout lanes was a favourite pastime. Nevertheless the turnpike trusts were for long accepted as the best successors to the hated statutory labour system. Indeed, about 1760 the number of roads and bridges began to increase and their quality grew better. In 1809 over £2 000 000 was spent on road-repairs by the trusts. On such roads the first steam-carriages made their experimental runs.

The failure of the turnpike trusts was mainly due to wretched administration and heavy capital charges. On the London–Holyhead road 23 trusts operated. Only half of the money collected was spent on the roads, and the debts of the trusts accumulated. By the nineteenth century taxation had killed voluntary effort at road-building. In 1829 the trusts responsible for 1119 miles of roads were expending £85 a mile against a revenue of £73 a mile. Their reign was over when the General Highways Act of 1835 created a new parish organization for highway-building, abolished statutory labour, and arranged maintenance.

Whatever blame may be laid on the turnpike trusts, they did create a better road-system. This is obvious from the growth of traffic. They made regular coach services possible. The new road surfaces made by Metcalf, Telford, and McAdam reduced the camber of the roads and drained them properly. Fewer coaches now overturned, and their speed was increased in proportion to the increased safety.

By 1834 English coaches drove at an average of 9–10 miles an hour, as compared with the 6 miles of the French *malle-poste*. Severe winter weather was the only serious cause of dislocation. In 1784 a strictly scheduled mail-coach system was started; armed guards protected it from highwaymen, and great speed was effected. The mail was carried from London to Birmingham in 12 hours, to Exeter in 17¼ hours. Now at last was speed back again to the limit imposed by equine capacity.

It is curious to read of protests in 1837 against the speed of the coaches in Britain—that travelling had become as dangerous as ever owing to the loads piled on the vehicles, and that the improved roads offered a temptation to fast driving. These better road-surfaces were the creation of great English road engineers working for the turnpike trusts and for the government.

Telford (1757–1834), originally a journeyman stonemason, was one of the great engineers of his generation. He is still remembered for his beautiful bridge over the Menai Straits (p 459) on the London–Holyhead road to Ireland. He had reconstructed the Shrewsbury–Holyhead section of the road, choosing the Trésaguet system, but over the hand-laid foundation course he applied only a fairly thin set of layers of chips (figure 298 B) [6]. In his own words:

> Upon the level bed prepared for the road materials the bottom course, or layer of stone, is to be set by hand in the form of a close, firm pavement. They are to be set on the broadest edges, lengthwise across the road, and the breadth of the upper beds is not to exceed 4 inches in any case. All the irregularities of the upper part of the said pavement are to be broken off by a hammer, and all the interstices to be filled with stone chips, firmly wedged together by hand with a light hammer. The middle 18 feet of pavement is

to be coated with hard stone as nearly cubical as possible, broken to go through a 2½-inch ring, to a depth of 6 inches, 4 of these 6 inches to be first put on and worked by traffic, after which the remaining 2 inches can be put on. The work of setting the paving-stones must be executed with the greatest care and strictly according to the foregoing directions, or otherwise the stone will become loose and in time may work up to the surface of the road. When the work is properly executed, no stone can move; the whole of the material to be covered with 1½ inches of good gravel, free from clay or earth.

Telford had wide experience of road-building in Shropshire and reconstructed many of General Wade's roads in Scotland (figure 299). He was very careful in selecting the small stones for the top strata, and differed from Trésaguet in making the road-bed level and in forming the crown of the road (with a fall of 1 : 60) with the stone itself, rather than making the finished surface parallel to the base. Most of his contemporaries did not like his use of a final layer of gravel, which 'by sinking between the stone diminishes absolute solidity to the surface of the road, lets in water and frost and contributes to preventing complete consolidation of the mass of broken stones'. This is partly correct, since at that time no good rollers were available. The cost of Telford's roads was relatively high because of the heavy foundation, and because when not properly and regularly repaired the top layers proved too thin for the wear of traffic.

The next step, combining proper drainage and low cost, was taken by John McAdam (1756–1836) of Ayr, who went into business in New York (1770–83) but returned to Britain to become deputy-lieutenant of Ayrshire and a Road Trustee, often spending his own money on road repairs and experiments. He was called to Bristol in 1789 and there tried different ways of building roads. By 1814 he had thoroughly inspected 30 000 miles of roads and spent some £10 000 of his own money on road construction. In 1815 he became surveyor-general of the Bristol Road Trusts, and started rebuilding their 180 miles of road according to his own system. His basic principles were:

That it is the native soil which really supports the weight of traffic; that while it is preserved in a dry state, it will carry any weight without sinking and that it does in fact carry the road and carriages also; that this native soil must be previously made quite dry and a covering impenetrable to rain must then be placed over it in that dry state; that the thickness of the road should only be regulated by the quantity of material necessary to form such impervious covering and never by any reference to its own power of carrying weight.

He believed that he could substitute for the costly hand-laid foundation a thin set of layers, less than 10 inches in all, of broken and graded chips.

As no artificial road can be made so good as the natural soil in a *dry state*, it is neces-

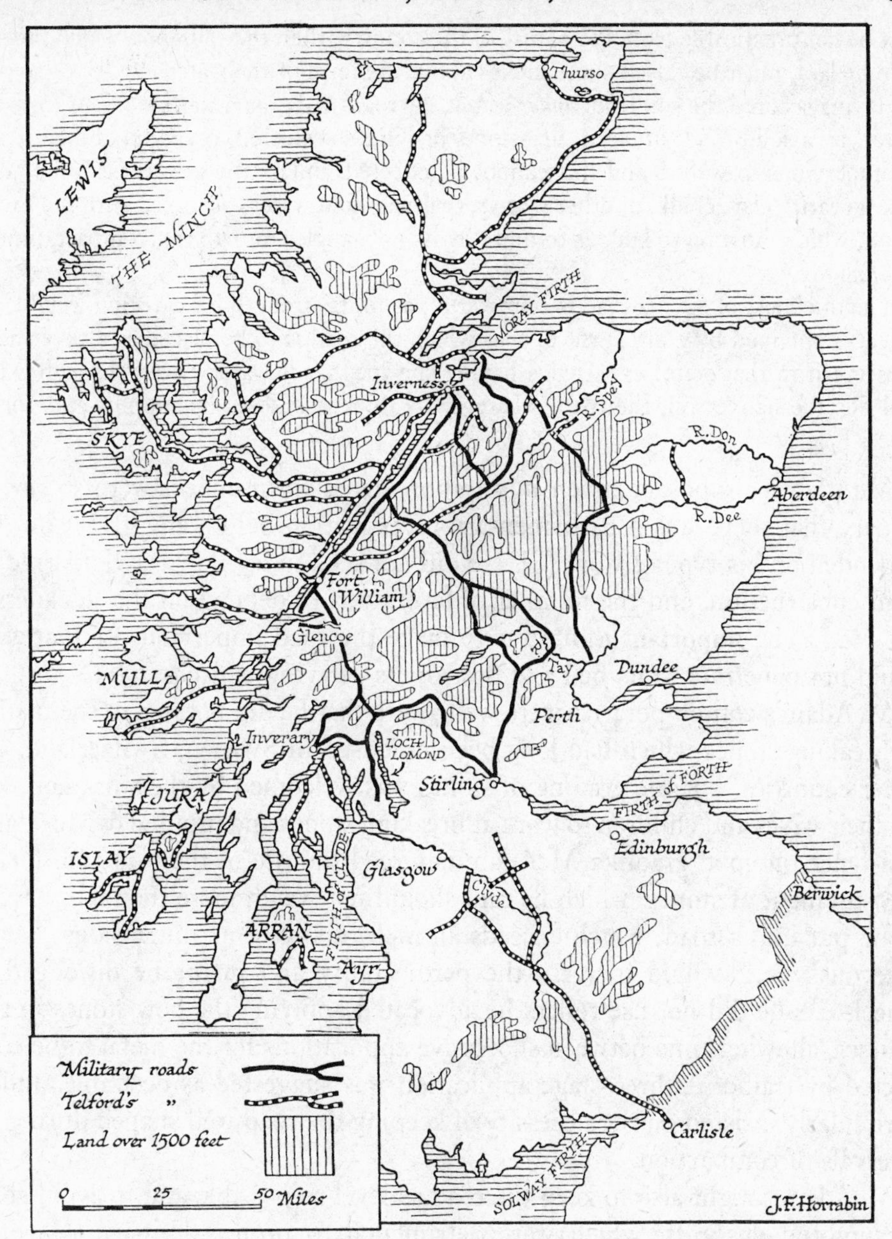

FIGURE 299—*Map of Telford's roads and military roads in Scotland.*

sary to preserve this state. The first operation should be the reverse of digging a trench. The road should not be sunk below, but raised above, the adjacent ground; that there be a sufficient fall to take off the water, so that it should be some inches below the level of the ground upon which the road is, either by making the drains to lower ground or, if that be not practicable from the nature of the country, then the soil upon which the road is to be laid, must be raised some inches above the level of the water.

Having secured the soil from *under* water, the road-maker is next to secure it from rain water, by a solid road, of clean, dry stone, or flint, so selected, prepared and laid, as to be impervious to water; and this cannot be effected, unless the greatest care be taken, that no earth, clay, chalk, or other matter, that will hold water, be mixed with the broken stone; which must be so laid, as to unite by its own angles into a firm, compact, inpenetrable body.

The thickness of such a road is immaterial; as to its strength for carrying weight, this object is obtained by a dry surface, over which the road is to be placed as a covering, to preserve it in that state: experience having shewn, that if water passes through a road and fills the native soil, the road, whatever its thickness, loses its support and goes to pieces [7].

McAdam's proposals, given in an abbreviated form above, were so revolutionary that there was a parliamentary investigation before any great sum was expended on his type of work [8]. He did not seek to lay down a rigid rule for road construction, and the number of layers was to depend on the thickness of the road. The important thing was to make the road impervious, so that water could not penetrate to its bed and destroy its carrying-capacity.

McAdam's contemporaries were well aware that he did not invent the method of breaking stones which had long been practised in Sweden, Switzerland, and other countries, but the grading of stones was welcomed by the workmen, who set their wives and children to work at breaking stones and profited byMcAdam's insistence on good grading. McAdam enforced the use of the 2-in ring for the measurement of stones, which he said should not weigh more than 6 oz. 'Every stone put into a road, which exceeds an inch in any of its dimensions, is mischievous', as it would increase the permeability and might be dislodged by wheels. As he did not use rollers he advocated applying the new stones in thin courses, allowing time between successive applications for the metal to be compacted by traffic. A three-stage application was suggested as desirable, and he particularly insisted on the necessity of keeping the road well shaped during the intervals of compaction.

McAdam sought also to keep the road as level as possible and to avoid sharp ascents and descents, which were detrimental to proper drainage. He often reconstructed older roads that had a proper foundation. Nowadays his idea of a soft, yielding foundation for the road is not accepted as good practice. But the older Telford foundations were very expensive and hence the custom of building a Telford–McAdam road grew up; that is, a road with a Telford base and a McAdam wearing-surface. For the repair and reconstruction of older roads

McAdam's system was excellent, and thus his name became attached to the 'water-bound macadam[1] road' that dominated in the nineteenth century. However, the filling of the interstices of the top layer by washing in sharp sand was not McAdam's invention and he actually condemned it. It was devised by Richard Edgeworth (1744–1817), whose road-building handbook was much praised by his contemporaries [9].

McAdam became surveyor-general of the Metropolitan roads (1827). In his first book he had indicated 'the state of the public roads, the alarmingly increasing debt, and the loose state of the accounts of the several Trusts' as the best proofs of the defects of the turnpike system. In his last book he proposed to centralize the administration and construction of roads under a committee of experts. Road-builders, he held, should not have other occupations and should be adequately paid for work that benefits agriculture, trade, and traffic. In Parliament it was suggested that the days of the road were over, now that the railways had come, but nevertheless American engineers came to study his results. His books were translated into several languages and had a profound influence in Europe. By the end of the nineteenth century some 90 per cent of the principal highways were macadamized.

The water-bound macadam system was further improved after 1876, when a third course was generally applied. The use of steam-rollers at this time effected much greater compaction, and justified the belief in the fairly light road-construction as urged by McAdam. A century of public pressure and hard work had gone by since Metcalf had obtained his first contract, but the results were encouraging:

LENGTH OF METALLED ROADS IN 1868–9

	Length (thousand miles)	*Area of country (thousand square miles)*	*Population (millions)*
United Kingdom	160	123	31
France	100	210	38
Prussia	56	140	24
Spain	11	198	16

IV. THE ADVENT OF THE RAILWAY AND THE MOTOR-CAR (1830–1900)

Many of McAdam's contemporaries feared to abolish the hand-laid foundation, and protested violently against such new-fangled methods. However, McAdam's principle of preventing water from reaching the foundation was

[1] In this form McAdam's name has become a part of the English language.

sound, and his system proved its worth. Was it necessary to keep the hand-laid foundation in the case of wet foundations? Thomas Hughes gave the proper solution in his 'Art of the Construction and Repair of Highways' (1838). The metalled surface of the road should cover not only the middle strip of the road but its full width, and the road-metal should be applied to an even depth over this full width. Proper drainage should be effected by digging ditches 5 ft deep and 2 ft wide alongside the road so that the water could be drained to the full depth of the foundation, leaving the latter in its natural state as far as possible. If necessary, drains in the form of earthenware pipes or trenches of compacted rubble should cross the road-bed to remove any water that in freezing might force the road up. His methods were applied to the macadam road with good results.

The French and English variants of McAdam and Telford's constructions spread over Europe. The older roads were mostly macadamized, stone setts or cobbles being sometimes used. Napoleon's conquests were the start of many national road-organizations in Europe, for he was very conscious of the strategic importance of roads. His ideal seems to have been a tripartite road, the middle paved with cobbles for the artillery, one side having a water-bound macadam surface for the infantry, and the other side carrying an earth-road, called the summer road, for the cavalry. Though few roads of this type were built, Napoleon certainly promoted scientific road-building between 1804 and 1814. His national roads still form the core of many highway systems and he made the Alpine roads accessible again to wheeled traffic.

Slowly the macadam road penetrated beyond Europe. In Australia there were some 275 miles of metalled roads by 1820, but the building of a proper highway system began much later. In the United States [10] the earliest roads were Indian trails. In 1632 Virginia obtained its first road-law, followed by Massachusetts in 1639. The Maryland law of 1704 provided for a 20-ft road and for road-signs. American development up to 1890 involved repairs by compulsory labour modelled on the statutory labour scheme developed in Britain. This lasted until the advent of the automobile brought more sophisticated road constructions, making skilled labour essential.

The first American turnpikes were built in Virginia, Connecticut, and Maryland. In 1785 a Turnpike Act was passed in Virginia, and a turnpike road was in operation a year later. As there was inadequate provision for repairs it was handed over to the Fairfax and Loudon Turnpike-Road Company, incorporated in 1795 to handle this road from Little River to Alexandria. The company was reorganized in 1802 and rebuilt the old road in 1805, operating it as a toll road for over ninety years. Meanwhile, other roads rapidly followed. In 1808 Albert

Gallatin, Secretary of the Treasury, could report that 770 miles of metalled road had been completed in Connecticut, and that over 3000 miles were under construction in New York State, with hundreds of miles in other states.

Such roads were usually 36 ft wide, but only 15 ft of the width was covered with gravel or pounded stones. Sometimes two courses of broken stone were applied; their size was large and there was no rolling or sprinkling. American engineers studied road-building in the Old World, and very capable men like Gillespie and Gillmore introduced better methods [11]. McAdam's principles were adopted by General Gratiot when repairing the surface of the Cumberland road east of the Ohio river in 1832.

The turnpike companies were in fact the first American public service corporations. In the beginning they made only graded roads; later, stone surfaces of water-bound macadam became the general type. By 1850 most had given up their charters as they were threatened by the canal boom (1810–40) and the railway boom (after 1840). In 1891 the legislature of New Jersey passed the first state-aid law assuming responsibility for part of the initial cost of construction. The era of modern road-building had begun.

Railways had become a serious menace to good road construction in the Old World also. As early as 1839 it was said: 'If the railways yield these supposed commercial advantages, we shall have no reason to regret their superseding stage-coaches.' By 1800 the average highway carried several thousand tons of goods a year, as compared with a thousand tons in the Middle Ages, but the real increase in traffic started only when the steam-engine began to play an important part in the actual manufacture of goods. However, by about 1875 road traffic had been largely displaced by the railways, whose load grew with the increased output of manufactured commodities.

A change came with the advent of the motor-car, which returned traffic to the roads; but before this could happen the engineers had to invent means of consolidating the road surfaces and combating the clouds of dust raised by the tyres. One solution was to secure better compaction during construction, and not to leave this to the action of traffic. The road-building equipment of the earlier phases consisted of tools such as hammers, sieves, spades, wheelbarrows, rammers, and pickaxes. Machines for proper compaction, such as rollers, had been used by the ancients, and in 1619 John Shotbolte proposed to use 'land stearnes, scowrers, trundlers and other strong massy engines . . . in the making and repairing of highways'. The first good roller is illustrated in Leupold's *Theatrum machinarium* of 1725, which pictures a horse-drawn iron roller weighing over a ton (figure 300). In Diderot's *Encyclopédie* (supplementary volume, 1777) is described a two-wheeled roller, with a box for additional stones to increase the weight when desired. In 1787 Louis Alexandre de Cessart (1719–1806) proposed a cast iron horse-drawn roller with a cylinder 8 ft wide and 36 inches in diameter, weighing about 3½ tons. Such rollers were used after 1815 in England, Hanover, and France, but it was feared that the horses or men drawing them would destroy the smooth road-surface before it was sufficiently compacted. However, horse-drawn rollers were gradually introduced in the 1830s. For the initial stage of compaction light types were used, followed by heavier ones when the road had been sufficiently compacted. During compaction sand was washed into the top layer of the macadam road.

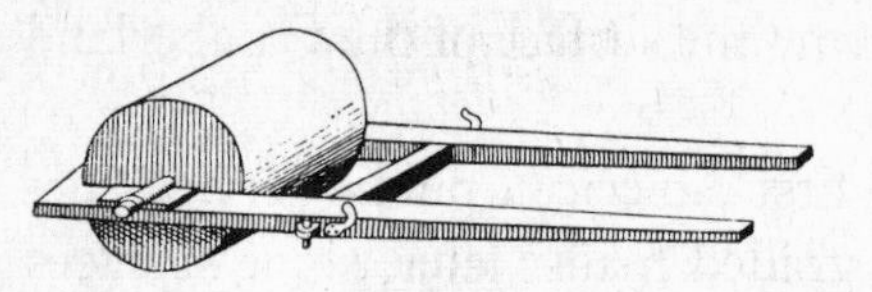

FIGURE 300—*Road-roller as drawn by horses.*

The first steam-driven roller was invented by Lemoine (1859), but its trial run was not a success (1861). Then came Ballaison (1862) with his 17½-ton roller driven by a 5-hp engine; this was produced by Gellerat et Cie of Paris from 1864 onwards, with other models of 8½ and 15 tons respectively. Despite its manifest advantages the steam-roller gained ground only gradually. The earliest British steam-roller was patented by W. E. Batho of Birmingham and W. Clark, chief engineer of the city of Calcutta, in 1863. The first American patent was awarded to Andrew Lindelof of New York in 1873. Aveling & Porter of Rochester, Kent, produced the first effective steam-rollers in 1866, and Green & Sons soon improved upon them (1879). At first glance, these steam-rollers appeared to be three-wheeled, but the roller actually consisted of a pair of cylinders set side by side: this made steering easier.

During the same period good stone-crushers were invented. In McAdam's days stones were broken by hand, and even as late as 1900 this was still economical: it cost no more than 1*s* 3*d* to 2*s* 6*d* a cubic yard. In 1858, however, Eli Whitney Blake, brother of the inventor of the cotton-gin and a manufacturer at New Haven, Connecticut, constructed the first stone-crusher. This treated stones for the roads in Central Park, New York City, which were then being built. It did not meet with enthusiasm, for a prize-winning essay of 1890 still assures us that 'hand-broken stone is much superior to that crushed by a machine, which is generally of irregular shape and seldom cubical, so that it does not readily bind together'. Nevertheless the stone-crusher had come to stay.

Besides new road-building equipment, two new constructions were evolved during the nineteenth century, though they came into common use only after 1900. The first was the concrete road. This began in antiquity, but was forgotten until William Hobson took out an English patent (1827) for grouting a macadam road with lime-mortar. His system found little recognition, though it was exactly the method adopted by the Romans in certain cities. MacNeill used concrete on a stretch of the Highgate–Archway (London) road where the subsoil water-level was fairly high. A 6-in concrete foundation was built as a water-tight base for grouted chips, its surface being roughened to carry the road-surface of macadam (1829). Concrete roads proper had to wait until the invention of Portland cement (p 448).

During the 1850s several concrete roads were built in Austria. The first English concrete road was constructed in 1865. In 1872 the first concrete road in Scotland was built in Edinburgh; France followed four years later with one at Grenoble. In 1887 the Blücher Platz at Breslau received a concrete surfacing, and concrete roads were constructed soon afterwards in Vienna (1898). The first American concrete road was built in 1892 at Bel-Fontaine, Ohio. Cheap concrete roads were closely bound up with the evolution of machinery to build them, which was first successfully constructed by P. Jantzen of Elbing (then in Germany, now in Poland) in 1879.

The second new-comer was the asphalt road. In 1712 Eyrinis d'Eyrinis, a Greek doctor, discovered the rock-asphalt at Travers near Neuchâtel (Switzerland) and learnt how to blend the powdered rock with hot pitch, making what we now call an asphalt mastic. He also applied his mastic to the making of floors and steps, some of which were examined by Fournel in 1838 and found in excellent state. d'Eyrinis interested a banker, de la Sablonnière, in his exploitation of rock-asphalt and obtained tax-exemption for it in France (1720).

This led others to the discovery of further rock-asphalt at Péchelbronn and Lobsann, Alsace. More thick oil and rock-asphalt were found at Wietze (Hanover), Osmundsberg (Sweden), and in Hungary and Rumania. In 1797 further sources were discovered near Seyssel (France) and mastic was made of it. The earlier work of Sécretan there was revived in 1832 by de Sassenay, who mixed the powdered rock-asphalt with bitumen from natural oil seepages and thus obtained a mastic of better quality. By 1835 his sales had gone up to 1000 tons a year. This asphalt mastic was used for footpaths at Lyons (1810), Geneva (1820), Strasbourg (1822), and other places. The first trials on roads were started on the pavements of the Pont Royal and the Pont du Caroussel in Paris. These were paved with mastic, as also was the Place de la Concorde (1835). Co-operative work by de Sassenay and Équem resulted in the foundation of a company with a capital of £30 000 to exploit the Seyssel rock-asphalt. Eventually, Seyssel regularly produced some 1000 tons of mastic a month. Attempts to introduce it into England met with little success until 1869, when part of Threadneedle

Street was paved with Travers rock-asphalt. This started a boom in asphalt streets in London.

Meanwhile new methods of construction with asphalt had been discovered. In 1849 Mérian observed that powdered rock-asphalt spread from carts became naturally compacted into a good road-surface. At first, he had powdered Travers rock-asphalt brushed and rolled into the interstices of a macadam road between Travers in Switzerland and Pontarlier in France. A few years earlier de Coulaine had covered a fresh macadam surface with hot powdered rock-asphalt and rolled it into a splendid road-surface (Bordeaux–Bayonne, 1837), but the under surface was wet and the trial failed. Malo, however, discovered a way to disintegrate the Travers rock by heating and rolling the powdered rock after spreading it over the road-base. Together with Vaudry he laid over 800 sq m of compressed asphalt in the Rue Bergère, Paris (1854). Its wear over fifteen years proved less than ¼-in. By 1858 compressed asphalt was in common use in Paris.

Travers now became a serious competitor with Seyssel. Asphalt from Limmer, Hanover, began to appear on the English market and Trinidad Lake asphalt also came to the fore, the latter notably in the United States. In 1848, the Earl of Dundonald had started advocating the use of Trinidad Lake asphalt with as much fervour as d'Eyrinis had devoted to Seyssel asphalt, but except for a floor in the Merchants' Exchange Building in Philadelphia it was not used until trial stretches of paving were built of compressed asphalt in front of Newark City Hall in William Street (1871) and in Union Square (1872).

American asphalt-paving was greatly promoted by the work of the Belgian engineer E. J. De Smedt, who used a mixture of sand, limestone-powder (as a filler), and mastic from Ritchie County (Virginia), and thus made the first sand-asphalt. He found other native asphalts in the United States suitable for such mixes. He and Clifford Richardson calculated the percentage of bitumen needed to fill the spaces of the mineral substances and thus obtained a good water-tight road-construction. In Cleveland (1873) a grout consisting of a mix of coal-tar and gravel was used on macadam, but with little success. In St Louis, De Smedt introduced asphalt blocks (1873) and compressed asphalt (1883). New Orleans had its first asphalt road in 1880 and in Philadelphia a few of the streets were asphalt-paved in 1884. The first successful Trinidad Lake asphalt pavement was laid in front of the Capitol in Washington by De Smedt in 1876.

Three types of asphalt roads were thus known before the end of the century: (*a*) compressed asphalt made by rolling rock-asphalt disintegrated by heating and spread on a base; (*b*) mastic asphalt, a mixture of mastic, sand, and a filler, poured on to the road surface and trowelled into shape; and (*c*) sand-asphalt, a hot mixture of bitumen, sand, filler, and sometimes larger stones, designed to leave no voids after compaction and spread and rolled after mixing at a temperature of 150–200° C. The invention of the steam-roller was a vital factor in the making of roads of this kind; they could not otherwise have been built.

Tar also now found use as a road-building material; crude tar was being distilled for the manufacture of solvents and dyes and the residues of heavy tars and pitches became available. Tar-macadam was first made in Nottinghamshire (1832–8), and was used for a section of the London road at Nottingham in 1845. Sheffield (1875) and Liverpool (1879) followed. The first tar roads in the United

FIGURE 301—*The water-cart helped to keep down the dust in the streets of the nineteenth century.*

States were built at Cleveland (1873). At Melbourne a three-layer tar-macadam was made in 1895. This tar-macadam was usually prepared by mixing tar and stones hot, then spreading them and consolidating the road with rollers after cooling. A final coat of sand was usually applied.

Concrete, asphalt, and tar roads came into their own with the advent of the motor-car. This gave road-building a new future, provided road-engineers could produce surfaces that stood up to the new forms of impact of traffic and vehicles. Until then the hammering action of hoof and wheel had been the main form of impact. Motor-traffic, however, with its rubber-tyred wheels, exerted a suction on the road-surface that was detrimental to macadam roads. Clouds of dust consisting of the finer particles sucked up from the interstices of the macadam structure were a great source of annoyance even before this (figure 301).

The obvious course in building new roads was to make them of the dustless concrete or asphalt types. However, something had to be done to cure the dust problem on the extensive network of older macadam roads. In 1902 Guglielminetti experimentally coated with tar an old macadam road near Monte Carlo. This treatment proved excellent, and in the course of the following decades both hot bitumen and tar, or emulsified forms of these materials, were extensively used for such surface-treatments.

V. CITY STREETS AND PAVEMENTS (1730–1900)

The history of city paving runs along much the same line as that of roads; it was the rise of the cities as economic units that determined the search for better streets and the financing of paving in general. Paris started paving its streets in 1184; London made some advance during the thirteenth century, and in 1280 the supervision of paving repairs in each ward was delegated to the aldermen.

In 1443 a road in front of the Savoy Palace was 'substantially performed with Stones and Gravel'. Such loads of new road-material were usually dumped on the old pavement and thus raised its level, to the annoyance of householders. During the sixteenth century most European cities had regular paviours on their pay-roll, for it had proved unsatisfactory to leave the work to the owners of property fronting the roads.

In most German cities a city engineer supervised the repair of street pavements. Cobbles were in common use. They were laid on a foundation of 6–8 in of clean sand, which was to be free from clay or loam to prevent swelling and cracking of the pavement. Methods of levelling had been devised and rollers were sometimes employed. The paviours were generally paid by the square yard of pavement, the footpaths being usually repaired by the city at the expense of the house-owner.

By the sixteenth century increased wheeled traffic in the cities had begun to turn the unpaved surfaces into mud-pools. Each city had to cope with this traffic problem. In London, Smithfield was paved in 1614 'to remove the Scandal the City was obnoxious to on account of its ruinous and dangerous condition; whereby instead of being a service, it was rendered a common nuisance to the City'. New regulations for the paviours were drawn up in 1662. The street gutters were to be covered in; narrow streets with cobble pavements sloping from both sides to an open sewer in the middle and crossed by innumerable transverse gutters were forbidden. Wheeled traffic demanded better pavements, though there were attempts to exclude such traffic from the cities. In Paris the size of the vehicles was limited in 1624, and the number of horses and the maximum weight drawn were prescribed in 1670. In Elizabethan times the number of carts in London was restricted to 420, and most merchandise was transported on pack-horses. In Dutch cities, where water transport was often available, wheeled traffic was completely banned until the eighteenth century. However, such regulations were ineffective in the absence of officers to enforce them.

The paving materials were usually cobble-stones, easily and cheaply available. The pavement was protected by posts at intervals. Paving-stones such as were used in the principal streets of London from 1616 onwards were mostly small and badly laid; after a shower they squirted mud and water when stepped upon. London received its cobble-stones from Guernsey and Kent, its flags from Purbeck. To provide good road-materials many cities enacted ordinances commanding all wheeled traffic to bring into the city a certain number of paving-stones. Even certain American cities like Boston and Washington started to pave some streets with cobbles about 1650, though Philadelphia had no paved street before 1761. During the seventeenth and eighteenth centuries the towns, as growing centres of manufacture and distribution, began to understand the need of rational and well organized paving.

In London, unfortunately, a great opportunity was missed after the Great Fire (1666): the street pattern was not recast (vol III, pp 296–8). In 1765, however, great improvement was effected in Westminster. Signs and posts obstructing traffic were removed, and the streets were raised or lowered to bring them nearer to a level. Footpaths on each side were elevated, defined by kerb-stones, and paved like the floor of a room. Attempts were made to construct a smoother pavement by forming the stones into blocks, at first of no particular shape but giving a comparatively smooth surface. Then the carriage-ways were paved with Scottish granite, gently sloping to the channels at each side. The City of London followed suit fairly quickly, after levying a rate on the annual value or rental of the houses.

Telford, in a report of 1824 (published in the second edition of Henry Parnell's 'Treatise on Roads'), recommended for street pavements a foundation of broken stones, 12 in deep; and above this foundation rectangular paving-stones of granite. The latter were to be worked flat on the face, straight and square on all the sides, so as to fit close together, with a base equal to the face, thus forming in fact an ashlar causeway. The dimensions of the stones were to be:

	Width (inches)	*Depth (inches)*	*Length (inches)*
For streets of the 1st class .	6 to 7½	10	11 to 13
" " 2nd " .	5 to 7	9	9 to 12
" " 3rd " .	4½ to 6	7 to 8	7 to 11

Stones of dimensions comparable to these were generally employed in street-paving, and proved to possess great durability. They have now been for the most part abandoned in favour of narrower paving-stones, 3 or 4 inches in width, though many secondary streets in London and elsewhere are still paved with 6-in stones. McAdam's system was introduced in some streets where the traffic was light, but it did not equal the granite paving.

In a pamphlet written by a Colonel Macirone of London in 1826, when the city had a population of 1 400 000, the author says: 'Florence, Sienna, Milan and other Italian cities have pavements with especially prepared wheel-tracks. These tracks are three feet in width, made of large and particularly well-laid stones. They are about four feet apart, and the space between paved with smaller stones.' He further states that these pavements, as well as those of Rome, are the best that he has seen, but that they would be too expensive for London. The pavements of London, even in the principal streets, were, he says, surprisingly bad, in marked contrast with the excellent turnpikes.

Although Paris had a number of pavements while London was still unpaved, it was many years before its streets were in even a decent condition. Martin Lister, writing of Paris in 1698, says: 'The pavements of the streets are all of square stones of about eight or ten inches thick; that is, as deep in the ground as they are broad on top, the gutters shallow and laid round without edges, which makes the coaches glide easily over them.' Elsewhere he says that the material was a very hard sandstone, and that all the streets and avenues were paved. A distinguished American traveller, Aaron Burr, in 1811 thus describes their condition in a letter to a friend: 'No side-walks—the carts, cabriolets and carriages of all sorts run up to the very houses. Most of the streets are paved as Albany and New York were before the Revolution, some arched in the middle and a little gutter on each side very near the houses.'

A pavement of broad, smooth, well jointed blocks of granite for wheel-tracks, with pitching between for horses, was laid in Commercial Road, London, in 1825 (figure 302). In the same year Telford recommended the use of stone blocks $4\frac{1}{2}\times7\frac{1}{2}$ inches for street use, and 3×9 inch granite setts, with mortar joints, were laid on Blackfriars bridge in 1840. This was probably the first attempt at a modern stone pavement. In London such granite setts were not laid on concrete before 1870. In passing, it may be noted that London pavements in the 1820s suffered much from explosions of the gas-mains, for the gas industry was still young and many difficulties in the distribution of gas had to be overcome.

However, street paving was rapidly improving in the first decades of the nineteenth century, but its concomitant noise and clatter remained an affliction.

Brick pavements had been suggested, and had indeed been used in certain countries where the production of bricks was cheap. They were generally introduced in Dutch cities (p 529) during the seventeenth century, and a hundred years later in Italian cities. One of the first roads to be paved with bricks was that leading from The Hague to Scheveningen. Brick pavements had some success in the United States, where they were first introduced at Charleston (1870) and Bloomington. Bricks were of some importance in the paving of footpaths in other cities.

Wood-paving came from Russia, where Gourief first used wooden pavement-

FIGURE 302—*Paving a London road with Scottish granite.*

blocks in St Petersburg about 1820 (plate 33 C). In 1836 he wrote a book on them, in which they are described as hexagonal blocks laid and washed in with sand and receiving a coating of tar or pitch. Fink proposed to use 16-cm wooden cubes for the carriage-ways of bridges. Experimental stretches of wooden pavement were laid in London in 1838, in Oxford Street and from Charles Street to Tottenham Court Road; they included a stretch of hexagonal pine-blocks. These were later laid on a lime-concrete base. Between 1840 and 1843 Carey and others patented forms square in plan but double-wedge-shaped in section. Creosoted wood-blocks had been proposed by L. Wagner in 1829. He claimed that they were better than stone, but they did not come into use until much later. They were first employed in America on a bridge at Sunderland (1867), though wood-blocks had been applied to New York (1835) and Chicago (1856) streets much earlier. In 1839 there were 1100 sq yds of wooden pavement in London. By 1842 this had increased to 60 000, when, according to a statement in the City Council by an alderman during a controversy over the relative merits of wood and stone pavements, there were 600 000 sq yds of the latter, probably almost entirely macadam. These two items without doubt represented the total amount of pavements in a city of nearly 2 000 000 people. But traffic was rapidly increasing in London: in 1850 no fewer than 13 099 vehicles crossed London Bridge in twelve hours.

REFERENCES

[1] BERGIER, N. 'Histoire des grands chemins de l'Empire Romain.' Paris. 1622.

[2] GAUTIER, H. 'Traité de la construction des chemins.' Paris. 1693.

[3] SCHMIDT, F. 'Geschichte der geodätischen Instrumente und Verfahren im Altertum und Mittelalter.' Pfälz, Neustadt a. d. Haardt. 1935.

[4] BIRK, A. *Beitr. Gesch. Tech. Industr.*, **11**, 75, 1921.
Idem. Z. öst. Ing.- u. ArchitVer., **76**, 171, 1924.

[5] CALETTI, P. 'Le strade da Roma imperiale all' Italia Fascista.' Bardi, Rome. 1932.

[6] TELFORD, T. 'Life of Thomas Telford, Civil Engineer, Written by Himself' (ed. by J. RICKMAN). London. 1838.
BAKER, J. F. and ARMITAGE, J. *Civ. Engng, Lond.*, **6**, 727, 1936.

[7] MCADAM, J. L. 'Remarks on the Present System of Road Making with Observations Deduced from Practice and Experience' (9th rev. ed.). London. 1827.
Idem. 'A Practical Essay on the Scientific Repair and Preservation of Public Roads.' London. 1819.
Idem. 'Observations on the Management of Trusts for the Care of Turnpike Roads, as Regards the Repair of the Road, the Expenditure of the Revenue and the Appointment of Officers.' London. 1825.

[8] BARRY, G. S. *Surveyor, Lond.*, **90**, 529, 1936.
DEVEREUX, R. 'John Loudon McAdam, a Chapter from the History of Highways.' Oxford University Press, London. 1936.

[9] ANDERSON, R. M. C. 'The Roads of England.' Benn, London. 1932.
BALLEN, DOROTHY. 'Bibliography of Roadmaking and Roads in the United Kingdom. King, London. 1914.
JEFFREYS, W. R. 'The King's Highway.' Batchworth Press, London. 1949.
COOKSON, R. B. S. *Road Tar*, **6**, 5, 1952.
EDGEWORTH, R. L. 'An Essay on the Construction of Roads and Carriages' (2nd ed.). London. 1817.

[10] LABATUT, J. and LANE, W. J. (Eds). 'Highways in our National Life. A Symposium', Pt I. University Press, Princeton. 1950.
MACDONALD, T. H. *Proc. Amer. Soc. civ. Engrs*, 1545, 1927.

[11] GILLESPIE, W. M. 'Manual of the Principles and Practice of Road Making.' New York. 1847.
GILLMORE, Q. A. 'A Practical Treatise on Roads, Streets, and Pavements.' New York. 1876.

BIBLIOGRAPHY

BIRK, A. 'Die Straße.' Kraft, Karlsbad. 1934.

GREGORY, J. W. 'The Story of the Road, from the Beginning Down to the Present Day (2nd ed., rev. and enl. by C. J. GREGORY). Black, London. 1938.

KNOLL, A. 'Geschichte der Straße und ihrer Arbeiter' (3 vols). Zentralverband der Steinarbeiter Deutschlands, Leipzig. 1925.
LAW, H. and CLARK, D. K. 'The Construction of Roads and Streets' (rev. with additions by A. J. WALLIS-TAYLER, 8th ed.). Crosby Lockwood, London. 1914.
LOESCH, K. L. VON. "Die Straße im Lebensgefühl der Völker." *Straße*, **4**, no. 17, 490, 1937.
MCCLOSKY, J. M. "History of Military Road Construction." *Milit. Engr, Wash.*, **41**, 353–6, 1949: **43**, 42–45, 192–5, 1951.
MERDINGER, C. J. "Roads Through the Ages." *Ibid.*, **44**, 268–73, 340–4, 1952.
PAGE, L. W. 'Roads, Paths and Bridges.' Sturgis & Walton, London. 1912.
PETER, A. "La route à travers les âges." *Schweiz. Z. Straßenwesen*, **17**, 325, 1931.
SHELDON, G. 'From Trackway to Turnpike.' Milford, London. 1928.
WEISE, A. 'Von Wildpfad zur Motorstraße.' Volksbund für Bücherfreunde, Berlin. 1929.
WILKINSON, T. W. 'From Track to By-Pass. A History of the English Road.' Methuen, London. 1934.

A stage-wagon with broad-dished wheels. Early nineteenth century.

18

PART I

CANALS:

INLAND WATERWAYS OUTSIDE BRITAIN

ROGER PILKINGTON

THE practice of canal-building was well established before the eighteenth century and the principle of overcoming differences in level by pound-locks had long been normal practice (vol III, ch 17). On the other hand, the great advances in hydraulic engineering that found expression in vertical lifts were not made until towards the end of the nineteenth century with the development of electrical methods and the internal combustion engine. The period from 1750 to 1850 is characterized by the great extension of the waterways themselves rather than by the introduction of important mechanical principles into their construction.

Yet during this period steam-power was gradually being developed. Thus as early as 1803 Fulton introduced a steamer on the Seine above Paris, and from 1817 a successful steamer service was run on the Mississippi between Louisville in Kentucky and New Orleans in Louisiana. This was soon to be succeeded by other packet-boats—so called because they carried not only passengers and general cargo but the United States mails. Similar paddle-wheelers were introduced on European rivers. In 1816 the London-built *Defiance* initiated the first service of powered craft on the Rhine, and the *Lady of the Lake*, built on the Clyde, began navigation on the Elbe. In 1830 steamers were plying on the upper reaches of the Danube, but the turbulence of their wash and the vulnerability of their paddles made such craft unsuitable for canal-work. A steam tug with a screw-propeller was used in 1844 on the canal from Charleroi to Brussels, but its destructive effects on the soft banks caused the temporary abandonment of such mechanical haulage.

The problem of supplying steam-power without a destructive wash was difficult, but in 1832 Tourasse and Mellet laid a submerged chain along much of the bed of the Seine between Paris and Rouen. The chain was picked up over the bows, passed round a steam-capstan on the tug, and dropped again over the stern. Unfortunately the chain proved too weak and this attempt, too, was abandoned, but many years later the idea was taken up once more and chains were employed with considerable success in a number of continental waterways. R. L. Stevenson's 'Journal of an Inland Voyage' contains an interesting account of the system in use on the Willebroek canal. In general, however, towage at this period was either by horse- or man-power, with help when possible from a sail.

The only lifting-system of any magnitude built during this period was the astonishing series of inclined planes on the Morris canal (figures 303 and 304).

FIGURE 303—*An inclined plane of the Morris canal.*

This canal was built between 1825 and 1831 to link the Hudson and Delaware rivers. It involved a rise of more than 900 ft to the summit pound at the watershed on the Alleghenies. Twenty-two locks were installed, each being at the head of an inclined plane running down to the pound below it, and descending on a gradient of 1 in 10 or 1 in 12. A 79-ft barge with a load of up to 30 tons was taken into the lock, and when the pen was emptied it came to settle on a trolley running on lines with a gauge of rather more than 12 ft. The lower gates were then opened, and the descent was made under gravity, checked by brakes. As the rails ran out into the lower pound and levelled off under water, the boat came to float again on an even keel. For the upward journey the procedure was reversed, and the cradle was hauled up the slope by a drum-and-cable mechanism, the power for which was supplied by a water-wheel. The device was remarkably efficient, and the total weight of 110 tons of cradle, barge, and cargo was raised through a vertical distance of 50 ft in $3\frac{1}{2}$ minutes for the expenditure of less than a twentieth of the amount of water required to raise a barge through a similar distance by conventional locking.

Navigation-works at this time were of several types. The simplest were concerned with improving the bed of a river which, either because of rapids or owing to silting, was unsuitable for commercial craft. The famous Iron Gates rapids on the lower Danube had impeded the use of this great river since antiquity. To by-pass them the Romans had cut a canal a mile and a half long. After the Roman period the Iron Gates remained an insuperable obstacle until 1830, when the Hungarian Count Szechenyi employed the engineer Vásráhelyi to survey the whole course of the lower river with a view to making it fully navigable. The count was tireless in his efforts to persuade the Russians and Turks to allow these improvements in the part of the river that ran through their territories, but the Russians were apathetic and the Turks actively hostile. Undaunted, he improved many sections of the river by cutting past rapids, but his scheme to by-pass the Iron Gates with a lock was abandoned.

Farther up, however, the Danube was regulated for 144 miles from Ennsmündung to Theuben, by work begun in 1849 and completed at a cost of more than half a million pounds, and by the end of the nineteenth century Hungary had nearly 2000 miles of navigable waterways. Much of this total was represented by the Danube and by the Nega canal from Themesvar to Titel, dug by the Romans and reconstructed in the eighteenth century. The Franz canal was opened in 1802 to join Bezdán and Bács-Földvár and so provide a cross-link between the courses of the Danube and the Tisza.

Navigation of the Rhône also was difficult. By 1840 the barge-traffic was in excess of 200 000 tons annually, but the splitting of the course into many winding, shallow channels was a serious impediment. The Canal de Miribel was therefore made just downstream of Lyons. By a system of dams and dikes the water was confined in this single course, but the speed of the current was so greatly increased that navigation remained difficult. Not until the middle of the twentieth century did thorough canalization of the river make upstream navigation easy for barges.

The Rhine showed a similar tendency in its Alsatian section. In 1840 the river was a maze of channels and backwaters, with shoaled reaches sometimes exceeding a mile in width. The flood-dikes were set more than a mile out to the sides, and the course was so diffuse that, although barges of 200 tons could work below Strasbourg, the river upstream of the city could accommodate only much smaller craft. At times of low water the river was sometimes impassable. Canalization of this section was begun in 1840, but once more the result was to increase the current to a degree that made upstream haulage practically impossible, and the faster flow of water scoured out the channel and obstructed the downstream reaches with silt and shingle.

The Mississippi with its tributaries drains two-fifths of the United States. Before the nineteenth century it carried considerable traffic, but only downstream, on account of swift and shallow passages. Rafts were the original form of transport, but they were soon replaced by flat boats. It was not until keeled boats were introduced that journeys up the river were at all possible, and such craft, manned by a crew of from 6 to 10, carried cargoes of 40 tons upstream by a combination of poling and warping.

Many rivers were improved by cutting off their bends, and in 1794 work was begun on the Guadalquivir which rendered it navigable as far as Seville and reduced the distance from 84 miles to 53. Making such cuts was usually accomplished by armies of workmen with pick and shovel, but at the end of the eighteenth century a labour-saving method was introduced in Germany, particularly on the Oder. This system involved digging the narrowest possible ditch along the line of the intended cut, and furnishing it with rectangular bays on either side alternately. At the time of the spring floods the upstream connexion with the river was opened through, and the torrent of flood water swirled down to erode a wide course. This simple system had its disadvantages, for, on the one hand, the flood easily got out of control and forged a channel in a direction different from that intended, and, on the other, the vast quantities of soil and subsoil swept away were sometimes deposited as banks in the lower reaches where, with increasing breadth of river, the force of the current was insufficient to dislodge them. In the nineteenth century, however, the system was much improved by laying finished banks in position beforehand, and by regulating the force of the incoming torrent.

Of all the river-improvement schemes of this period none offered greater possibilities than the work on the St Lawrence river in Canada, culminating in the drastic enlargements in the mid-twentieth century. These are to make inland navigation available to large ocean-going tankers as far as the terminus of the oil pipe-lines from Alberta, which reach the shores of the Great Lakes more than 2200 miles above the entrance to the St Lawrence. Much of the work has necessarily consisted of by-passing the rapids on the section of river between Montreal and Lake Ontario (figure 304). In 1821 the first successful cut was made between Montreal and Lachine, to overcome the Lachine rapids which had a fall of 46 ft. Originally this by-pass was limited to a depth of 5 ft, but within twenty years it was reconstructed with a minimum of 9 ft. At the time when the Lachine canal was built the sets of rapids at Les Cascades, Coteau du Lac, Mill Rapids, and Split Rock had already been overcome by a comparatively shallow canal 14 miles long and rising more than 80 ft; between 1834 and 1847 the navigable route through to Lake Ontario was completed by the Cornwall canal and the three shorter Williamsburg canals. As the lake was already connected to Lake Erie by the Welland canal (figure 304), cut in 1824–9 by a private company to by-pass the 327-ft drop of the Niagara river and falls, navigation right through to Lake Huron was now possible for grain-ships and lumber-floats of moderate draught.

A further connexion through to Lake Superior was already provided by the Sault Ste Marie canal (figure 304), since enlarged on several occasions. Though only 1 mile in length, it is today one of the busiest waterways in the world. In the first canal, opened in 1798 by the Northwest Fur Company, there was one lock only; this had a depth of no more than 1½ ft on the sill and was the first to be constructed in the American continent. It was destroyed by American troops in 1814.

In the same period a second route was begun between Montreal and Lake Huron, linking together the numerous small lakes lying to the northward of Lake Ontario to form a 224-mile waterway between the Bay of Quinte on Lake Ontario and Georgian Bay, but the marine railways involved at two points on the descent of the Severn river still limit the use of the through connexion to 20-tonners drawing not more than 4 ft of water.

Work parallel to that on the St Lawrence river was also undertaken in the first half of the nineteenth century on the Ottawa river, to provide through navigation between Montreal and Ottawa. Once again it was a matter of three small canals to by-pass the St Anne, Carillon, and Long Sault rapids (figure 304). But in 1826 the Canadian government decided to construct the Rideau Navigation from Ottawa to Kingston at the head of Lake Ontario to facilitate movements of goods and troops. This was in case war with the United States should render the St Lawrence route unusable—the boundary between the two countries passing down the river itself for a distance of nearly a hundred miles. This waterway was fortified, and crossed the summit of the watershed between the Rideau river (a tributary of the Ottawa) and the St Lawrence, and involved forty-seven locks. It exists today much in its original form, but is now more used by yachtsmen than by commercial craft, the depth having been left at the original 5 ft.

A more important route commercially was that of the St Ours and Chambly canals built between 1830 and 1850 to improve the course of the Richelieu river, which flows from Lake Champlain to reach the St Lawrence 46 miles below Montreal. By these navigations a through connexion to New York was eventually established when the 66-mile Champlain canal was constructed on the American side of the frontier to join the southern end of Lake Champlain to the Hudson River at Albany.

Quite apart from river-improvement schemes the era was one of canal-

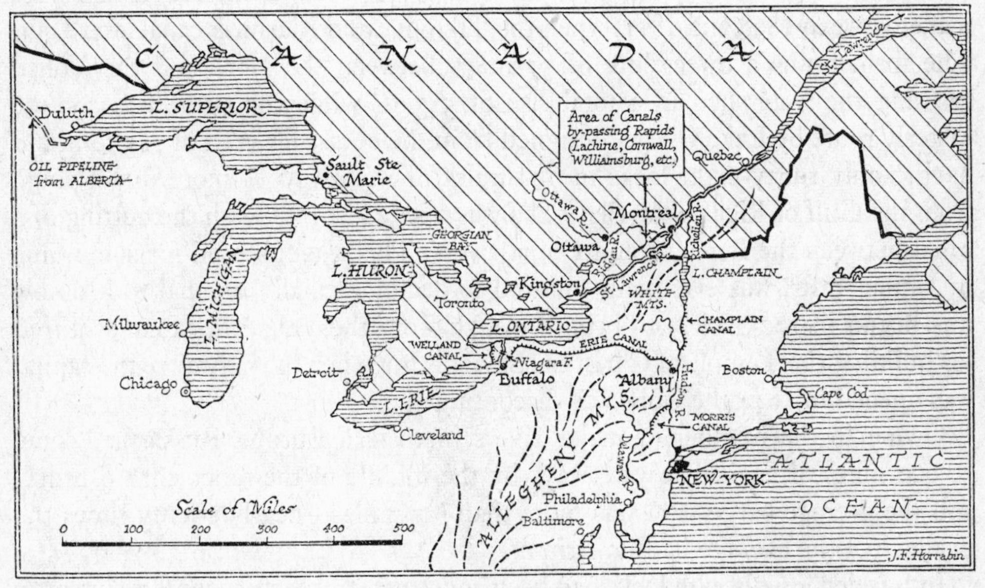

FIGURE 304—*Principal canals and waterways of the Great Lakes–St Lawrence region.*

development in many parts of the world. Some of these, such as the Franz canal of Hungary, were cut to join two already navigable river-courses, and if these flowed into different sea areas the effect was to provide an inland route to replace a lengthy sea voyage. Amongst the more astonishing projects was that of Maire, the Belgian engineer, who in 1786 planned an elaborate system of continental waterways based on Vienna and incorporating a canal that should cross the Alps and reach the sea at Fiume or Trieste, so providing a transcontinental route to the Adriatic. The Holy Roman Emperor Franz II sent his engineer Maillard to study the methods of building canals over hilly country. It was intended to cut through the highest ranges with tunnels, and, though the scheme was abortive, 40 miles of this canal were completed at the Vienna end of the line, and furnished with thirty-six locks.

As early as 1701 Peter I of Russia had begun the construction of a navigable link between the Volga and the Don, which at one point approach within 48 miles of each other. The work was abandoned because of war, but it was succeeded by two even more ambitious schemes that linked the Baltic with the Caspian Sea. The first line connected the Neva and the Volga by way of Lake Ladoga, but owing to poor water-supply it was soon replaced by the Vychnyvolotschok canal, which in spite of a draught of only 18 in at the sills of the locks was conveying more than 3000 eighty-ton craft annually in 1760. Further improvements were made between 1808 and 1811, when the Tikhvine and Mariinsk canals were cut. The former was a direct link of 57 miles between the Neva and the Volga, crossing the watershed in a total rise of 543 ft, while the latter was a more easterly route by Lake Onega, designed from the outset for craft of 165 tons and having only thirty-eight locks in 757 miles of waterway. A more direct route from the Gulf of Riga to the Black Sea was opened in 1805 with the cutting of a canal between the Beresina and Dvina rivers. This, though used for some time by timber-rafts, was eventually allowed to decline. Finally, a canal to Moscow was begun in 1825 solely to bring through from the Volga the stone required for building the Temple of Christ the Saviour, but when the railway to the capital was opened in 1844 the work was discontinued.

Owing to the number of major rivers in eastern Europe, Russia had some 50 000 miles of navigable waterways by the middle of the nineteenth century, and the average barge-haul was more than 600 miles—nearly twenty times the distance of the average haul in Britain.

In Sweden, canals with locks had been constructed as early as the late sixteenth century, but the waterway of most importance was the Gotha route, spanning the country from the Kattegat to the eastern Baltic with sixty-three locks. Constructed between 1810 and 1832, it was built partly for strategic reasons but carried considerable produce and particularly timber.

In Spain two canals, begun as far back as the sixteenth century, were completed within our period. Pignatelli completed the Imperial canal of Aragon, which had a two-step staircase lock at Casablanca. By 1795 a flourishing passenger service was operating there, and the carriage of grain was bringing in dues of a third of a million reals annually, but when the Saragossa to Pamplona railway was opened the waterway declined and was suppressed. Strangely enough it was to be reopened in 1918, the railway track being starved of materials for the repair and maintenance of the permanent way as a result of the 1914–18 war. The Castille canal from Valladolid to Medina de Rioseco, with forty-two locks, was completed in 1849.

In Germany the Ludwig canal, completed in 1845, was to form a link between the North Sea and the Black Sea by connecting the rivers Main and

Danube. Through insufficient water-supply, however, it remained virtually impassable until much later, when further works were carried out.

Some canals were constructed not only for navigation but for irrigation. Such was the Pavia canal, built under a decree of Napoleon, which connected the Naviglio Grande (a twelfth-century canal) with the Ticino by way of Milan; it was furnished with twelve locks, each of which carried a water-mill operated by the irrigation spill-over. In Egypt the dual-purpose Mehmondieh canal was dug between 1800 and 1825, to carry the waters of the Nile to Alexandria. 350 000 navvies worked on it, but the line was not marked out in advance and the result was a 50-mile course of odd straight sections connected by sharp bends which made navigation difficult. In India a magnificent project was begun in 1848 to the designs of Sir Proby Cautley, and when completed the Upper Ganges canal had a length of more than 500 miles and involved spanning the Solani river with an aqueduct 300 yds long and 50 yds broad. Other streams were carried across the top of the canal in smaller aqueducts.

The most enterprising canal on the American continent was constructed by de Witt Clinton from Albany to Buffalo between 1817 and 1824, and involved crossing two watersheds by means of seventy-two locks. This, the 364-mile Erie canal, provided an artery down which the grain from the Great Lakes could flow to New York. It was navigated by barges drawn by pairs of horses. The round trip, including the Hudson River section of the voyage, took about 4 weeks, but, being ice-bound from December to May, a barge could not deliver more than six or seven loads a year at best. Yet the volume of traffic was so great that within eleven years the cost of construction had been met by the tolls. Before 1850 double locks had to be installed to cope with the ever-increasing number of packet-boats and barges plying between the Great Lakes and New York Harbor. In the twentieth century the Erie canal was greatly enlarged, and its course came to form part of the New York State barge-canal system, navigable for vessels of 300-ft length.

The greatest developments of inland waterways, however, were taking place in France and the Low Countries. In 1810 the famous St Quentin canal was opened to link the North Sea and the Scheldt and Lys systems with the English Channel by way of the Somme, and with Paris and Le Havre by way of the Oise and Seine. This canal still carries a great volume of traffic. A system of horse-relays was organized over the whole length of the 60 miles from Chauny to Cambrai and quickly extended to the Canal Lateral à l'Oise, which led from the St Quentin canal to the Oise proper at Janville, near Compiègne. With no appreciable current on the canal section, two horses were adequate for laden barges, but on the Oise eight were often needed for the return haul upstream from Conflans St-Honorine.

The St Quentin canal incorporated two tunnels. The longer, or Grand souterrain de Riqueval, was 3¼ miles long, and when in due course the canal was opened no boatman dared to enter it. In desperation the authorities offered freedom from all canal dues in perpetuity to the first boat to pass through the tunnel, and one man volunteered. His boat was renamed the *Grand Souterrain* in celebration of the occasion, and until nearly the end of the nineteenth century it was still navigating tax-free. At that time, however, the dues on the canal were remitted entirely, and the *Grand Souterrain* retired honourably.

Other important links made at this time were the Canal du Centre (1793), constructed by Gauthey to connect the Loire at Digoin with the Saône at Chalon and thus complete the first inland route from the English Channel to the Mediterranean; the Canal de Bourgogne (1832), which linked the Seine to the Saône at a more northerly point and provided a more direct route from Paris to Lyons; the Rhine–Rhône canal (1834), completing a direct north to south route across western Europe; and the Canal de la Sambre à l'Oise, which today is part of the main trunk route from Antwerp and Liège by way of the Meuse to Paris.

In Belgian territory a canal was all but built which if completed would have vitally affected the development of both Rotterdam and Amsterdam by diverting their trade to Antwerp. As early as 1598 Spinola, the general holding the southern Netherlands for Philip II of Spain, conceived the idea of a Rhine–Meuse–Scheldt canal which would provide a route from the Rhineland to the sea passing only through territory held by the Spaniards. Work upon the canal was begun in 1626, but the Hollanders, seeing that the Rhine trade would be taken from them, destroyed the canal and wrecked the works. In 1804 Napoleon chanced to see the remnants of the works and at once planned to construct for strategic reasons the great Canal du Nord, though on a route slightly farther south. Two years later, however, the assimilation of Holland within his empire made the canal no longer necessary and work was suspended, but the completed portion in Germany was used until 1848.

Any scheme to connect the Rhineland with the Scheldt would inevitably deal a heavy blow to the Dutch ports at the mouth of the Rhine, and the idea has always been extremely unpopular in Holland. When in 1828 and again in the twentieth century the merchants of Antwerp clamoured for the canal to be finally cut, the Dutch opposed the proposal with every means in their power.

Many Belgian waterways (figure 305) have been traffic arteries for centuries. Visitors to Ghent can see the magnificent row of canal-side warehouses and note among them the tiny house of the toll-collector, next to a huge granary which from the Middle Ages was used to store the grain exacted as a toll upon the cargoes carried by barge through the city waterways. The main extension of the canals, however, took place towards the end of the eighteenth century and particularly during the first half of the nineteenth, to carry the coal of Bergen (Mons) and Charleroi southward to Paris and the areas of northern France, and northward to Brussels, Ghent, and Antwerp. In the coalfields the Mons–Condé canal

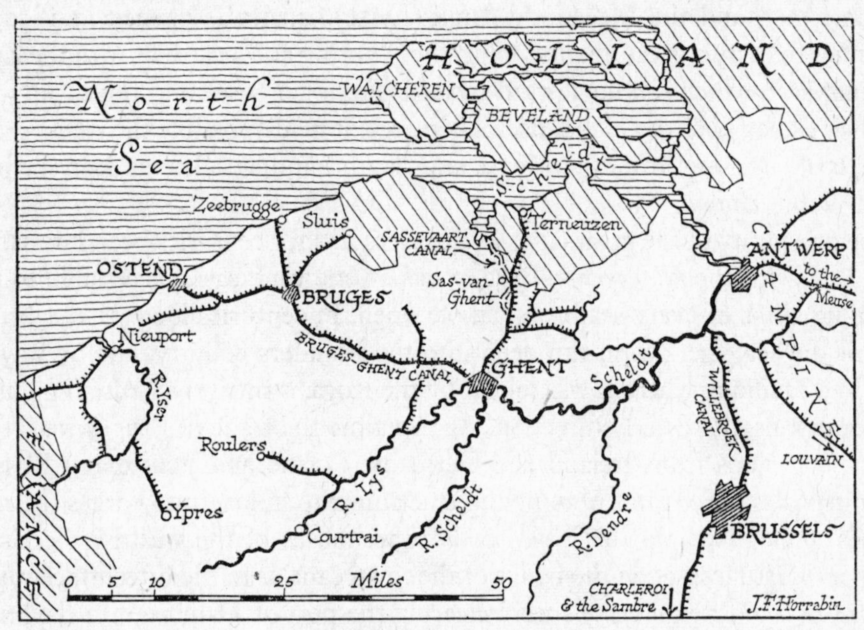

FIGURE 305—*Some Belgian canals.*

was built (1818), the Pommeroeul–Antoing canal was opened to connect the Haine and Scheldt basins (1823), the Sambre river was canalized (1828), and the Charleroi–Brussels canal was opened in 1827 as a southward extension of the Willebroek canal—known in our own day as the Brussels Ship Canal but in reality one of the oldest artificial canals in Europe. Later, the great routes of the Campine were laid down to carry the agricultural produce of that area to the port of Antwerp, and to form a connexion between the Meuse and the Scheldt (1846).

Towage on the Charleroi–Brussels canal was mostly by man-haulage, though horses could be used between lock 40 and Brussels, but since there was a great demand for both labour and horses in the mines of the area through which the canal passed, traffic was sometimes brought almost to a standstill for lack of haulage. A towing-company was formed which imported donkeys from England, but they proved difficult animals, particularly in the tunnel, and their use was discontinued. Brussels itself ran short of fuel in the hard winter of 1837–8, entirely owing to lack of haulage for the many laden coal-barges accumulating on the canal.

Not all the northward-bound supplies from the Sambre area were routed to Brussels and Antwerp, however, for the Dutch, too, extended their network of canals to link with the same industrial field. Maastricht and Liège are both on the Meuse, but the river above Maastricht was still unregulated (as it is in one section today) and the Maastricht–Luik (Liège) canal was opened in 1850; it continues to carry a great quantity of traffic. Uniting at Maastricht with the Zuid Willemsvaart, which ran northward towards Hertogenbosch and linked up with the river estuaries of the Hollandsch Diep area, it made possible the transport of stone, coal, and steel from the Meuse and Sambre industrial areas to every part of the Netherlands.

The prosperity of the great cities of Flanders had for centuries been intimately bound up with the waterways. Bruges was at one time easily accessible to the sea-going ships of every seafaring nation when, in centuries long past, a broad inlet of the sea, the Zwijn, ran deep into the Flanders country-side by way of Sluis and Damme, where it was joined by the Roya, a small river running out of Bruges in a north-easterly direction. At that time the trade of Bruges was at its height, and ships from Ireland and Germany, Poland and Venice and Russia, Scandinavia and Scotland were plying to Damme to unload into barges the rich cargoes to be taken up the Roya to the warehouses of the wealthy merchant burghers of Bruges, set on the banks of the town canals. In the fifteenth century, as many as 150 foreign vessels were clearing the port of Damme in a day, and Bruges contained the consulates of a score of countries, but today Damme has shrunk to a mere fiftieth part of its former size. Its fate was inseparably linked with that of Bruges, and both were ruined when in the early part of the fifteenth century the sea began to desert them. The banks then beginning to form south of the mouth of the Scheldt were soon to close for ever the mouth of the estuary, and the Zwijn itself silted up until navigation was impossible. The harbour at Damme was left on dry land, the Zwijn disappeared, the marshes were reclaimed, and the most prosperous city of northern Europe fell into inevitable decline.

Bruges eventually made an effort to regain her lost trade, and in 1722 the river Yperlée was canalized to form the present course of the canal from Ostend to Bruges, so that sea-going ships could once again reach the city. In the middle of the nineteenth century British schooners of more than 200 tons regularly plied to Bruges by this canal, most of them carrying cargoes of salt from the Mersey.

The Ostend–Bruges canal carried a flourishing packet-service, and when

Robert Southey visited Bruges in 1815 he travelled by the *trekschuit* or fly-boat, drawn by four horses and making a speed of 5 mph. It was a fine affair, the better of the two cabins being splendidly fitted up with crimson plush.

The anonymous writer of 'What may be done in Two Months' went by the canal boat *Élégante Messagère* on this same canal in 1834, and wrote that 'there never was a cleaner or better fitted up packet-boat: the little cabin with its beautiful sofas, mirrors and chairs, rivalled the nicest drawing room: and breakfast was served in it with so much propriety and order'. The boat was drawn by two horses at 4 mph and the charge for the trip was only 2 francs, which included the breakfast. At Bruges the passengers were taken by carriage to the Ghent packet, an equally smart boat that ran on the Canal de Bruges à Ghent.

The history of Ghent was similarly bound up with its outlet to the sea. At first sight it seems strange that this should have been a matter of concern for a city situated on the navigable reaches of the Scheldt, but the lower reaches of the river ran through states that were not always on good terms with Ghent, and the city could ill afford to remain in a position where her entire export trade could persist only on the sufferance of others. Accordingly in 1251 the Lieve canal was begun, leading all the way to Damme, which port Ghent then shared with Bruges until the disastrous silting of the Zwijn rendered it useless.

For many years afterwards Ghent used the Scheldt as an outlet, but the growth of the textile industry led to new thoughts about an alternative route to the sea, and in 1549 the Sassevaart was opened to bring sea-going ships from a point on the south side of the Scheldt estuary, opposite the island of Beveland, right into the city.

Luck was against the citizens, however, and the Treaty of Münster in 1648 gave control of the outlet of this canal, and also of the main Scheldt itself, into the hands of the Dutch. Article XIV stated that 'The rivers of the Schelde, as also the canals of Sas, Zwijn and other mouths of rivers disemboguing themselves there shall be kept shut on the side of the Lords the States'; and to make sure that their monopoly of navigation should remain unbroken the Dutch built a fort at Lillo (the present frontier-post in the estuary) to cover the Scheldt route, and another at Sas-van-Ghent to cover the canal. Nothing could pass without paying crushing dues, so the city of Ghent had once again to plan a new export route or die. This new canal was the Canal de Bruges à Ghent, begun in 1724 and reconstructed in 1751 and on three later occasions. From the outset it was designed to carry 100-ton craft, and it enabled the exports of Ghent to flow down through Bruges to Ostend and thence to such parts of Europe as were independent of Dutch control.

In 1795 the French Republican government reopened the Sassevaart for traffic, but when in 1800 an enterprising burgher named Lieven Bauwens succeeded in acquiring a Crompton spinning-mule in England and smuggling it out of the country in pieces and bringing it home to Ghent, busy cotton-mills sprang up, and the increased trade demanded something bigger and better than even the Sassevaart and the Ostend route together could provide. Accordingly, after the departure of the French the big modern Ghent ship canal was cut through to Terneuzen and opened in 1827. It followed much of the line of the old Sassevaart, but was shorter and straighter and it made certain the rise of Ghent to a flourishing port in our own day. It now passes 25 000 ships annually.

Elsewhere, two other canals for sea-going vessels were constructed. Amsterdam was accessible by way of the Zuider Zee, but the continual silting of this shallow area of water progressively made the position of the port more precarious. In 1825, therefore, a long and admirably constructed ship canal was opened, by-passing the entire Zuider Zee coast and reaching the North Sea in the Texel roads opposite the western end of the chain of the Frisian islands. Half a century later it was to be succeeded by the much shorter ship canal to Ijmuiden, but the smaller cargo-vessels still use the North Holland canal if bound from the north for Alkmaar. It was originally constructed with a minimum depth of 18 ft (as against 11 in the Zuider Zee) and the locks at each end had a length of 213 ft. Forty yards broad and fifty miles long, it was a handsome piece of canal construction across soft and very difficult land.

The other great work of the period, which was to prove so valuable when improved at a later date, was the bold stroke of making a waterway which would by-pass the Kattegat and the dangerous Skagerrak, and so give direct access from the Baltic to the North Sea. Earlier attempts had been made; the Vikings portaged their ships across a 10-mile watershed on rollers, and as early as 1398 a canal for small craft was cut by way of Lübeck on the line of the present Elbe-Trave canal. In 1784 the Eider canal was laid down between the Kiel fiord and the Upper Eider lakes, on the instructions of the Danish King Christian VII. This waterway was cut to a depth of 10 ft and had three locks (see plate 38 A) on either side of the watershed, and from where it connected with the Eider river at Rendsburg the river-course westwards was dredged and deepened. Originally intended for Danish ships only, the Eider canal (figure 306) was opened to craft of all nations in 1785, and it was not until more than a hundred years later that the increased size of modern ships made it essential for the course to be widened, deepened, and straightened to form the Kiel canal—a waterway which today carries more than 2 million tons of shipping a month.

The Kaiser Wilhelm or Kiel canal was opened in 1895, with a length of 59 miles from the locks at Brunsbüttel at the North Sea end, where there is a tidal range of some 13 ft, to the Holtenau locks in the Kiel fiord, where the tide ranges through only a few inches. Crossing low and undulating country, and with plenty of water available from the Eider (figure 306), its construction did not present any special problems, but the railway-bridge at Rendsburg is a notable feat of engineering. Sufficient height is gained by a loop of track which

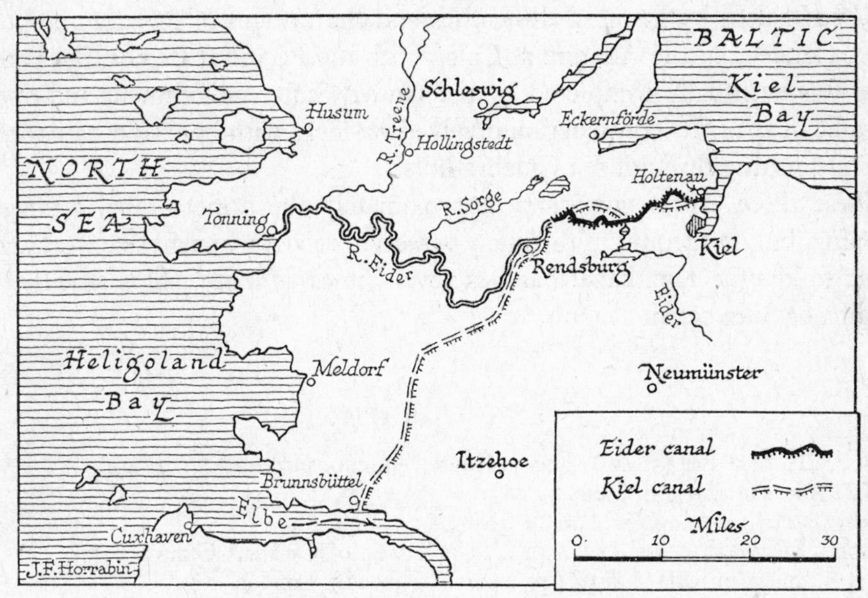

FIGURE 306—*Lines of the Kiel and Eider canals.*

encircles the city on a rising viaduct and crosses over itself before running on to the main span above the water, while the underside of the bridge serves as a carrier for a trolley from which a road transporter is suspended at bank level.

The Kiel canal not only by-passed the dangerous Skagen area of northern Denmark, where millions of tons of shipping had been lost, but cut the distance from the English Channel to the southern Baltic by several hundred miles. An even greater shortening of commercial seaways was the object underlying the construction of the two other great inter-sea or inter-oceanic canals, work on which was begun during the latter half of the nineteenth century. The scheme of a canal to link the Mediterranean with the Red Sea dated back to pre-Christian times, but it remained for Ferdinand de Lesseps (1805–94) to construct the existing Suez canal, a waterway 99 miles long and without locks at either end. Opened in 1869, this waterway was taking £2 500 000 annually in dues before the end of the century, but the deposition of sand eroded by wash or carried by the wind has made continual dredging necessary in order to preserve the depth of water (plate 38 B).

The narrow isthmus of Central America also offered attractive possibilities for a link between the Atlantic and Pacific oceans, and work was in fact started on the Nicaragua canal in 1889. It was abandoned, however, in favour of the Panama route which had already been begun by de Lesseps, but work on which had been halted by financial difficulties and the ravages of malaria and yellow fever. Connecting the Atlantic at Colon with the Pacific at Balboa, the Panama canal was eventually completed by the United States government and opened to traffic in 1914. Its construction involved six locks with bankside haulage, and a 7-mile cutting through the Culebra hills.

These three canals now carry approximately the same annual tonnage of shipping, but on account of the many vessels of relatively small size working the Baltic routes the Kiel canal handles seven times as many ships as either the Panama or Suez canal.

BIBLIOGRAPHY

ADAMS, S. H. 'The Erie Canal.' Random House, Toronto. 1953.

"A.K." 'Afloat in Belgium.' London. 1871.

Annales des Ponts et Chaussées. Paris. 1850–83.

CANADIAN DEPARTMENT OF TRANSPORT. 'The Canals of Canada.' Ottawa. 1937.

CRESY, E. 'Encyclopaedia of Civil Engineering' (new ed.). London. 1861.

DUMONT, M. E. 'Gent — een stedenaardrijkskundige studie.' Rijksuniv. te Gent, Werken uitgegeven door de Faculteit van de Wijsbegeerte en Letteren, 107e Aflevering. De Tempel, Bruges. 1951.

'The Emperor's Claims . . . together with Extracts from the Articles of the Treaty of Munster . . . whereby the Dutch found their Right to the Blocking up of the Schelde.' London. 1785.

'Haven van Gent.' Report published by the Harbour Authority, Ghent. 1955.

HOERSCHELMANN, E. F. DE. 'Aperçu historique du développement des voies navigables de l'Empire de Russie.' Kiev. 1894.

'Map of the Inland Waterways of France.' Imray, Laurie, Norrie & Wilson, London. 1950.

'Der Nord-Ostsee Kanal.' Wasser- und Schiffahrtsdirektion, Kiel. 1955.

PILKINGTON, R. 'Small Boat through Belgium.' Macmillan, London. 1957.

SOUTHEY, R. 'Journal of a Tour in the Netherlands in the Autumn of 1815.' Heinemann, London. 1902.

STEVENSON, R. L. 'An Inland Voyage.' London. 1878.

THOMAS, B. F. and WATT, D. A. 'The Improvement of Rivers and Canals' (2nd ed.). John Wiley, New York. 1913.

Verhandlungen des III Internationalen Binnenschiffahrts=Kongresses. Frankfurt. 1888.

VERNON-HARCOURT, L. F. 'Rivers and Canals' (2nd ed., 2 vols). Oxford. 1896.

'What may be done in Two Months.' London. 1834.

18

PART II

CANALS:

INLAND WATERWAYS OF THE BRITISH ISLES

CHARLES HADFIELD

BRITAIN was slow to begin building canals, but, once started, they were quickly extended as the industrial revolution developed. In 1750 there were over 1000 miles of navigable river in Great Britain (figure 308), and in

FIGURE 307—*The Duke of Bridgewater's canal crossing the Irwell.*

1850 about 4250 miles of inland navigation, in addition to a considerable mileage in Ireland (vol III, ch 17).

The first modern canals, the Sankey Brook from the St Helen's coalfield to the Mersey (1757), and the Duke of Bridgewater's from the Worsley mines to Manchester (1761) (figure 307 and tailpiece), presented few engineering problems other than the building of the Irwell aqueduct. Later canals had to surmount hilly country and, because no state finance was available, had to be cheap and bring returns quickly. The Trent and Mersey canal, for instance, was begun in 1766 and completed in 1777; it was 93½ miles long with 75 locks and five tunnels (figure 309).

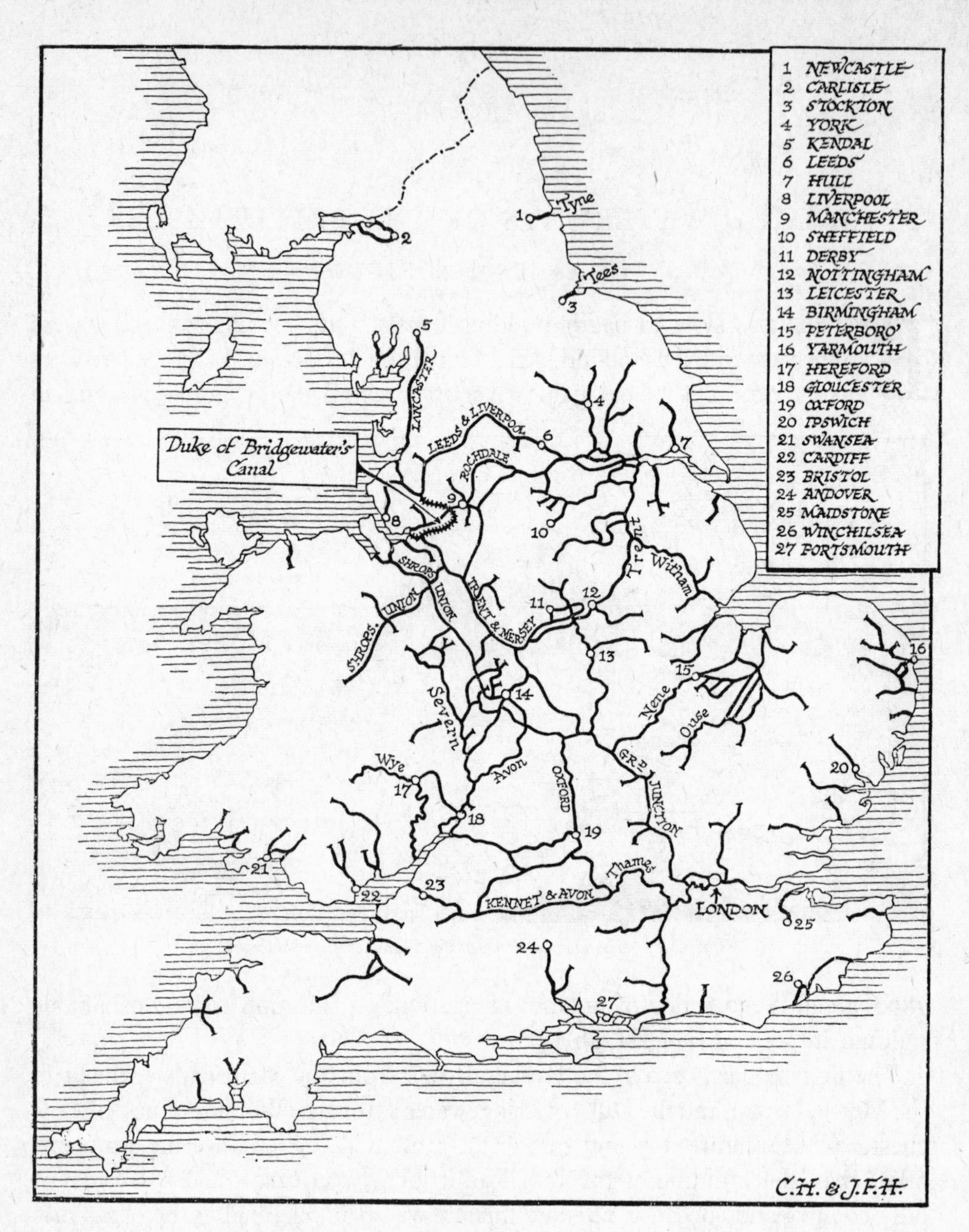

FIGURE 308—*The inland waterway system of England and Wales at its greatest extent. 1858.*

Three types of canal were developed: wide for some main lines with ambitious shareholders; narrow with 7-ft locks for cheaper routes, especially those with poor water supplies; and the tub-boat canal for the steepest gradients. Wide

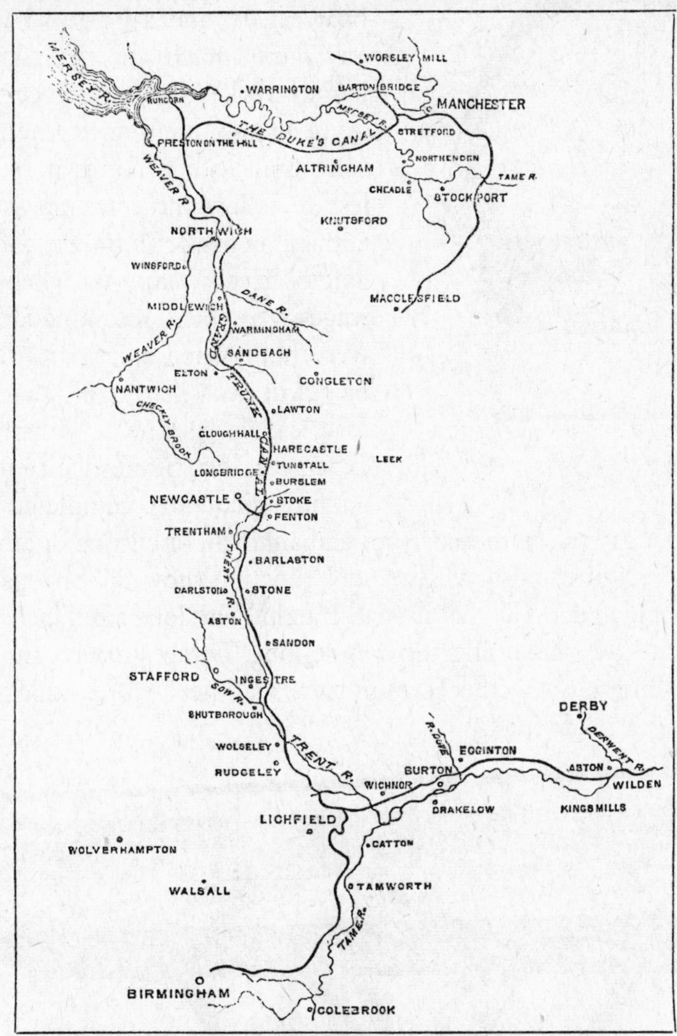

FIGURE 309—*The Grand Trunk (Trent and Mersey) and Duke of Bridgewater's canals, with early proposed extensions to Birmingham and Macclesfield. The latter was in fact continued through Macclesfield to rejoin the Grand Trunk at Lawton.*

canals were mainly in the north-east and north-west of England and in Scotland; narrow canals in south Wales and around Birmingham, the ascent to which is by flights of locks on all sides; the tub-boat canals in the south-west and in Shropshire. Within these groups variations were developed, but broadly

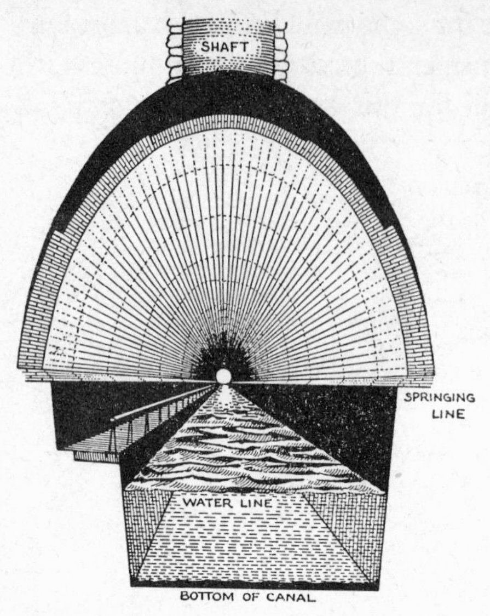

FIGURE 310—*Section of the Strood tunnel on the Thames and Medway canal.*

speaking a narrow boat 70 ft by 7 ft could travel anywhere south of the rivers Trent and Mersey except on the tub-boat canals, and a barge 58 ft by $13\frac{1}{2}$ ft anywhere north of that line. Larger barges worked upon the river navigations.

As already mentioned, the early canals were built as cheaply as possible. It cost less to follow the contours than to make embankments or cuttings, and the extra length hardly mattered when boatmen's wages were low. Accommodation bridges were built when a farmer's land had to be cut in two (plate 39 B). Later, as wages rose, canals became straighter and more expensive. The Staffordshire and Worcestershire (plate 37), completed in 1772, is a typical contour canal, with hardly an embankment or cutting of any size upon it; while the Birmingham and Liverpool Junction (now the Shropshire Union main line), completed in 1835, is almost straight, with long stretches on embankments or in cuttings, including the 2-mile-long Tyrley cutting, the deepest in the country. In two cases, the Birmingham and the Oxford canals, a contour canal was later straightened.

FIGURE 311—*The iron aqueduct conveying the Shrewsbury canal over the river Tern at Longdon in Shropshire.*

Where hills had to be passed, tunnels were cheaper than cuttings. About 45 miles of canal tunnel were built in Great Britain, most of them not big enough to allow boats to pass each other. Earlier tunnels, except the shortest, had no towpath, boats being legged or shafted through, or pulled with chains fastened to the walls. Paths were later provided, the first, on timber stretchers over the water, being in the Berwick tunnel of the Shrewsbury canal. Later, the bores were enlarged to take a single or double tow-path. The longest tunnel built was at Standedge on the Huddersfield canal, 5415 yds long; the largest in dimensions

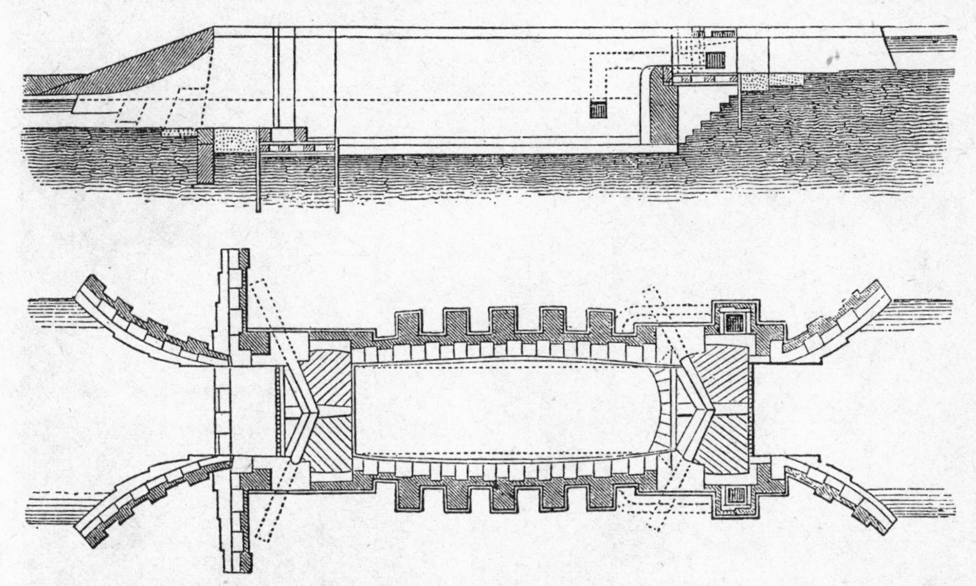

FIGURE 312—*Section and plan of a lock on the Duke of Bridgewater's canal.*

was the Strood tunnel on the Thames and Medway canal, 35 ft from the bottom of the invert to the top of the arch, and 26 ft 6 in from wall to wall (figure 310). The usual tunnelling practice was to work outwards from shafts sunk from above, up which the spoil was drawn by horse-gins (plate 7 A). There were, for instance, 25 such completed shafts in the Sapperton tunnel (3808 yds) on the Thames and Severn canal.

Aqueducts carried the canals over river valleys. Early canal engineers built them immensely strong of stone or brick, within which frame the waterway, usually narrowed, was carried in a puddled bed. A major development was the substitution of an iron trough, first used on the Longdon-on-Tern aqueduct on the Shrewsbury canal (figure 311). The most notable was at Pont-y-Cysyllte on the Ellesmere canal, the aqueduct being 1007 ft long with 19 arches, and 121 ft above the river Dee. The trough is 11 ft 10 in wide, the tow-path being carried over it on iron supports, so allowing a wider waterway than at Longdon-on-Tern, where it lay beside the waterway in a separate trough.

Locks (figure 312), inclined planes (figures 313 and 314), and lifts (figures 315, 317) were used to raise or lower boats from one level to another. The gate,

FIGURE 313—*A medium plane for use in small canals with a rise of only 20–30 ft. A water-wheel was used as a source of power on a number of planes in the West of England.*

counterbalanced by a beam, and its heel-post revolving in a quoin, was commonly used for locks, though occasionally a vertically-rising counterbalanced gate is found, as on the Shrewsbury canal or on the Stratford on Avon canal at King's Norton, Birmingham. Double locks placed side-by-side appear first to have been used on the Regent's canal in London, opened in 1820, while staircase locks, in which two or more were built together and had gates in common, were frequent, the biggest being the five-lock staircase at Bingley on the Leeds and Liverpool canal. Water was passed into or out of locks by almost every possible combination of ground- and gate-paddles. The normal arrangement was to have both the ground- and the gate-paddles on the upper gates, and gate-paddles alone on the lower, the paddles rising vertically by ratchet and pinion worked by a detachable windlass, though sideways-moving paddles and fixed windlasses are also found.

Inclined planes for moving tub-boats from one level of canal to another were used in hilly parts of the country (figure 313). Fourteen were worked in south-western England, two in south Wales, and six in Shropshire. One was built in Scotland at the end of our period, and one in Leicestershire after it, both for

FIGURE 314—*A double inclined plane, where the boats were lowered on rails. The weight was counterbalanced by a large tub of water in a pit. The tub, which was about 9 ft in diameter and 5 ft deep and contained about 8 tons of water, was filled from the upper canal. When it reached the foot of the pit, which was on a level with the lower canal, the water was released and escaped through a trough. A plane using this method was built at Hobbacott Down on the Bude canal.*

larger craft. The first incline, at Ketley in Shropshire (plate 48 C), began work in 1788, and the last, at Trench not far away, was closed in 1922. These planes were slopes upon which single or double lines of rails were laid: upon the rails the boats were carried either in wheeled caissons full of water, or dry in wheeled cradles, or ran on their own wheels (figure 314). Water was the usual, steam the occasional, motive-power. The greatest vertical height of any British plane carrying boats was 225 ft, on the Hobbacott Down plane of the Bude canal in Cornwall. In addition to the boat-carrying planes, one carrying trucks, into and out of which boxes of coal were lifted, for some years connected two pounds of the Somerset coal canal. Several others using trucks either fed canals with loads brought down from mines and quarries, as at Froghall in Staffordshire, or carried canal cargoes down to a river-wharf, as at Morwellham on the Tavistock canal, or delivered them to a works, as at Coalbrookdale on the Shropshire canal.

Lastly, a few vertically-rising lifts counterbalanced by water were built (figure

FIGURE 315—*The perpendicular lift. The cranes move the boats, and the weight is counterbalanced by the tub of water in the pit. This was an idea that never became practicable.*

315), the only ones successfully operated under working conditions being the set of eight designed by James Green for the Grand Western canal and used from 1838 to 1867. A device patented by Robert Fulton is illustrated in figure 316. Fulton wrote on canals and took out patents, but the development work on the subjects of his study had already been largely done by others. After our period a larger lift, worked at first hydraulically and later by electric power, was built at Anderton in Cheshire; it is still in use.

The craft on the canals developed little during the period (plate 39 A and figure 317). The single boat drawn by one horse or a pair of donkeys was almost uni-

FIGURE 316—*Device patented by Fulton in 1794 for conveying loaded boats from one level to another on canals.*

versal; bow-haulage by men was not unusual on rivers, and sails were sometimes used. Boats carrying boxes of goods or tramway wagons were occasionally used. Specialized boats were developed on many canals for carrying passengers by day, and on the Forth and Clyde canal there were sleeping-boats for night travel. Light passenger-boats travelling at some 10 mph were run for many years on the Glasgow, Paisley, and Ardrossan canal.

In 1789 Symington tried the second of his steam-boats on a canal in Scotland, and in 1802 his tug, the *Charlotte Dundas*, worked there for a time, till she was abandoned because of her wash. Later, many experimental steam cargo-carrying boats were run on canals, but the only regular development of the steam-boat within our period was as a tunnel-tug, one of the first being that which started work through the Islington tunnel on the Regent's canal in 1826.

Between 1750 and 1850 the great British canal engineers—Brindley, the elder Rennie, Outram, the Whitworths, the Jessops, the Dadfords, Telford, and

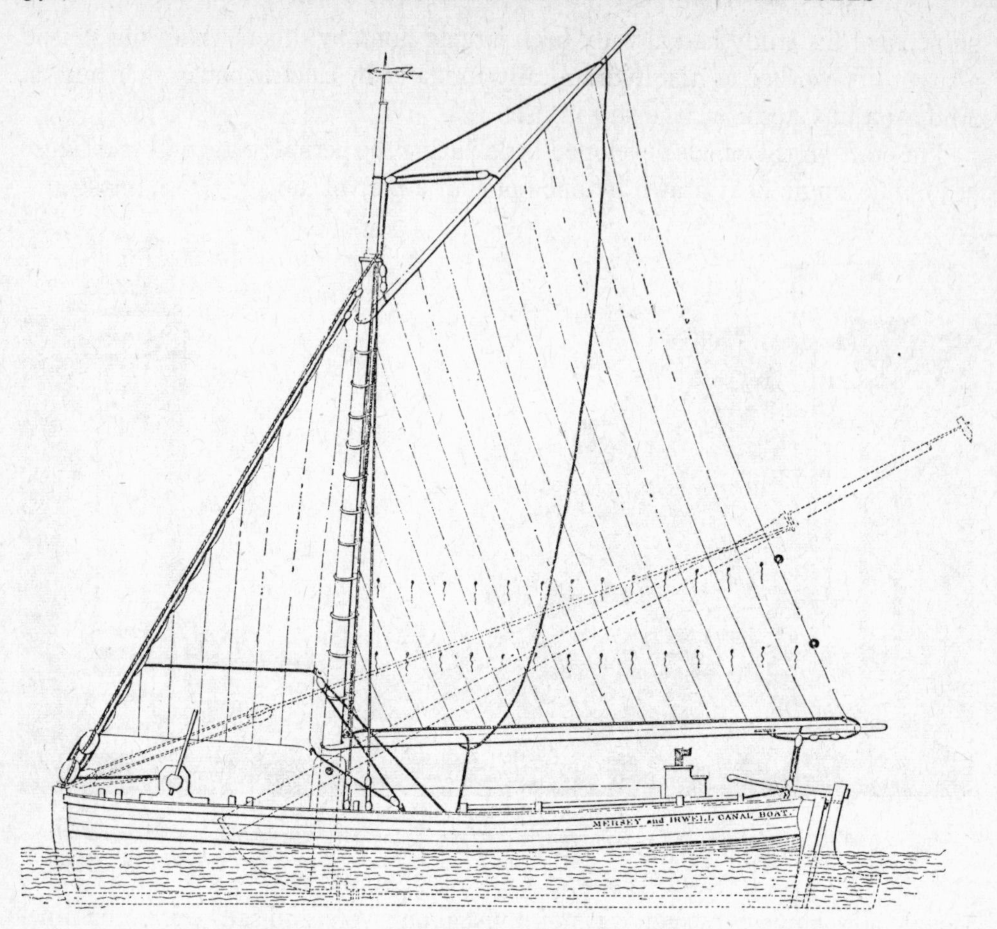

FIGURE 317—*Canal boat as used on the Mersey and Irwell navigation. The mast could be lowered.*

Green—had joined the Thames, Severn, Mersey, Trent, and Aire by trunk canals, from which many branches had been built, while a number of separate canal systems had been developed. In Wales, canals brought coal and iron from the hills to the ports; in Scotland, two great waterways had been built from sea to sea, the Caledonian in the north and the Forth and Clyde in the south; and in Ireland two crossed the country from the Shannon to Dublin. They made an invaluable contribution to the great nineteenth-century development of Britain.

BIBLIOGRAPHY

DE SALIS, H. R. 'A Chronology of Inland Navigation in Great Britain.' London. 1897.
FORBES, U. A. and ASHFORD, W. H. R. 'Our Waterways.' John Murray, London. 1906.
HADFIELD, C. 'British Canals: an Illustrated History.' Phoenix House, London. 1950.
Idem. 'The Canals of Southern England.' Phoenix House, London. 1955.
JACKMAN, W. T. 'The Development of Transportation in Modern England.' University Press, Cambridge. 1914.
PHILLIPS, J. 'A General History of Inland Navigation.' London. 1792.
PRIESTLEY, J. 'Historical Account of the Navigable Rivers, Canals and Railways throughout Great Britain.' London. 1831.
Report of Royal Commission on Canals and Waterways (12 vols). H.M. Stationery Office, London. 1907–9.
ROLT, L. T. C. 'The Inland Waterways of England.' Allen & Unwin, London. 1950.
SMILES, S. 'Lives of the Engineers with an Account of their Principal Works' (3 vols). London. 1861–2.
'The History of Inland Navigation.' London. 1766.
VERNON-HARCOURT, L. F. 'Rivers and Canals' (2nd ed., 2 vols). Oxford. 1896.

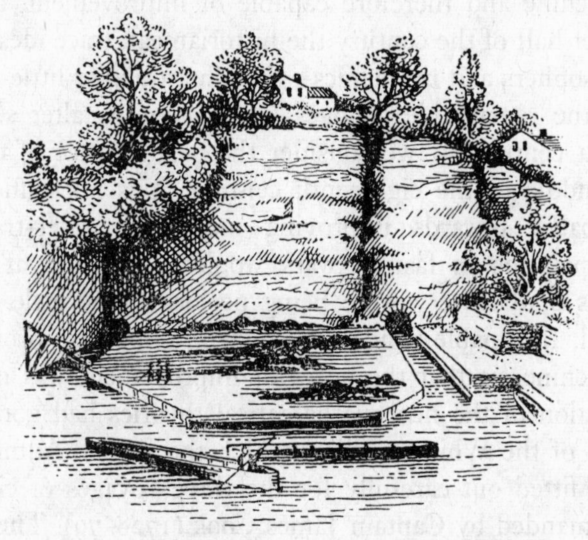

The basin at Worsley, showing the canal entrance to the coal-mine.

19

SHIP-BUILDING

GEORGE NAISH

I. PERFORMANCE AND TYPES OF SHIP

THE fact that there had been no startling progress in the development of the ship during the eighteenth century was noted by the author of the article on seamanship in the third edition of the 'Encyclopaedia Britannica' published in 1797: 'What a pity it is that an art so important, so difficult, and so intimately connected with the invariable laws of mechanical nature, should be so held by its possessors that it cannot improve, but must die with each individual.' The seaman, having no advantages of education, 'cannot think'. Yet a ship was a machine and therefore capable of improvement, and particularly during the latter half of the century the historian can trace ideas stirring in the minds of philosophers and mechanics—though attracting little public attention—that herald the remarkable changes which were to alter ships completely during the next century. If we consider the performance of certain ordinary ships in the middle of the eighteenth century, it is not difficult to condone the general apathy towards improving means of water-transport. Trade by sea was expanding as fast as wars would allow, and at the same time notable voyages of discovery were being performed by little ships otherwise undistinguished. In capable hands the wooden sailing-ship proved itself a very satisfactory machine, so that the need for improvement was not obvious. No great consideration of the new mathematical theories had gone, for example, into the design of the Whitby colliers which the British Admiralty bought in succession and fitted out carefully for the three voyages of circumnavigation (1768–80) commanded by Captain James Cook (1728–79). These colliers were described as 'cat-built barks'. Bark was a common term for a small three-masted ship, and was used by Shakespeare and Hakluyt in this sense. Cat was a word of Scandinavian origin for a type of hull, common to the maritime countries of northern Europe, having a bluff bow and straight stem, without the beak-head and figure-head common to larger ships. The broad, round stern had a narrow, flat piece above the transom, with stern windows in it looking out of the after-cabin or coach; this type of stern was called a 'pink' stern. Cat-built vessels were very roomy for their size and were not only colliers but carried goods across the

North Sea and Atlantic. They were, however, best known as colliers, and having flat bottoms could be unloaded into carts on beaches at low water. They could be sailed close to the wind, for the narrow upper part of the stern enabled the main yard to be braced sharp round. Their anchors were weighed with powerful windlasses in the bow.

Cook considered this type of ship ideal for exploring unknown coasts, and with reason. Thus when the *Endeavour* was holed on the Great Barrier Reef of Australia she was run ashore on a beach and repaired, which could not have been done with a bigger ship. The *Endeavour* (plate 40 A) was 97 ft long on the lower deck and of 29 ft beam: her burthen was 368 tons. In this vessel Cook rediscovered New Zealand, sailed round the North and South Islands, and discovered and explored the Great Barrier Reef. The *Resolution*, a similar ship, was called upon to sail in high southern latitudes, voyaging 3660 leagues in 117 days without sighting land. Yet the *Resolution* might well never have set sail, for she proved so 'crank' (top heavy) working down the Thames from Deptford before Cook's second voyage that her first lieutenant wrote: 'I think her by far the most unsafe ship I ever saw or heard of.' The Admiralty had added a poop deck in the stern to provide accommodation for Sir Joseph Banks (1743–1820) and his staff of artists and botanists, but Banks gave up the expedition. Cook wrote: 'She was a stiff ship before we got her', and advised the removal of the top-hamper, after which the *Resolution* proved herself one of the finest sea-boats of all time.

The story of Cook's ships, which were typical of the smaller European merchant ships of the day, shows that such vessels, well found and competently handled, were generally speaking incapable of being overwhelmed by heavy weather in the open sea. Shipwreck was another matter, however. For example, a gale might spring up when a ship was unloading on the sands at low water and she might be lost when the tide came in. Errors of navigation were frequent; in fact, they could not be avoided by the most skilful ship-master because of the insufficiency of the charts (ch 20). Nevertheless, Nelson once wrote cheerfully, when he commanded his favourite 64-gun ship, the *Agamemnon*: 'To me it is perfectly indifferent to what quarter of the world we go: with a good ship and a good ship's company we can come to no harm.' Cook felt equally secure in the *Endeavour*. 'Her best sailing is with the wind a point or two abaft the beam; she will then run 7 or 8 knots and carry a weather helm', he wrote. And again: 'No sea can hurt her laying-to under a main sail or mizzen ballanced.' He had had little opportunity of sailing her in company with other ships, but enough to notice that she made more leeway than most, about a point or a point and a half.

The biggest merchant ships were those trading with the east and managed by the English, French, and Dutch East India Companies (plate 42 B). At the end of the century the English company was taking up ships of three sizes, the largest being officially 1200 tons, which in effect meant anything up to 1500 tons. These ships were well armed with from 30 to 36 guns, and while not fast were well found and well manned and very safe. They usually made three voyages out and back, taking six years, and then were thoroughly repaired and perhaps taken up by the company again. Heavily built and bluff-bowed as these Indiamen were, it is on record that a naval frigate convoying three of them had difficulty in not losing company by running ahead out of sight—the frigate under bare poles and the Indiamen staggering along under a press of canvas which included studding-sails. Nevertheless, the Indiamen were outwardly almost indistinguishable from small warships. The latter, however, were built for speed rather than for cargo-space and were heavily armed, but not necessarily heavily laden, and well manned. The larger naval vessels were considerably larger than any merchant ships.

The ships of the Royal Navy were administratively divided into six rates, according to size and armament. The first three rates were deemed suitable for the line of battle. British ships were usually built a little smaller than French, Spanish, or Dutch ships of the same calibre, and this was a cause of frequent complaints by British naval officers, because the larger ship was both roomier and faster and able to fight better in a sea-way. It was a common fault—arising from attempts to put a quart into a pint pot—for English ships to carry their lower gun-ports nearer the water than was designed by the naval architect. In 1782 Great Britain had 105 ships of the line, France 89, Spain 53, and Holland 32. The financial struggle to maintain this lead was the cause of the niggardly economy of building British ships a little too small. However, a good many French, Spanish, and Dutch ships found their way into the Royal Navy.

A solitary survivor of the line-of-battle ships of those days, H.M.S. *Victory* (plate 42 A), is still in commission as the flagship of the Commander-in-Chief, Portsmouth. The *Victory* deserves our consideration as a very successful ship, so popular that she was always chosen as a flagship throughout her long and active career. She was laid down at Chatham in 1759 and launched in 1765. The length of her gun-deck is 186 ft and her beam is 52 ft. Her armament is 100 guns, the heavier firing a 32-pound ball, with two 68-pounder carronades (short guns) on the forecastle. Between 1778 and 1812 she flew the flags of fourteen admirals and took part in eight major actions, including the battles of Cape St Vincent (1797) and Trafalgar (1805). Her longevity was not due to the careful choice of her timber, because before Trafalgar she had undergone two expensive repairs, in 1787–8 and 1800–3. She was repaired again in 1814–16, and brought up to date in the light of experience gained at Trafalgar. In 1922, after being placed in dry dock, she was restored to her Trafalgar appearance. A visitor to the ship can imagine the cramped life on board, the enormous quantity of timber that went into the building of a wooden ship, and, perhaps above all, the skill and strength needed to handle such a ship under sail and to man-handle her spars, anchors, and boats. One of her officers at Trafalgar, Lieutenant Rivers, compared her with the *Dreadnought*, of much the same dimensions, launched at Portsmouth in 1801. The latter was a heavy, dull sailer, but he records that the *Victory* sailed beautifully, was very weatherly, and steered like a fishing-boat. He calls attention to a fact that was well known: two ships, even if built to the same draught, would never behave alike.

Evidence of the efforts made to improve the theory and practice of shipbuilding will be found in the number of books published on various aspects of the subject. Works by Frenchmen which were widely studied, translated, adapted, and copied were M. Bouguer's *Traité du navire, de sa construction, et de ses mouvements* (1746) and H. L. Duhamel Dumonceau's *Élémens de l'architecture navale ou traité pratique de la construction des vaisseaux* (1752). The Swiss mathematician Leonhard Euler (1707–83) wrote on the form of ships and why they sail to windward; written originally in Latin and published at St Petersburg, his books were translated and he was regarded as the great authority on ship-design. He favoured the full-bowed and clean-tailed, or cod's-head and mackerel-tail, hull. On the whole, however, the scientific reasoning of the mathematicians seems to have resulted in theories that did not work out in practice. A well laden ship with bluff bows drove before her a great swell of water which impeded both sailing and steering, not merely in stormy conditions but in fine weather and over a smooth sea. When running before the wind in bad weather she was liable, even with a good helmsman, to broach-to when yawing about, and her fine lines under the stern made her liable to be pooped by a following sea. On the other hand, a ship with wedge-shaped bows could not carry sufficient sail when upon a wind or close-hauled in a rough sea, because she would plunge dangerously deep, and the water would come on board and fill her main deck.

Ship-builders ignored the theories and strove in the light of experience to find successful designs that represented a compromise between the opposing factors. Most of the many draughts prepared for the Royal Navy during the eighteenth and nineteenth centuries have survived and can be studied (plate 41 A). While merchant ships were built with full-bodied hulls to carry the greatest amount of cargo, warships were designed with many little variations—made within very narrow limits—that represented the testing of various suggested improvements in design. Good use was made of a successful design, and it was often employed for many decades as a basis for later ones. When a ship was captured, her lines were recorded as soon as she reached a naval dockyard, and thus it is possible directly to compare English ships with those of French, Dutch, Spanish, American, and all other navies that came into conflict with that of Britain. The comparison is interesting, and shows the interest in ship-design taken by the British Admiralty. However, admiration for captured French ships was such that there was a tendency for their faults to be copied as well as their virtues. Gabriel Snodgrass, surveyor to the Honourable East India Company, wrote: 'In my opinion, a great deal too much has been said in favour of French ships. I cannot, myself, see anything worthy of being copied from them but their magnitude.'

Warships were commonly built with their top-sides pinched in, so that they had a greater beam at the water-line than at the level of the upper deck. This feature was called the 'tumble-home'. It kept the weight of the upper-deck guns inboard and the hull was supposed to be stronger because of it, but, on the other hand, the tumble-home gave less buoyancy when the ship was heeled. Straight sides also gave more room on deck. Snodgrass did not approve of the tumble-home, which was not the fashion with East Indiamen and other merchant ships. It was excessive in French warships. 'It must appear very extraordinary,' continued Snodgrass, 'that there are several line of battle ships and large frigates now building [1796] for the Government from draughts, copied from those ridiculous ships.' Snodgrass had no use for this 'absurd old fashion of tumbling in', which also wasted crooked or 'compass' timber. The British government was in this period very concerned over the timber situation, and an inquiry brought to light many interesting facts which were probably common to other seafaring countries. Keeping large supplies in the royal dockyards led to wastage because much decayed before it was used, but there need have been no shortage if the forest lands had been replanted at all systematically.

From his experience in building and inspecting ships for the East India Company, Snodgrass made suggestions that were of real practical value; they were generally adopted, though not always immediately. He thought ships should be built more strongly: 'I have no idea of a ship of war, that is properly built, foundering, or not keeping the seas in the worst weather.' His proposals included thicker planking on the bottom, from four to six inches in the case of line-of-battle ships; straight sides to give greater spread for the shrouds and to make the masts more secure; firm, flush, upper decks to strengthen the hull and prevent a weight of water collecting between decks in the waist; moving the foremast farther aft to lighten the ship in the bows; and removal of the quarter galleries to lighten the stern, which should also be strengthened with strong dead-lights in place of the weak stern windows. A great advance was his suggestion for iron knees, standards, and diagonal braces to prevent the ship from 'working'. The use of iron not only saved timber but gave greater strength. Snodgrass advised the Admiralty and other government departments from 1771 onwards, and gathered his experience from ships of all countries.

It seems probable that the urge to improve ships, which began to take effect at the end of the eighteenth century, was common to all European countries that possessed shipping. The French led the way in trying to unite theory with practice. For example, much space was given in French books on the subject to descriptions of all possible ways of rowing Greek triremes, and the canoes of the South Sea islands are fully illustrated from the descriptions of Cook and Anson. But, as has been shown by the modern use of testing-tanks, it is difficult to apply theory to ship-design, and the improvements came generally from cautious trial and error. In 1791 a privately formed group in London carried out a series of experiments in the Greenland dock, and although the society for the improvement of naval architecture which they formed got into difficulties and failed, its transactions were privately printed and given away. At the same time, Captain John Schank (1740–1823) was experimenting with sliding keels or centreboards. Various ships were also built with peculiar hull-forms or rigs which achieved a certain amount of success but no lasting favour. Examples are the sloops *Arrow* and *Dart*, designed by Sir Samuel Bentham (1757–1831). They had sharp ends, the stem and stern-post raking, and their sides spread outwards so that they had more beam on deck than at the water-line, which was supposed to make them very stiff. They were armed with carronades mounted on non-recoil carriages. They were fairly successful and more were built. An officer of the East India Company, Richard Gower (1767–1833), built and had launched from Itchenor, in 1800, a four-masted ship, also with sides spreading out and with a rig of his own design in which the sails were very flat. This vessel, the *Transit*, was exceedingly fast sailing to windward. Such trials were followed with interest, and encouraged further practical experiments.

II. COPPER SHEATHING FOR SHIPS' BOTTOMS

Weeds and barnacles attach themselves to the bottoms of ships, and unless they are cleared off the ship is made slow and unhandy. In the tropics, the bottom of a wooden ship will quickly be destroyed by the mollusc known as the shipworm (*Teredo*) unless it is protected. In the eighteenth century it was usual to sheath the bottom of a ship with thin fir-boards over hair and tar; and when, in addition, the bottom was covered with the broad heads of nails the ship was said to be sheathed and filled. In the West Indies it was very difficult to careen ships and burn off or 'bream' their bottoms, and in 1761 the Navy Board suggested to the British Admiralty that a ship's bottom might be covered with plate copper as a protection against worm. This suggestion had been made before, for example in 1708, but it was now carried out, the frigate *Alarm* being sheathed with thin copper by way of experiment. She came home in August 1763. The copper had been on for twenty months; it had somewhat wasted away, but it was clean of weed and barnacles and had kept the caulking in place, and the worm had not got into the planking. On the other hand, much to everyone's surprise, the false keel had fallen off and the iron fastenings of the rudder were so decayed that the rudder would very soon have followed. By replacing with copper the iron fastenings on the hull below the water-line, rudder and keel were made safe, but weed grew on the copper, which was disappointing. The electrolytic action between the copper and the iron was not understood until later. In 1776 twelve vessels in the Royal Navy, all frigates or smaller, were coppered. In 1781 there was a great drive to copper ships, and in that year Admiral Rodney was sent with a coppered fleet to relieve Gibraltar.

III. THE INDUSTRIAL REVOLUTION AND THE SAILING-SHIP

Until the end of the eighteenth century the heavy labour of ship-building was being performed in England with little mechanical assistance, despite the example of the revolution that was altering the character of many industries. Foreigners, however, did not seem to think England backward in this respect. Daniel Lescallier (1743–1822) in 1791 was full of praises for the great merchant yards on the Thames where Perry and Wells were building East Indiamen and whaling-ships. At the end of the century Thomas Pennant (1726–98), on his last tour, visited Portsmouth and inspected the dockyard. He saw the anchorsmiths: 'seventy or eighty brawny fellows were amidst the fires busied in fabricating those securities to our shipping'. He saw the faultless anchor of the unfortunate *Royal George*, bearing the motto: 'Fear not; I will hold you fast.' He saw the rope-walk, 870 ft long: 'The making of a great cable is a wonderful sight; a hundred men are required for the purpose, and the labour is so hard that they cannot work at it more than four hours in the day.' The sawing was all done by hand over saw-pits, and it was sometimes cheaper to buy planks from Scandinavian countries where sawing was done in mills by wind- or water-power. Pumping water out of the dry docks was another heavy labour, in this case performed by horses.

Sir Samuel Bentham, the brother of Jeremy Bentham, had early training as a shipwright. He gained his military rank in the Russian service and had returned to England on leave when he visited the dockyards to advise on improvements in 1795. He left the Russian service, became inspector-general of naval works (a new office), and laboured with a small staff to bring the naval yards up to date. In 1798 he wrote: 'I lost no time in considering the means of enabling inanimate force to perform some of the most important of the preparatory operations subservient to naval works.' He suggested a steam-engine, but the idea found little favour. He conferred with the First Lord of the Admiralty, Lord Spencer, who

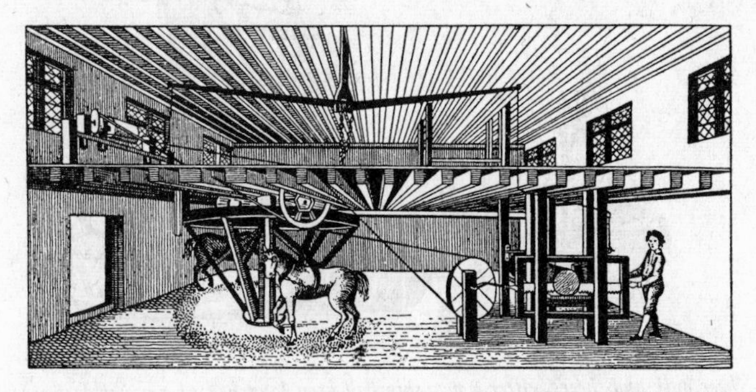

FIGURE 318—*Blockmaking. The horses work both a saw and a lathe. The parts of the block are the shell, of elm or ash; the pin, of lignum vitae, greenheart, or iron; and the wheel, of lignum vitae.*

allowed him to try out a steam-engine at Redbridge, near Southampton, where new ships of his own design were building for the Navy. The ships were ready before the engine, which he was then allowed to introduce into Portsmouth Yard.

This engine, made by Sadler, seems to have worked at about 12–14 hp; its first job, when set up by a master millwright in 1799, was to replace the horses used for pumping out a new dock, and to work saws. Sadler's engine cost £800, the pump £550, and the saws £600. The total of £1950 compared very favourably with the cost of the horse-pump for the dock alone, which was £2758. The new engine was to pump by night and saw by day. It also raised fresh water from a well and pumped water through the fire-engine hoses. A second engine was ordered from Boulton and Watt; it appears to have produced 30 hp. In 1801 there were discussions about a movable steam-engine and apparatus 'calculated to perform the work of from 30 to 40 labourers': this seems to have been equivalent to six horses. Block-making (figure 318) was an operation of great importance to the sailing Navy, and in 1802 Bentham was inquiring about the block-making contract and very shortly was submitting his own plans for making the blocks in the dockyard by steam. The blocks for the Navy were then made under contract by Dunsterville at Plymouth and Taylor at Southampton: the latter owned quite an elaborate plant driven by a water-mill. Under Bentham a large works was established for block-making machinery, but the story of this has been told elsewhere (p 426). It employed ten men and produced 160 000 blocks annually. By this time, too, the steam-engines were harnessed to both the rope-walk and the iron- and copper-works. Bentham was responsible for many other

FIGURE 319—*Sheer hulk and sheers. After a new ship had been launched at a naval dockyard she was taken alongside the sheer hulk and her lower masts were stepped. The rope was cut to the proper length and worked up into standing and running rigging on board by the ship's company, blocks were stropped and fitted, and the masts and spars sent up aloft.*

improvements in the dockyards, such as building covered slips. This had often been suggested, but he was in a position to carry it out. Some of the slips can still be seen at Chatham and Devonport dockyards.

IV. THE SAILING WARSHIP, 1800–40

The Napoleonic wars naturally focused attention on the warship, though certain merchant ships and privateers were built with a particular view to speed. The Royal Navy blockaded the coasts of Europe, and Admiral Mahan, the naval historian, has told us how 'those far distant, storm-beaten ships, upon which the Grand Army never looked, stood between it and the dominion of the world'. Admiral Cornwallis was off Brest, Collingwood off Rochefort, Pellew off Ferrol, and Nelson off Toulon. It is sufficient indication of the endurance of ships and men to mention that from 16 June 1803 Nelson did not set foot out of the *Victory* for very nearly two whole years.

Nelson must have considered the ship of the line as almost incapable of improvement. At Trafalgar the foremost ships of the two British lines were some time getting into action, and suffered much from raking fire into their bows, where the beak-head bulkhead afforded little protection from the enemy shot. As a result of this lesson, various forms of bows and sterns were proposed which

FIGURE 320—*'Hooping' a mast, that is, driving on iron rings.*

afforded better protection. Sir Robert Seppings (1767–1840), one of the surveyors of the Navy, was responsible for a much stronger round stern, which was very unpopular amongst naval officers because of its ugliness. Before this an officer fighting an action astern, as in the famous retreat conducted by Admiral Cornwallis before a superior French force in 1795, was forced to mutilate the stern of his ship in order to make gunports through which to fire at the enemy; a gun was fired from within to blow out the stern frame.

Seppings devised a new way of framing ships that was adopted in the Navy. Declaring that 'partial strength produces general weakness', he pointed out that the frame of a 74-gun ship, 170 ft long, was formed of 800 different timbers placed at right angles to the keel (plate 41 B); there the ribs were each made of several pieces, about 14 in thick, and there was a space of from 1 to 5 inches between each 'frame', as the complete rib was called. The ribs were planked within and without, and the deck beams tied the sides together and supported the deck-planking. All the timbers composing the hull were placed at right-angles to each other, which allowed the hull to work in a sea-way. Seppings devised an elaborate system of diagonal trusses to hold a ship rigid, and filled the spaces between the frames. The trusses and the fillings also prevented the ship from 'hogging', that is, sagging at the bow and stern when the middle of the ship was on the crest of a wave. Hogging came about from the want of a continued succession of support from the centre to the extremities. Seppings omitted the inside planking, called the ceiling.

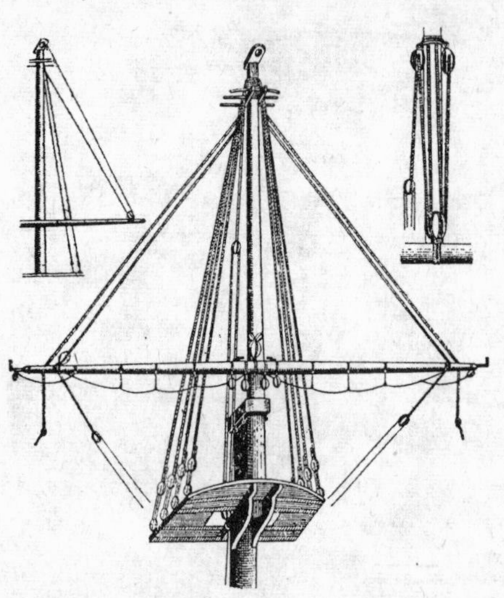

FIGURE 321—*Rigging of the topsail yard. When a ship was rigged, everything had to go on or up in the right order.*

In 1811 a school of naval architecture was established in Portsmouth dockyard. Forty-two students were educated there in a few years, though the Admiralty could employ only 25 men so highly trained and educated. The principal of the school, James Inman (1776–1859), was a brilliant mathematician, and many of the pupils became famous in later years. Once again, however, mathematics provided no short cut to improvement; the ships designed by the school were undistinguished and it was closed down as a failure in 1832. At the same time the Navy Board, the department of the Admiralty that looked after ship-building, was abolished and its administrative work reorganized under the Admiralty. A naval officer, Sir William Symonds (1782–1850), who had a flair for designing ships but no especial training, was appointed surveyor of the Navy. He built many ships, of all classes, which had a great reputation for speed and stability. They could carry a press of sail, but had a violent motion which made them bad gun-platforms; they also had a V-section which sometimes meant that stores had to be stowed on deck because there was too little room in the hold. It was suggested that while there was too much mathematics in the ships designed by the school of naval architecture, Symonds's designs suffered because he was untrained. Despite his claims to originality, such a man as

Symonds found no pleasure in designing hulls for the new steam-engines. Instead, he delighted in trying to improve the sailing qualities of the already old-fashioned wooden warship, frigate, or line-of-battle ship. The hooped masts (figure 320) would be stepped in the hull as she lay alongside a sheer hulk (figure 319); and when they had been stepped would be clothed with the appropriate standing and running rigging; then the tops and caps could be placed over the mastheads and secured. The topmasts and topgallantmasts would follow and be rigged in the proper order; after which the yards could be crossed and the sails bent (figure 321); then the spectators had the wonderful sight of the full-rigged ship

FIGURE 322—*Sails of a ship. These are named after the masts, and each mast of a full-rigged ship was in three parts: the lowermast, topmast, and topgallantmast. The squaresails on the foremast are the foresail, fore topsail, fore topgallantsail, and fore royal. The extensions to the squaresails are the studding sails. There are staysails between the masts, and the mizzen is brailed up and the spanker or driver set. The jib and two staysails are set from the bowsprit, and the spritsail-topsail and spritsail under the bowsprit.*

with her acres of canvas (figure 322), of which the individual sails had been stitched and roped by hand (figure 323) by the sail-makers sitting on their characteristic benches. The progressive rigging of a warship just put into commission was carried out by the newly raised ship's company under their own officers. It was skilful work founded on the stored experience of many generations of sailormen.

V. INTRODUCTION OF CHAIN ANCHOR-CABLE

In 1808 Sir Samuel Brown (1776–1852) of the Royal Navy proposed the use of iron cables and rigging. The iron cable came into general use in the Navy—one chain-cable to each ship—in 1811, and the fleet under Admiral Lord Exmouth which bombarded Algiers in 1816 lay at anchor with chain-cables, which could not be shot away. The original cost of the chain was not much greater than that of the hempen cable, which, in the *Victory* for example, was some

20 inches in circumference. Chain was not affected by alternate wetness and dryness, which quickly rotted hempen cables, especially in the tropics, and it did not easily part amongst rocks. The chain could be stowed in a locker, whereas the ablest men in a ship were required to coil down the hempen cable in the cable-tiers so that it would run out quickly without a kink, which might jam. The chain was, however, difficult to handle in deep water, and the hawse-holes in the ship's bows, as well as the riding-bitts, had to be cased in iron to take it. The difficult task of splicing the hempen cable, and the 'puddening' or padding of

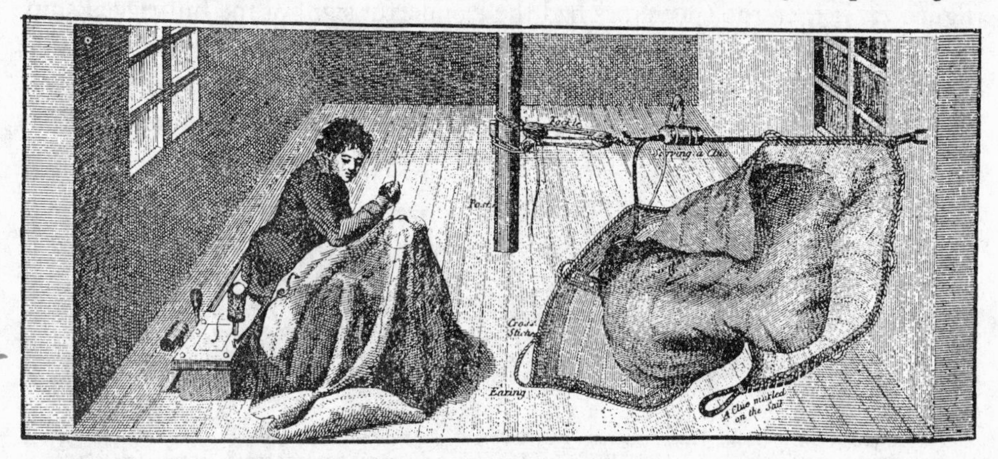

FIGURE 323—*Sailmaking. Tools illustrated include a sail hook, used with a tackle for stretching the bolt rope when sewing it to the sail; seam rubbers and mallets; and palm and needles.*

the anchor-ring, were no longer necessary. Merchant ships gave up carrying hempen cables, though men-of-war carried two or three for laying out anchors. By 1840 chain slings for lower yards, chain topsail sheets and ties, chain gammonings, and chain bobstays were common.

VI. LAST DAYS OF THE SAILING NAVY

During the Napoleonic wars there was very little difference between the ships of the navies of the principal powers: Great Britain, France, Holland, and Spain. At the end of the wars, however, Great Britain was supreme except for a young but sturdy rival, the United States of America. In the war of 1812 the United States built large frigates which inflicted startling losses on the ships of the Royal Navy. On the other hand, the commerce of the United States was cleared from the seas and most of these powerful frigates were ultimately captured. Their lines were recorded by their captors and so have been preserved.

In 1815 it was not apparent to the directors of naval strategy that the new steam-engine, still uncertain, could be of any use for purposes of war except for powering tug-boats. Certain far-seeing officers thought otherwise, and it is not surprising to find the Earl of Dundonald and Charles Napier advocating better use of this new method of propulsion. Contemporary engines were unreliable, fuel was bulky, and early ocean-going steamships were therefore fully rigged. Paddle-wheels interfered with sailing, especially when the ship was heeled, and the screw-propeller was introduced to aid sailing-ships. Moreover, paddle-wheels were very vulnerable to gun-fire, and it was the screw-propeller that made the steam-warship practicable. In the navies of the world steam-propulsion slowly found favour, though the larger navies were more reluctant to countenance drastic changes than the smaller ones. Meanwhile the grand old wooden line-of-battle sailing-ships completed their slow development, and reached a remarkable climax to their long and steady progress. The last three-decker launched for the Royal Navy was the *Victoria* of 121 guns; this was in 1859.

A ship with a more active career, the *Queen*, of 110 guns, was launched at Portsmouth in 1839; the length of her gun-deck was 204 ft and of her keel 166 ft; her breadth was 60 ft; and her tonnage 3104. Her main truck, that is, the top of her main-mast, was 240 ft above the water-line, and her main yard was 111 ft long. Her lower-deck ports were 6 ft 6 in above the water-line. Her main armament consisted of 32-pounders, the guns on the lower decks being longer and heavier than those on the upper. The *Queen* was flagship in the Black Sea during the Crimean war; she was towed into action with the tug-boat lashed along her disengaged side, and was set on fire by Russian shells. In 1859 she was cut down to a two-decker, and fitted with engines of 500 hp. She was sold out of the service in 1871. H.M.S. *Duke of Wellington*, of 131 guns, was launched at Pembroke in 1852. The length of her gun-deck was 240 ft and her tonnage was 3771. She was one of the largest wooden warships and, although designed as a sailing-ship, was given engines on the stocks. She saw active service as a flagship in the Baltic campaign in 1854, and in 1855 during the Crimean war. She was screw-propelled, and her engines, built by Robert Napier & Sons, were of 700 hp. H.M.S. *Marlborough*, 131 guns, launched at Portsmouth in 1855, was a little larger than the *Duke of Wellington* and can therefore be regarded as the climax of the wooden warship, driven by sail and steam (plate 40 B).

In the merchant service, iron construction started with small vessels; it both saved timber and, in the case of steam-vessels, lessened the risk of fire. The navies, especially the Royal Navy, long looked askance at iron construction. A shell that could be fired from ships' guns had been invented in 1822 by the

French general H. J. Paixhans (1783–1854). Although the *Duke of Wellington* could fire shells from her 68-pounders their destructive powers on the wooden ships of the enemy received less consideration than the danger of filling them in the magazines of ships also constructed of wood. In 1853, in the preliminaries which led up to the Crimean war, a very superior Russian fleet destroyed a Turkish squadron at Sinope, firing shells from their 68-pounders against the wooden hulls of the enemy, who could retaliate only with the old-fashioned solid shot. The massacre at Sinope underlined a lesson that should have been obvious before, and the French navy immediately ordered armoured 'floating batteries' for service against the Russians.

Another lesson, that of the superiority of the steam-propelled ship, was still not so obvious. The last days of the sailing navy saw very efficient sailing-ships, smartly handled. In H.M.S. *Queen*, for example, all three topsails could be reefed together in about a minute. The sailing-ship was, however, helpless in a calm and might be prevented by a head-wind from leaving port. The existence of small steamships made surprise attacks possible. Nevertheless, particularly in England, it was unthinkable that the traditional wooden walls should be abandoned. The ship-building industry was prepared to go on building wooden ships, claiming that we should lose our advantage if there were a change.

VII. THE FULLY-RIGGED IRONCLAD, 1859

The French government had led the way in building floating batteries, armoured against shell-fire. In 1859 they had a wooden two-decker on the stocks cut down a deck, and her sides armoured. The removal of her upper deck compensated for the weight of the armour, so that the ship was not made top-heavy. The British Admiralty replied to this French ironclad, *La Gloire*, with a new design of their own, a ship iron-hulled and iron-armoured, originally planned by John Scott Russell and Isaac Watts. H.M.S. *Warrior* was epoch-making as being the first armoured ship in the Royal Navy; when put in commission she could have taken on the navies of the world single-handed. The necessity of protecting a broadside with hundreds of tons of iron slabs meant that to retain stability a ship either had to be much broader, and therefore much slower, or much lower in the water and therefore impracticable as a three-decker with the customary three tiers of guns. In the *Warrior* the answer was to increase the length and to mount the guns in one tier; thus, the old nomenclature of the Royal Navy being retained, she was rated as a frigate.

Wooden ships had already reached a limit in length, and the *Warrior* was built on an iron frame. She was divided into watertight compartments by bulkheads, and her machinery and equipment were distributed between these compartments. She was 380 ft long between perpendiculars, and her beam was 58 ft; her tonnage was 9140. A length of 208 ft of her hull was armoured, but her hand-steering gear was left unprotected. Her 4½-in armour was backed by teak topsides and could resist the heaviest gun then afloat, namely the 100-pounder such as she herself mounted. She was rather unhandy because of her length, and her handsome beakhead with figure-head and the old-fashioned frigate-stern made her wet at sea. Her graceful head concealed a ram bow below water. She was fully rigged, unlike *La Gloire* which had a schooner-rig as auxiliary to her screw and engines. The *Warrior* had powerful engines, by J. Penn & Son of Greenwich, which drove her at over 14 knots—much faster than foreign warships. On occasions she logged 13 knots under sail. Her single screw was fitted with lifting-gear and came up into a trunk in the stern of the hull; for this operation the ship had to be hove-to and 600 men of her complement of 705 tailed on to the falls. Her anchors were weighed by hand. Her armament was three 100-pound Armstrong rifled breech-loaders on the upper deck; below, she carried eight more 100-pounders and twenty-six smooth bore muzzle-loaders on the gun deck. The government yards had no facilities for iron construction, so the *Warrior* was built on the Thames in a private yard. She was ordered in 1859 and completed in 1861. She was paid off from service in 1884, by which time she was well out of date. The armament race between warships, rightly feared by the British Admiralty, had begun.

The *Warrior* was copied and improved upon, and the screw-driven ironclad warship continued to be fully rigged with masts and sails. The warships of the European navies were always fully manned, and ready to visit distant parts of the globe away from stocks of coal. Masts and their supporting shrouds and other rigging did not get in the way of broadside ordnance, and warships were generally sailed whenever possible, to save coal. In 1861, however, during the American civil war, John Ericsson (1803–89) persuaded the Federal government to build an ironclad 'monitor', and the name was indeed a warning to all the old-fashioned navies of Europe. The features of the *Monitor* were complete armour above the water, low free-board, and a revolving gun-turret. The revolving turret made the fitting of mast and sail impossible. The *Monitor* was the first of the modern warships to be designed to carry a chosen weapon at the expense of the usual sea-going conveniences of a ship. Turret-ships were added to the Royal Navy, and in 1869 the *Captain* (plate 43B) was launched, embodying some of the features of the *Monitor* in a much bigger and sea-going ship of 4272 tons; she was fully rigged. Her armament included four 12-in 25-ton guns in two turrets. The ship's low free-board amidships was accentuated because of a mistake in her design: designed to be 8 ft it was in fact 6 ft. She capsized in a squall off Cape Finisterre in 1870 with the loss of most of her complement of 500 men, including her designer Captain Cowper Coles (b 1819). When she was heeled so that the edge of the deck went under water she quickly lost stability and capsized.

The sailing ironclad's days were numbered. The turret-ships *Glatton* and *Devastation*, both launched in 1871, each had one mast for signalling-purposes only; but until the turn of the century the Navy had use for some sailing-ships on foreign stations.

VIII. THE CLIPPER SHIP

The British East India Company enjoyed a monopoly of trade with the Far East until 1833, when its charter was revised. Even then firms such as Green & Wigram of Blackwall on the Thames and T. and W. Smith of Newcastle took over the trading responsibilities and carried on the old traditions. Their comely ships were 'snugged down' each night, that is, sail was reduced. The ships were not slow, but they were not driven; they could do 12 knots on occasion and made Calcutta in about 90 days. For example, the *Blenheim*, constructed in 1848, was frigate-built and in the event of war would have been taken into the Royal Navy. She was 175 ft long by 42 ft beam, and measured 1314 tons.

Meanwhile, however, the idea that ships must hurry was gaining ground. Queen Victoria, for instance, visited Scotland in 1842 in her sailing-yacht the *Royal George*, which was towed all the way by a naval steamer. Nevertheless the Queen found the voyage very tedious and vexatious, and came home in the *Trident* belonging to the General Steam Navigation Company, which in a head-wind soon left the *Royal George* and the naval steamers out of sight. Speedy passage was particularly desirable for passengers and mails, and the American-owned packets which sailed backwards and forwards across the Atlantic were well known for their quick passages and their regularity. An American who visited England in 1833 tells the story of a packet-ship sailing from London to New York and back and finding still sheltering in the Downs, awaiting a fair wind, an Indiaman and several other ships that had sailed in company with her from London. The Americans had studied how to build fast ships and they drove these ships hard. In 1849 Great Britain repealed the Navigation Acts which for long had made the eastern markets practically the monopoly of British ships. In reply, fast soft-wood ships which had been built in the United States set about chasing British shipping off the seas. Emphasis was placed on speed under sail at the expense of capacity for carrying cargo. The first ship each year to arrive back in Europe with the new tea crop from China earned a handsome premium. British owners took up the American challenge and turned to the ship-builders for help. The racing was very keen and captured the attention of the public.

There has been much argument as to what constitutes the clipper ship.

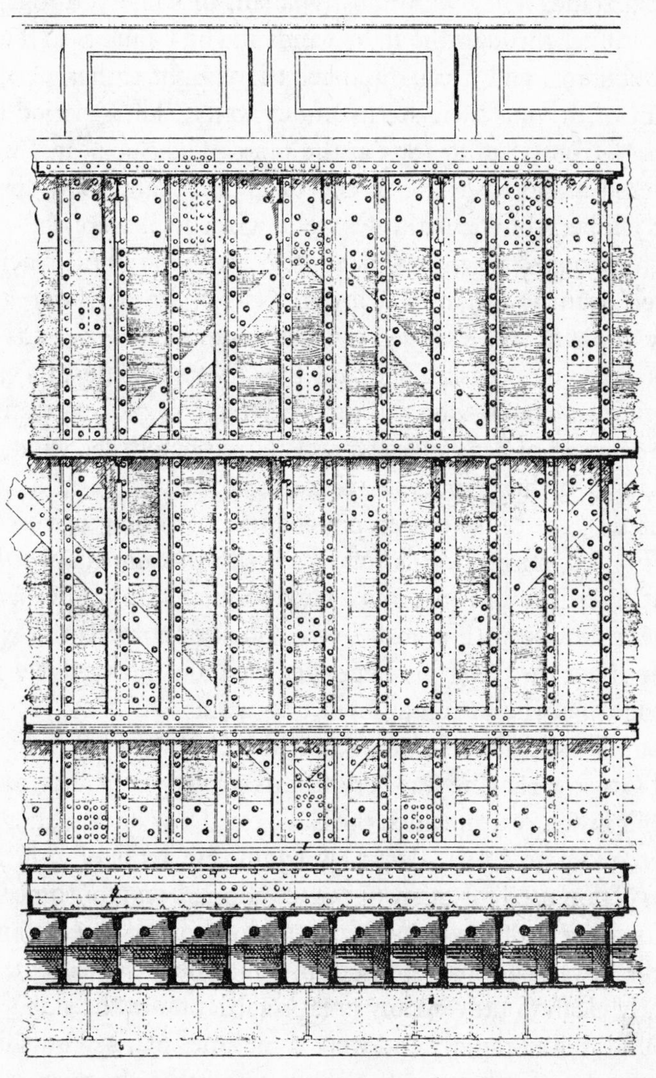

FIGURE 324—*Suggestions for the construction and classification of composite ships. Before the opening of the Suez canal many clipper ships were composite built, as it was called, that is, their bottoms were wooden planking over an iron frame, the advantage being that the bottoms of such ships could be sheathed with copper, Muntz metal, or zinc, and kept reasonably clean so as not greatly to retard their speed. However, composite building was not suitable for steamers with full engine-power, and after the opening of the canal it went out of fashion for merchant ships, though remaining in use for small naval vessels which still made passages under sail.*

Schooners built at Baltimore proved very fast as privateers in the war of 1812 and were copied in both Britain and America. The ship-builders of Aberdeen developed fast schooners whose lines were copied for larger vessels. In fact, the building of fast ships was being undertaken on each side of the Atlantic even before the repeal of the Navigation Acts in 1849. Tea clippers were ships built for that special trade. They were mostly small, of some 700 tons, and heavily canvassed for sailing through the light winds in the China Sea. Their fine ends made them wet ships, and if caught aback they might gather stern-way and be lost as a result of driving their sterns under water. Their period of fame was, however, short—from 1849 to 1875 at the most. The Suez canal was opened in 1869 and offered a shorter route to the east, practicable only for steamships. Two famous clippers built on the Clyde at Greenock were the *Ariel* and *Sir Lancelot*, both launched in 1865 and built to the same lines. Their length was 197 ft and their beam 33 ft 9 in. The lower masts of the *Ariel* were of iron. They were extreme clippers, and excelled in light winds. The *Ariel* was very seldom passed at sea—on one occasion she and the *Taeping* (plate 43 A) raced up the Channel logging 14 knots—but she was very tender, and in strong winds had quickly to be relieved of her canvas when running before the wind, as otherwise she was in danger of being pooped. She was lost in 1872 on a voyage out to Sydney and is thought to have been pooped when running her easting down in the Roaring Forties, strong winds for which she was unsuitable. The *Thermopylae*, built at Aberdeen in 1868, was a very popular ship, rather larger than the *Ariel*, being 212 ft long with a 36-ft beam. She never raced the *Ariel*, but was the better ship if not the faster, for she sailed well to windward and was also very fast and manageable when running in strong winds.

The only survivor of these famous ships, the *Cutty Sark*, is now preserved in a dry dock at Greenwich. She was very fast in strong winds, having once logged 17½ knots. Built in the year in which the Suez canal was opened, her active career lasted until 1922. The *Cutty Sark* was composite built of iron and wood, a form of construction used for many of the tea clippers and for some small vessels, sloops and gun-vessels, of the Royal Navy (figure 324). Wooden planking on iron frames had the advantage that the bottom could be sheathed with copper and kept sufficiently clean to prevent any great retardation in the ship's sailing. Iron hulls were found to foul rapidly and were sometimes planked outside with wood and then sheathed with copper over all, but care had to be taken to prevent the copper from coming into contact with the iron, as electrolytic action would then have been set up (p 580). Iron lower masts and wire rigging were introduced, to support the heavy strains when big sailing-ships were raced. The clipper ship

Caliph, launched in 1865, had wire standing-rigging and wire lifts. Wire standing-rigging was introduced into the Royal Navy in 1838.

IX. SAIL AND STEAM

The iron hull was developed to withstand the vibration of the steam-engine, but it proved suitable for sailing-ships also, except for the fact that the bottom fouled quickly. Steamships were fully rigged as long as engines were unreliable, but as engines improved so the top-hamper of masts and yards was cut down. French steamships were often rigged with three short masts and jib-headed schooner-sails. Some British shipping-lines retained sails to steady the ship, but when ships came to steam at higher speeds square canvas was useless (plate 44 A). They steamed at a steady pace throughout the voyage, and already mail-steamers were making some 360 nautical miles a day. Hence by 1883 merchant ships favoured fore-and-aft canvas only: they had planned voyages and regular arrangements for the replenishment of fuel, so that sails became less important. Again, few ships had enough crew to see that a steamer's sails were properly set. The screw-propeller had been developed for use in sailing-ships (p 587), and naval ships with large ships' companies were able to make full use of sail and steam, but in the merchant service, where crews were relatively small, the tendency was for steamers to give up sail. The Orient Line, however, kept full rig on their ships which voyaged to the Cape and Australia. There was still a large tonnage of iron sailing-ships, which they could afford to let wait in port warehousing a cargo. A further advantage of the sailing-ship was that the hull is relatively more capacious than that of the steamship, which has a large engine-room.

At different times auxiliaries were tried, but in several ships the engines were afterwards removed. An example was the *Lancing*, a four-masted iron ship, built at Glasgow in 1866 as the steamer *Pereire*. With the engines removed, the *Lancing* was still sailing in 1924 under the Norwegian flag. Various labour-saving devices helped to improve the sailing-ship. An example was the patent reefing-gear invented by Henry Cunningham in 1850, which enabled topsails to be reefed from the deck. The topsail was bent to a smaller yard, below the topsail-yard and hanging from it, which could be rotated by means of chains so as to roll up the head of the topsail on it. The gear necessitated a split down the middle of the sail; this was covered by a laced patch called the bonnet. It was claimed that the sail could be close-reefed in heavy weather by one man and a boy in 2½ seconds. By such means small crews were able to handle large sailing-ships, such as the iron barques, often four- or five-masted, which at the end of the nineteenth century still crowded the ports of the world (plate 44 B). This was the final development of the ocean carrier, fully rigged. A five-masted ship, the *Preussen*, built of steel at Hamburg in 1902, was 433 ft long overall with a beam of 53 ft, and carried a sail area of 60 000 sq ft of canvas, divided into six square-sails on each mast and eighteen fore-and-aft sails. She could log seventeen knots and had steam-power on board for weighing her anchors and working her cargo. She was the only five-masted ship square-rigged on all five masts ever built (figure 325).

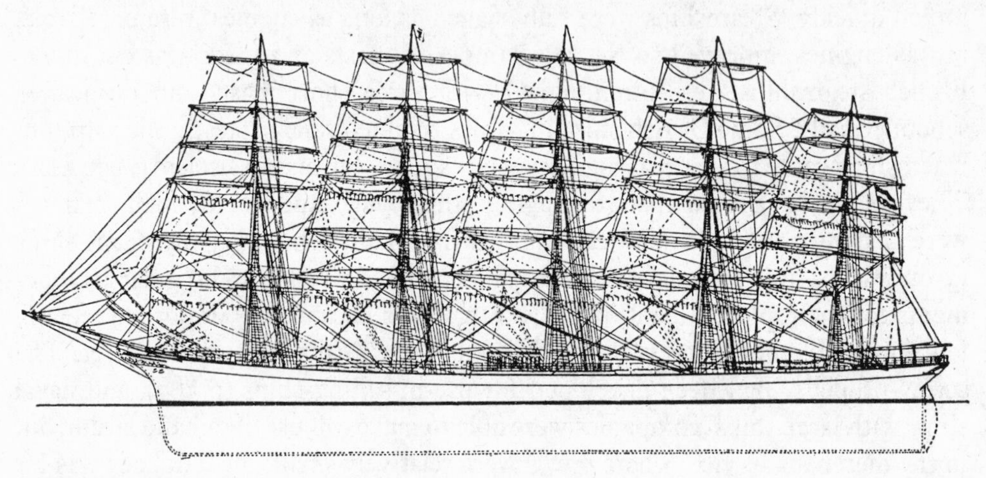

FIGURE 325—*Five-masted ship* Preussen, *the only five-masted full-rigged ship ever built. She marked the climax of the big merchant sailing-ships.*

X. LLOYD'S REGISTER OF SHIPPING

Lloyd's[1] register deserves mention here as it reflects the major changes in ship-construction during this period. The earliest register is of ships sailing in 1764, 1765, and 1766. The ships were classified according to hull and equipment, and the list was issued to subscribers for the use of underwriters, who were to regard it as private and not for publication. The list gives particulars of some 4500 ships, several of from 400 to 600 tons, two of 800 tons, and one of 900 tons. 8271 ships are classed in the register for 1800. Iron cables appeared in 1813, and a steamship, the *James Watt* (294 tons), in 1822. There were 81 steamships in 1827 and 100 in 1832. In 1834 a permanent committee representing merchants, shipowners, and underwriters was set up, and there was competition with a Liverpool register of shipping. In 1836 the description 'built of iron' first occurs, and rules for iron construction were framed in 1854, the committee co-operating with the ship-builders. Lloyd's rules for classing ships have been of the greatest

[1] From Lloyd's coffee-house, originally in Tower Street, London, where from 1687 merchants and others interested in shipping used to meet.

value in improving ship-building practice, and the testing of equipment has done much to prevent loss of life at sea.

BIBLIOGRAPHY

ABELL, SIR WESTCOTT S. 'The Shipwright's Trade.' University Press, Cambridge. 1948.
ALBION, R. G. 'Forests and Sea Power.' Harvard University Press, Cambridge, Mass. 1926.
ANDERSON, ROMOLA, and ANDERSON, R. C. 'The Sailing Ship.' Harrap, London. 1926.
'Annals of Lloyds Register, Centenary Edition.' Lloyds, London. 1934.
BENTHAM, M. S. 'The Life of Brigadier General Sir Samuel Bentham.' London. 1862.
CHAPELLE, H. I. 'The History of American Sailing Ships.' Putnam, London. 1936.
CLARK, A. H. 'The Clipper Ship Era.' Putnam, New York. 1911.
COTTON, E. 'East Indiamen.' Batchworth Press, London. 1949.
CUTLER, C. C. 'Greyhounds of the Sea.' Putnam, New York. 1930.
FALCONER, W. 'A New and Universal Dictionary of the Marine.' London. 1769. See also the enlarged edition by W. BURNEY. London. 1815.
FINCHAM, J. 'A History of Naval Architecture.' London. 1851.
GREENHILL, B. 'The Merchant Schooners', Vol. 1. Percival Marshall, London. 1951.
LESCALLIER, D. 'Vocabulaire des termes de marine anglois et françois' (new ed., 2 vols). London. 1783.
Idem. 'Traité pratique du gréement des vaisseaux et autres bâtiments de mer' (2 vols). Paris. 1791.
LEVER, D. 'The Young Sea Officer's Sheet Anchor' (2nd ed.). London. 1819.
LUBBOCK, B. 'The China Clippers.' Brown, Glasgow. 1922.
MACGREGOR, D. R. 'The Tea Clippers.' Percival Marshall, London. 1952.
DUHAMEL-DUMONCEAU, H. L. 'Elemens de l'architecture navale.' Paris. 1752.
MOORE, A. 'Last Days of Mast and Sail.' Clarendon Press, Oxford. 1925.
Idem. 'Sailing Ships of War, 1800–1860.' Halton & Truscott Smith, London. 1926.
NATIONAL MARITIME MUSEUM. 'Catalogue of Ship Models in the National Maritime Museum', by R. C. ANDERSON. H.M. Stationery Office, London. 1952.
PARKINSON, C. N. 'Trade in the Eastern Seas, 1793–1813.' University Press, Cambridge. 1937.
PLIMSOLL, S. 'Our Seamen—an Appeal.' London. 1873.
SCIENCE MUSEUM. 'Sailing Ships—their History and Development as Illustrated by the Collection of Ship Models in the Science Museum', by G. S. LAIRD CLOWES. H.M. Stationery Office, London. 1932.
SHARP, J. A. 'Memoirs of Rear Admiral Sir William Symonds.' London. 1858.
SHEWAN, A. 'The Great Days of Sail.' Heath Cranton, London. 1927.
SOCIETY OF NAUTICAL RESEARCH. *The Mariner's Mirror.* The Quarterly Journal of the Society of Nautical Research. 1911–.
STEEL, D. 'The Elements and Practice of Rigging and Seamanship' (2 vols). London. 1794.
Idem. 'The Shipwright's Vade Mecum.' London. 1805.
UNDERHILL, H. A. 'Sailing Ship Rigs and Rigging.' Brown Son & Ferguson, Glasgow. 1938.
Idem. 'Masting and Rigging the Clipper Ship and Ocean Carrier.' Brown Son & Ferguson, Glasgow. 1946.
Idem. 'Deep Water Sail.' Brown Son & Ferguson, Glasgow. 1952.
VILLIERS, A. 'The Way of a Ship.' Hodder & Stoughton, London. 1954.
WATSON, H. 'A Compleat Theory of the Construction and Properties of Vessels.' London. 1776.

CARTOGRAPHY

R. A. SKELTON

I. THE WORLD MAP

THE construction of the framework of an accurate world map, depending on determinations of the shape and size of the Earth and the accurate fixing of the latitude and longitude of a sufficient number of points on its surface, was the work of geodesists and cartographers of the late seventeenth century and the eighteenth century, initiated by the *Académie des Sciences* of Paris.

Jean Picard's (1620–82) measurement of a degree on the meridian of Paris in 1669, and the measurement of arcs of this meridian to north and south by Jean Dominique Cassini (1625–1712) and his son Jacques (1677–1756) between 1700 and 1718, had given a diminishing figure for the degree of latitude as it approached the pole, suggesting that the polar diameter of the Earth was greater than the equatorial. The French expeditions which measured arcs of the meridian in high and low latitudes (in Lapland and Peru) between 1736 and 1745 established the figure of the Earth as an oblate spheroid, flattened at the poles, and provided estimates for the length of a degree in various latitudes which served as the basis for eighteenth-century cartography (vol III, pp 553–4).

In the seventeenth century numerous tables of positions had been published; a geographical textbook of 1661 listed no fewer than 2200 places whose latitude and longitude were 'certain or probable'. The wide variation in the estimates made by different authors and map-makers pointed, however, to their fallibility. Without a series of accurately determined positions and, in particular, without any reliable method of ascertaining longitudes, cartographers could not lay down the land-masses and oceans of the world with any approximation to their correct extent and shape. Ptolemy's world map had been shattered by the geographical discoveries of the fifteenth and sixteenth centuries, but his acceptance of too low an estimate for the circumference of the globe was reflected in the exaggeration of longitudinal distances in seventeenth-century maps. Thus the east-to-west width of continents was generally too great, the coast of China being drawn over 25° too far to the east; and the Mediterranean, to which Ptolemy had ascribed a longitudinal extension of 62°, was still laid down 15° to 20° in excess of its true length.

From 1672, the year after the opening of the Paris observatory, French scientists were systematically making astronomical determinations of longitudes from shore stations; these were mainly derived from observation of eclipses or of the occultation of Jupiter's satellites, for which tables were published in 1668. By 1682 the latitude and longitude of 24 places on the French coasts had been established, and a corrected outline of the country could be laid down. *La Connoissance des temps*, an ephemeris published by J. D. Cassini from 1679, recorded the gradual increase in the number of positions accurately fixed: in Europe, 32 in 1684 and 83 in 1691; in the world, 40 in 1682 and 109 in 1706.

The observations thus collected were incorporated in the maps published from 1700 to 1726 by Guillaume Delisle (1675–1726), who has been called the first modern cartographer. While Delisle had little new information on the interiors of the continents, their coastal outline on his world map was notably correct, and the Mediterranean was reduced in length to 42°. Delisle also introduced a useful reform in his choice of a prime meridian. A French decree of 1634 had prescribed that longitudes should be taken from the west point of the island of Ferro (Hierro) in the Canaries; but its exact longitude from Paris was not known. Delisle ran his longitudes from the meridian 20° west of Paris—the 'reputed Ferro'; and this became the general practice until, with the publication (from 1767) of 'The Nautical Almanac' containing astronomical tables calculated for Greenwich, the Greenwich prime meridian attained gradual—though not universal—acceptance.

The critical method of appraising the cartographer's materials was applied even more rigorously by J. B. Bourguignon d'Anville (1697–1782). Rejecting all traditional data that failed to satisfy his searching collation of ancient authorities and modern travellers' reports, he re-drew the maps of the continents. The conventional Ptolemaic representation of the African river systems, as interpreted by sixteenth-century geographers, was finally discredited, and d'Anville's map (1749) became the starting-point for the exploration of inland Africa during the next century. For eastern Asia he was able to use the maps and determinations of the Jesuit astronomers established in Peking; and for the interior of North America the results of the recent French explorations from the Great Lakes to the Gulf of Mexico.

From the second half of the eighteenth century cartographers were supplied with an ever increasing volume of reliable information on positions, topography, and coastal outlines. This was due not only to activity in exploration but to refinements in the technique of exploratory survey and to the organization of systematic topographical surveys in European, and a few extra-European, countries. The voyages of Louis de Bougainville, 1767–9, and James Cook, 1768–79, drew the modern map of the south Pacific Ocean; and Matthew Flinders charted the coasts of Australia, 1798–1803. Cook, 1778–9, and La Pérouse, 1785–7, surveyed the American and Asiatic shores of the north Pacific; Malaspina, 1791–2, and Vancouver, 1792–4, its American coasts. Between 1770 and 1855 British, French, and German expeditions revealed the geography of northern Africa, and the oceanic coast-line of the continent was surveyed in 1822–6. The Antarctic continent was discovered in 1819, and by 1850 extensive sectors of its coast had been traversed. From the third quarter of the eighteenth century the traveller was equipped with lighter precision-instruments (ch 13) which, unlike the cumbersome astronomical quadrant and theodolite, could be used in a route-traverse or on the deck of a ship. The reflecting sextant—'a portable observatory'—and the chronometer allowed him to determine the latitude and longitude of his discoveries with sufficient accuracy to enable them to be re-identified from his map or chart.

For the determination of longitude on his first Pacific voyage (1768–71), Cook had only 'that great natural chronometer presented by the moon in her orbital motion round the earth'; that is, he employed the method of 'lunar distances', obtaining Greenwich time, at the moment of his sextant observations, from the tables printed in 'The Nautical Almanac'. These tables enabled the seaman, for the first time, to make his computations for longitude rapidly and in sufficient numbers to reduce, by 'meaning', the errors of individual observers and instruments. By lunar observations, 'when multiplied to a considerable number, made with different instruments, and with the sun and stars on both sides of the moon', Cook claimed to be 'sure of finding a ship's place at sea to a Degree and a half and generally to less than half a Degree'. In 1769, in fact, he determined the longitude of the north point of Tahiti within one minute of the modern reckoning (and the latitude, by meridian altitudes of the Sun, within one second); and the longitudes on his chart of New Zealand, made by a running survey in 1769–70, are seldom more than half a degree out. Although on his second and third voyages he carried chronometers made to the design of John Harrison (1693–1776), Cook and his officers continued to make lunar observations in extraordinary numbers; for instance, at Tongataboo in 1777, 131 sets of lunars were taken, 'amounting to above a thousand observed distances'. These, however, were used only for comparison with 'the Watch'; and the accurate timekeeper, designed independently by Harrison of London between 1729 and 1761 and by Pierre Leroy (1717–85) of Paris in 1766, and developed by later horologists, was to become the standard instrument for finding the longitude (ch 13).

The cartographer of the early nineteenth century therefore disposed of a vastly greater number of accurately fixed positions for his world map than were available to Delisle; in 1817 they were estimated to amount to over 6000. By the middle of the century trigonometrical surveys, proceeding from a network of

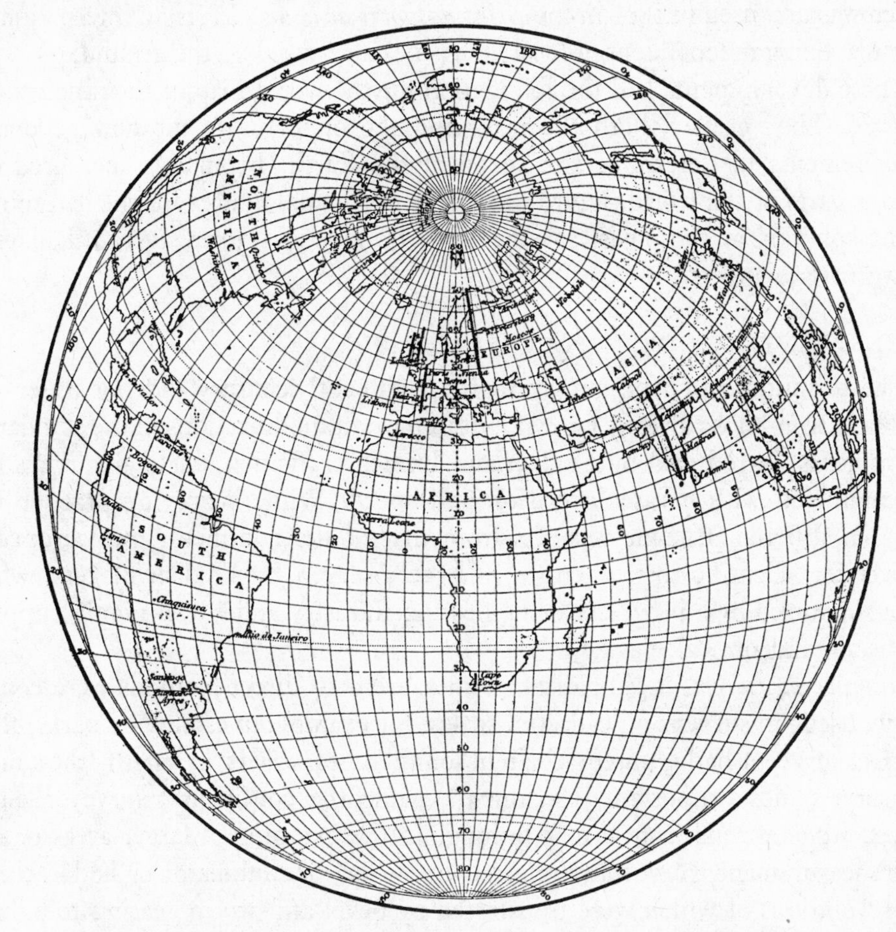

FIGURE 326—*Measured arcs of meridian in the nineteenth century.*

triangulations made with improved instruments for the measurement of angles and distances, had been undertaken in every major European country and in a few overseas territories, notably India, and the initial steps had been taken to co-ordinate these materials so that they could be used as the basis of an 'international' map. When the *Académie des Sciences*, in 1791, defined the metre as 1/10 000 000 of a quadrant of the terrestrial meridian, the various national standard measures of length could be converted into a 'natural' linear standard, the basic unit of which was proportionate to the circumference of the Earth. The adoption of the metric system led to the concept of a 'natural scale' for maps, expressed as a fraction relating one unit of length on the map to the number of like units on the Earth's surface represented by it. The 'representative fraction', which was first used in 1806 in the *Atlas national de la France*, is an international formula, being independent of local linear measures used on the ground.

These developments laid the foundation for the world map of the nineteenth century. They created both the need and the opportunity for new geodetic measurements to determine the shape of the Earth. From arcs measured in various parts of the world (figure 326), seven principal figures for the flattening of the spheroid at the poles, varying from 1/293·5 to 1/300·8, were calculated between 1830 and 1910.

II. INSTRUMENTS FOR TOPOGRAPHICAL SURVEY

The techniques of land-survey in the eighteenth century did not differ in principle from those already known, but important modifications in the standard instruments, introduced by English and French craftsmen, enabled surveys to be conducted with greater precision and speed. While surveying practice in England differed in some respects from that of the continent, the European market for scientific instruments was largely served by English makers, who were supported by a progressive engineering industry and by an ample supply of metals and optical glass.

Distance measurement. For distance measurement direct methods were commonly used: in surveys on cadastral scales, for example of estates or parks, the English surveyor had Gunter's chain of four perches (22 yds) in length, 'the land-measurer's most important instrument', while the continental surveyor employed wooden rods from 2 to 5 m long. In the mapping of larger areas or in road measurement, surveyors preferred the wheel-perambulator or hodometer, the revolutions of which were transferred by bevel-and-worm gearing to a dial (plate 23B). Regional maps, in the eighteenth century as in the sixteenth, were still generally made from road-traverses with cross-bearings taken by alidade, that is, with the plane-table or surveying compass, on points off the measured route. The private surveyor was slow in adopting more refined techniques for the indirect measurement of distances. In the second half of the eighteenth century, every English county was mapped on a scale of one inch to a mile or greater; but only six of these maps are accompanied by a diagram of triangulation.

The traditional instruments were liable to variations of length, in conditions of changing temperature or humidity, and to displacement of adjoining members when placed in contact. These defects could not be tolerated in the accurate measurement of an extended line, such as the base for a triangulation, in which the resultant angular errors would become cumulative throughout the survey. Italian and French surveyors, using copper- or brass-tipped wooden rods for the measurement of base lines, reduced the contact error by leaving an interval, which was measured with beam compasses, between adjacent rods. To mitigate and correct temperature errors, materials with a low coefficient of expansion were used, and the mean temperature of every section of the base was measured and reduced. In his triangulation of 1733–40, Cassini de Thury (1714–84) used both 24-ft wooden rods, tipped with iron, and iron bars 15 ft long. William Roy

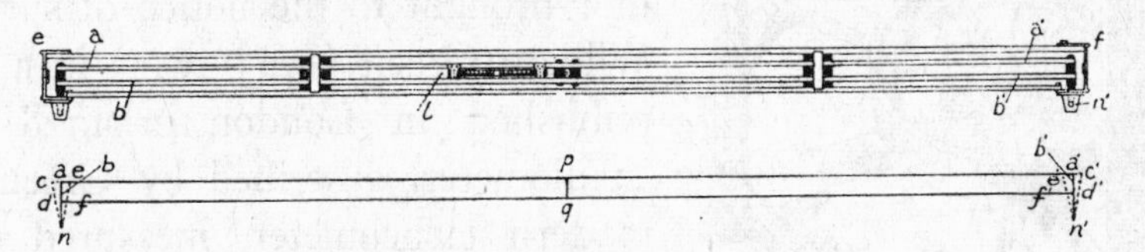

FIGURE 327—*Diagram illustrating the principle of Colby's compensation-bars.* aa′, *brass bar;* bb′, *iron bar;* pq, *steel connecting bar;* cc′, dd′, *brass bar, iron bar, at higher temperature* (62°+*n*°)*;* ee′, ff′, *brass bar, iron bar, at lower temperature* (62°−*n*°)*;* abn, a′b′n′, *position of steel tongues at* 62°*;* cdn, c′d′n′, *position of steel tongues at* 62+*n*°*;* efn, e′f′n′, *position of steel tongues at* 62°−*n*°*;* n, n′, *compensation points;* l, *longitudinal level.*

(1726–90) in 1784, taking a base of over 5 miles for his triangulation of south-east England, made a preliminary measurement with a 100-ft steel chain; and, after overlapping rods of Riga pine had proved too unstable in varying humidity, the final measurement was made with glass tubes. Roy's base of verification was measured in 1787, however, with the steel chain. Various applications of the principle of compensation, already familiar in horology, were made in apparatus for base-measurement. The French scientist J. C. de Borda (1733–99) in 1792 used bars of two metals (copper and platinum), with unequal coefficients of expansion, to determine more exactly the effect of temperature changes in different sections of the base; and F. W. Bessel (1784–1846), in his triangulation of East Prussia in 1836, employed compensated rods of iron and zinc similarly constructed. About 1825 Thomas Colby (1784–1852), director of the Ordnance Survey, invented an apparatus in which two parallel bars of brass and iron were rigidly connected at their centres and linked at the ends by pivoted metal tongues; the compensation-point marked at the extremity of each tongue was thus maintained at an invariable distance from the centre of the bar in all temperatures (figure 327). Colby's compensation-bars were used in 1827–8 in measuring bases for the primary triangulation of Ireland, and in 1849 for that of England; the average rate of measurement was six bars an hour, or 461 ft in a day, and the error in the Irish base amounted to about 1:200 000. A base-apparatus designed by F. G. W. von Struve (1793–1864) for the primary triangulation of Russia (1817–55) used spring-contact levers by which the effects of temperature could be accurately allowed for; for this a mean probable error of 1:1 240 000 was claimed.

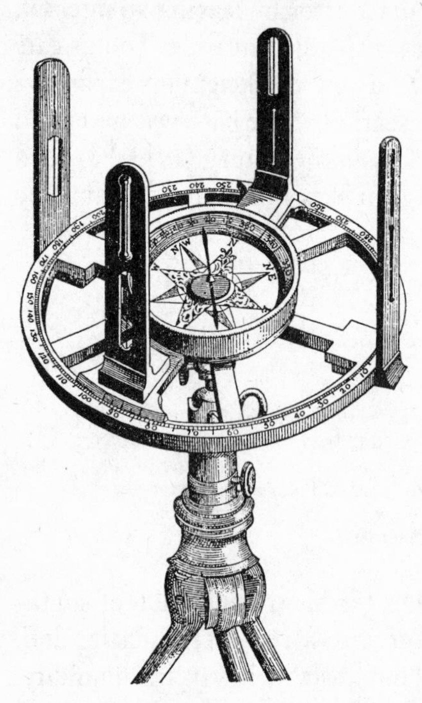

FIGURE 328—*'Common theodolite' with open sights, by George Adams. Eighteenth century.*

Tacheometry, the basic process for indirect distance measurement in modern medium-scale surveys, had been practised as early as the seventeenth century, and was first brought to the notice of surveyors by William Green (1725–1811) in a pamphlet published in London in 1778 [1]. The 'stadiometer' described by Green, like the modern tacheometer, measured the angle subtended at the optical centre of the instrument by rays from two points at a known distance apart on a staff, and thus enabled the distance of the staff, and of distant points in the same vertical plane, to be calculated. The 'anallatic' lens invented by Ignazio Porro (1801–78) in 1823 enabled the observer to read the subtended angle directly (that is, on the vertical axis of his instrument), without making allowance for the focal length of the object-glass. The tacheometer, as a combined range-finding instrument and level, became popular with engineers engaged in rapid surveys for canals (ch 18) and railways (vol V, ch 15) during the early nineteenth century.

Angle measurement. For azimuthal observations, that is, the measurement of horizontal angles, topographical instruments derived from the magnetic compass were still generally used in the eighteenth century: in England the circumferentor or surveying compass, in France the graphometer or surveying semicircle. These instruments, incorporating a compass and an alidade with open sights, allowed the surveyor to read the bearing of a line of sight; they were said to be liable to an error of 2° or more, and the early Ordnance surveyors detected in the English county maps 'an error of nearly three miles . . . in a distance of eighteen'. Other surveying circles had both fixed and movable pairs of sights and gave the angle between two lines of sight: such were the *cercle hollandais* (perhaps developed from the nautical astrolabe) and the so-called 'common theodolite', a modification of the circumferentor (figure 328). The surveying quadrant or *quart de cercle*, also with both fixed and movable sights, was widely used on the European continent. Picard, during his triangulation in 1669, had been the first to fit telescopes with micrometer-wires to his quadrants; for the smaller quadrants, of 2-ft radius, used in the eighteenth-century triangulation of France, Cassini de Thury claimed an accuracy of from 8 to 10 seconds of arc, and his detail survey was made with graphometers fitted with telescopes, in which a probable error of up to 10 minutes was expected.

Plane-tabling, by which lines of sight were directly plotted in the field, was extensively practised. English writers of the seventeenth and eighteenth centuries considered that its use should be confined to 'Townships and small Inclosures' and recommended 'in laying down of a spacious businesse [that is, a large area]' the circumferentor or theodolite [2]. The plane-table was the standard topographical instrument of military engineers employed in surveys of fortifications.

Various types of altazimuth instruments had been developed during the sixteenth and seventeenth centuries; in the eighteenth, London instrument-makers perfected the altazimuth theodolite which was to become the fundamental instrument in trigonometrical survey. This resulted from a series of improvements in the design and construction of angle-measuring instruments, affecting their optical accuracy, the mechanical trueness of the circle and alidade, and the precise division and reading of the graduated limb.

In the first half of the century Thomas Wright (1711–86) and Jonathan Sisson (1694?–1749), followed by other makers, replaced the open slotted sights of the common theodolite by a telescope with cross-hairs, which was mounted on a graduated arc so as to permit the vertical movement of the sight required to align the telescope, with its more restricted field of view, on the object. Thus the surveyor could observe horizontal and vertical angles simultaneously. The function of the compass still incorporated in the instrument was now subsidiary. Spirit-levels were fitted to level the horizontal circle of the theodolite and to bring the vertical arc to zero; the graduated circle was read by verniers. The achromatic lenses introduced by John Dollond (1706–61) in 1758 permitted shorter refracting telescopes to be constructed. John Bird (1709–76) developed a method for graduating astronomical quadrants more accurately, and Jesse Ramsden (1735–1800) (plate 1) invented circular dividing-engines in 1766 and 1775 (p 392).

The theodolites that Ramsden constructed for the geodetic and topographical surveys of England initiated by Roy and carried on by the Board of Ordnance were designed and machined to permit perfectly smooth rotation and freedom from 'central shake' [3]. Roy remarked that the 'mode of centering [was] one of the chief excellencies' of the 'great instrument', 3 ft in diameter, completed for him in 1787 (cf figure 223). The transit-telescope of this theodolite could be completely rotated round its horizontal axis; tangent-clamps and slow-motion screws enabled the telescope to be smoothly and correctly aligned; and three microscopes allowed the horizontal and vertical scales to be read to 1 second of arc—a degree of precision never before reached. Ramsden's 'great instrument', which proved itself capable, in the primary triangulation of England, of measuring angles at a distance of 70 miles to 2 seconds of arc, is the prototype of the modern theodolite.

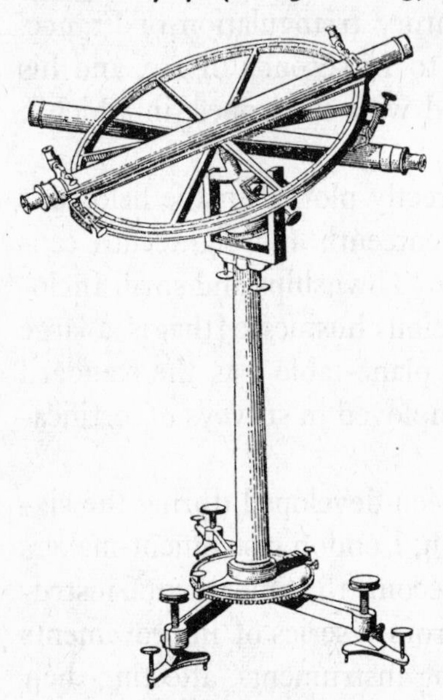

FIGURE 329—*Repeating circle, 33 cm in diameter, by Étienne Lenoir. (See figure 222.)*

In the French triangulation, continued by the fourth Cassini (Jacques Dominique, 1748–1845) and carried across the Straits of Dover to connect with Roy's in 1787, the azimuthal observations were made with a repeating circle (p 402), 33 cm in diameter, developed by Borda in 1775 and constructed by Étienne Lenoir (1744–1832) (figure 329). This employed the method of repetition of angles, using different arcs of the circle, introduced by Tobias Mayer (1723–62), so that mechanical errors were reduced by 'meaning'. Borda's reflection circle, embodying the principle of Hadley's quadrant, with repeating angles, became the preferred instrument of French marine surveyors (p 618).

Altitude measurement. In the measurement of altitude, the altazimuth theodolite gave vertical angles from which relative height could be determined; but levelling operations, at first for engineering projects and later in topographical surveys, demanded a direct method of observation. At the beginning of the eighteenth century the spirit-level (air- or bubble-level), which had been described by M. Thévenot (1620?–92) in 1661, quickly superseded the old plummet and water-level and facilitated the construction of compact levelling-instruments and clinometers. Among these was the Y-level, first made by Sisson.

Early barometric determinations of height, uncorrected for air-temperature and depending on no agreed correlation of pressure and altitude, gave widely divergent results. After 1772, when J. A. Deluc (1727–1817) published rules for the construction and use of the mercury barometer and his formula for relating pressure with altitude, the barometer enabled surveyors to obtain heights more rapidly and simply than by trigonometrical methods. Such observations, notably by H. B. de Saussure (1740–99) in the Alps, Alexander von Humboldt (1769–1859) in South America in 1799–1803, and L. Ramond (1755–1827) in the Pyrenees in 1802–3, supplied absolute hypsometric data both for topographical mapping and for the applied cartography by which the altitudinal distribution of physical phenomena was to be recorded (p 614). Deluc's comparative study of the fall in the boiling-point of water with diminishing atmospheric pressure and increasing height provided the theoretical basis for the hypsometer, developed in the early nineteenth century as the characteristic altitude instrument of exploratory survey.

III. NATIONAL SURVEYS

The eighteenth century established the general principle of modern survey, which, proceeding from the whole to the part, constructs a rigid geometrical framework of triangles before filling in the topographical detail by local observation of angles and distances. Such a system depends on no more than one linear measurement, that of the primary base-line; only the angles of the triangles are measured, and the sides are computed from them by spherical trigonometry. The survey is correctly located on the Earth's surface by astronomical observations to define the latitude and longitude of the principal stations.

France was the first country to be wholly mapped by these methods. The astronomical fixes made by Picard and P. de La Hire (1640–1718) on the coasts in 1679–81 enabled a revised outline of the country to be drawn (figure 330). This revealed errors of longitude in the older maps, which had displaced the Atlantic coast up to one-and-a-half degrees too far west, and errors of latitude in the south amounting to about half a degree in a southerly direction.

These determinations of position, to which the coastal surveys later published in the *Neptune françois* were adjusted (p 615), prompted a proposal by Picard, in 1681, for a trigonometrical survey of the kingdom. The geodetic operations of J. D. Cassini and his son during 1700–18 produced a band of triangulation along the meridian of Paris from Dunkirk in the north to Roussillon in the south; and in those undertaken in the years 1733 to 1740 by Cassini de Thury, G. D. Maraldi (1709–88), and others, as a check on the length of a meridian degree yielded by the earlier observations, triangles were run along perpendiculars to the Paris meridian and round the coasts and frontiers of France. By 1745 the country was 'enclosed' by a net of nearly 800 triangles developed from 19 measured bases. The necessary geodetic and trigonometrical data for the map of France had now been supplied, and two years later Cassini received a royal

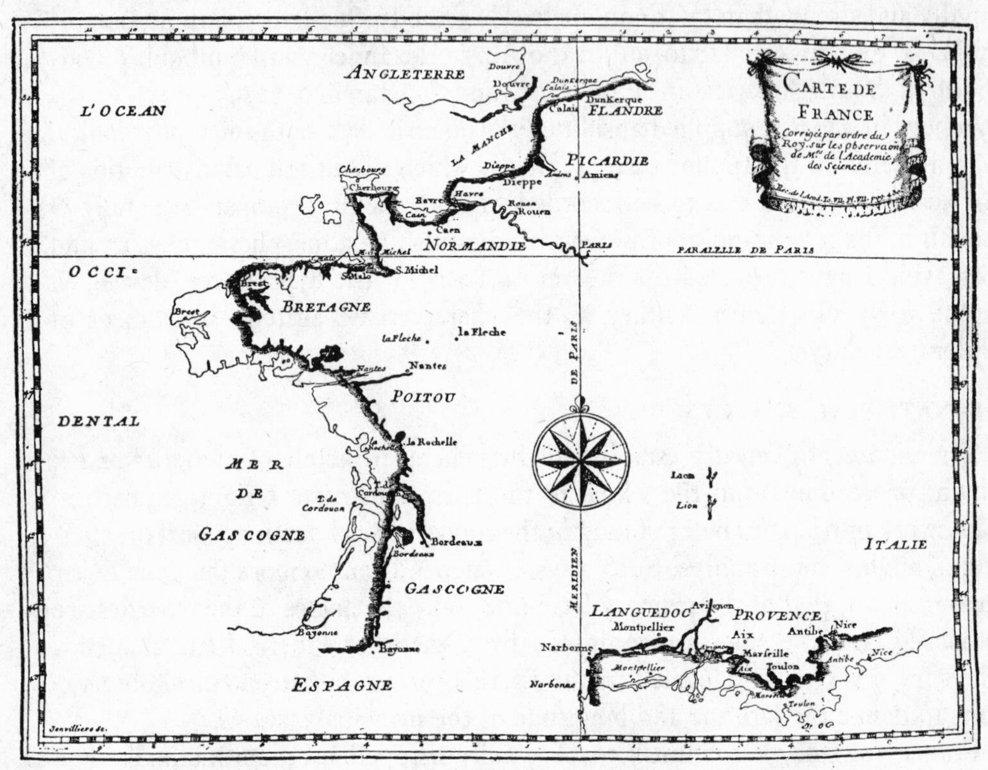

FIGURE 330—*Outline map of France by Philippe de La Hire, 1693, superimposed on that by Sanson, 1679. The new outline is shown in shaded line.*

order to map the whole kingdom. By 1783, when Cassini de Thury published his *Description géométrique de la France*, the secondary triangulation, comprising 40 000 observed triangles, and the infilling topographical survey had been completed. The *carte de Cassini*, on a scale of 1:86 400, was published in 182 sheets between 1756 and 1793. In 1818 a new survey of France was begun, and the *carte de l'État-Major*, on a scale of 1:80 000, was completed by 1878.

Cassini de Thury had in addition carried out in 1748 a 'geometrical' survey in Flanders, by which he connected the triangulation along the Paris meridian to that carried out by Willebrord Snell (1591–1626) in Holland in 1615; and in 1762 he was able to carry the triangulation along the perpendicular to the Paris meridian as far east as Vienna. Twenty-one years later he presented a memorial to the British government, proposing triangulation from London to the French coast in order to establish the difference in latitude and longitude between the observatories of Paris and Greenwich. This operation was directed by the Royal Society and executed by William Roy, who had long advocated 'a general survey of the whole island at public cost' and had already in 1783 observed a series of triangles round London. Roy's base-line was measured on Hounslow Heath in 1784, by means of glass rods, with an error of only 1/158 000 (about 2 inches in the whole length of 27 404 ft, over 5 miles). After a delay of three years while Ramsden completed his 3-ft theodolite, the principal triangulation was in 1787 carried, with the help of 'white lights' as signals, to Dover and across the Straits to the French coast; and a base of verification was measured on Romney Marsh (figure 331).

Roy's was the first accurate triangulation to be made in Britain; and it was to be, as he recommended, 'the foundation of a general survey of the British Islands'. In 1791 administrative provision was made by the Duke of Richmond, Master-General of the Ordnance, for the continuation of the trigonometrical survey and the preparation of a map of the country on the scale of 1 inch to 1 mile (1:63 360), a scale familiar to military surveyors. The survey was equipped with two 100-ft steel chains by Ramsden, for base measurement, and a new 3-ft theodolite by the same maker for the 'great triangles'. The secondary triangles were observed with smaller theodolites constructed by Ramsden and by Troughton and Simms; and the field survey, at 2 in to 1 mile, was made by traversing with the measuring-wheel and circumferentor. By 1825 the whole of England and Wales had been triangulated, all but the six northern counties mapped, and the triangulation of Scotland was nearly complete. Under William Mudge (1762–1820), director of the Survey from 1799 to 1820, an arc of the meridian had been measured from Dunnose in the Isle of Wight to Clifton in Yorkshire, using a zenith sector with an 8-ft telescope, made by Ramsden. This very accurate operation, while inconclusive in determining the figure of the Earth, gave a mean curvature of the meridian that served as a basis for the one-inch map. In practice, the latitude and longitude of all the principal stations were computed in relation to the Greenwich meridian; and, whenever the operations were 'extended in eastern or western directions over spaces of sixty miles from fixed meridians', the 'directions of meridians', or azimuthal bearings, of selected stations were determined by observing the maximum east-and-west distance of Polaris from the celestial pole. Unlike the French survey, Mudge's triangulation was formed not in narrow belts or chains but as a mesh gradually spreading from south-east

England over the whole country. The 'great theodolites' of Ramsden were the earliest instruments 'capable of detecting spherical excess' in terrestrial triangles; and the effects of refraction near the horizon were carefully noted, with the accompanying circumstances of temperature, air-pressure, and wind.

In 1825 the resources of the Ordnance Survey were diverted to a cadastral survey of Ireland, ordered by Parliament as a basis for land valuation, on a scale of

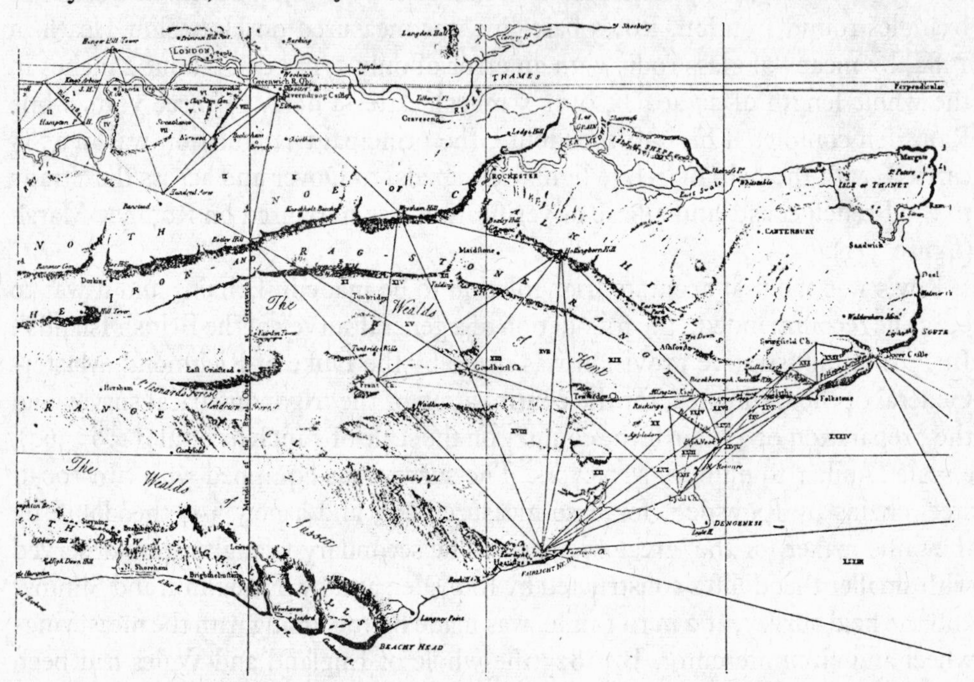

FIGURE 331—*Roy's triangulation of south-east England and the Straits of Dover, 1787, shown in hair-line.*

6 inches to 1 mile (1 : 10 560). The base was measured on Lough Foyle with Colby's compensation-bars (p 601), and the major triangulation was carried out in 1826–32. The observation of very long rays, up to 102 miles, was made possible by the use of light-signals invented by Thomas Drummond—the heliostat, or solar reflector, and the lime-light.

The larger scale of the Irish survey led to some important changes of practice, introduced for greater precision. In the field survey, chaining superseded traversing. From 1839 altitude measurement was carried out by levelling, based on a low-water datum in Dublin Bay. The observation of vertical angles hitherto practised was a less accurate method, which did not lend itself to continuous representation of relief and slope so readily as levelling, and the series of heights produced by the level could be easily plotted as contours. The projection of the maps of Ireland followed the system of rectangular co-ordinates adopted in the *carte de Cassini*, the origin being the point of intersection of a selected central meridian with a great circle at right-angles to it. The plotting of the curved and

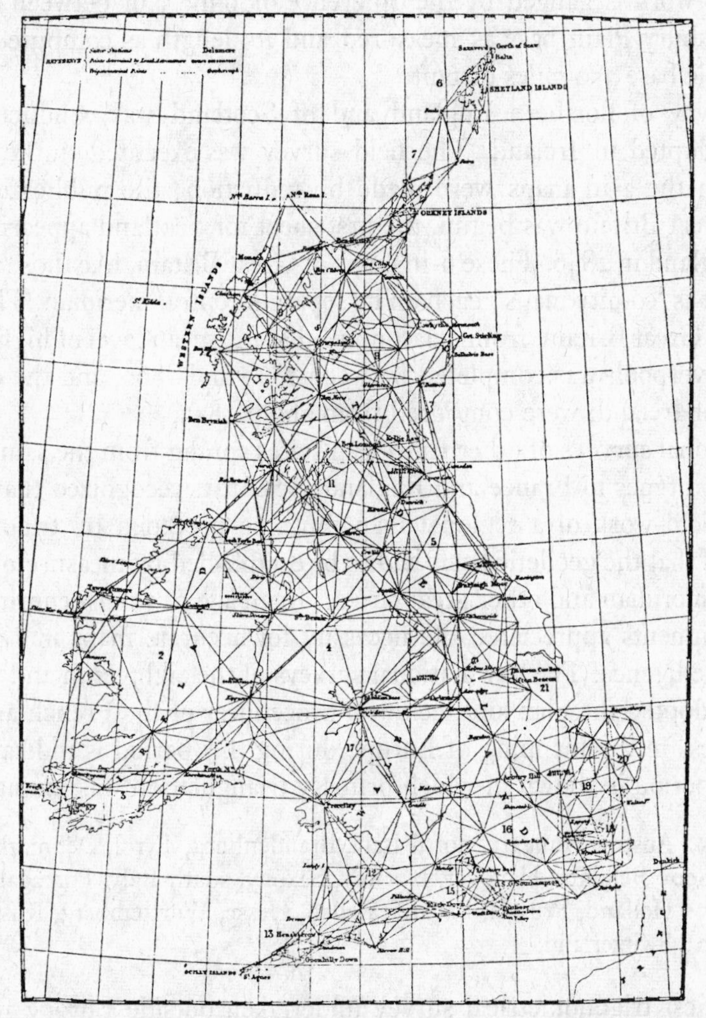

FIGURE 332—*The principal triangulation of the British Isles, completed in 1852.*

converging meridians as parallel straight lines on the map leads to an exaggeration of the scale to north and south along all meridians except the central one. While Cassini had plotted his map of the whole country on the meridian of Paris, the surveyors of Ireland reduced the contingent error by plotting the map of each county on a central meridian appropriate to it.

The survey of Scotland was resumed in 1838, and by 1852 the principal triangulation of Great Britain had been completed (figure 332). This depended on the two base-lines measured with Colby's apparatus, verified by four check bases. In the great triangles, 66 sides exceeded 80 miles in length, and the precision of the work is gauged by the difference of only 5 in between the length of the Salisbury Plain base as measured and its length as computed from the Lough Foyle base 350 miles distant.

The survey of northern England and of Scotland was conducted by the methods adopted in Ireland. The field survey was executed on the 6-in scale, from which the 1-in maps were made by reduction; the publication of 6-in maps of Great Britain was begun, the first sheet for Scotland appearing in 1843 and for England in 1846. These 6-in maps of Great Britain, like those of Ireland, were issued as 'county maps', each on its separate central meridian. The primary levelling of Great Britain, from a datum fixed at the mean level of high- and low-water at Liverpool, was completed between 1840 and 1860, and the 6-in maps, like those of Ireland, were contoured from about 1843.

The national surveys of other European states sprang from the same impulses as their prototypes in France and England. Scientists recognized that the topographical field-work of a regional map must be preceded by trigonometrical survey, and that the geodetic basis had to be established by measurement of long arcs of the meridian and other great circles. In an age of almost continuous warfare, governments appreciated the necessity for accurate maps in political and military intelligence. The new national surveys of the eighteenth and nineteenth centuries adopted the plan and technical procedures of the French and British. The progress in the mapping of Europe during this period is indicated below, where the period is shown in which primary triangulation was initiated:

1750–75: Austria-Hungary, north Italy, Brandenburg, Tyrol, Denmark, Sweden.
1775–1800: Belgium, Hanover, Norway, Saxony, south Italy, Portugal.
1800–25: Holland, Prussia, Bavaria, Baden, Hesse, Württemberg, Russia.
1825–50: Switzerland.

The earliest trigonometrical survey undertaken outside Europe was that of India. Between 1763 and 1777 James Rennell (1742–1830) had surveyed Bengal by route-traverses adjusted to observations for latitude and longitude. Triangulation, from a base line measured near Madras in 1802, was begun by William Lambton (1756–1823) with the object of measuring an arc of the meridian. By 1840 a 'great arc' of 20° of latitude, extending from Cape Comorin to the Himalayas, had been triangulated, and chains of triangles had been run across the subcontinent from east to west. These provided the framework for the Great Trigonometrical Survey of India.

IV. METHODS OF CARTOGRAPHIC REPRESENTATION

Relief. The effective delineation of relief—the third dimension in topography—by the map-maker enables the configuration of land-forms to be clearly visualized and the altitude and gradient of the land-surface at any point to be ascertained. Before the eighteenth century none of these conditions was satisfied by land-maps, which commonly employed pictographic symbols drawn in half-perspective or bird's-eye view, with hatching 'obliquely' shaded as if illuminated from the north-west. Such a method conveyed a general impression of relative elevation, but failed to disclose the plan of relief features, their absolute altitude, or their slope.

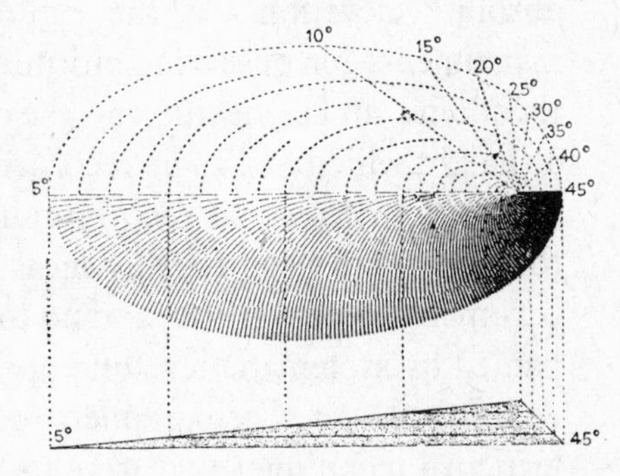

FIGURE 333—*Diagram illustrating the principle of J. G. Lehmann's graded hachures.*

Early in the eighteenth century, cartographers began to draw their hill-hatching as if vertically shaded or illuminated from a source above the object. From this method, which facilitated the representation of relief features in plan, developed hachuring by parallel lines drawn in the direction of the slope, the steepness being indicated by the thickness of the hachures and the interval between them. This convention was used with plastic effect in 1757 in the physical maps of Philippe Buache (1700–73) to illustrate the morphology of river-systems and watersheds. An original, if ingenuous, application of it was made by Christopher Packe (1686–1749) in his 'Philosophico-chorographical Chart of East Kent' (1743) to demonstrate the pattern of valleys and 'their use in draining the waters from the surface of the earth' [4].

The Cassini map of France employed an insensitive style of hachuring which suggested two levels only—erosion valleys divided by a scarp from the surrounding table-land. Cassini, who recognized the need for a comprehensive levelling of the country, had to admit the limitations of his topographical surveyors, and they were required only to sketch relief from rough field-notes, such as D or F for '*pentes douces ou fortes*'. Although Cassini's method of delineating relief was widely imitated in military and topographical surveys, it was superseded by the 'theory of mountain drawing' published by J. G. Lehmann (1765–1811) in 1799 (figure 333). In the scientific system of hachuring introduced by Lehmann the gradient was accurately represented by equidistant parallel lines, the thickness of which was made proportionate to the angle of slope. Lehmann's system was widely adopted on the continent, and in the first national survey of Switzerland —the 'Dufour map'—a notably plastic effect was achieved by emphasizing the hachures on the south and east slopes as if obliquely illuminated.

Hill-shading and hachuring, even in their most refined forms, have only a limited range in the differentiation of slopes, and unaided they cannot indicate absolute elevation. As the eighteenth-century surveyor learnt to use field-instruments for observing altitude—the surveying level, barometer, altazimuth theodolite, and tacheometer—the cartographer was supplied with determinations of height which had to be recorded on his map, though it is true that these were not yet numerous. In 1807 Humboldt noted that no more than 122 altitudes in the world had been reliably measured, nearly half of these being from his own barometric observations, and no topographical survey of a large area was accompanied by systematic levelling operations before that made for the French *carte de l'État-Major*. Cartographers of the eighteenth century, however, evolved the principal techniques that were to be used in the nineteenth for representation of absolute altitude.

Marine charts had since the sixteenth century recorded the relief of sea-bottom or river-bed by depth-figures obtained by sounding. Altitude-figures, or 'spot heights', were not marked on land-maps until the middle of the eighteenth century. Packe's map of 1743 provides the earliest English example, from barometric observations, and at about this time French military engineers began to insert altitude-figures, obtained by levelling, in their plans of fortifications.

The isometric line had been introduced into cartography by Edmond Halley's (1656–1742) chart of magnetic variation (1701), and hydrographers were accustomed to the use of form-lines on charts to indicate the coastal shelf and the limits of shoals. By an easy development, lines run through points of equal sounding produced underwater contours or isobaths. This step was first taken by the Dutch engineer N. S. Cruquius (1678–1754), in whose chart of the river Merwede (1729) depth was depicted by contours at a vertical interval of 1 fathom, referred to the low-water mark (itself a contour). A bathymetric chart of the English Channel, prepared by P. Buache in 1737 and published in 1752, drew submarine contours at 10 fathoms interval and was accompanied by a vertical section of the sea-bed (figure 334).

Contouring was not generally adopted in marine charts for over a century after the initial essay by Cruquius; it was introduced on the Russian official charts in 1834, and on the British in 1838. Meanwhile theoretical studies of its application to topographical survey had been made in France in 1771. While making a gravity survey of a Scottish mountain in 1777 Charles Hutton (1737–1823) em-

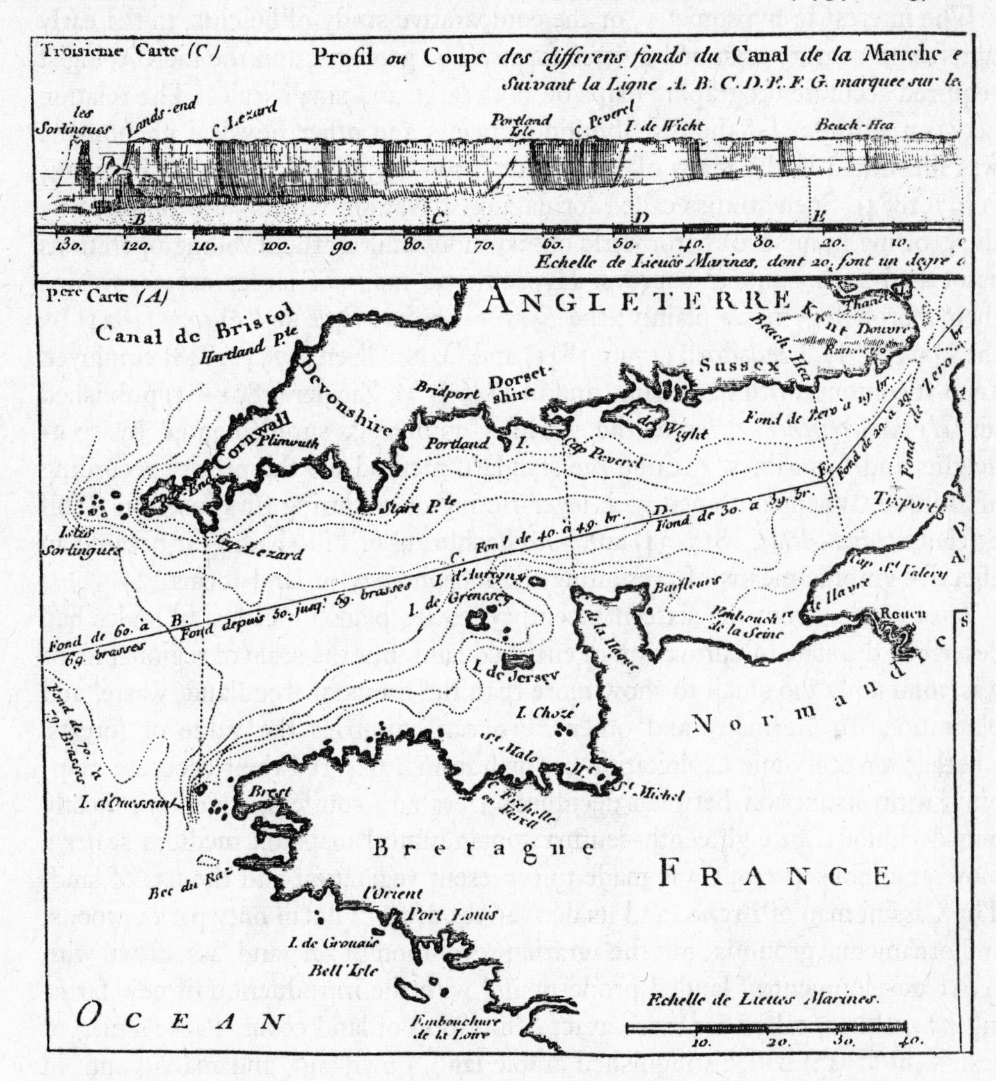

FIGURE 334—*Contoured chart and vertical section of the English Channel by P. Buache (detail), 1752.*

ployed the method, 'connecting together by a faint line all the points which were of the same relative altitude'; and the first map of a larger land-area in which it is found is that of France (1799) by J. L. Dupain-Triel (1722–1805?). Here, in an attempt to show the configuration of country '*par une nouvelle méthode de nivellements*', altitude was represented by contours above mean sea-level, at a vertical interval of 20 m, together with spot-heights, hachures with oblique shading, and a vertical section across the country.

The interest in hypsometry, or the comparative study of heights, in the early nineteenth century assumed diverse forms. The geologist and the meteorologist required accurate orographic maps on both large and small scales. The relation between altitude and the distribution of plants and other physical phenomena was illustrated in the maps of Humboldt (1769–1859) and H. C. W. Berghaus (1797–1884). Such studies called for data on elevation, which were supplied by the growing number of barometric observations and by the levelling operations associated with national surveys. Hypsometric maps of larger areas revealed their morphology more plainly; the *Esquisse orographique de l'Europe* (1824) by the Danes J. H. Bredsdorff (1790–1841) and O. N. Olsen (1794–1848) employed 1000-ft contours with hachuring, and in 1856 J. M. Ziegler (1801–84) published his *Hypsometrischer Atlas* of the world. Contouring, supplemented by spot-heights and form-lines, became the standard method for the precise recording of altitude. When combined with layer-tinting or colouring (first used in Adolf Stieler's *Hand-Atlas*, 1817–34) and with hachuring or hill-shading it became an effective graphic means of presenting the morphology of land-forms.

Land cover. From the sixteenth century, estate plans on cadastral scales had described the state of cultivation of enclosed land, but the scale of regional maps was commonly too small to show more than the limits of woodland, waste, and plantation. In Germany and other European countries the value of forests, whether for economic exploitation or for hunting, ensured their accurate mapping, with distinction between deciduous trees and conifers, which are mostly non-deciduous. In eighteenth-century topographical maps on medium scales a more ambitious attempt was made to represent vegetation and the use of land. The Cassini map of France and its derivatives drew in detail only parks, woods, and ornamental grounds; but the agrarian revolution in England, associated with active development of landed property and with the introduction of new farming procedures, called for more exact delineation of land cover. Packe's map of east Kent (1743) had distinguished arable land, downland, and marsh, and, in the English county maps of the second half of the century, the cartographers—who were usually also estate surveyors—employed a varied vocabulary of symbols, adapted from large-scale plans, for crops and vegetation cover. In the 2-inch to a mile maps of John Rocque (*c* 1704–62), for instance, appropriate conventions defined arable and pasture, hop-lands, formal and landscape gardens, parks and woodland, heath and marsh.

A more systematic technique was applied in a map of the London region published by Thomas Milne (fl 1788–1800) in 1800, from a survey made in 1795–9 and covering an area of 16 miles by 14 on a scale of 2 inches to a mile [5]. The boundaries of enclosures, unlike those of Rocque's maps, were carefully surveyed, and each field (whether open or enclosed) was marked by a characteristic letter or colour denoting its cultivation. No fewer than 17 forms of land-use were thus differentiated, and Milne's map strikingly anticipates the practice of land-utilization surveys of the twentieth century.

Special maps. The observation of the inorganic and organic phenomena of the Earth's land and water surfaces, and the investigation of their physical composition, called into being maps of special types, whose individual modes of expression are studied in a later section (p 620).

V. HYDROGRAPHY AND OCEANOGRAPHY

At the opening of the eighteenth century the charting of the seas and coasts of the world fell far short of the seaman's needs. Three factors essential to precise hydrographic survey were still lacking. The number of points whose latitude and longitude had been reliably determined was few; neither instruments nor methods for accurate survey of a coastline had come into general use; and the technique of chart-drawing had developed little since the sixteenth century.

The reformation of hydrographic survey followed that of land-survey. The sea-atlas *Le Neptune françois*, published in Paris in 1693, introduced a number of innovations in its charts of western Europe. They were drawn on the Mercator projection ('*cartes réduites*'), enabling the navigator to plot bearings as straight lines, and were graduated in latitude and longitude; the positions of many coastal stations were laid down from the astronomical determinations of Picard and Cassini; and a shore-survey, with more accurate instruments than could be used on shipboard, preceded the plotting of the marine details. The example thus set was followed in the charts compiled by J. N. Bellin (1703–72) in the Dépôt des Cartes, Plans et Journaux de la Marine between 1737 and 1752 and published in 1756 as a sea-atlas of the world with the title *L'Hydrographie française*.

The accurate graduation of charts of the world, other than the European coasts, was, however, not possible until the introduction of the reflecting quadrant and sextant, and of the chronometer, enabled the seaman to find his latitude and longitude with confidence on board ship. Throughout the eighteenth century he continued to carry compass-charts oriented to magnetic north, not graduated in longitude and seldom in latitude, and covered with the traditional network of bearing-lines radiating from centres arranged on the periphery of a circle (vol III, pp 523–6).

Before the second half of the century the methods of hydrographic survey lagged behind those of land-surveyors. Although ships of the Royal Navy were occasionally issued with survey-equipment, including theodolite, plane-table, and chain, this part of a seaman's education was neglected. As late as 1770 Cook could write of 'the few [seamen] I have known who are capable of drawing a Chart or Sketch of a Sea coast', and Cook himself received his first training in survey, in 1758, from a military engineer. A coastal survey, like that of Great Britain, 1681–8, by Greenvile Collins (fl 1669–93), whose charts remained in use to the end of the eighteenth century, was commonly constructed from compass intersections on landmarks, taken from the ends of a sailed traverse which was measured by the ship's log, that is, by dead reckoning; or, in a 'geometric' survey on land, the coastline was traversed with measuring-wheel (plate 23 B), or chain and angular observations were made by surveying-compass or theodolite.

By the middle of the century the fallibility of these methods had become apparent, and surveys were being developed through a framework of triangulation from a level base-line measured on shore (figure 335). In his survey of the Orkney Islands, 1747–9, Murdoch Mackenzie (fl 1747–97) measured two bases on land with an iron chain, observed the primary triangles by theodolite, and defined prominent points on the coast by secondary triangulation. Finally the coastline was filled in by a boat-survey, compass bearings being taken to fix the position of marks, soundings, and reefs. Between 1751 and 1770 Mackenzie charted the west coast of Great Britain and the coasts of Ireland for the Admiralty; and in the same period (1763–7) Cook was making a trigonometrical survey of Newfoundland. Cook's survey, adapted to the charting of a difficult and 'practically unknown shore', combined Mackenzie's 'stasimetric' method with that of a running survey: a harbour was carefully planned from a measured base, the triangulation was carried as far afield as possible, and the surveying ship then sailed for the next harbour, sounding and sketching-in the coastline and fixing the ship's position by quadrant angles or compass bearings on the shore stations, determined by the theodolite. Cook's work was extended southward by surveys made for the Admiralty between 1763 and 1773 by J. F. W. Des Barres (1722–1824), Samuel Holland (1728?–1801), and their deputies. Their charts, covering 1000 miles of the Atlantic coast of North America, from the St Lawrence to Florida, were published in the sea-atlas 'The Atlantic Neptune' (1777–81).

By now the reflecting sextant, developed from Hadley's quadrant in 1757, was becoming the marine surveyor's tool-of-all-work. Not only was it employed in the observation of altitudes, for which it had been designed, but it was to supersede the compass as the standard instrument for taking horizontal angles. It was, as Mackenzie pointed out, 'more portable . . . and generally more accurately . . . divided' than the theodolite; and Dalrymple remarked that Hadley's quadrant

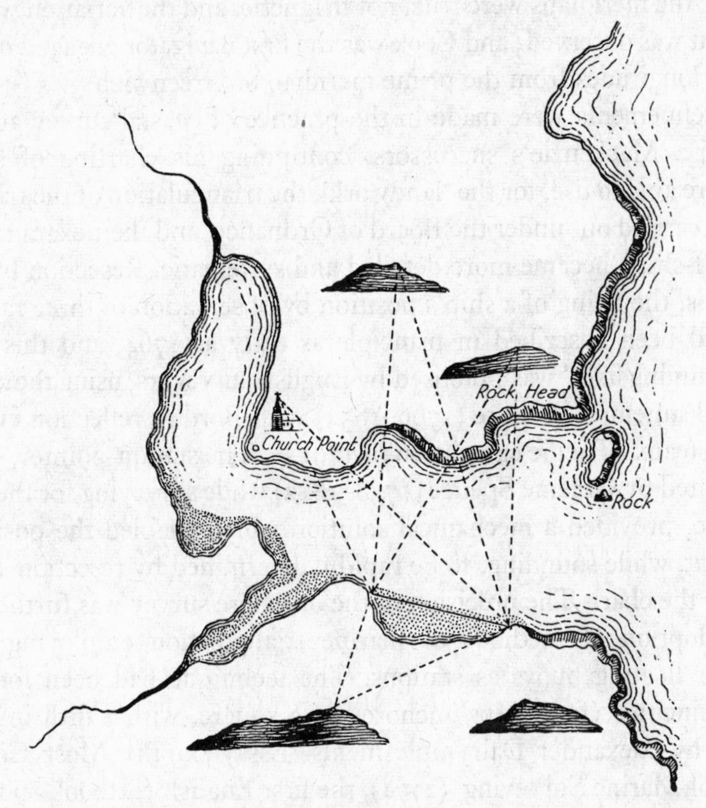

FIGURE 335—*Murdoch Mackenzie's diagram of a 'stasimetric' survey, 1774.*

could be 'used with equal facility at Mast-head as upon Deck, and therefore the Sphere of Observation is . . . much extended'. These qualities were of special value where coasts had to be charted by a continuous running survey from the ship, as in exploration. The use of the sextant contributed to the accuracy and the rapidity of Cook's surveys during his three voyages to the Pacific, the outstanding hydrographic achievement of the century. In his circumnavigation of New Zealand in 1769–70, in the course of which he charted 2400 miles of coastline in six months, Cook made no use of dead-reckoning; he plotted his track by fixing the ship's position from his courses and from intersecting rays on landmarks, adjusting it from time to time to the astronomical observations; and he 'made no farther use of the log than to connect those points of the track which the ship was in when he took his angles and bearings'. The drawing of the charts from these voyages, we may add, conformed to modern practice. Unlike those of Cook's Newfoundland survey, they were habitually graduated in latitude and longitude; the meridians were true, not magnetic, and the variation was recorded wherever it was observed; and Cook was the first navigator engaged on discovery to run his longitudes from the prime meridian of Greenwich.

Many refinements were made in the practice of coastal survey at the end of the century. Mackenzie's successors, continuing his charting of the English coasts, were able to use, for the 'landwork', the triangulation of the trigonometrical survey carried out under the Board of Ordnance, and their examination of the sea-bed off-shore became more detailed and systematic. Resection by the quadrant, that is, the fixing of a ship's position by observation of three rays on shore marks, had been described in principle as early as 1764, and this method of making 'running fixes' was practised by English surveyors, using the sextant, and by C. F. Beautemps-Beaupré (1766–1854) with Borda's reflection circle during d'Entrecasteaux's Pacific expedition of 1791–3. The station-pointer, said to have been invented by Graeme Spence (1758–1812) while surveying for the Admiralty about 1780, provided a mechanical solution which enabled the position of the survey-boat, while sounding, to be rapidly determined by resection and directly plotted on the chart. The precision of the off-shore survey was further increased by the adoption of methods of marine triangulation employing temporary beacons or floating buoys as stations. The technique had been foreshadowed by the 'quincunx' (four ships anchored in a square, with a fifth in the centre) proposed by Alexander Dalrymple in his 'Essay on the Most Commodious Methods of Marine Surveying' (1771), the first English textbook on the subject. By this method, using beacons and buoys, Admiralty surveyors charted the banks and channels of the Thames estuary in 1818–20 and 1832.

The Hydrographical Office was established by the Board of Admiralty in 1795 and was charged with the custody, compilation, and issue of charts for naval ships. About 1811 the surveying service of the Admiralty was brought under the administration of the Hydrographer, and in 1814 the first surveying-ships were entered in the Navy List. From this time British naval surveys, recorded in the Admiralty charts, were extended over the coasts and waters of almost the entire world.

The French hydrographic service had for half a century continued the work of Bellin, expanding the *Hydrographie française* into a series of 'Neptunes' (sea-atlases) compiled for the different '*navigations*'. A new survey of the coasts of France from a shore-triangulation was made between 1816 and 1836 and published in *Le Pilote français*. This was directed by Beautemps-Beaupré, as chief hydrographer; and the boatwork, using his method of fixing positions by the reflection circle and taking samples of the sea-bottom by means of a new type of sounding-rod, produced an extremely detailed survey of the marine features.

For want of suitable equipment, little physical study of the deep sea beyond coastal waters was possible before the nineteenth century. Sailors had regularly deduced the existence of surface currents from discrepancies between their dead-reckoning and their observed positions, and charts of oceanic circulation associated with the wind-systems had been produced since the seventeenth century. The introduction of the chronometer led to greater precision in records of the direction and velocity of currents, and the early nineteenth century saw the first systematic studies in oceanography, notably those of James Rennell, whose charts of the currents of the Atlantic Ocean were completed in 1827. Water-sampling instruments had been used during the eighteenth century, for instance by the scientists of Cook's expeditions, to measure the temperature and salinity of sea-water. Temperature observations to determine the limits of the Gulf Stream were made with Fahrenheit's thermometer by Benjamin Franklin (1706–90) in 1775 and Sir Charles Blagden (1748–1820) in 1776–7.

The floor of the ocean, however, could not be charted, and remained 'a sealed volume', until deep-sea sounding apparatus had been devised. In 1773 Captain C. J. Phipps, in 65° N 3° E, on his return from Spitsbergen, spliced together all his lines and, using a lead of over 150 lb, obtained 'a very fine soft blue clay' from a depth of 683 fathoms; this is the earliest deep-sea sounding recorded. On his Antarctic expedition (1839–43), Captain James Clark Ross (1800–62) made numerous deep soundings with a hemp line over 4 miles long, marked at every 100 fathoms. Lieutenant M. F. Maury (1806–73), as head of the U.S. hydrographic service, recommended a lighter line and lead—'a common twine thread for a sounding-line, and a cannon-ball (of 32 pounds) for a sinker'. With this equipment measurements of depths to over 5000 fathoms were claimed, and Maury's chart of the north Atlantic (1853) showed more than a hundred soundings in excess of 2000 fathoms. Maury also experimented unsuccessfully with echo-sounding by underwater explosions, and he introduced a deep-sea sounding rod, invented by Midshipman J. M. Brooke, which enabled specimens of the ocean-bottom to be recovered.

Maury is rightly regarded as the founder of systematic oceanography, and his textbook 'The Physical Geography of the Sea' (1853) remained in use for over half a century. During his service in the U.S. hydrographic office (1841–61), he compiled, from the tracks and observations of ships whose logs came into his hands, a series of 'Wind and Current Charts', the first of which appeared in 1847, employing an ingenious combination of colours and symbols. These charts pointed to the shortest sailing-routes, and Maury asserted that their use had reduced the average duration of the passage between New York and California from 183 to 135 days, and that between England and Australia from 124 to 97 days. In 1853 an international conference held at Brussels adopted the standard form of abstract log proposed by Maury.

VI. ATLASES AND SPECIAL MAPS

By the beginning of the nineteenth century maps on medium and large scales could describe with much greater precision the topographical elements of location, direction, distance, extent, and altitude. Of the general atlases which, continuously revised from contemporary sources, served as an index to the progress and current state of world cartography, the prototype is Adolf Stieler's (1775–1836) *Hand-Atlas*. The first edition of this was issued, in parts, between 1817 and 1834 by the great geographical publishing house of Justus Perthes (1772–1843) at Gotha, and new editions and supplements appeared regularly until 1930.

At the same time cartographic techniques were elaborated to represent geographically, in structural or spatial relationship, the data of other sciences. This enlargement of the map-maker's field embraced on the one hand the physical phenomena of the lithosphere, the hydrosphere, and the atmosphere, and, on the other, the material of various branches of human geography.

The earliest meteorological example is Edmond Halley's wind-chart, published to accompany his 'Historical Account of the Trade Winds and Monsoons' (1686). Halley drew tapering lines to indicate wind-directions, and the more familiar arrow appeared on eighteenth-century maps; the 'feathers' or lateral strokes denoting wind-strength were added after the introduction of the Beaufort scale in 1806. The isopleth, or 'curve-line' of equal value, introduced by Halley in 1701, was adapted to the representation of meteorological facts in the nineteenth century. Isotherms—lines of equal mean annual temperature—were drawn by Humboldt in mapping the distribution of plants (1817). Isobars—lines of equal mean pressure—were first plotted by Heinrich Berghaus (1797–1884), in his barometric world-chart (1838), as straight lines, parallel to the equator, drawn across the oceans to show pressure at sea level. Alexander Buchan's (1829–1907) world-maps of isobars for the months and the year, published in 1868–9, established that pressure varied with longitude as well as latitude. In synoptic weather charts, such as those of the eastern United States (1846) by Elias Loomis (1811–89), the data of winds, cloud, precipitation, atmospheric pressure, and temperature were brought together. Daily weather-charts from telegraphic reports were produced at the Great Exhibition from August to October 1851.

The association of longitude with the phenomena of terrestrial magnetism was illustrated, in the eighteenth century, by maps of magnetic declination (variation) and inclination (dip). In Halley's isogonic charts of the Atlantic and of the world, lines of equal variation for the year 1700 were drawn over the oceans, and J. H. Lambert (1728–77) in 1770 extended isogones over the land-surfaces of the globe. Isoclines, or lines of equal magnetic dip, were first used by William Whiston (1667–1752) in the maps of eastern England and north-west France published with his essay 'The Longitude and Latitude found by the Inclinatory or Dipping Needle' (1721), and in 1768 J. C. Wilcke (1731–96) produced an isoclinic world chart. On his South American travels (1799–1803) Humboldt had made observations of the decrease of magnetic intensity from the poles towards the equator, and in 1805 he drew a sketch of isodynamic zones. The earliest isodynamic maps, with lines of equal magnetic force, were those of north-west Europe (1825) and of the world (1826) by C. Hansteen (1784–1873).

The cartographic description of the physical materials of the Earth's crust also begins in the period now under consideration. Mineral resources and workings had been shown on maps since the sixteenth century, and geological sections of coal-seams in south-west England were drawn early in the eighteenth. The development of scientific agricultural methods was accompanied by an interest in soils, exemplified in Packe's physiographic map of east Kent (p 611) and in the 'soil maps' published with the reports of the Board of Agriculture (1794–1810), in which soils were characterized by their texture and fertility. The extension of geological observations, the systematic study of the sculpture of land-forms, and the classification of successive rock-formations—all these aspects of the young science of geology were to be served by a new kind of map.

In the mineralogical maps of France and north-west Europe (1746) drawn by Philippe Buache from the investigations of J. E. Guettard (1715–86), the first attempt was made to summarize the results of geological observation over a large area (plate 32 B); the pattern of rocks and sedimentary deposits was defined, and the location of fossils and minerals was indicated by distinctive symbols. At the end of the century William Smith (1769–1839), 'mineral surveyor', made his momentous correlation of rock-formations with their associated fossils, and the tables of strata which he drew up supplied the key to his geologically coloured maps, from that of the Bath district (1799) to his mature work in the map of the whole of England and Wales on a scale of 5 miles to an inch ('A Delineation of the Strata of England and Wales', 1815) and his 21 geological maps of English counties.

A geological map of the eastern United States was published by William Maclure (1763–1840) in 1809, and between 1825 and 1835 France was geologically mapped by J. B. A. L. L. Élie de Beaumont (1798–1874) and O. P. A. P. Dufrénoy (1792–1857) on the basis of the English stratification. These were independent enterprises. Geological surveying at the public expense was initiated in Great Britain. In 1814 John MacCulloch (1773–1835) was appointed geologist to the Ordnance Survey; in 1826 a geological branch of the Survey in Ireland was set up; and in 1832 H. T. De la Beche (1796–1855) was authorized to add geological colours to the 1-in topographical maps for south-west England. Three years later, when eight of these sheets had been published, the Geological Survey was established as a branch of the Ordnance Survey, with De la Beche as Director, to continue the geological mapping on the 1-in scale; this was the first national geological survey department. Before 1850 the study of the phenomena of glaciation led to the making of the earliest drift-maps.

The mapping of agricultural and mineral resources pointed the way to economic cartography. A pioneer essay in this field, anticipating work of a century later, was the map of Europe by A. F. W. Crome (1753–1833), published at Dessau in 1782. Here symbols were used to show the distribution of 56 commodities, and the principal commercial centres; and the map was accompanied by tables of the area and population of countries.

A synoptic view of the development of physical geography in the first half of the nineteenth century was presented in the notable *Physikalischer Atlas* compiled by Heinrich Berghaus (p 620) and published in parts from 1838 to 1848 by Justus Perthes. The data of the several divisions of the science—meteorology, hydrology, geology, terrestrial magnetism, the geography of plants, animals, and man—were co-ordinated and interpreted in 90 plates, accompanied by memoirs, in which Berghaus effectively applied the novel cartographic techniques introduced during the century.

In his sections on 'anthropogeography' and 'ethnography' Berghaus had treated human geography only in biological terms; but maps were already being brought into service to collate and depict quantitatively the facts of social geography, abstracted from statistical records. During the seminal period 1835–55, it has been claimed, 'almost every technique now known for representing population numbers, distribution, density and movements seems to have come into being'.

The earliest population maps were made in the British Isles, where a regular census had been instituted in 1801. The final report of the railway commissioners for Ireland, published in 1838, was illustrated by an atlas of six maps, drawn by H. D. Harness (1804–83) 'on a new design', which anticipated a num-

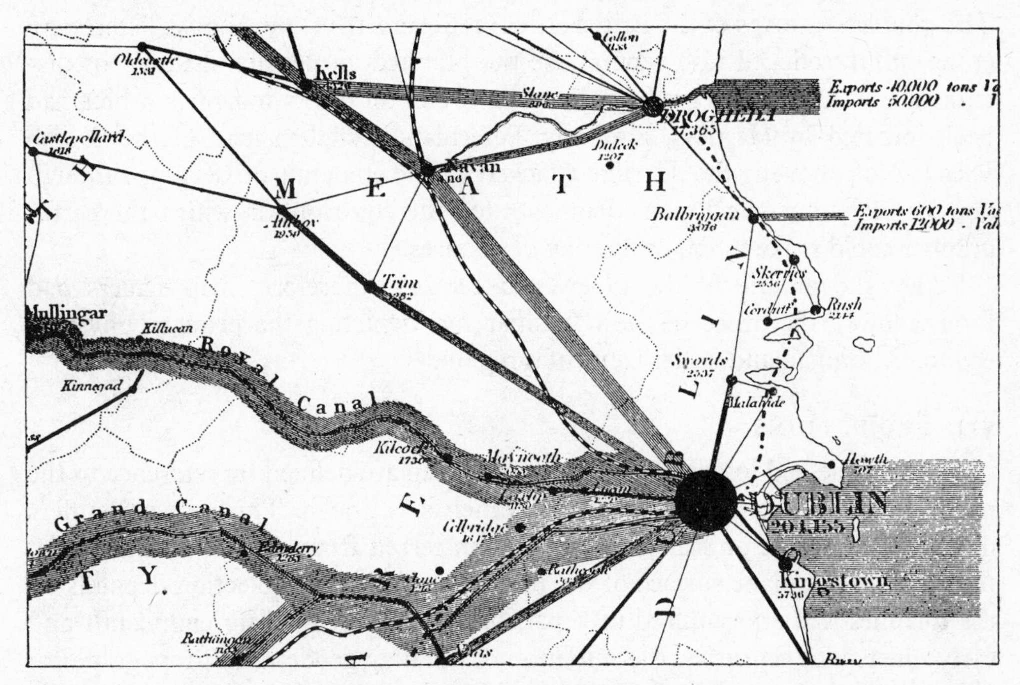

FIGURE 336—*Traffic-flow map of Ireland by H. D. Harness, published in 1838 (detail). This illustrates the use of 'flow lines' for traffic density and of graduated circles or dots for population.*

ber of modern cartographic techniques [6]. In his two traffic maps, showing the number of passengers carried by public conveyances and the volume of goods-traffic, Harness drew 'streams of shade', the thickness of which was proportional to the movements represented; this is the earliest example of the use of 'flow lines' (figure 336). In his map showing 'the comparative density of the population', as in his traffic maps, Harness indicated towns and cities by solid black circles proportional in size to the population as given by the 1831 census. The population map also represented the density of rural population by four degrees of aquatint shading, supplemented by occasional figures for the number of persons to the square mile. The density-shades are not delimited by boundaries of the administrative divisions for which the census returns were made, but correspond to zones of settlement, and Harness was thus also the first cartographer to employ the so-called dasymetric technique.

The originality of Harness's methods does not seem to have attracted attention, but it bore fruit in the maps published with subsequent census reports, such as that of 1841 for Ireland, in which similar distribution techniques were adapted to indicate population, housing, education, and agricultural property. The population maps of the British Isles (1849 and 1851) by August Petermann (1822–78) introduced into general use the practices of density-shading for distribution by area, and of graduated dots or circles for towns and cities, which had been initiated by Harness. Similarly, Petermann's cholera map of the British Isles (1850), showing the districts attacked by the epidemic of 1831–3, although not the earliest medical map, demonstrated the contribution which the cartographer could make to the geography of diseases.

Before the middle of the nineteenth century, therefore, map-makers had foreshadowed the processes now familiar for 'depicting the primary physical, economic, human and social facts' of a region.

VII. PROJECTIONS

The latitude and longitude of points on a map are defined by reference to the network of parallels and meridians on which it is drawn. This network suffers distortion, in shape or scale, when it is transferred from the curved surface of the globe to the plane surface of the map. The choice of projection depends on the qualities that are required in a particular map. In the late eighteenth and early nineteenth centuries, the initiation of accurate geodetic and topographical surveys and the extension of the applications of cartography gave a new impulse to the mathematical study of projections. J. H. Lambert laid the foundations for this study in an essay published in 1772 under the title *Anmerkungen und Zusätze zur Entwerfung der Land- und Himmelskarten*. Here he analysed the properties of the two principal methods of projection: the conformal (or orthomorphic), in which angles and the true shape of any small area are preserved on the map, and the equivalent (or equal-area), in which the area of any tract on the map is equal to that of the same tract on a globe to the same scale.

Lambert's work marked 'the beginning of a new epoch in the science of map projection', not only by its enunciation of basic principles but by the forms of projection that he devised. His equal-area conic projection, with one standard parallel, was modified in 1805 by H. C. Albers (1773–1833), who employed a cone intersecting the globe at two standard parallels; this gave a projection that greatly reduced the errors of scale in the north and south of the map and was especially suitable for areas with wide extension in longitude. The French *carte de l'État-Major* and other national surveys of the nineteenth century, however, adopted an older conic projection, also equal-area, used by Rigobert Bonne (1727–95) in 1752 and named after him. Lambert's conformal conic projection was revived for military mapping in the twentieth century.

Equivalence is plainly an essential property in the mapping of distributions or densities; but correlation of these factors with differences of latitude and climate, as required by many physical maps, is not clearly evoked by the equal-area conic projections, which have curved parallels of latitude. In the nineteenth century, projections with horizontal and rectilinear parallels were accordingly brought into use. The older sinusoidal, or Sanson-Flamsteed, projection became popular in atlas maps; and in 1805 K. B. Mollweide (1774–1825) constructed his homalographic projection, which, as specially suitable for circular hemispheric maps, came into general use in the second half of the century.

The Mercator chart, drawn on a conformal projection and therefore correctly representing angles between intersecting lines, such as parallels and meridians, had by the middle of the eighteenth century established itself as the standard navigational chart, enabling the seaman to lay off his compass course as a straight line. Its formal properties, with rectilinear parallels and meridians drawn parallel to the edges of the map, led to its adoption for some special types of map, such as meteorological charts; and its ease of construction made it the standard projection for world-maps in the general atlases of the nineteenth century.

VIII. THE PRINTING OF MAPS

From the middle of the sixteenth century the great majority of maps were printed from incised copper plates. Intaglio engraving on copper reproduced the cartographer's line with unequalled sharpness, precision, and delicacy; details could be deleted or corrected when the map required revision; and the plate if properly husbanded had a long life. These qualities recommended the process as much to the cartographer of the nineteenth century as to his less scientific predecessors, and it was employed in printing both the topographical maps of national surveys and the special maps described in a preceding section.

Nevertheless, copper-plate engraving had some disadvantages. It was a slow, highly skilled, and expensive process; in the eighteenth century the cost of engraving a medium-scale map was as great as that of surveying and drawing it. When a large number of impressions had been pulled from it, the relatively soft plate lost its sharpness unless it was reworked. Line-engraving was not suitable for the rendering of tones or surface colours, which had to be added by hand.

While few nineteenth-century cartographers doubted the superiority of copper-plate engraving, its limitations encouraged the introduction of rival or supplementary processes for map-printing. Engraving on steel plates, softened by heat to take the burin and then annealed, had a brief vogue in England and France from about 1820. This gave the fine line required by the cartographer, and the harder surface of the steel permitted larger printings, but the plate was less easily corrected than copper. Lithography, in which the design to be printed is drawn or traced on a chemically prepared stone surface, was applied to maps soon after its invention by C. Senefelder (1771–1834) about 1798. Its flexible line, although less brilliant than that of the incised metal plate, was a suitable vehicle for the cartographer's drawing, which could be applied directly to the stone without suffering the risk of corruption by the engraver. The lithographic stone was challenged, for the surface-printing of maps, by the much cheaper and lighter zinc plate, and in 1855 the Ordnance Survey adopted zincography for the reproduction of its large-scale plans at 25 inches to the mile.

Meanwhile, maps continued to be printed from engraved copper plates, as they have been to the present day. Revision was facilitated by the use of electrotypes, in which corrections or additions could be made without risk of injury to the original plate. This method, employed in Stieler's atlas from 1842, also enabled different maps to be prepared on the same topographical base; thus the Ordnance Survey issued three versions of the first edition of its 1-in map—with contours, with hill-hachuring, and with hill-hachuring and geological outlines.

Before the second half of the eighteenth century, colouring was employed principally to distinguish political divisions and the main physical features, such as water and woodland, or to enhance the decorative elements of a map. Its functions were immensely widened when maps were called into service by the physiographer (and especially the geologist) and by the social geographer. For applied cartography in these fields, the use of tones and colours was indispensable. Until the middle of the nineteenth century all colouring of maps was still done by hand; aquatint tones were occasionally used in distribution maps, such as that of Harness (1838). The introduction of chromolithography placed at the printer's disposal a process apt for reproducing flat colours, and therefore suitable for the colouring of geological maps and of layered orographic maps. Thus, while the maps in the *Physikalischer Atlas* (1838–48) of Berghaus were still hand-coloured, the layer colouring in Ziegler's *Hypsometrischer Atlas* (1856) was printed from lithographic stones. The first edition (1838) of H. von Dechen's geological map of Germany used only eight colours, added by hand, but the second edition (1869) was in 32 colours printed by lithography.

REFERENCES

[1] GREEN, W. 'Description and Use of the Improved Reflecting and Refracting Telescopes, and Scale for Surveying, etc.' London. 1778.
[2] LEYBOURNE, W. 'The Compleat Surveyor.' London. 1657.
[3] ROY, W. *Phil. Trans.*, **80,** 137, 1790.
[4] CAMPBELL, E. M. T. *Imago Mundi*, **6,** 79, 1949.
[5] BULL, G. B. G. *Geogr. J.*, **122,** 25, 1956.
[6] ROBINSON, A. H. W. *Ibid.*, **121,** 440, 1955.

BIBLIOGRAPHY

General:

CRONE, G. R. 'Maps and their Makers.' Hutchinson, London. 1953.
ECKERT, M. 'Die Kartenwissenschaft' (2 vols). De Gruyter, Berlin and Leipzig. 1921, 1925.
PESCHEL, O. 'Geschichte der Erdkunde' (2nd rev. ed.). Munich. 1877.

The World Map:

PERRIER, G. 'Petite histoire de la géodésie.' Presses Universitaires de France, Paris. 1939.
SANDLER, C. 'Die Reformation der Kartographie um 1700.' Oldenbourg, Munich. 1905.
WOLF, C. 'Histoire de l'Observatoire de Paris, de sa fondation à 1793.' Gauthier-Villars, Paris. 1902.

Instruments:

ADAMS, G. 'Geometrical and Graphical Essays.' London. 1791.
DAUMAS, M. 'Les instruments scientifiques aux XVIIe et XVIIIe siècles.' Presses Universitaires de France, Paris. 1953.
LANCASTER-JONES, E. 'Catalogue of the Collections in the Science Museum: Geodesy and Surveying.' H.M. Stationery Office, London. 1925.
LAUSSEDAT, A. 'Recherches sur les instruments, les méthodes, et le dessin topographique' (2 vols). Paris. 1898, 1903.

National Surveys:

BERTHAUT, H. M. 'La Carte de France, 1750–1898' (2 vols). Service Géographique de L'Armée, Paris. 1898–9.
CASSINI DE THURY, C. F. 'La description géométrique de la France.' Paris. 1783.
CLOSE, SIR CHARLES (FREDERICK). 'The Early Years of the Ordnance Survey.' Institution of Royal Engineers, Chatham. 1926.
MUDGE, W. *et al.* 'An Account of the Operations carried on for accomplishing a Trigonometrical Survey of England and Wales' (3 vols). London. 1801–11.

Hydrography and Oceanography:

DEACON, G. E. R. "Exploration of the Deep Sea." *J. Inst. Navig.*, **7,** 165–74, 1955.
ROBINSON, A. H. W. "The Early Hydrographic Surveys of the British Isles." *Emp. Surv. Rev.*, **11,** 60–65, 1951.
SKELTON, R. A. "Captain James Cook as a Hydrographer." *Mariner's Mirror*, **40,** 92–119, 1954.

Applied Cartography:

HELLMANN, G. 'Neudrucke von Schriften und Karten über Meteorologie und Erdmagnetismus', No. 4: "Die ältesten Karten der Isogonen, Isoklinen, Isodynamen"; No. 8: "Meteorologische Karten." Berlin. 1895–7.

WOODWARD, H. B. 'History of Geology.' Watts, London. 1911.

Projections:

AVEZAC, A. B. d'. 'Coup d'œil historique sur les projections des cartes de géographie.' Paris. 1863.

Surveyors' instruments drawn from a vignette on an early eighteenth-century map.

21

DREDGING

G. DOORMAN

WHILE the development of the European canal system (ch 18) was of great importance it was not a wholly unmixed blessing, for much dredging was necessary to keep the canals clear. Many ports, too, had to be dredged, especially as ships grew larger. In some cases fast-flowing rivers, such as the Scheldt, Meuse, and Rhine, kept the ports at their entrances free, but many towns had to move their harbours nearer to the sea. Thus Grevelingen (Gravelines) and Dunkirk became the ports for St Omer; Dixmude, later Nieuport, for Ypres; and Damme, later Sluis, for Bruges.

The various methods of deepening rivers, canals, and harbours that have been used may be classified as follows:

(*a*) removal of silt in suspension;
(*b*) scoops;
(*c*) ladle-dredgers;
(*d*) grab-dredgers;
(*e*) wheel-dredgers;
(*f*) chain-dredgers or bucket-dredgers.

(*a*) *Removal of silt in suspension.* In order to deal with local shoaling in a river it is sometimes sufficient to bring the silt into suspension merely by narrowing the river by crib-dams or, more simply, by hauling a heavy rake or harrow across the stream by means of a winch set up on the bank. Conradis [1] illustrates work of this kind during the sixteenth to eighteenth centuries, and also shows horses wading in a river to drag a harrow downstream. A defect of this method, however, is that the silt so removed will settle again farther down the river.

A similar system was the *spoelsluis* (cleansing sluice), which was applied in some sea-ports of Holland and Zeeland. Smeaton [3] saw it working satisfactorily in 1755. In this method a dock or lake was filled by the sea at high tide, and by closing a sluice-gate the water was kept there until low tide, when it was suddenly released by opening the sluice. The sudden rush of the released water carried off much of the silt (cf p 467).

This scouring effect was often increased by a special ship, called a *mol* (mole) or *krabbelaar* (scraper). A model of such a ship is seen in figure 337. The ship had a broad stern, widened by hinged lee-boards, so that it would be swept along by the current. As it moved downstream it tore up the bed of the river by means of adjustable rakes and harrows. An early *mol* with iron teeth is mentioned in the municipal accounts of Middelburg (Zeeland) for the year 1435.

Faustus Verantius of Venice, about 1600, refers to a boat similarly used on a

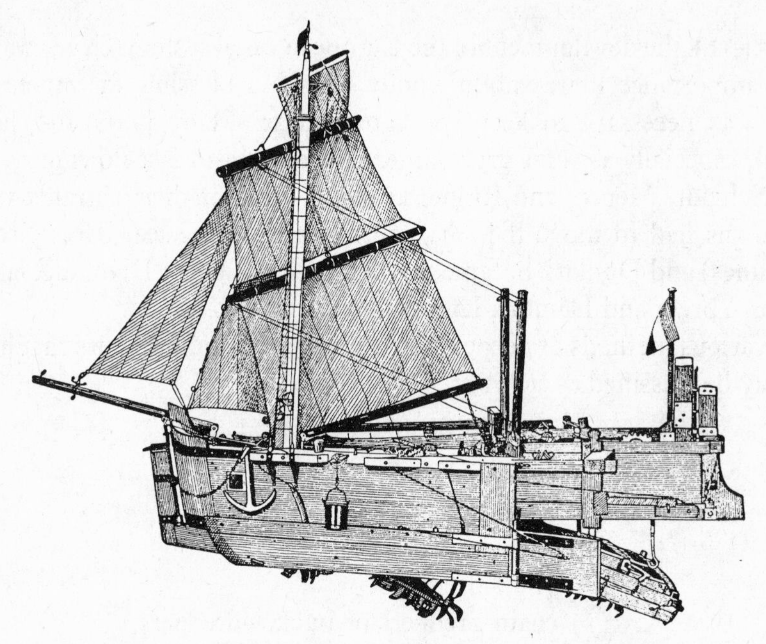

FIGURE 337—*Model of an eighteenth-century* krabbelaar *or scraper.*

river; it had a horizontal shaft carrying at each end a paddle-wheel, rotated by the stream, and in the middle a number of arms for tearing up the river-bed.

In a patent of 1589 Simon Stevin (1548–1620) claimed *inter alia* the process of conveying mud, clay, sand, or other suspended matter through tubes to deposit it on land [2]. It is remarkable that Stevin formulated such an advanced idea, for it was incapable of realization at the time. Had the patent system not then been in an immature state the States-General would have rejected the claim, since it failed to disclose the means by which it could be performed. In fact, it could be realized fully only much later, in the nineteenth century, when the steam-driven centrifugal pump reached a useful stage. An early practical solution was the 'squirting-dredger', designed for the Suez works. In this, a chain of buckets delivered the mud into a high tank, in which it was mixed with water from a centrifugal pump. The mixture was discharged through a gutter with a gradient of 1:20 and a length of 30–70 m. It is believed that this method of removing mud from the Suez canal is still adopted in principle.

Another system, also used for the Suez canal, was Bazin's steam-driven sand-pump (figure 338), a model of which was shown at the Paris exhibition of 1867. A rotating harrow beneath the forepart of the ship loosens the ground, and the resulting silt is taken up by four suction-tubes at the stern; these rest on a frame which can be adjusted in order to bring the ends of the tubes to the desired

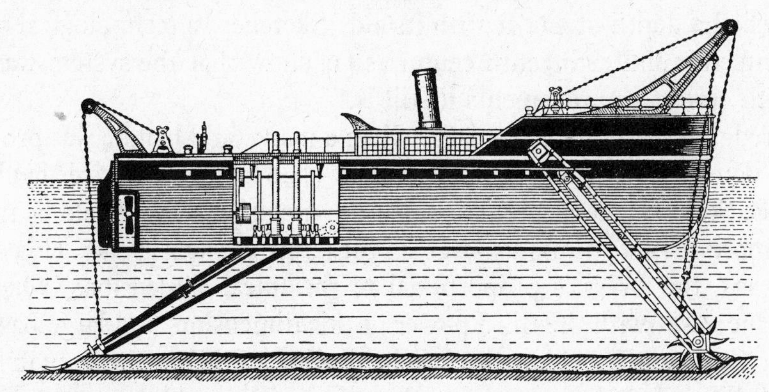

FIGURE 338—*Model of Bazin's steam-driven sand-pump. The rotating screw loosened the sand, which was then sucked up by tubes at the stern.*

height. Marcaire mentions *refoulement par une charge d'eau*, indicating that certain tubes beneath the suction-tubes (not shown) served to direct a jet of water on to the sand in order to bring it into suspension. Centrifugal pumps delivered the mixture into lighters. Such a dredger could daily lift 3000 cu m of material with a specific gravity of 1·8 to 2·0 from a depth of 8 to 12 metres. From about the same time dates Woodford's sand-pump, provided with a vertical centrifugal pump; this pump was lowered until its inlet was just above the river-bed, when it took up a mixture of water and mud.

The conduction of liquid mud by applied pressure seems first to have been used by English contractors when cutting the *Noordzeekanaal* for Amsterdam (1865–76). They worked with the Burt and Freeman sand-pump, an improved vertical pump of the Woodford type fed by a chain of buckets. The pump forced the mixture through a floating pipe-line consisting of a series of wooden tubes reinforced with iron. These tubes, each 6 m long, were joined by linen (later leather) sleeves. The pipe-line was about 100 m long and in some cases its outlet was 2½ m above the water.

From such devices have developed modern suction- and pressure-dredgers.

(*b*) *The scoop.* The simplest implement for dredging is the scoop, in Britain known also as the bag-and-spoon. The scoop is derived from the spade by bending up the edges of the blade in order to hold the semi-liquid mud. At an early stage the blade was replaced by a bag of permeable fabric, made of hemp or leather, attached to a strong metal ring. This instrument still forms a useful means for dredging; it has also been used in well-sinking. For the latter purpose, the bag was carried at the lower end of a vertical pole which was rotated from above by two men. The method was patented in 1602 by Pieter Pietersz Enten [2], who reached a depth of 232 ft with its aid. Sketches in technological works of the seventeenth and eighteenth centuries [1] show that the system was widely used; with certain improvements it still is.

For dredging purposes a bag larger than a man could handle was proposed at an early date. In his patent of 1589 Stevin claims such a device, hauled by a winch: the States-General stipulated that the exclusive right should be restricted to bags more than 1½ times as large as those up to then in use. However, for similar bags, the stress is proportional to the linear dimensions, whereas the capacity increases with the third power of this dimension, and large bags therefore wear very rapidly. Although a mechanically hauled bag was seen in Amsterdam in 1830 [1] most designers of dredgers have followed other ways, which will now be discussed.

(*c*) *The ladle-dredger.* A model owned by the *Hoogheemraadschap Rijnland* at Leiden (figure 339) shows an early design of ladle-dredger, doubtless the one patented in 1627 by Dominicus Van Wesel [2]. As indicated in the patent, this dredger was designed for cutting channels under water. It had a pontoon carrying '4, 5, 6, 8 or more instruments for clearing a broad cut of uniform depth and width with incredible rapidity'. The model shows six winches on the pontoon, each worked by hand. The cable of every individual drum has each end connected to the end of one of a pair of ladles, so that while one ladle rises, the other is lowered. After every stroke the rotation is reversed. Each of the twelve ladles is manœuvred by a man standing on one of a pair of floats; he pushes the ladle into the mud, and after it has been lifted he makes it unload into a mud-hopper or mud-scow. The cutting of polder-canals before the marsh had been drained, as is done today, may have been a novel feature of the invention. About the year 1645 Van Wesel's dredger was used by Van der Wel for land reclamation in Holland. A patent of 1603 [2] taken out by two carpenters of Hoorn shows that Van Wesel was not the first to design a ladle-dredger with winches. This earlier dredger had iron buckets 5 ft long and with a width of 3–6 ft. A dredger with a davit for bringing the bag of a ladle inboard after it had been hoisted by means of a winch seems to be typically English. A sketch of about 1760, in the Hamburg state archives (see tailpiece), reproduces such a device [1].

Little more is heard about ladle-dredgers until the eighteenth century, when the French constructed their famous pontoon-dredgers. de la Balme's design of 1718 was only a modification of dredgers already working in the harbours of Brest and Toulon. Far more complicated and effective were the French designs

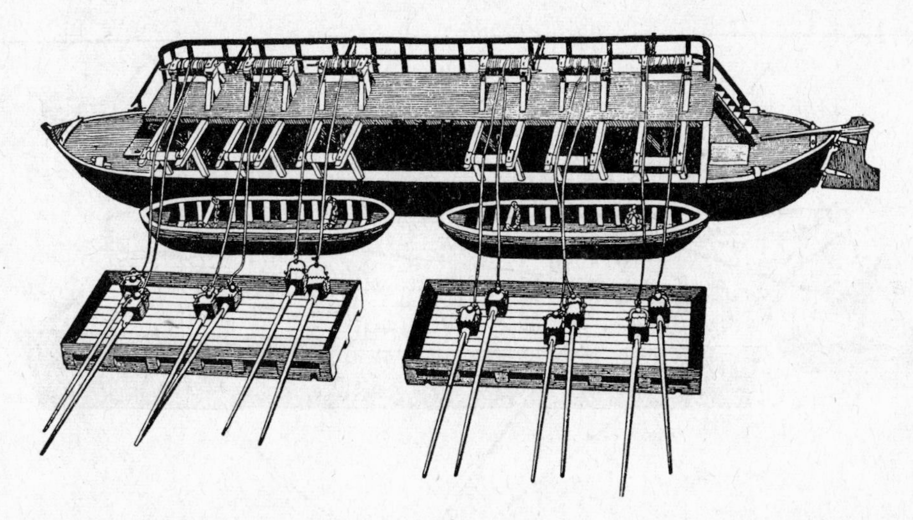

FIGURE 339—*Model of an early ladle-dredger, showing the ladles which were raised and lowered by the winches. Men standing in the small boats used the long handles to guide the ladles.*

with two treadmills, the larger one for hauling and lifting the bucket and the smaller one for its return movement. An example of such a dredger, dated 1745, is shown in figure 340. At first sight these designs are bewildering: a large bucket at the end of a heavy pole, about 14 m long, seems to move through water and air as if some giant handled the pole. It is reminiscent of Goethe's poem *Der Zauberlehrling* which inspired Paul Dukas's well known symphonic poem *L'apprenti sorcier*; in that tale, an incantation made a broom start its sweeping action without being touched by man.

In the French dredger the movements of the hand-operated device were faithfully followed when it was mechanized: such imitation in a mechanical device is commonplace in the history of invention. As in digging with a spade or dredging with a bag, the spoon was first applied to the ground, then moved forward towards the stern of the boat. The pole was tilted a little to prevent spilling during the raising of the bucket.

The two treadmills are mounted on the same boat, which has on each side a pole with a metal bucket. Each pole passes through a horizontal guiding-slot about 3 m above the water. A chain passes from each bucket over a pulley (E) on the stern of the boat and then horizontally to the shaft of the large treadwheel. Here the chains are wound on the shaft, one clockwise, the other anti-clockwise, and the last link of each chain is attached to the shaft near the nave of the tread-wheel. Thus, when one bucket is hauled to the stern and finally raised, the chain

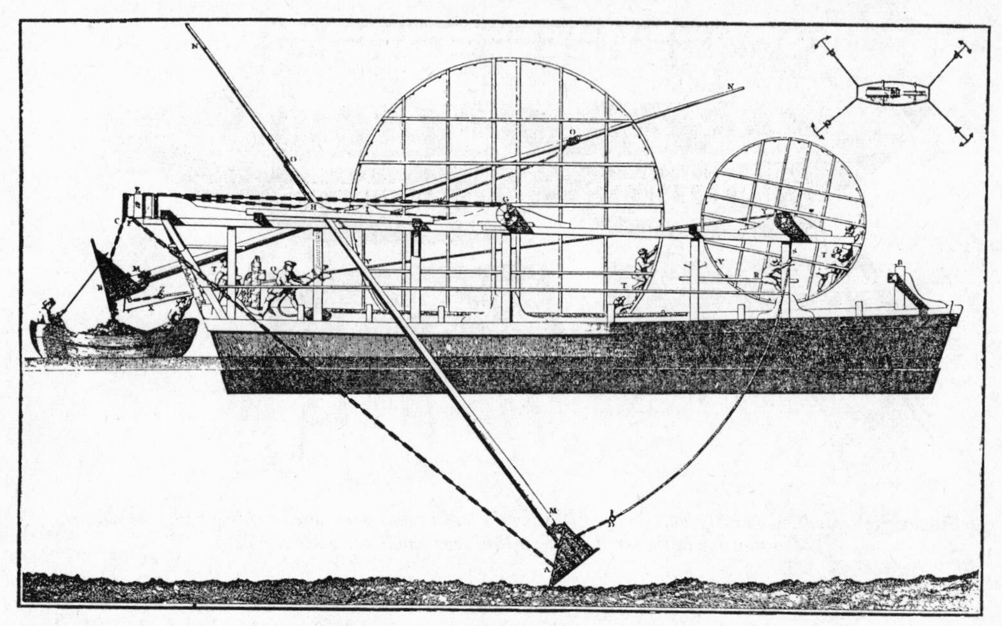

FIGURE 340—*French pontoon-dredger, with power supplied by treadmills, 1745.*

of the other one is paid out, as in Van Wesel's dredger. Cables are similarly wound on the shaft of the smaller wheel. This dredger carried a crew of six—a foreman (shown twice), two workmen in each wheel, and an ordinary seaman (S).

When on the bottom of the river, in the position shown in figure 340, the bucket is hauled to the left by the chain, and would fail to dig into the soil were it not for the fact that the foreman restricts the upward movement of the pole by means of a rope fixed to it at O. This rope passes over a pulley (H) and is controlled by the foreman at P. The pole gradually comes into a perpendicular position and then tilts from one end (H) of the guiding-slot to the other end (I). As a result the bucket comes into a position in which it will hold the mud that it has grasped. Meanwhile the smaller wheel has paid out the rope attached to the bucket, but this is then stopped, or at least checked, by the seaman, with the result that the bucket is lifted out of the water. The foreman leaves his position and opens the rear door of the bucket by releasing a catch on it with a boat-hook (X), thus discharging the mud into a mud-hopper brought under the bucket.

In both treadwheels the workmen then go to the other side (from T to V) in order to reverse the motion, bringing the bucket back to its original position relative to the boat. Before the next cut begins the boat can be moved transversely by means of the moorings, shown in the corner of the drawing.

The development of the French pontoon-dredgers cannot be attributed to a single inventor, but Antoine Macary seems to have had a great share in it. He shows the construction in its most perfect form in his Dutch patent [2] of 1763. This was for a dredger built in 1756 for deepening the canal and the harbour of Dunkirk. In a complete cycle, taking 8 to 9 minutes, it raised 72 cu ft of mud and sand from a depth of 15 ft. The smaller treadmill was mounted on a separate boat, in front of the main pontoon and connected to it by means of a wooden frame. This frame had slots for the poles of four buckets, again working in couples, each bucket containing 18 cu ft of mud. The mud was discharged into a mud-hopper brought between the two boats. Otherwise the construction was practically the same as that described above.

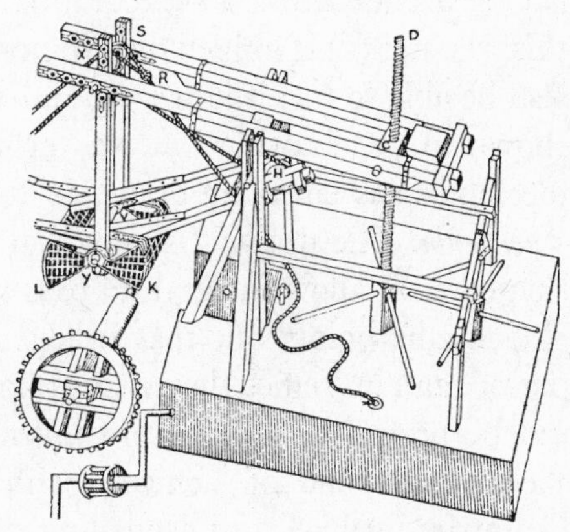

FIGURE 341—*Grab-dredger, 1597.*

Such pontoon-dredgers worked in several French harbours (for example, Toulon and Brest) and in Holland (Middelburg, Helvoet, Enkhuizen).

(*d*) *The grab-dredger.* Verantius informs us that in his time (about 1600) several devices could be seen in Venice for removing silt and sand from the bottom of the sea, but that one he had invented [1] could reach deeper and worked faster. It had two pontoons, between which was suspended a grab in the form of a pair of tongs. This could be lowered to the bottom and, after being closed by means of the cables of two windlasses, could be lifted by a winch turned by a treadmill. The mud-hopper was brought under the grab when this was lifted.

In a book of 1597 Lorini (b 1540) describes one of the Venetian dredgers improved according to his own proposals. As shown in figure 341, a wooden frame has been mounted on a square pontoon and carries a horizontal beam. Also mounted on the pontoon is a vertical screw (D) passing through a nut on the inboard end of the beam. Adjustably hinged to the outward end of the beam are two vertical bars (XY) bearing at their lower end the axle (YV) of a grab (LK). The outer half (L) of the grab has two arms reaching above the pontoon, where their ends are connected by cross-bars carrying a pulley (H). In the same way the inside half of the grab has two arms with cross-bars and pulley, though these are not included in the drawing. A rope divides (R) into two branches running over pulleys (S). One of these branches passes over the pulley (H) and its end is brought back and fixed to some point near the pulleys (S). The other branch is in the same way connected to the other half of the grab, so that by hauling the rope the grab is closed. The lifting of the grab is effected by turning the screw (D); to allow this, the nut (C) is hinged on two horizontal pins of the beam. The screw should also be able to turn slightly around a horizontal axis on the pontoon; this is not shown in the drawing but was probably well known in the art, for a similar mechanism is correctly drawn in the figure of a crane in folio 37 of Besson's *Theatrum*. The drawing shows that the front side of the pontoon has been so shaped as to allow the grab to pass with its arms and pulley.

Conradis points out that dredgers of this sort were employed over a long period, and in Venice they were still in common use in the nineteenth century. It can be proved that they were invented before 1561. In February of that year Pietro Venturino of Venice obtained in Brussels a patent [2] for the Low Countries for his art of deepening rivers and other waterways. In November of the same year he was allowed to co-operate with one or two experts who were to act as licensees under his supervision. The text of the patent of February is not known, and the additional patent of November gives no description of the new dredger. However, in 1562 the council of Kampen sent Otto Tengnagel, one of its members, to Antwerp to negotiate with an Italian dredging expert about deepening the Kamperdiep. By July, Tengnagel had accomplished his task, and on 11 September a large committee, together with the town carpenter and 'the Italians who wished to deepen', sailed out in four pilot-boats to examine the situation [4]. Again there is no description of the dredger, but at this stage a complete specification was given of the wooden planks and bars required to make the pontoon. At the author's request Mr W. Hildernisse, a shipbuilding engineer, made a drawing of the pontoon from these data, and evolved the design shown in figure 342. In this he has found a place for all the parts in the specification except one 27-ft bar which was probably intended as a spare part or to make the beam. This investigation gives us the dimensions of the dredgers then in use.

The figure shows that the pontoon has a deeper draught in the bow than in the stern; this, as stated by Lorini, serves to give the necessary buoyancy when lifting the grab. The pontoon has a flat front, not recessed for the passage of the arms of the grab as in Lorini's dredger; but Lorini informs us that his improvements consisted only in the longer beam and in the construction of the grab. It is therefore likely that Venturino was the inventor of the original Venetian dredger.

A few grab-dredgers are known from the eighteenth century, some with ingenious devices for closing the grab. Today the appliance is still widely used to remove mud from confined spaces and corners inaccessible to the bucket-dredger, and occasionally for lifting heavy objects from the water. It is now more commonly employed, however, for moving dry material such as coal and sand.

(*e*) *The wheel-dredger.* As a first example of a dredger with buckets on a rotating wheel a sketch by Leonardo da Vinci has been instanced [1], but this is evidently one of the many sketches he rapidly drew without giving much attention to how the design might be realized. It shows a horizontal shaft, driven by a handle and reduction-gearing. Mounted crosswise on the shaft are four arms ending in open beaks and reaching into the water between two boats, each carrying brackets with bearings for one end of the shaft. The mud was supposed to fall into a mud-hopper between the two boats, but much would have been spilt sideways from the open beaks during the preceding two-thirds of each revolution. There would also have been a difficulty inherent in all wheel-dredgers discharging outwardly, namely that, in order to be able to bring a mud-hopper or even a collecting-plate near enough to the rotating wheel, the latter would have to be of large diameter. In a project of de la Balme, in 1718, a wheel 30-ft in diameter was proposed. In the case of a vertical bucket-chain a movable collecting-plate was applied which was moved below each bucket as soon as it came into the unloading position, and was withdrawn again to allow the next one to pass. It is interesting to note that in Leonardo's sketch the dredging-mechanism served also for hauling on a rope fastened to a pole fixed in the canal; this device would give the whole system a slow forward movement during the dredging. The same feature is found in many later dredgers. Leonardo further conceived the idea of making the wheel-shaft adjustable in height, but he did not describe a method of doing so. A wheel-dredger is said to have been constructed in Berlin in 1630, but if this were ever more than a project it seems to have been unsuccessful.

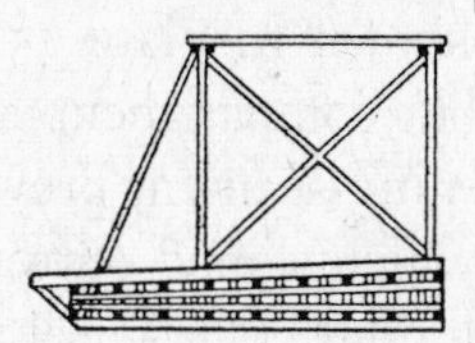

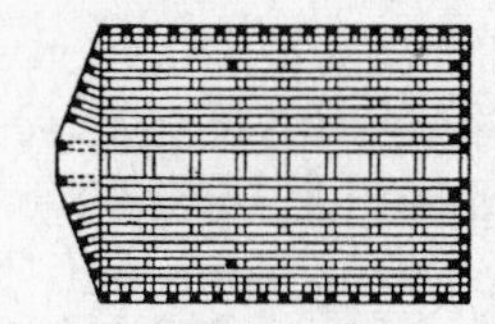

FIGURE 342—*Reconstruction of the dredger of 1562 for the Kamperdiep.*

While the discharge of buckets to the outside of a wheel was difficult, discharge to the inside had its own inconveniences. A project by M. Peltier (1742) for conducting the mud through the spokes to a hollow wheel-shaft would not have been successful, for clogging would soon have occurred. A better method was found earlier, in 1674, by the Dutch painter Jan Van der Heyden, inventor of the fire-engine with suction- and delivery-hoses. We have no drawing of his complete dredger, but there is one of a preliminary model; this forms part of a report made by Van der Heyden in 1675, now in the municipal archives of Amsterdam. As shown in plate 45 A, the wheel had eight compartments for taking up mud. The compartments were open towards the inside of the rim, but a stationary screening-segment prevented the mud escaping until it came above a second screen which sloped outwards and protected the bearing of the wheel against the falling mud. The wheel moved through an opening in the bottom of the pontoon and its shaft was supported by a frame which could be raised or lowered through a short distance: to allow for this the wheel was driven by a lantern-gear with long staves. Van der Heyden reported that he had to surmount great difficulties, but he eventually succeeded, and for some time the dredger did its work on the Voorzaan. The cost of building it was nearly 6000 guilders.

One of the last wheel-dredgers was described by Bouvier in 1831 [1, 5]. This *roue dragueuse* was used in the Beaucaire canal. To make it adjustable in depth a lantern-gear was used, as in the Van der Heyden dredger. The compartments of the wheel delivered the silt at their circumference by way of the outside of the preceding compartment and over a screen. A mud-hopper was kept as near as possible to the screen by guiding-rods that allowed some relative vertical movement.

In general the wheel-dredgers were not successful. They could be used only in shallow waters, and it was difficult to find a satisfactory way of throwing off the mud without soiling shafts and other moving parts.

(*f*) *Chain-dredgers or bucket-dredgers.* A chain fitted with buckets, each carried by a link of the chain, for raising water was known as early as 16 B.C. Marcus Vitruvius Pollio gives a sketch of such an instrument [6]. A tumbler-wheel is mounted on a horizontal shaft driven by a treadwheel. A chain with a bucket on every other link is suspended on the tumbler and its end hangs freely in the water. The buckets throw out their water when turned over by the tumbler. Drawings by Leonardo da Vinci, Agricola, Lorini, and Ramelli [6] prove that water-raising instruments of this character had continued in use.

The first known application of the chain for dredging purposes was the mud-mill, invented in 1589 by Cornelis Dircksz. Muys, the town carpenter of Delft [2].

There is a small illustration of this mill in an engraving of 1606 showing a view of Amsterdam, but a much clearer drawing, reproduced in plate 45 B, accompanied a booklet, *Grondighe Beschrijvinghe van Noort-Hollandt* . . ., annexed to the third edition of Joost Jansz.'s (Bilhamer's) map of that province. In this connexion several authors mention what they call 'an old engraving by E. Vermorcken of 1600'; however, the fact is that this Flemish illustrator lived in the nineteenth century and his drawing does not add to our knowledge of the mud-mill.

A good drawing [7] of the device was made between 1600 and 1620 by Roelandt Savery (certainly not by Pieter Brueghel the elder as assumed by the Vasari Society). The dredger consisted of a boat fitted with two treadwheels each worked by two men. These wheels were mounted aft and drove the top tumbler of a chain. The chain was guided through an inclined wooden sleeve or trough, carrying the other tumbler at its lower end. In contrast with modern bucket-dredgers, the chain moved in such a direction that its ascending part ran below the descending part. The chain had no buckets, but was furnished with flat wooden boards working as pushing-plates in the sleeve, in which they fitted as closely as the movement allowed. At its lower end the sleeve had an entrance reinforced with pointed iron plates for taking up the mud; the latter was forced upwards by the boards as they moved round the lower tumbler. The whole sleeve, with the chain, could be lowered about the axis of the top tumbler by means of a winch. During transport it could be lifted out of the slit in the bottom of the ship through which it reached the bed of the river when working.

Later drawings, for example plate 46 A, show the main parts more clearly. Here the treadwheel on the fore part of the ship is replaced by a horse-mill on the stern, driving the shaft of the top tumbler by means of gearing and a transmission-shaft below the deck. This was the ordinary arrangement, also shown in drawings of 1660, 1700, and 1761. D. Hudig & Company, at Rotterdam, and the Science Museum in London, possess models with the horse-mill carried forward. In this case the long transmission-shaft would have been unnecessary, but the mud would have had to pass below the mill. There is no evidence that such a dredger was built.

The first suggestion for placing a horse-mill on a chain-dredger came from Jacob Jacobssen of Haarlem in 1622 [2]. His construction—with 60 or 70 iron buckets, each taking up as much as half a wheelbarrowful of mud—was said to lift even hard ground, such as sand and clay, from a depth of 14 or 15 ft. This dredger would have been much like a modern bucket-dredger, but it seems doubtful whether such a heavy chain could have been driven with the mechanical means then available. Much later (1785), however, a dredger of this type was worked with a horse-mill by Grundy, at Kingston upon Hull [9].

Muys's mud-mill, with its flat boards, was meant to deal with the soft mud of canals and harbours. Although it has been much used in England, Denmark, Italy, and Germany it is generally known as the mud-mill of Amsterdam, where it did its work until well into the nineteenth century in competition with the first steam-dredgers [1]. In the eighteenth century about five mud-mills were constantly at work on the IJ,[1] each with four men and about three horses; two reserve horses were kept in a stable on board. Van Veen [8] mentions that Amsterdam levied mud-taxes to cover the expenses of dredging, and that between 1778 and 1793 the tax totalled 1 598 000 florins; this large sum gives an idea of the scale on which the dredging of the IJ was necessary. However, the bar across the Zuiderzee (Pampus) could not be removed by such means, and large laden ships could pass it only with the aid of 'camels'.

Muys obtained a patent both from the States of Holland and from the States-General, after the former had satisfied themselves that a machine which he had built in Delfshaven would be of great value to the country. They stipulated that Muys should not proceed with his invention before a committee had fixed the remuneration payable to him by towns wishing to build such dredgers during the twelve-year term of the patent. Two months later (May 1589) this committee fixed the sum as 200 carolus guilders for each of the eleven largest towns and 150 for each of the smaller.

In those days the States used to ask for some specification, drawing, or model before granting a patent. In most cases such documents are unhappily lost, but in the case of Muys they were not required, since the States had seen the dredger at work. It is only by a lucky chance that we have been able to ascertain the nature of the invention Muys had patented. Some competitors, wishing to praise their own inferior dredging-method, wrote in their patent of August 1589 that it worked much better than the dredger of a master-engineer of Delft (doubtless Muys) 'where the mud is pushed upward along planks'. For those who know the mud-mill this is a clear definition of Muys's invention.

In general terms, Muys's invention was a dredger with an inclined chain running over an upper and a lower tumbler, taking up the mud near the bottom and throwing it out above, its depth in the water being adjustable by a swinging movement of the chain around the axis of the top tumbler. Such a definition would cover all modern bucket-dredgers.

A vertical chain-dredger with buckets was designed and built in 1752 by

[1] In Dutch, IJ is a single character.

de Lonce [1]; it had one top tumbler and two below, 1 m apart. The chain had four buckets, which took up mud during their horizontal travel between the tow lower tumblers. This dredger was used in clearing foundations for bridges on the Loire. A note on a sketch preserved at the university of Leiden proves that a dredger of this type was built at Rouen in 1797.

It was also in the second half of the eighteenth century that dredgers with inclined chains began to be fitted with buckets; improved mechanical devices—especially geared wheels and steel plates for the buckets—made this possible.

In some cases the buckets were hauled over the ground by a slack part of the chain [1]; but on a trip to London in 1830 Henz, a German engineer, saw a dredger fitted with an 8-hp steam-engine in which the buckets passing the bottom tumbler-wheel were pressed into the ground by the weight of the inclined chain of buckets. This machine had guiding-bars fitted with cast iron rolls, to reduce the friction, along which the buckets moved. It was used to raise gravel for making macadam roads.

The first steam-dredger was built about 1796, when Boulton & Watt mounted a 4-hp steam-engine on an existing ladle-dredger employed in Sunderland harbour [1], in order to save the wages of the men operating the four ladles. In 1802 John Rennie advised the Hull dock company to replace the horse-mill of a bucket-dredger by a steam-engine. It was not until 1804 that this project was carried out, however, and in the meantime Oliver Evans had forestalled Rennie by building the first steam-dredger with a bucket-chain, for the Philadelphia docks. The introduction of steam raised new problems. A treadmill or the horse-mill stopped when the resistance on the chain became too strong—for example, when a bucket met a heavy stone. In the case of a steam-engine some yielding part, such as a friction-coupling or belt-drive, became necessary. An alternative was to provide some easily replaceable element which would break at a certain load; this was proposed by Jessop, who designed a steam-dredger for the Caledonian canal in 1805 [1].

Accessories. The mud-hopper, discharging from underneath, was very suitable for dumping the mud into the sea. It was proposed by Stevin in his patent of 1589 [2], and later, in 1594 or possibly 1617, Verantius claimed to have invented a mud-hopper of that type.

A drawing made in 1742 by Martin Peltier [1] shows a construction in which the side-walls of the central compartment for the mud converge to the discharging-doors in the bottom of the vessel. Buoyancy was obtained by compartments between this central one and the side of the boat. This is still a common arrangement, but it seems to some extent to have fallen out of use in the nineteenth century. In his patent of 1830 [10] a well known Dutch contractor of dredging-works, S. T. Kater Czn, says that the discharging of 40 cu m used to take 2 days, whereas it was performed in from 12 to 20 minutes by a boat that he had invented. In this boat, which was used with great success, the buoyancy compartment was at the bottom, under the floor of the mud compartment, which sloped towards doors in both sides of the boat.

It is not possible to discuss here the various means developed for the destruction of rocks, heavy trunks, or roots on the bottom of canals or rivers, but one of the earliest devices for that purpose deserves mention. The Bayerische Staatsbibliothek at Munich possesses a manuscript of Giovanni Fontana which, according to the catalogue, dates from about 1420. It contains two sketches of pontoons fitted with a spike, reaching to the bottom of the river through a central opening in the pontoon. Underwater obstructions could be broken up by repeated blows with the spike, and possibly the idea derived from contemporary agricultural practice. In one of these appliances the spike is dropped vertically. The other has an interesting mechanism, shown by Conradis [1] though without a clear description of its working. To the drawing a cryptographic note[1] has been added. The drawing shows an inclined semicylindrical sleeve hinged on a horizontal axis above the pontoon. The spike is chisel-shaped and its rounded end is guided by the sleeve. Both the sleeve and the spike are sharpened at the end. Initially the sleeve is lowered to the bottom, its hinged suspension allowing regulation of its setting with regard to both depth and inclination. The spike is then dropped several times, its downward movement being effected both by gravity and by the cable of a winch. In this way obstructions consisting of stone or wood could doubtless have been broken up.

REFERENCES

[1] CONRADIS, H. 'Die Naßbaggerung bis zur Mitte des 19. Jahrhundert.' Verein Deutsche Ingenieure, Berlin. 1940.

[2] DOORMAN, G. 'Patents for Inventions in the Netherlands during the 16th, 17th and 18th Centuries.' Netherlands Patent Board. Nijhoff, The Hague. 1942.

Idem. 'Octrooien voor uitvindingen in de Nederlanden uit de 16e-18e eeuw.' Netherlands Patent Board. Nijhoff, The Hague. 1940.

STEVIN, S. Patent G.7.

ENTEN, P. P. Patent G.68 (for his original drawing, see DOORMAN, G., *Ingenieur*, *'s Grav.*, **67**, A220, 1955).

[1] We are indebted to the Bayerische Staatsbibliothek for the text, as deciphered by Herr W. Meyer: Cavum canale dicitur opus novum eo quod cavare lectos potest aquarum ruere primo permititur unum lanceatorium deinde reliquam per illud et frangit nedum molua sed dura similiter. ('A new work in which the beds of streams are dug out is called a hollow canal. First, a spike is allowed to fall down heavily; then the other piece [scoop] after it; not only soft material but hard likewise is broken up.')

VAN WESEL, D. Patent G.278. (For D. Van Wesel and also J. van der Heyden, see DOORMAN, G., *Ingenieur*, *'s Grav.*, **63**, A414–18, 1951.)

VENTURINO, P. Patent K.2. (See DOORMAN, G., *Ingenieur*, *'s Grav.*, **56**, A213, 1941.)

MUYS, C. D. Patents G.6 and H.5. (See DOORMAN, G., *Ingenieur*, *'s Grav.*, **63**, A415, 1951; **64**, A83, 1952.)

JACOBSSEN, J. Patent G.209.

MACARY, A. Patents H.250 and G., Dec. 1763. (See CONRADIS, H. Ref. [1], p. 113.)

[3] SMEATON, J. 'John Smeaton's Diary of his Journey to the Low Countries, 1755, from the original MS. in the Library of Trinity House, London' (with an introduction by A. TITLEY), p. 24. Newcomen Society Extra Publication No. 4, London. 1938.

[4] UITTERDIJK, J. N. *Bijdr. Gesch. Overijssel*, **10**, 66–73, 1890.

[5] 'Annales des ponts et chaussées, 1831 à 1840', 1831, 2e semestre, p. 352, Pl. XVI. Paris. 1843.

[6] BECK, T. 'Beiträge zur Geschichte des Maschinenbaues' (2nd enl. ed.). Verein Deutsche Ingenieure, Berlin. 1900.

[7] ZIMMER, G. F. *Trans. Newcomen Soc.*, **4**, Pl. II, 1923–4.

[8] VAN VEEN, J. 'Dredge, Drain, Reclaim', p. 78. Nijhoff, The Hague. 1948.

[9] "History of the Dredging Machine." *Mechanic's Mag.*, **39**, 307, 1843.

[10] DOORMAN, G. 'Het Nederlandsche Octrooiwezen en de techniek der 19e eeuw', figure on p. 173. Netherlands Patent Board. Nijhoff, The Hague. 1947.

Ladle-dredger, c *1760*.

22

TELEGRAPHY

G. R. M. GARRATT

It has been said that the history of the art of communication is the history of the human race. While such a statement is perhaps too sweeping, it is undoubtedly a fact that the development of communication is an integral part of the growth of civilization. Every improvement in the speed and facility with which thoughts and ideas can be exchanged has had its social or economic effect, and we can appreciate fully the significance and trend of historical, social, and political developments only if we view them against the background of the contemporary state of the art of communication.

The hundred years with which we are here particularly concerned was one of special interest, for at its beginning the fastest means of communication over long distances was that of a rider on horseback, while by its end the electric telegraph was firmly established. Although the earliest proposal for a system of electric telegraphy was made as early as 1753, it was nearly ninety years before a really practicable scheme was evolved. The intervening period was, as we shall see, filled with suggestions and experiments, mostly of a somewhat unpractical nature but all indicative of that instinctive urge towards the improvement of communication which has been such a marked characteristic of the human race.

Before describing the stages by which the electric telegraph evolved from its earliest beginnings, it is necessary to devote some attention to a review of the system of visual telegraphs which matured in France during the Revolutionary period, and which was for nearly forty years an important factor in contemporary naval and military operations.

The scene may be set by recalling the situation in France during 1793–4. The Revolution was at its height, and France was assailed on every side by the allied forces of Britain, Holland, Prussia, Austria, Spain, the Italian States, Hanover, and Hesse. The cities of Marseilles and Lyons were in revolt, and a British fleet held Toulon. Three factors alone were on the side of the French in their seemingly hopeless position: the lack of co-ordination between the allied forces due to their inadequate lines of communication; the disunity of allied purpose; and the single-minded determination of Lazare Carnot in establishing coherence among all sections of the French army.

In this situation, the advent of the Chappe telegraph was one of the major factors that eventually turned the scale in favour of the French forces. It must not be supposed, however, that Claude Chappe (1763–1805) was the sole originator of visual telegraphs. Primitive methods of signalling were almost certainly in use 4000 years ago, and the Romans are known to have made wide use of towers for signalling purposes. The invention of the telescope did much to make visual telegraphy more practicable, and Robert Hooke (1635–1703), in a discourse to the Royal Society in 1684, gave a vivid and comprehensive outline of the requirements for an effective system. There were few practical details to which Hooke did not refer, but it was one thing to describe such an invention and another altogether to carry it through all the troubles of development, and then to operate it over hundreds of miles in the conditions existing at the close of the eighteenth century.

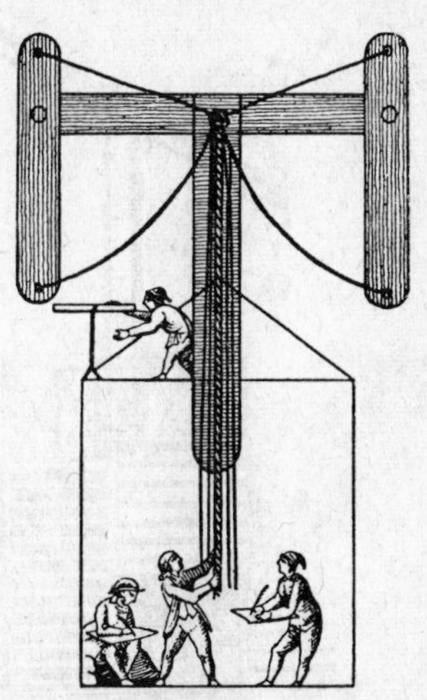

FIGURE 343—*Chappe's semaphore telegraph.*

Claude Chappe was one of a family of ten of whom only seven survived infancy. In the disturbed conditions of the times, he and his brothers found themselves without regular employment, and early in 1790 they allied themselves enthusiastically to the new régime of republicanism then sweeping the country. During a period of enforced leisure in the summer of that year, Chappe determined to devise a system of communication (figure 343) that would enable the central government to receive intelligence and transmit orders in the shortest possible time. His investigation included a study of the electric telegraph (p 651). During the next two years he experimented with several different forms of visual telegraphs. On two occasions his apparatus at the Étoile in Paris was destroyed by fanatical mobs in the belief that he was communicating with the imprisoned Louis XVI. Not discouraged by these reverses, he persevered with his experiments and by the summer of 1793 the value of his proposals had been recognized. He was accorded the title of *Ingénieur-Télégraphe* and was ordered to establish a line of telegraph stations between Paris and Lille, a distance of 144 miles. Within a year the line of fifteen stations, each within sight of the next, was complete, and the first telegram to be transmitted over such an organized system was that sent from Lille to Paris on 15 August 1794 informing the government that their forces had retaken Le Quesnoy. A fortnight later, another message, which gave rise to scenes of wild enthusiasm in the French capital, told of the recapture of Condé. The Chappe semaphore consisted of a wooden beam pivoted at its centre so that it could be rotated in a vertical plane. At each end of the beam were additional movable arms, and a large number of configurations was therefore possible (figure 344).

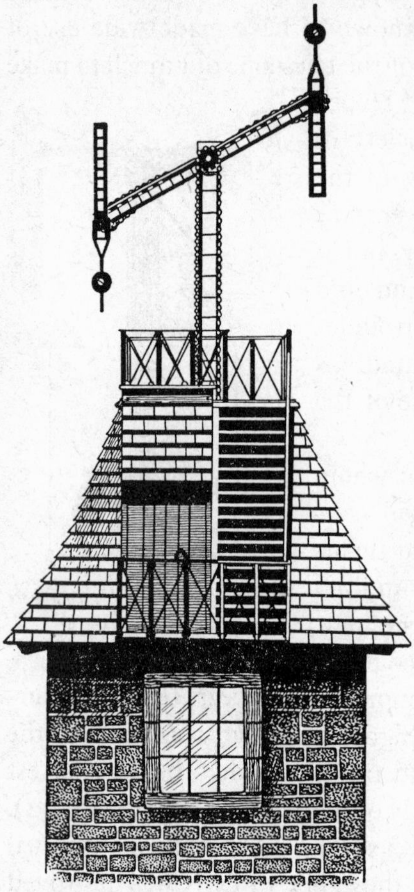

FIGURE 344—*Model of a Chappe telegraph tower.*

Lines of Chappe telegraphs were established during the next few years between Paris and Strasbourg and between Paris and Brest, but since each station in the line had to be within sight of the next—there were fifty between Paris and Strasbourg—the difficulties of administration and the wages of the staff were considerable. It is not surprising that financial troubles were incessant, at least until the service was linked with a lottery scheme.

Chappe died in 1805, probably by suicide occasioned by the strain and anxiety to which he had been subjected, but for fifty years the system of telegraphs he had instituted covered the greater part of France. In 1852, when the Chappe system was finally superseded by the electric telegraph, the network covered a total distance of more than 3000 miles and included 556 separate stations.

In England, reports of the working of the Chappe line between Lille and Paris were received during the autumn of 1794, and an illustrated description appeared in 'The Sun' on 15 November. Although it is not uncommon for similar inventions to be made quite independently yet almost simultaneously in widely different places, it seems likely that it was these reports from France that stimulated Lord George Murray and John Gamble to propose schemes for visual telegraph systems to the Admiralty early in 1795. Murray's scheme, which was adopted, was very similar to one of Chappe's earlier proposals. It employed a large wooden framework provided with six movable shutters which, exhibited in different combinations, provided sixty-three distinct signals. A chain of these stations, fifteen in all, was erected for the

Admiralty between London and Deal at an expenditure of nearly £4000—including the cost of an eight-guinea clock and two twelve-guinea telescopes at each station—and it was reported that a signal could be sent and acknowledged within two minutes.

A similar chain of ten stations was erected to link the Admiralty with Portsmouth, and some of the prominences upon which the stations were erected are still known locally as 'Telegraph Hill'. Yet another chain was projected in 1801, to link London with Yarmouth, but during the brief lull in the fighting with France marked by the Peace of Amiens (1802) the plan was postponed; it was not in fact completed until 1807. Another important chain was that between London and Plymouth, completed during the summer of 1806.

The first visual telegraph, on the semaphore principle, in the United States was built in 1800 by Jonathan Grout. It was a 65-mile line connecting Martha's Vineyard with Boston, and its purpose was to transmit news about shipping.

Between 1811 and 1814 the shutter system was gradually replaced in Britain by the superior Chappe semaphore, but with the defeat of Napoleon and his banishment to Elba all sense of urgency was lost and many of the telegraph stations were abandoned. The relaxation was but an interlude, however, for when Napoleon escaped and landed in France in the spring of 1815 the telegraph-lines were hastily restored, and were converted to the semaphore system where this had not already been done. The revival was short-lived, however, for such was the dependence of the telegraph on a state of war that upon the final defeat of Napoleon at Waterloo, and the ending of the long struggle with France, the telegraph stations were abandoned.

Within a few years an effort was made to revive them, and the line to Portsmouth was not finally closed until 1847. Essentially, however, the visual telegraphs had been an instrument of Admiralty, and it is not surprising that the service tended to fall into disuse when deprived of the stimulating effect of war. The semaphore telegraphs were extravagant in man-power, for the stations were seldom more than 8 miles apart; they were subject to interruption by adverse weather conditions; and they were of little use to the individual citizen. With these handicaps it was perhaps inevitable that they should fail to survive a long period of peace; in any case, the advent of the electric telegraph about 1840 rendered the semaphore system obsolete.

The history of the electric telegraph is generally considered to start in the year 1753, when a remarkable letter, signed only with the letters C. M. (p 649), appeared in the 'Scots Magazine' of 17 February. Before describing the proposals made by C. M., however, it is appropriate briefly to review the background against which they were made, and to bear in mind that knowledge of the science of electricity (vol V, chs 9 and 10) was still only rudimentary.

It had been known from very early times that a piece of amber, when rubbed, acquired the property of attracting small pieces of straw or paper. Such phenomena, however, attracted little attention and were considered of no practical significance until near the close of the sixteenth century, when William Gilbert (1540–1603) of Colchester collected together various scattered observations on them and, adding many of his own, laid the foundations of the science of electricity in his great work, *De magnete*, published in 1600. It was Gilbert who coined the word 'electric' from the Greek *ēlektron*, meaning amber. Some advance was made by Robert Boyle (1627–91), who in 1675 published a small book on the origin and production of electricity, but though he speculated on the causes of electrical phenomena he was no more able to offer a satisfactory explanation than the Greek philosophers had been, more than 2000 years earlier.

An important advance was made between 1660 and 1663 by Otto von Guericke (1602–86) when, in the course of some experiments that he was carrying out on another subject, he constructed a large ball of sulphur that could be rotated on a spindle. Pressing his bare hand against the ball as it revolved, he observed that it became strongly electrified, and he thus unintentionally became the inventor of the first machine to generate electricity.

Development of the frictional machine proceeded slowly. The sulphur ball was replaced by one of glass, probably by Newton in 1675. In 1733, J. H. Winckler (1703–70) mounted a leather cushion in contact with the glass to act as a rubber, and G. M. Bose (1710–61) introduced the prime conductor in 1738. In 1742 Andrew Gordon (1712–51) substituted a glass cylinder for the rather awkward globe, and thus by the middle of the eighteenth century the frictional machine was established as a fairly reliable generator of electricity.

Familiar as we all are today with the basic facts of electrical practice—that metallic wires act as conductors, and that rubber, porcelain, mica, and other such substances act as insulators—we must remember that there was once a time when even these elementary facts were unknown. It would take too long to describe here the remarkable series of experiments carried out by Stephen Gray, a pensioner of the Charterhouse, between 1720 and his death in 1736, but his discovery of the basic principles of electrical conduction and insulation in 1729 laid the foundations upon which the electric telegraph was to be built. Before his time there had been no attempt to transmit electric charges over a distance, even of a few feet.

Among Gray's many experiments were a number carried out in the summer of

1729, in which he showed that electric charges could be transmitted along such materials as moistened pack-thread and brass wire, but not along silk threads, glass rods, or sticks of resin. In the course of his experiments, he succeeded in transmitting electric charges to a distance of nearly 300 yds, and it is of interest to note that, in so doing, he had in fact set up all the essential elements of an electric telegraph: a source of electricity at the sending-end, an insulated line, some form of indicator at the receiving-end (Gray used a down feather), and an earth-return circuit, although the function of this last was not suspected at the time.

Before we come to C. M.'s electric telegraph, one further invention must be briefly mentioned—that of the Leyden jar in 1745. This was important not so much for its uses in telegraphy—to which, indeed, it had little direct application —as for the manner in which the discovery of its properties aroused widespread interest in electrical phenomena throughout Europe. For the first time, electric charges could be stored. Popular demonstrations and experiments were carried out in many places, and it became commonplace to transmit an electric shock through a circle of twenty or thirty persons, each holding hands with the next. It was shown that the shock was experienced simultaneously by all those in the circle. The experiment was repeated on a grand scale by the Abbé Nollet (1700–70), and when a shock was passed round a circle, more than a mile in circumference, in which some 200 Carthusian monks were linked together by lengths of iron wire, it became evident that the speed of transmission was exceedingly high. Here, then, were all the requirements for an electric telegraph, and it is not surprising that within the space of a few years a fully detailed proposal was published for the employment of electricity for the transmission of intelligence.

It is convenient to classify the various forms of electric telegraph proposed between 1750 and 1850 under three headings, according to the basis of their operation:

(*a*) Telegraphs employing static electricity.
(*b*) Electrochemical telegraphs.
(*c*) Electromagnetic telegraphs.

This classification serves to indicate how the development of the telegraph was influenced and stimulated by the discoveries of Galvani, Volta, Ampère, and others in the basic science of electricity.

Telegraphs employing static electricity. The name of the author of the remarkable letter published over the initials C. M. in the 'Scots Magazine' in 1753 is not known. Although it has been attributed by some to Charles Morrison and by others to Charles Marshall, the evidence in favour of either is weak and the author's identity must remain uncertain. Whatever his name, his letter constituted a fully detailed specification for an electric telegraph employing static electricity. Although it is doubtful whether he ever carried his proposals to the stage of practical experiment, it is clear that he foresaw nearly all the difficulties that would be encountered.

C. M.'s letter is too lengthy to quote in full but, briefly, he proposed that 'a set of wires, equal in number to the letters of the alphabet, be extended horizontally between two given places, parallel to one another and each of them about an inch distant from the next to it. At every twenty yards let them be fixed in glass, or jewellers' cement, to some firm body, both to prevent them touching the earth, or any other non-electric,[1] or from breaking by their own gravity. . . .' The letter goes on to explain in detail how the wires are to be connected to the prime conductor of the electric machine when it is desired to signal a particular letter. At the receiver, 'let a ball be suspended from every wire, and about a sixth or an eighth of an inch below the balls, place the letters of the alphabet, marked on bits of paper, or any other substance that may be light enough to rise to the electrified balls. . . . Having set the electrical machine a-going as in ordinary experiments, suppose I am to pronounce the word Sir; with a piece of glass or any other *electric per se* I strike the wire S, so as to bring it in contact with the barrel, then i, then r, all in the same way; and my correspondent, almost in the same instant, observes these several characters rise in order to the electrified balls at the ends of the wires. . . .'

C. M.'s letter attracted little attention at the time and, detailed though it was, it did not contribute materially to the development of practical telegraphy. Of historical and technical interest for the manner in which it proposed to apply the latest advances in the electrical art, it may have failed to find practical uses for economic reasons. Moreover, it is to be doubted whether the civilized world was yet ready for an electric telegraph, especially one which required the use of twenty-six insulated wires for its operation.

During the thirty years that followed the publication of this letter, a number of somewhat similar schemes were suggested, notably by Bozolus (1767), Odier (1773), and Le Sage (1782), but, so far as is known, none ever reached the stage of practical experiment. In 1787, however, M. Lomond in Paris gave demonstrations on a small scale, his scheme being an improvement on C. M.'s in that he employed only a single conductor, with a pith-ball electroscope as an indicator.

[1] An electric material was one which could be electrified by rubbing, that is, an insulator. A non-electric was thus what we term a conductor.

By means of a pre-arranged code, the receiving-operator was able to translate the motions of the pith-balls into letters of the alphabet, but perhaps the very slow rate of signalling discouraged development on a larger scale.

The semaphore telegraph developed so successfully by Chappe has already been noticed, but it is not generally known that before this work he had, in 1790, carried out extensive experiments with an electric telegraph. His scheme made use of two clocks, the pendulums of which were carefully adjusted to swing in unison. Around the seconds dials, he marked the numerals 1–9 and 0. Signalling was achieved by the discharge of a Leyden jar, the receiving operator noting the numeral indicated by the seconds-hand at the instant of discharge. Chappe seems, however, to have been discouraged by the difficulties he encountered in insulating the conducting wire, and abandoned his electrical scheme in favour of the visual telegraph which seemed, at that time, to offer prospects of more immediate success.

Less daunted by the apparent difficulties inherent in an electrical system was Don Francisco Salvá of Barcelona who, in 1795, put forward a multi-wire scheme in which he proposed that the discharge of Leyden jars at the transmitter should be detected as electric shocks experienced by the operators at the receiver. His proposals, which included a scheme of submarine telegraphy, were described in great detail, but in spite of the patronage of the Spanish court it does not appear that his ideas ever found more practical application than that of a purely local demonstration. There is a report that in 1798 a modification of Salvá's scheme, using only a single wire, was actually constructed between Madrid and Aranjuez, a distance of about 26 miles, but the absence of reports on the working of this line is in such striking contrast to the wealth of detail regarding the original proposals that its existence must be regarded as uncertain.

The last, and perhaps the most interesting, of the telegraphs employing static electricity which we shall notice is that described and demonstrated by Francis Ronalds in 1816. Born in 1788, and originally intended for a career in commerce, Ronalds seems to have taken unkindly to such prospects and from 1812 onwards devoted himself to chemistry and physics, experimenting in static electricity. He had probably observed the slow, cumbersome, and unreliable system of semaphore telegraphs then employed by the Admiralty, and it is evident that he devoted a great deal of time and expense during the summer of 1816 to a large-scale experiment on the use of electricity for the purposes of telegraphy.

At that time Ronalds was living at a house in Hammersmith, London, the garden of which was 600 ft long. In order to demonstrate the speed at which electrical impulses travelled, he erected a pair of large wooden frames, from the bars of which he suspended a total of eight miles of wire. To one end of the wire he connected a frictional machine which charged the line; to the other he connected an indicator in the form of a pair of pith-balls which diverged when the line was charged. At the sending-station Ronalds provided a dial which was marked with the letters of the alphabet and could rotate behind a plate through an aperture in which one letter at a time could be seen. A similar dial was provided at the receiver, and both were rotated synchronously by means of clockwork, a scheme not unlike that proposed, but abandoned, by Chappe in 1790. The line was charged continuously by the frictional machine, but was discharged by the sending-operator at the moment when the desired letter appeared in the aperture of his instrument. The receiving operator would see the pith-balls of his indicator collapse and he would note the letter which was at the same moment exposed in the aperture of his dial.

Having satisfied himself that the system would work with an overhead line, Ronalds then proceeded to construct an underground line 525 ft in length in a trench 4 ft deep in his garden. He insulated the copper wire with lengths of glass tube, which were encased in soft pitch in long troughs of wood. Many years later, in 1862, a length of this line was discovered in the Hammersmith garden, and a short specimen is preserved in the Science Museum at South Kensington.

Were Ronalds's proposals really practicable? Had they the makings of an efficient electric telegraph? In the light of later knowledge, the answers must almost certainly be in the negative, but there is no doubt that his experiments constituted a serious attempt to solve what was, at that time, a very difficult problem. Their scale and success were certainly such as to merit official investigation. It was unfortunate, therefore, that when Ronalds offered to demonstrate his telegraph to the Admiralty he was informed that 'telegraphs of any kind are now wholly unnecessary and no other than the one now in use will be adopted'.

Electrochemical telegraphs. In the closing years of the eighteenth century, the work of Galvani and Volta was responsible not only for introducing a completely new era in the field of electric telegraphy but for laying the essential foundations upon which the practical application of electricity was to be built. In consequence of their work, electricity became available in a low-pressure form, the supply of which was to prove as copious and tractable as that of static electricity had been elusive and capricious. Sooner or later, it is safe to assume, telegraphs dependent on static electricity would have developed into reasonably acceptable forms for practical use. There can be no doubt, however, that the provision of low-pressure voltaic electricity very greatly facilitated the development of convenient and simple devices for the purpose of communication, and in the telegraphs now to be described we shall see how the basic discoveries of Galvani and Volta, and later of Oersted, Ampère, Arago, and Sturgeon, were applied in the development of practical systems.

Very briefly, Galvani showed in 1791 that contact between metals and animal tissues often produced muscular contractions which seemed to be of an electrical origin; Volta showed that the effect was due to the generation of electricity arising from the conjunction of two dissimilar metals in a moist body. This led him in 1800 to the invention of his well known column or pile of zinc and silver disks, each pair being separated by pasteboard moistened with brine. Volta's pile constituted the first electric battery. It was soon observed that the maintenance of an electric current was associated with chemical action on the disks of the pile, and it was also shown (Nicholson and Carlisle, 1800) that water could be decomposed into its constituent elements, oxygen and hydrogen, by the passage of an electric current from the pile.

This association of electricity with chemical action quickly resulted in suggestions for a variety of electrochemical telegraphs, the first of which was due to Salvá in 1804. Salvá, as was mentioned earlier, had previously developed a static-electricity telegraph; he now proposed to employ the bubbles of hydrogen that appear at the negative electrode during the electrolytic decomposition of water as the indicator in a telegraph, with one of Volta's piles as the source of electricity. His proposals were published but, lacking development, they were quickly forgotten; thus it was once again shown that an inventor needs both to develop and to exploit his schemes before he can expect either acknowledgement or reward.

Prominent among other inventors of electrochemical telegraphs was S. T. von Soemmering, whose apparatus (figure 345) was described in considerable detail to the Munich Academy of Sciences in the summer of 1809 and was subsequently demonstrated on many occasions. His apparatus, which he had installed at his residence, was very similar to that proposed by Salvá, the only original contribution made by von Soemmering being the fitting of an alarm (seen on the right in the figure) to call the attention of the receiving operator; but so earnestly did he advocate his scheme over a period of several years that he has been widely regarded as its original inventor. Employing no fewer than thirty-five wires between the sender and receiver, however, it was clearly too costly and unpractical for general use, and it is not surprising that the many officials and governments whom von Soemmering approached showed little desire to adopt it.

Among those to whom von Soemmering demonstrated his telegraph in 1810 was Baron Schilling, an attaché at the Russian Embassy at Munich. Greatly impressed with the possibilities of an electric telegraph, Schilling devoted much of his time during the next twenty-seven years to the development of an acceptable system. Since Schilling's instrument later provided the basis of the Cooke and Wheatstone inventions, the friendship between von Soemmering and Schilling was of the utmost consequence in the history of the electric telegraph.

Other forms of chemical telegraph were proposed by a number of inventors during the thirty or forty years following von Soemmering's demonstrations, notably those of Sharpe (1816), Coxe (1816), E. Davy (1838), Smith (1843), and

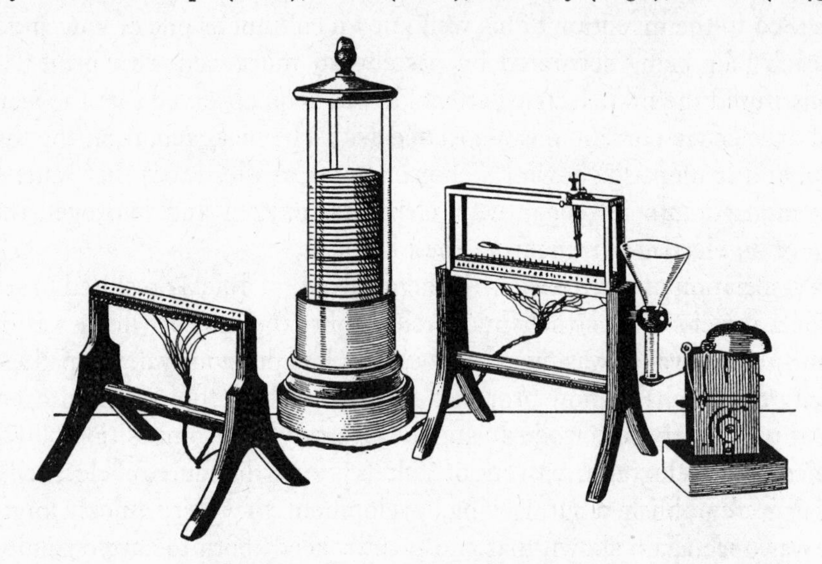

FIGURE 345—*von Soemmering's telegraph, 1809.*

Bain (1846), but none proved of practical value. With the coming of electromagnetism, telegraphy underwent a new orientation.

Electromagnetic telegraphs. For at least one hundred and fifty years preceding 1820, if not a great deal longer, the relationship between magnetism and electricity had been obscure. There were so many obvious analogies that some sort of connexion seemed certain, but in the absence of any steady source of direct current the real nature of the link between magnetic and electric phenomena had not been understood. With the invention of Volta's pile, however, and the subsequent development of various primary cells, it was inevitable that, sooner or later, the true relationship should be disclosed. During the winter of 1819–20 Hans Christian Oersted (1777–1851), professor of physics in the university of Copenhagen, made the vital observation that a magnetic needle was deflected when a current flowed through a wire above it. His observations, first published in Latin in July 1820, aroused the greatest interest, and were immediately followed up by Ampère and Arago in France; by Humphry Davy, Faraday, and Sturgeon in England; by Schweigger and others in Germany; and by Henry in America. Within a few weeks Ampère had published his first memoir on electromagnetism, and Arago had announced his discovery of the magnetizing effect of an electric current.

A few months later, an invention of the greatest importance to telegraphy—that of the galvanometer—was announced by J. S. C. Schweigger (1779–1857) of Halle. Observing that a magnetic needle was deflected in one direction by a current flowing in a wire above it and in the same direction by a reverse current in a wire beneath, he found he could obtain almost twice the deflexion if he arranged the outward-flowing current to pass above the needle and, simultaneously, the return current to pass beneath. The deflexion was doubled again by giving the wire an extra turn around the needle, while a third turn gave nearly six times the original deflexion.

Schweigger's galvanometer, or multiplier as it was first called, was a primitive device consisting merely of a small magnetic compass with a few turns of wire around it, but improvements in its construction were soon made by Ampère and others. It quickly attracted the attention of von Soemmering and Baron Schilling.

Schilling's experience in the diplomatic and military fields, and the close interest that he had paid to the subject of electricity over a number of years, enabled him fully to appreciate the possibilities of Schweigger's multiplier for the purposes of telegraphy. Details and dates in regard to Schilling's early experiments are lacking, but it seems probable that he began experimenting in his spare time about 1822. During the next fifteen years—until his death in 1837—Schilling devised a number of separate arrangements, sometimes using a single multiplier as indicator and sometimes five or six (figure 346). In the case of the single-needle instrument, he used a code, not unlike the later Morse code.

An interesting feature of Schilling's telegraph was the alarm device (figure 346 B), which bore a striking resemblance to that employed some fifteen years earlier by von Soemmering. This device consisted of an additional galvanometer-movement fitted with a horizontal arm so arranged that, when the needle was deflected, it struck a delicately balanced lever which, in falling, operated the detent of an ordinary clockwork alarm.

Although Schilling appears to have travelled widely and to have brought his telegraph to the notice of many, he seems to have made no serious attempt to put it into practical use until 1836. In that year a commission was appointed by the Emperor Nicholas of Russia with a view to installing the telegraph between St Petersburg and the imperial palace at Peterhof. Unfortunately, Schilling died before the plans could be carried into effect. In 1835, however, he had demonstrated his instruments to a Heidelberg professor named Moncke, who had a copy made for use in his own lectures. In March of the following year this instrument was seen by W. F. Cooke.

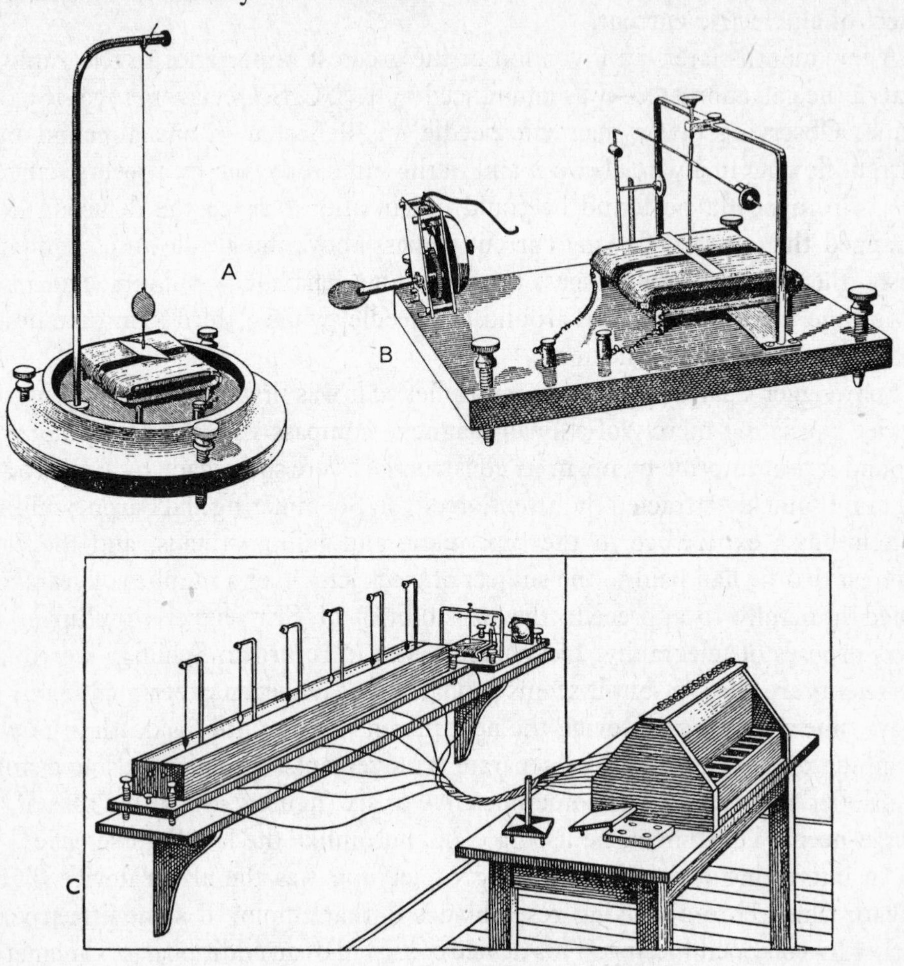

FIGURE 346—*Schilling's telegraph*, c *1825*: (A) *indicator*; (B) *alarm mechanism*; (C) *complete installation.*

William Fothergill Cooke was born in 1806, the son of a doctor, and at the age of twenty joined the East India army. Compelled to relinquish his commission on account of ill health, he had begun to earn a living by anatomical modelling, but his interest in Moncke's instrument led him to devote his whole attention to telegraphy. Returning to England in April 1836, Cooke constructed several forms of telegraph during the following months. One of these it was proposed to install on the Liverpool and Manchester railway, but he met with certain difficulties in the working of the electromagnets and as a result called on Charles Wheatstone (1802–75), professor of natural philosophy at King's College, London. Wheatstone had himself been conducting experiments with telegraphic apparatus, and in view of their joint interests they eventually decided to form a partnership. Their first patent was granted in June 1837, and in the

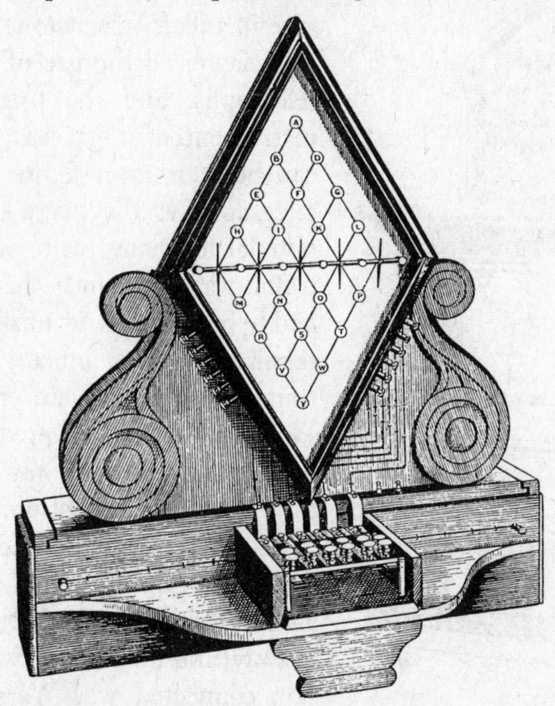

FIGURE 347—*Cooke and Wheatstone's five-needle telegraph. 1837.*

following month a demonstration of their five-needle telegraph (figure 347), working between Euston and Camden Town, a distance of about a mile, was given to the directors of the new London and Birmingham railway.

Disagreement between the directors of the railway company as to the need for a telegraph delayed further action, but in the following year, the directors of the Great Western railway company approved the installation of the telegraph between Paddington and West Drayton, a distance of about 13 miles. This was completed in May 1838, and proved so successful that it was extended to Slough in 1842.

The instruments employed on the Paddington–Slough line were of the double-needle type in which particular letters were signalled by the momentary deflexions of the needles in accordance with a pre-arranged code (figure 348). With the exception of Schilling's telegraph, to which the needle-instruments of the Cooke and Wheatstone telegraphs bore a close resemblance, most earlier telegraphs had been of the type in which each letter had to be specifically indicated, either by a pointer, by bubbles of hydrogen, or, as in Ronalds's instrument, by the appearance of a letter behind an aperture in a dial. Wheatstone himself particularly favoured the use of letter-indicating telegraphs, and the original five-needle instrument of 1837 was of this type, as can be seen from figure 347. His ABC. telegraphs, as they were known, remained popular for many years, particularly where traffic was light and where the telegraph had to be operated by unskilled persons. In regular telegraph offices, however, where trained operators were employed, it was soon found that a predetermined code formed a far quicker way of operating; in time it became almost universal.

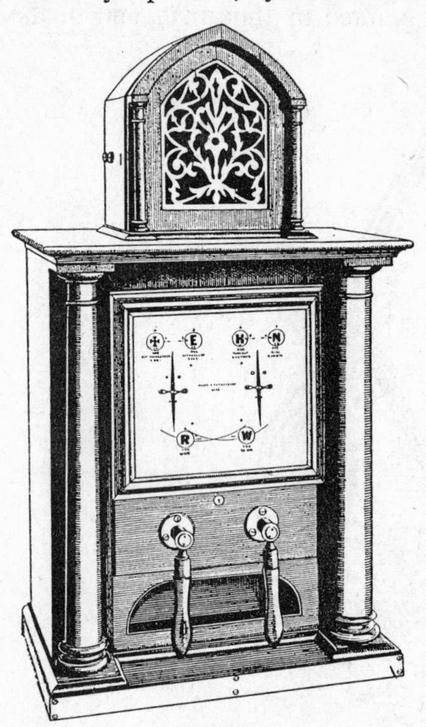

FIGURE 348—*Cooke and Wheatstone's two-needle telegraph. 1842.*

The success of the Paddington–Slough line led to rapid progress. A telegraph had already been installed on the Blackwall railway, and in the next two years Norwich was connected with Yarmouth; London with Gosport and Southampton; Tonbridge with Maidstone; and Wolverton with Peterborough. In 1846 London was linked with Dover. The rate of growth at this period may be deduced from the fact that in 1844 Wheatstone received only £444 in respect of his share of the royalties for newly laid lines, whereas in the following year he received £2775.

The telegraph had as yet attracted little public notice, but in 1845 there occurred an incident that strikingly demonstrated its possibilities. A woman was murdered at Slough and the suspected murderer was seen to board a train for Paddington. A full description of him was telegraphed to Paddington, as the result of which he was recognized on arrival, arrested, and subsequently hanged. It will be remembered that in more recent times a similar incident—the arrest of Crippen in 1910 as he was about to step ashore from an Atlantic liner when fleeing from England—drew public attention to the far-reaching powers of wireless telegraphy.

Until the close of 1845, the commercial interests of Cooke and Wheatstone remained under Cooke's personal management; he also acted as the contractor responsible for the installation of the telegraphs. Upon receiving the order for the London–Dover line, however, it seemed opportune to form a company, and the Electric Telegraph Company was incorporated early in 1846. Such was the progress of the company that by 1852 it was estimated that some 4000 miles of telegraph-lines had been completed in Britain.

Unhappily, a quarrel had persisted between Cooke and Wheatstone since the early days of their partnership, and it is beyond question that the strained relations between them retarded the technical development of the telegraph. As early as 1838, Cooke had had occasion to remonstrate with his partner about his often-repeated claim to be the exclusive inventor of the telegraph. Cooke, while not claiming to have invented the telegraph, had done more than anyone else to make it a practical device, and he strongly resented the manner in which his partner claimed all the credit for himself. The quarrel became almost childish in the manner in which charge and counter-charge were published during a period of some fifteen years. One's sympathy undoubtedly tends to rest with Cooke, but truth lies in the statement made in 1841 that 'it is to the united labours of two gentlemen so well qualified for mutual assistance that we must attribute the rapid progress which this important invention has made during the five years since they have been associated'.

With the founding of the Electric Telegraph Company, Cooke continued to be fully employed with the commercial development of the telegraph and its ever-extending lines, and he was far too busy to undertake any major technical developments. Wheatstone, however, with his academic background, had opportunities for making technical progress, and for many years he continued to devise new and improved forms of telegraphic apparatus. In 1840 he had been responsible for the first serious proposal for a cross-Channel telegraph, and in the same year he brought out the first of his many forms of ABC. telegraphs. In 1841 he invented the first type-printing telegraph, but this particular instrument was before its time and did not come into general use.

The Cooke and Wheatstone telegraph is an example of an invention that evolved more or less logically from previous discoveries and inventions. It was consequently founded upon well tried and established principles, and its success was substantially due to these circumstances. By contrast, the telegraph invented by Samuel Morse about 1835 was original, but as he was technically inexperienced his instrument was crude and unpractical (plate 47 A). His receiver consisted of a pen held in contact with a moving strip of paper. When the receiver was energized the pen was moved by an electromagnet and a notch appeared in the track drawn by the pen. Morse was an artist of some distinction—he was appointed professor of art in the university of New York in 1832—but his idea of developing an electric telegraph would have been frustrated by his lack of technical knowledge if it had not been for the assistance he received from his friend L. D. Gale, and from Joseph Henry (1797–1878), secretary of the Smithsonian Institution. Towards the end of 1837, Morse found an assistant and supporter in Alfred Vail (1807–59), who early in 1838 completely redesigned the telegraph and was instrumental in bringing it to the notice of influential congressmen. Two notable improvements were made: the introduction of relays to extend the range of transmission, and the adoption of the now well known dot-dash code (plate 47 B).

At the end of 1842, Congress was persuaded to vote 30 000 dollars for establishing a telegraph between Washington and Baltimore, a distance of about 40 miles, and this was successfully completed in June 1844. As in England, the next decade was a period during which widespread expansion of the telegraph system took place. A whole network of lines was set up, often by companies that competed with each other until their amalgamation into Western Union in 1856.

In England, as we have seen, many lines were laid down in the years immediately following 1842. The telegraph between London and Dover, opened in 1846, attracted considerable notice and can scarcely have failed to stimulate thoughts of an extension of the line across the Straits of Dover to the continent. Though Wheatstone had first proposed such a link, it fell to the two brothers John and Jacob Brett to pioneer the first submarine telegraph cable between England and France. This was laid on 28 August 1850 (figure 349), but it proved a failure on account of inadequate mechanical strength; a second and successful cable was laid in September 1851.

If the development of the electric telegraph represented one major milestone in the progress of human communications, the development of the submarine cable was another of equal importance. While the one speeded communication within countries, the other linked countries and continents overseas. With the successful laying of submarine cables across the North Sea and in the Mediterranean, it was natural that thoughts should next turn to the laying of a cable across the Atlantic.

The story of the early Atlantic cables is an epic of enterprise, courage, and perseverance in the face of heart-breaking disasters and calamitous losses. The first attempt was made in 1857, but the cable broke and was lost when nearly 350 miles had been laid. A second attempt was made in the spring of 1858, but fresh disasters occurred and it was not until August of the same year that the laying of the cable was completed. Unfortunately it was far from perfect—it had almost certainly been damaged and mishandled in the various mishaps—and although messages could at first be sent slowly over the cable, the signals became unintelligible after only four weeks; six weeks later the cable failed

FIGURE 349—*The first submarine telegraph cable ever laid: the tug* Goliah *on 28 August 1850.*

completely. A fresh attempt was made in 1865 with a cable of greatly improved design, which was laid by the *Great Eastern*, but further accidents were experienced and the cable finally broke, being lost in mid-Atlantic at a depth of 2000 fathoms. A still further attempt was made in 1866, and at last, on 27 July, a sound cable, again laid by the *Great Eastern* (plate 46 B), stretched from Valentia in Ireland to Trinity Bay in Newfoundland. Credit for this final achievement was due to many, but to none more than Cyrus W. Field (1819–92), a great American citizen whose untiring efforts had constituted the mainspring of the whole undertaking for nearly thirteen years. The *Great Eastern* rounded off this success by recovering one end of the cable that had parted the previous year and splicing a new length to it, thus providing a second complete cable. Since that time transatlantic telegraph cables have been in continuous use.

BIBLIOGRAPHY

APPLEYARD, R. 'Pioneers of Electrical Communication.' Macmillan, London. 1930.
FAHIE, J. J. 'A History of the Electric Telegraph to the Year 1837.' London. 1884.
HAMEL, J. VON. 'Historical Account of the Introduction of the Galvanic and Electro-magnetic Telegraph.' London. 1859.
SABINE, R. 'History and Progress of the Electric Telegraph.' London. 1869.
TURNBULL, L. 'The Electro-magnetic Telegraph.' Philadelphia. 1853.

The electric telegraph office, Lothbury. c *1850.*

23

THE BEGINNINGS OF THE CHANGE FROM CRAFT MYSTERY TO SCIENCE AS A BASIS FOR TECHNOLOGY

A. R. J. P. UBBELOHDE

I. CRAFT EXPERIENCE AND CRAFT MYSTERIES

UNTIL the advent of the scientific age, technological advances were based on craft experience, and the personal element in transmitting such experience from one generation to another, and from one place to another, was exceptionally strong. In these volumes several instances have already been recorded of the transportation of a technology even involving the physical movement of the craftsmen from one centre to another—as in the importation into Britain of Flemish brick-makers and of French glass-makers.

Such imported craftsmen would naturally be particularly secretive in handing on essential details of their craft, but craft skill and experience were at all times valuable personal possessions that needed to be protected by secrecy. This can be conveniently summarized by stating that ancient technologies were based on craft mysteries learnt and handed on privately, a circumstance that makes any comprehensive survey of craft technologies difficult. Other factors, discussed below, contribute to the incompleteness of our knowledge of craft mysteries, some of which involved a remarkable degree of practical knowledge.

As modern science grew in stature, roughly from the scientific renaissance of the mid-seventeenth century onwards, a basic change in the foundations of technology gradually took place. The object of this final chapter of the present volume is to describe and to discuss various aspects of the beginning of the change from craft mystery to science as the basis of modern technology. The subject will be further developed in the concluding chapters of volume V.

The permeation of craft mysteries before 1750

Different sections of this and earlier volumes have surveyed the growth and decay of various crafts in different parts of the world. Though our present knowledge is far from complete, these surveys make it clear that, in the past, copying from other communities—often by the importation of more advanced craftsmen—and local innovation have gone hand in hand, whenever the conditions of material welfare have been sufficiently stable in a community to allow wealth to accumulate.

History records many instances of the rise and fall of nations. Each such consolidation of power, stability, and wealth fostered to high levels of refinement and skill the growth of a diversity of crafts; each might serve to illustrate the permeation of craft mysteries. When the nation declined, a concomitant decline in its technology was inevitable and was often severe. Considered in space and time, world history thus exhibits zones of high-level skills separated by transition regions in which the permeation, and even the survival, of such skills was much more uncertain and obscure.

It is possible to draw contours around centres of culture in the world in successive ages to illustrate the appearance and disappearance of zones of high-level craft skills, but no complete tracing of the permeation of craft mysteries in past ages will be attempted here, fascinating though the story is. For the present survey it is sufficient to refer to the technological consequences of the rise of the Roman Empire, and of the establishment of a firmly administered *Pax Romana* over considerable portions of the world. This encouraged the permeation of craft mysteries on a quite extensive scale. Examples quoted previously (vol II) include the practices of metallurgy (ch 2), of military engineering (ch 20), of building and civil engineering (ch 12), of glass-making (ch 9), and of the production of ceramics (ch 8).

The decline of the Roman Empire led to a general dissipation of the accumulated wealth and craft experience of the ancient world. Zones of high craft-skills of the Roman Empire are, as it were, separated from the technology of medieval and modern times by a deep valley with marshy bottom not yet fully explored. The submergence of Roman civilization took place earlier in the west European fringe than in the east. As a result, when the upheavals due to barbarian invasions in the west were subsiding, east to west permeation of technological improvements, though variable in intensity, persisted in this direction at least until the Renaissance. This contrasts with technological improvements based on science, which have mainly flowed from west to east.

Craft mysteries and a managerial class

One of the unsolved problems about the handing on of craft mysteries is how supervisors and managers were trained in such of the ancient technologies as called for managerial supervision. The methods used for such training are important for the present survey, since they could provide one of the most systematic approaches to the technological foundations of ancient crafts.

By way of example, in at least two instances capital accumulation in ancient technologies reached a level which called for a class of supervisors; these were mining and metal-working. There is evidence (vol II, ch 4) that well paid mining managers were employed in Roman times to supervise slave labour, but it is not fully known in what form technical secrets were handed on within this managing class. Notwithstanding their relative prosperity, such *technites* did not enjoy full civic rights (vol II, ch 4); and for this reason only incomplete descriptions of their functions are given in ancient records.

In Renaissance mining, the Fuggers of Augsburg had founded a *Bergschule*, for instructing overseers of mines and analysts of metals and ores, at Villach in Carinthia. The father of Paracelsus, who was also town physician, taught chemical theory and practice at this school shortly after 1500 [1]. Apart from such fragmentary information, it is difficult to arrive at an understanding of the managerial foundations of ancient crafts, because of the very way in which they were practised. More is known about the various levels of recognized proficiency in medieval trade-guilds. These regularized the teaching and handing on of craft mysteries, which still remained, however, on a basis of personal skills.

Some handicaps to applied science in ancient civilizations

One essential factor in the gradual introduction of a scientific outlook and scientific procedures into modern technology was the increasingly active leadership in this direction given by men in relatively prominent social positions, especially from the seventeenth century onwards. This arose from the widespread growth of interest in natural science amongst this class, who were also concerned in exploiting new economic opportunities. Roman capitalism, and ancient capitalism generally, were greatly handicapped in this respect by the old contempt for applied science, which resulted in the supervisors of ancient craft-processes having apparently been quite out of touch with any scientific thinking.

Various authoritative statements show the general attitude of the actual leaders of ancient civilized communities towards technology. For example, Plutarch (A.D. 46?–120) [2], in his life of the Roman general Marcellus (270?–208 B.C.), has recorded various details about the life and opinions of the greatest of the Greek applied mathematicians, Archimedes (287–212 B.C.). The latter is famous amongst other things for having invented, or having had attributed to him, many highly original mechanical inventions connected with warfare. The pressing demands for increasingly effective means of attack and defence led to quite distinctive applications of science to military technology even in ancient times. Plutarch states that Archimedes

> did not think the inventing of [military engines] an object worthy of his serious studies, but only reckoned them among the amusements of geometry. Nor had he gone so far, but at the pressing instances of Hiero of Syracuse, who entreated him to turn his art from abstracted motions to matters of sense, and to make his reasonings more intelligible to the generality of mankind, applying them to the uses of common life.
>
> The first to turn their thoughts to mechanics, a branch of knowledge which came afterwards to be so much admired, were Eudoxus [fl 366 B.C.] and Archytas [428?–347 B.C.], who confirmed certain problems, not then soluble on theoretical grounds, by sensible experiments and the use of instruments. But Plato inveighed against them, with great indignation, as corrupting and debasing the excellence of geometry, by making her descend from incorporeal and intellectual, to corporeal and sensible things, and obliging her to make use of matter, which requires much manual labour, and is the object of servile trades. Mechanics were in consequence separated from geometry, and were for a long time despised by philosophers [2].

Geometry, astronomy, and similar pure sciences were relatively advanced even in Greek and Roman times, but among the intellectual leaders there was little interest in the scientific foundations of technology. The social submergence of technology in the ancient civilizations, and the social inferiority of craftsmen, can be illustrated from many old records. Ecclesiasticus [3] admirably summarizes an attitude of mind that persisted for many centuries:

> ... every workman and master workman, that must turn night into day. Here is one that cuts graven seals; how he busies himself with devising some new pattern! How the model he works from claims his attention, while he sits late over his craft! Here is blacksmith sitting by his anvil, intent upon his iron-work, cheeks shrivelled with smoke, as he battles with the heat of the furnace, ears ringing again with the hammer's clattering, eyes fixed on the design he imitates. All his heart is in the finishing of his task, all his waking thoughts go to the perfect achieving of it. Here is potter at work, treadles flying, anxious continually over the play of his hands, over the rhythm of his craftsmanship; arms straining at stiff clay, feet matching its strength with theirs. To finish off the glaze is his nearest concern, and long must he wake to keep his furnace clean. All these look to their own hands for a living, skilful each in his own craft; and without them, there is no building up a commonwealth. For them no travels abroad, no journeyings from home; they will not pass beyond their bounds to swell the assembly, or to sit in the judgement seat. Not theirs to sift evidence and give verdict, not theirs to impart learning or to make award; they will not be known for uttering wise sayings.

Resurgence of craft technologies and the impact of science: some precursors

With the decay of Roman administration and Roman rule throughout the world, many of the more refined crafts gradually lost impetus. It is not the purpose here to describe the decay in the west of crafts derived from Greek and Roman times. The resurgence of craft mysteries under the more stable social and economic conditions of medieval times likewise does not concern us directly. Historical research is paying increasing attention to the upsurge of medieval science, but these activities of the human intellect could not properly be described as having any profound scientific influence on technology. What must be considered in some detail is the strengthened interest in natural science and in the experimental method which spread to a marked extent in the sixteenth, and particularly in the seventeenth, centuries among the very class of social leaders who had for so long held aloof from it.

By far the most complete and well documented record of this new growth of the influence of science on technology can be found in the history of the foundation of the Royal Society under the patronage of Charles II. Before discussing this it must, however, be emphasized that all strong movements in history show precursors; this can certainly be said of the precursors of the seventeenth-century revolution in pure and applied science.

Two brief biographical examples must suffice to throw light on some of these precursors. One was a Renaissance artist whose genius for applied science was at least comparable with that of Archimedes. Leonardo da Vinci (1452–1519) has left a long list of projects and inventions, which showed at least an intuitive grasp of the many technological possibilities of applied science. However, there appears to be no evidence that these inventions were based on theoretical scientific studies of anything like the same degree of advancement. The continued and urgent practical demands of the arts of war for new applications of science stimulated Leonardo to devise a number of war machines, including a breech-loading cannon, fire-arms rifled to impart a spin to the bullets, a wheel-lock pistol, and a steam-cannon, the *architronito* [4]. Leonardo is also reputed to have invented a submarine ship, details of which he never divulged because he was apprehensive of its wrongful use by tyrants.

A second precursor of those who founded the Royal Society was Sir Walter Ralegh (1552?–1618) [5]. This prominent Elizabethan followed many projects of high adventure, but when imprisoned in the Tower (*c* 1604) he spent his time in writing a 'History of the World' and in chemical experiments, probably chiefly concerned with distillation.

Foundation of the Royal Society

The history of the early years of the Royal Society is particularly important for the present chapter because it records three factors that became important in the mid-seventeenth century in promoting the shift from craft mysteries to science as a basis for technology. First, the Royal Society united a new class of men interested in natural philosophy and its applications. Secondly, it sponsored 'Histories of Nature, Arts or Works', which provided, often for the first time, scientific descriptions of craft technologies as they were practised in the seventeenth century. Thirdly, it stimulated the publication, so that all might know of them, of important new scientific and technological discoveries.

(i) *The new class of men.* A somewhat biased but historically interesting description of the 'new men', and of the shift of interest brought about by the new developments of natural philosophy, is due to Joseph Addison, writing in the 'Spectator' (No. 262, 1711): 'It draws men's minds off from the bitterness of party, and furnishes them with subjects of discourse that may be treated without warmth or passion. . . . The air pump, the barometer, the quadrant, and like inventions were thrown out to those busy spirits, as tubs and barrels are to a whale, that he might let the ship sail on without disturbance, while he diverts himself with these innocent amusements.'

An even more closely contemporary, and less patronizing, view of the new men can be obtained from a history of the Royal Society published in 1667 soon after the grant of the Royal Charter (1663) [6]. Thomas Sprat's (1635–1713) description of the wide range of interests in pure and applied science of one of the early members, Christopher Wren, refers to 'so much excellence covered with so much modesty'. According to Sprat, Christopher Wren's works included:

A doctrine of Motion . . . an Instrument to represent the effect of all sorts of Impulses, made between two hard globous Bodies, either of equal, or different bigness, and swiftness, following or meeting each other, or the one moving, the other at rest . . . of all which he demonstrated the true Theories. . . .

A History of the Seasons . . . because the difficulty of a constant observation of the Air by Night and Day seemed invincible, he therefore devised a Clock to be annexed to a Weather-cock, which moved a rundle, covered with paper, upon which the Clock moved a black lead pencil so that the observer by the Traces of the Pencil on the paper might certainly conclude, what Winds had blown in his absence, for twelve hours space. After a like manner he contrived a Thermometer to be its own Register. . . . He contrived an Instrument to measure the quantities of Rain that falls . . . many subtile wayes for the easier finding the gravity of the Atmosphere, the degrees of drought and moysture . . . new Discoveries of the Pendulum . . . many ways to make Astronomical Observations more accurate and easie. . . .

He has attempted to make Glasses of other forms than Spherical. Other works include the Theory of Refraction and Dioptrics, Observations on Saturn, Selenography, Magnetical Experiments, Studies of the Geometrical mechanics of rowing, of the dry way of Etching, of the Emendation of Water works, the devising of Instruments of respiration for straining the breath from fuliginous vapours, to try whether the same breath so purifyd will serve again, long lived lamps and registers of furnaces for keeping a perpetual temper, in order to various uses; as hatching of eggs, insects, producing Fossils and Minerals, keeping the motion of Watches equal, in order to longitudinal and astronomical uses, and infinite other advantages; and injecting liquors in the veins of Animals . . . transfusing blood.

Sprat makes it clear that some of Wren's inventions 'he did only start and design and they have since been carried on to perfection, by the Industry of other hands'. But even with this reservation, it is clear that the breadth of ideas and originality of inventions cited are in the same class as those of Leonardo da Vinci.

(ii) *Scientific surveys of craft technologies.* The 'Histories of Nature, Arts or Works' sponsored by the Royal Society included the following:

Histories of English Mines and Oars . . . of Iron making, of Lignum Fossile: of Saffron: of Alkermes; of Verdigreace: of Whiting of Wax, of Cold, of colours, of fluidity, and firmness. The Histories of Refining: of making Copperas: of making Allum: of Saltpeter: of refining Gold: of making Pot-Ashes: of making Ceruse: of making Brass: of Painting, and Limning: of Chalcography: of Enamelling: of Varnishing: of Dying:

The Histories of making Cloth: of Worsted-Combers: of Fullers: of Tanners, and Leather making: of Glovers, and Leather dressing: of Parchment, and Vellum making, and the way of making transparent Parchment: of Paper making: of Hatters: of making Marble Paper: of the Rowling Press.

The Histories of making Bread: of Malt: of brewing Beer and Ale in several places: of Whale-fishing: of the weather for several years: of Wind-mills and other Mills in Holland: of Masonry: of Pitch and Tar: of Maiz: of Vintners: of Shot: of making Gun powder: and of making some, that is twenty times as strong as the common Pistol powder.

These openly accessible surveys of contemporary craft technologies were an essential first step towards applying scientific principles to technology generally.

(iii) *The new inventions.* An impressive list of instruments is attributed by Sprat to the activities of the new Society. His list includes:

Astronomical instruments.
Clocks and watches.
Instruments for compressing and rarefying the Air.
Barometers.
Gravity scales.

Magnetic scales.
Surveying instruments.
Geological augers.
Instruments to measure the velocity of movement of objects in water.
Diving apparatus, a Diving Bell, means of supplying air to divers.
Apparatus to measure wind velocity.
Rotary-vane water pump.
Thermometers.
Corn planters.
Hygroscopes.
Water analysers.
Engines to determine the force of gunpowder by weights, springs, etc.
Do. to measure the recoiling and other properties of guns.
Several instruments to improve hearing.
Several chariots for progressive motion.
A chariot way-wiser measuring exactly the length of the way of a chariot or coach to which it is applyd.
An instrument for making Screws with great dispatch.
A way of preserving the most exact impression of a Seal, medal or Sculpture.
An instrument for grinding optick glasses.
Several excellent telescopes of divers lengths including one sixty foot long, with a convenient apparatus for the managing of them.

Seventeenth-century views about applied science

Sprat records interesting contemporary views about how far new discoveries in science could benefit the advancement of technology. He criticizes—on grounds similar to those we have already discussed—the complete failure of the Greeks and the Romans to apply science. Sprat takes a balanced view about contemporary applications. He refers to 'corruptions of Learning, which have been long complained of but never removed: The one, that Knowledge still degenerates to consult present profit too soon; the other, that Philosophers have bin always Masters, and Scholars; some imposing and all the others submitting; and not as equal observers without dependence.' He quotes as a significant defect of learning 'the rendering of Causes barren: that when they have been found out, they have been suffered to lie idle; and have been onely used, to increase thoughts, and not works. . . . To this the Royal Society has applyd a double prevention; both by endeavouring to strike out new Arts, as they go along; and also, by still improving all to new experiments.' These views about the interaction between pure and applied science remain apposite today.

In the rest of seventeenth-century Europe, this growth was paralleled under the leadership of scientists such as Descartes (1596–1650), Huygens (1629–94), Leibniz (1646–1716), and many others who openly published their scientific discoveries. Open publication, even when limited to discoveries in pure science, is in marked contrast to the concealment traditional and necessary in the writings of early alchemists and inventors. Such publication of discoveries in applied science was undoubtedly helped by the granting of limited but effective patent protection. The change in attitude to knowledge is clearly marked, for example, in the diary of John Evelyn, a Fellow of the Royal Society, covering the period 1640–1706. He records both attendances at the public experiments sponsored by the Royal Society, and the claims of contemporary alchemists who kept their methods secret from him.

II. THE FIRST OF THE NEW TECHNOLOGIES—THE DEVELOPMENT OF POWER-ENGINES

The stimulating effect of scientific ideas and methods on long-established crafts is easy to grasp. In addition, from the seventeenth century onwards entirely new technologies, without any craft precursors, were developed to meet new demands created by the reorganization of manufactures and of town and country life generally described as the industrial revolution. But often, until the economic and social pressure of these new demands became really strong, entirely new technological applications of the new scientific principles met with only limited success. In contrast with present times, money to support adequate research and development was not then readily mobilized. Methods of actually creating new demands did not appear with any prominence until the twentieth century. In the development of the earliest new technologies demand had to spring from the general economic development of a community.

For example, in the seventeenth century one pressing demand was for new sources of power to run pumping-engines for mining operations. When mines got deeper, as shallow veins of ore were exhausted, the need to pump out water and to provide ventilation systems became progressively more urgent (ch 3). Quite elaborate pumping arrangements had to be driven by humans—or horses, or even goats and lesser animals—in a treadmill. In his *De re metallica* (1556) Agricola gives rather pathetic illustrations of some mechanical contrivances recommended for harnessing the driving-power of animals of various sizes.

Even before the seventeenth century, scientists had considered various ways of harnessing the power of fire [7], but no useful application of steam-power was made in the ancient world, partly because there was no effective demand in a society organized to use the driving-power provided by men and animals.

Some mining enterprises in the seventeenth century had both the urgent need for new sources of driving-power and the money to pay for rather costly contrivances to meet this need. The incentive is clearly described in a report written in 1688 by Sir Samuel Morland (1625–95), Master Mechanic to Charles II, for the king's information: 'Water being evaporated by fire, the vapours require a greater space, about 2000 times that occupied by the Water. And rather than submit to imprisonment it will burst a piece of ordnance. But being controlled according to the laws of statics, and by science reduced to the measure of weight and balance, it bears its burden peaceably, like good horses, and thus may be of great use to mankind, especially for the raising of water.'

Many inventors in the seventeenth century were attempting to harness the power of fire and steam (ch 6). Hero's book on 'Pneumatics' had been translated from the Greek at Bologna in 1547. At least two suggestions derived from this book were to use his aeolipyle—a small steam-jet rotor—instead of dogs to turn a roasting-spit, and to use the jet of steam from a bronze kettle to drive an impulse-wheel (Branca). Another inventor with many ideas was the Marquis of Worcester (1601–67); his close collaboration with his mechanic, Caspar Kaltoff, illustrates both the increasingly active part in the development of applied science taken by socially prominent men and their dependence on collaboration with craftsmen practising traditional methods. No clear description of the Marquis's 'water-commanding engine', constructed around 1663, appears to be available; the details were no doubt kept secret deliberately.

Other scientists, such as Denis Papin (1647–1712?) and Huygens, are known to have experimented with the expansive force of gunpowder and of steam in cylinders fitted with pistons. Thomas Savery's (1650–1715) first pumping-engine for raising water was a pistonless vacuum-producing device; when exhibited to William III in 1698 it raised water to a height of about 16 fathoms. Savery was a versatile military engineer much interested in profitable inventions. He collaborated with Thomas Newcomen to produce, about 1712, the first successful piston steam-engine for pumping water from the mines at Dudley Castle. The working of this stationary engine has been described by Smiles: 'the working of a Newcomen engine was a clumsy and apparently a very painful process, accompanied by an extraordinary amount of wheezing, sighing, creaking and bumping. When the pump descended, there was heard a plunge, a heavy sigh, and a loud bump. Then as it rose, and the sucker began to act, there was heard a creak, a wheeze, another bump, and then a rush of water as it was lifted and poured out.'

The Savery-Newcomen venture, though evidently economic for certain pumping stations in mines, had only limited appeal in other applications of inanimate power, because of its inefficiency and low ratio of power to weight. Its development illustrates the effectiveness of collaboration between the craftsman Newcomen and the more theoretical inventor Savery. However, really scientific principles concerning heat and mechanical power were not applied to the steam-engine before the work of James Watt (1736–1819). Watt's development of a condenser for the steam, separated from the cylinder in which the piston moved, was closely linked up with and inspired by the scientific researches of Joseph Black (1728–99), then professor of chemistry at Glasgow University. As will appear more fully below, Black was the first to measure heat-energy quantitatively, and this led to his discovery of latent heat. James Watt began his technical work as mathematical instrument-maker to Glasgow University. His many discussions with Black, and his own scientific experiments, undoubtedly contributed to the much closer dependence of his steam-engine on scientific principles and on the theory of heat, compared with the Savery and Newcomen engine.

Application of Watt's designs of piston steam-engines was at first hampered by the difficulty of financing the necessary research and development, although Black assisted further by lending Watt £1500. This difficulty was finally overcome when Watt made a partnership agreement with Boulton: the first commercially successful Boulton & Watt engine was ordered in 1776. Subsequent applications of steam-power to requirements other than pumping water from mines developed slowly but steadily. They do not concern us in this section, which aims to trace the shift from craft to science in the foundations of power-technology, but it is worth noting that Watt's early collaboration with the scientists in Glasgow University was followed by a continued friendship and collaboration with scientists in later years. Both Boulton and Watt were members of the 'Lunar Society' at Birmingham, which included active scientists such as Erasmus Darwin, Samuel Galton, James Keir, and Joseph Priestley.

III. PERSONAL INFLUENCES FAVOURING THE PERMEATION OF TECHNOLOGY BY SCIENCE

The life of James Watt provides an important illustration of the personal influence during the eighteenth century of scientific leaders like Joseph Black. Similar instances may be found in the lives of other leading scientists of the period under review. It would be particularly valuable to have records of the kind of consulting work undertaken, since this has the most direct bearing on applied science, but unfortunately such records are often very incomplete. However, four examples relating to the period from about 1750 to about 1850 may be quoted. In addition to advising Watt, Black was also the first to recommend the use of hydrogen for filling balloons, on the basis of the specific gravity of the gas as determined by Henry Cavendish. Many instances are on record of his contributions as a scientific consultant to the bleaching industry, to the ceramic industry, to Lord Hopetoun's project for working Scottish ores, to the coal-tar industry, to distilleries, and to the malleable and cast iron industry [8]. The French chemist Antoine Laurent Lavoisier (1743–94) acted as consultant on the Paris water-supply, on the production of gunpowder in the French arsenal, on prisons, on balloons, and on the hospitals of Paris. He was also particularly active in advising on applications of science to agriculture, which was then a matter of great importance in France. In England, Michael Faraday (1791–1867) was a member of the scientific advisory committee of the Admiralty, scientific adviser to Trinity House, and a member of the committee for the improvement of glass for optical purposes [9]. The Ulster-Scottish physicist William Thomson, later Lord Kelvin (1824–1907), played an extremely active part in the development and laying of the first transatlantic cables (1856–66), and was responsible for many improvements to navigation instruments.

In addition to the instances recorded above, many other examples might be found to illustrate the permeation of technology by a scientific outlook through the personal influence of eminent scientific consultants. In the late eighteenth and early nineteenth centuries other more broadly based modes of permeation can be plausibly attributed to the influence of messianic or philanthropic concepts of the social functions of applied science. Four examples, of differing degrees of importance, illustrate the kinds of influence referred to:

(i) The work of the French encyclopaedists.

(ii) Count Rumford's philanthropic plans at the Royal Institution to promote new applications of science for the relief of poverty.

(iii) Contemporary enthusiasm for the messianic power of applied science as a liberator from the servitude of hard labour.

(iv) The formation in 1831 of the British Association for the Advancement of Science.

(i) *The French encyclopaedists.* The famous *Dictionnaire raisonné des sciences, des arts et des métiers* under the editorship of Denis Diderot (1713–84) and Jean d'Alembert (1717–83) first appeared, in 39 volumes, during the period 1751–72. Its general form is obviously inspired by earlier encyclopaedias, such as that produced by Ephraim Chambers (d 1740) in 1728. But by reason of its amplitude the French encyclopaedia, like the 'Histories of Nature, Arts or Works' sponsored by the Royal Society in the preceding century, had an important systematizing influence on contemporary technology in France, which was then in a state of transition from a craft to a scientific basis. As is well known, Diderot's encyclopaedia is also widely considered to have made an important contribution to the ferment of controversies that led to the French Revolution, but this aspect of the work does not directly concern us here.

(ii) *Count Rumford* (1753–1814), was an American born in Massachusetts of English stock, and had been concerned with a number of philanthropic schemes in Munich during his services to the Elector of Bavaria: the history of his ideas for developing applied science is of considerable interest for the present survey. In 1796 Rumford put forward proposals for an establishment in London for 'feeding the poor and giving them assistance . . . connected with an Institution for introducing and bringing forward into general use new inventions and improvements, particularly such as relate to the management of heat and the saving of fuel, and to various other mechanical contrivances by which domestic comfort and economy may be promoted . . .'.

Originally the plan was to collect 'perfect and full sized models of all such mechanical inventions and improvements as would serve these ends. . . . Cottage fireplaces and kitchen utensils for cottages, a farm house kitchen with its furnishings, and a complete kitchen with all utensils for the house of a gentleman of fortune, a laundry, including boilers, washing, ironing and drying rooms for a gentleman's house or for a public hospital . . . models of newly invented machines and implements of husbandry, models of bridges of various constructions.'

Rumford also made interesting comments about the applications of science to technology in his day. In his 'project' he refers to the causes of the slowness, indifference, and jealousy under which improvements made their way—the influence of habit, ignorance, prejudice, suspicion, dislike of change, and the narrowing effect of the subdivision of work into many petty occupations. According to him,

> between workmen and merchants comes in a class of men who have devoted themselves to the labor of observing, analysing, inventing. The movements of the Universe, the relations and habitudes of men and things, causes and effects, motives and consequences, are the powers on which they meditate for the development of truth. . . . It is the business of these Philosophers to examine every operation of Nature or of Art, and to establish general theories for the direction and conducting of future processes. Invention seems to be particularly the province of the men of science.

The immediate outcome of the founding of the Royal Institution turned out rather differently from Rumford's project. This was partly due to the fact that its members, who commissioned lectures and discourses in its early days, stemmed from a social class not at that time widely interested in technological progress or philanthropy, but keenly stimulated by the brilliant scientific discoveries made by such men as Humphry Davy and Michael Faraday in the laboratories of their Institution.

(iii) *Applied science as a liberator from servitude.* The enthusiasm that possessed some of the early technologists sprang from an almost supernatural confidence in the power of applied science to lighten the burdens that weigh down mankind. This thesis could be established in a number of ways; one of the most direct is to record two extracts from contemporary praise of the new benefits brought by applied science.

The first of them comes from 'The Philosophy of Manufactures. The Scientific Moral and Commercial Economy of the Factory System of Great Britain.' This rather pompous-sounding book by A. Ure (1778–1856) was first published in 1835: the quotation that follows is from the third edition of 1861.

> . . . tens of thousands of old, young and middle aged of both sexes, many of them too feeble to get their daily bread by any of the former modes of industry, earning abundant food, raiment, and domestic accommodation, without perspiring at a single pore, screened meanwhile from the summer's sun and the winter's frost, in apartments more airy and salubrious than those of the metropolis in which our legislative and fashionable aristocracies assemble. In those spacious halls the benignant power of steam summons around him his myriads of willing menials, and assigns to each the regulated task, substituting for painful muscular effort on their part, the energies of his own gigantic arm, and demanding in return only attention and dexterity to correct such little aberrations as casually occur in his workmanship. Magnificent edifices, surpassing far in number, value, usefulness, and ingenuity of construction, the boasted monuments of Asiatic, Egyptian and Roman despotism, have, within the short period of fifty years, risen up in this kingdom. . . .

The second extract is taken from a practically contemporary French book by Marc Seguin, *Traité sur l'influence des chemins de fer* (1839) [10].

> To increase the well-being and the enjoyment of material life is today the dominant idea of civilised nations. All their efforts are turned to industry because it is from that alone that one can expect progress. It is industry that gives birth to and develops in mankind new needs and gives them at the same time the means to satisfy them. . . . A thousand inventions are simultaneously born and lead to other discoveries and these in turn will become the starting point for new progress; all these changes concur to the profit of the whole public and tend to make well-being common property. . . . So look, everything is changed around us—the towns, the face of the countryside, the course of the rivers,

the work of the peoples, the production of the soil and industry, the distribution of property....

Finally, in our own valleys and across our hills wind and spread long ribbons of iron, along which rush, rapid as thought, those formidable machines which seem to eat up space with spontaneous impatience and which seem almost alive in their breathing and their movement... when one remembers that these results are the work of an industry which is only very imperfect, and an art which is in its infancy, one asks what will be the last prodigies to be realised by the perfecting of this art, and one feels a noble desire to contribute to the realisation of these incalculable blessings....

(iv) *Founding of the British Association for the Advancement of Science in 1831.* In civilized countries, the pursuit of science and of its applications seems almost inevitably to undergo cycles of activity that are difficult to explain. The foundation of the British Association in 1831 marks one deliberate attempt to counter, by co-ordinating the powers and enthusiasm of a band of experts, what was felt to be a contemporary decline of science in Britain. Its proclaimed objects were 'to give a stronger impulse and a more systematic direction to scientific inquiry, to obtain a greater degree of national attention to the objects of science, and a removal of those disadvantages which impede its progress, and to promote the intercourse of the cultivators of science with one another and with foreign philosophers'.

Subsequent history has recorded only fluctuating preoccupation of the British Association with applications of science to technology. Nevertheless, during the period of its existence the Association has often provided a platform for important debates, and the publicity of such debates has from time to time promoted new applications of science.

IV. SOME DEVELOPMENTS IN APPLIED SCIENCE LEADING TO NEW KINDS OF TECHNOLOGY

One of the ways in which the scientific approach to practical problems permeated age-old craft-technology was through accounts of various crafts compiled by scientists—for example, those sponsored by the Royal Society in the seventeenth century, and those by the French encyclopaedists in the eighteenth. Besides transforming long-established branches of technology, new scientific discoveries in some cases formed the basis of quite novel ones, which never had a craft ancestry, though the full efflorescence of this trend occurred after the period we are now considering. During that period, the most important fundamental advances of science that ultimately led to new kinds of technology were mainly those concerned with the study of various forms of energy.

There were also many new advances in applied science. In a short space it is difficult to list all the applied discoveries without distorting the historical perspective. Two obvious, and often quoted, examples refer to the use of coal-gas for providing artificial light, and to the controlled removal of carbon from molten iron to produce steel in bulk.

The development of the gas industry (ch 9) for the first time made it reasonably inexpensive to supply artificial light for large rooms, as in factories. Work was no longer regulated by the length of daylight, and the practicability of working several shifts made possible the use of machinery too expensive to be left idle for long.

The partial decarburation of molten iron to form steel was another extremely important new discovery, though its practical application was completed just after the period now under review. It provided cheap steel for constructional uses. The first Bessemer converter for blowing air through molten iron, to remove combustible impurities such as excess carbon, was in operation about 1856. The first Siemens-Martin open-hearth furnace, for melting iron under oxidizing conditions to produce steel in large quantities, was erected at about the same time.

As has been noted, the scientific discoveries productive of new technologies were in the main those concerned with energy changes: among these, discoveries in the field of electricity were of exceptional importance.

(i) *Electricity from chemical sources.* Up to the time of the invention of the now historic pile by Volta (1745–1827), electricity had been chiefly known and studied as produced by friction, but the quantity of electrical energy involved is extremely small in most electrostatic manifestations. Somewhat larger quantities of electricity could be studied after the invention of electric condensers or Leyden jars in the middle of the eighteenth century. Researches on electricity by Benjamin Franklin during the period 1746–52 led to his highly practical invention of the lightning-conductor for the safe discharge of low thunderclouds without danger to buildings.

The voltaic pile consisted of alternate disks of copper or silver separated from disks of zinc or tin by disks of absorbent paper soaked in brine. By building up long columns of such sequences of disks high voltages were obtained between the topmost and lowest disks, and large currents could be obtained. The voltaic pile formed a crude electric battery, and more efficient ones were later produced. They all have in common the production of electricity as a result of internal chemical changes. Electric batteries were highly important to the development of the science of electricity. By their means Davy in 1807 isolated sodium and potassium by electrolysis of the corresponding fused caustic alkalis. In this discovery were the seeds of great modern electrochemical industries, such as the aluminium industry, though they were long in germinating.

(ii) *Electromagnetism.* Studies of magnetic effects around a wire carrying a current obtained from a battery led to the discovery of a number of the basic phenomena of electromagnetism. From these stem the whole of the great electric power-generating and power-using industries of today, though again the rate of progress was very slow. In 1820 the Danish physicist, H. C. Oersted (1777–1851), first observed the magnetic field present around a copper wire carrying a current. Various laws concerning this electromagnetic force-field surrounding a conductor carrying a current were established by scientists such as A. M. Ampère (1775–1836).

The complementary discovery to that of Oersted was made by Faraday in 1831: an electric current is generated in a conductor when this is moved in a magnetic field. Faraday's observation of electromagnetic induction completed the scientific knowledge of interdependent electromagnetic phenomena associated with currents and conductors, and led to dynamos that can generate large electric currents when their coils are rotated in a magnetic field. The industrial significance of this development needs no emphasis.

In an inverted use of the dynamo, electric current is made to pass through coils of wire mounted on a movable frame in a magnetic field, so producing a force on the coils that leads to the rotation of the movable frame. This is the basic principle of electric motors, now of outstanding importance, though the development of the electric motor is again a little beyond the period now under consideration.

(iii) *Precision measurements of energy: discovery of the laws of thermodynamics.* During the first half of the nineteenth century discoveries less tangible, but quite as fundamental, as those in electromagnetism were made through precise measurements of energy. Such measurements led to a clear understanding of the laws of thermodynamics, which today permeate the whole of power-production on the one hand, and are a determining factor for large sections of chemical industry on the other. For the reasons that follow, however, these very important scientific discoveries affected technology only slowly.

It is comparatively easy to grasp how certain scientific discoveries could be applied to whole groups of craft technologies based on cognate natural phenomena. For example, the discovery of how to harden copper by adding tin affected all users of metal in the Bronze Age: the discovery of how to control the carbon content of iron accurately and cheaply on a large scale affected all users of steel in the Iron Age. But more abstract discoveries, such as those about the electrochemical production of electricity, required a considerable lapse of time before they acquired extensive technological influence. Even more abstract are the laws of thermodynamics, which were finally established during the period 1800–50.

Measurements of heat-energy and of other forms of energy are conceptually difficult compared with, say, measurements of length, because suitable standards of comparison are by no means obvious. Nevertheless, it is technologically very significant that the first steam-engine built on scientific principles was closely associated with Black's discovery of how to measure quantities of heat-energy (p 673). Black used the rise in temperature of a given mass of water as a measure of the quantity of heat it had taken up. This mode of measurement permitted fairly exact assessment of the quantity of heat-energy taken up in unit time by a steam-engine. By means of it, Black discovered that on being converted to steam at the same temperature water takes up large quantities of heat which become 'latent' in the steam. Latent heat-energy can be partly transformed into useful mechanical energy by means of a steam-engine. James Watt, working closely with Black, discovered how to measure mechanical energy, or mechanical work, in terms of the force exerted by a pulling horse lifting weights over a pulley. Combining these measurements of heat-energy and mechanical energy, Watt was the first power-engineer who could in principle determine the efficiency of his engine, that is, the ratio of the quantity of heat-energy taken up to the mechanical energy obtained; though not all these concepts were as yet clearly understood.

At this stage there was still an awkward gap in the group of basic energy-measurements relating to steam-power. Black's method for measuring heat-energy, though quantitative, was based on a standard of comparison different in kind from Watt's method for measuring mechanical energy. This gap was bridged through the experimental researches of J. P. Joule (1818–89) over the period 1840–50. Using a system of churning paddles, Joule determined the mechanical equivalent of heat by finding the rise in temperature of a known mass of water when a definite quantity of mechanical energy was transformed into heat within the water. From that time, power-production could be based on extremely accurate energy balance-sheets. Exact balance-sheets recording interchange of different forms of energy are based on the first law of thermodynamics, which states that, in any physical process, energy is neither created nor destroyed. Energy may appear in new forms but these are quantitatively equivalent to the other forms of energy that disappear.

The second law of thermodynamics, as enunciated in 1851 by R. J. E. Clausius (1822–88) and by Lord Kelvin, makes a statement which in appearance is even milder: that there is a theoretical maximum to the efficiency of any engine which converts heat-energy into useful work. Its enormous importance derives from the discovery by Lord Kelvin that the vast majority of observable transformations, if these involve heat-energy in any way, can be proved to be governed by the second law of thermodynamics. The technologies of power-production and the technologies of chemical industry both involve heat-energy in a very basic way, and so are governed by the second law of thermodynamics. This law imposes natural limits to the efficiency of any energy-transformation that can be devised, and so provides fully reliable standards whereby practical operations can be controlled.

As with many other scientific discoveries, the technological significance of the second law of thermodynamics was only slowly appreciated, despite its vast practical importance. Its formal enunciation, however, was an important event in the changing relationship between science and technology, and with it this chapter can most appropriately end.

REFERENCES

[1] HARGRAVE, J. 'The Life and Soul of Paracelsus', p. 26. Gollancz, London. 1951.
[2] 'Plutarch's Lives' (trans. by J. LANGHORNE and W. LANGHORNE): Life of Marcellus, Vol. 3, pp. 119 ff. London. 1821.
[3] *Ecclesiasticus*, chap. 38 (trans. by R. A. KNOX): 'The Old Testament Newly Translated from the Latin Vulgate', Vol. 2, p. 1053. Burns, Oates & Washbourne, London. 1949.
[4] MCCURDY, E. 'The Mind of Leonardo da Vinci.' Cape, London. 1952.
[5] CREIGHTON, LOUISE. 'Life of Sir Walter Raleigh.' Longmans, Green, London. 1902.
[6] SPRAT, T. 'The History of the Royal Society of London for the Improving of Natural Knowledge.' London. 1667.
[7] VITRUVIUS *De architectura* (Loeb ed. with Eng. trans. by F. GRANGER, 2 vols). Heinemann, London. 1931, 1934.
[8] CLOW, A. and CLOW, NAN L. 'The Chemical Revolution.' Batchworth Press, London. 1952.
[9] THORPE, SIR EDWARD. 'Essays in Historical Chemistry', ch.: "Michael Faraday". London. 1894.
[10] BERNAL, J. D. 'Science and Industry in the Nineteenth Century.' Routledge & Kegan Paul, London. 1953.

I. INDEX OF PERSONAL NAMES

II. INDEX OF PLACE-NAMES

III. INDEX OF SUBJECTS

Jesse Ramsden (1735–1800) with his dividing engine. (pp 392, 603)

PLATE 2

A. *Model of the Rotherham plough. Eighteenth century.* (p 2)

B. *Model of the Kent turnwrest plough. Eighteenth century.* (p 4)

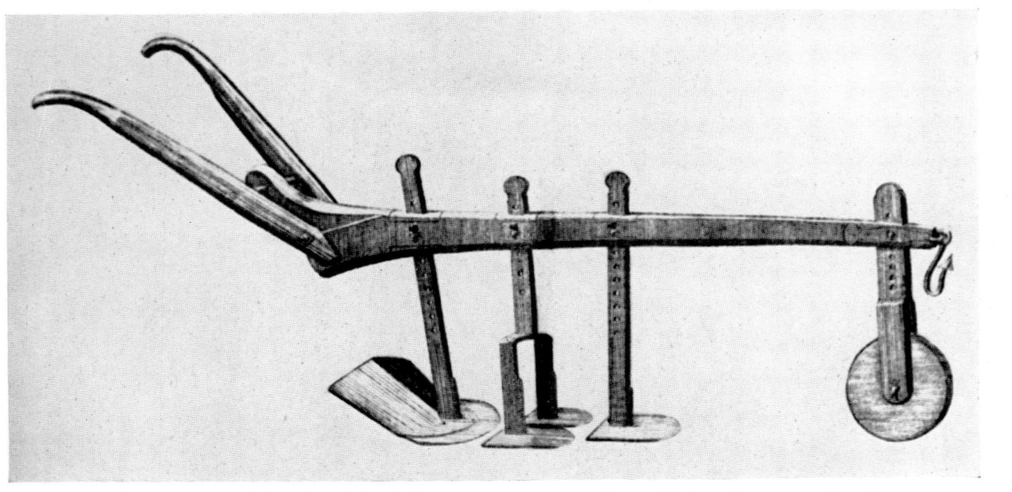

C. *Drawing of horse-hoe for weeding and earthing between plants. Eighteenth century.* (p 13)

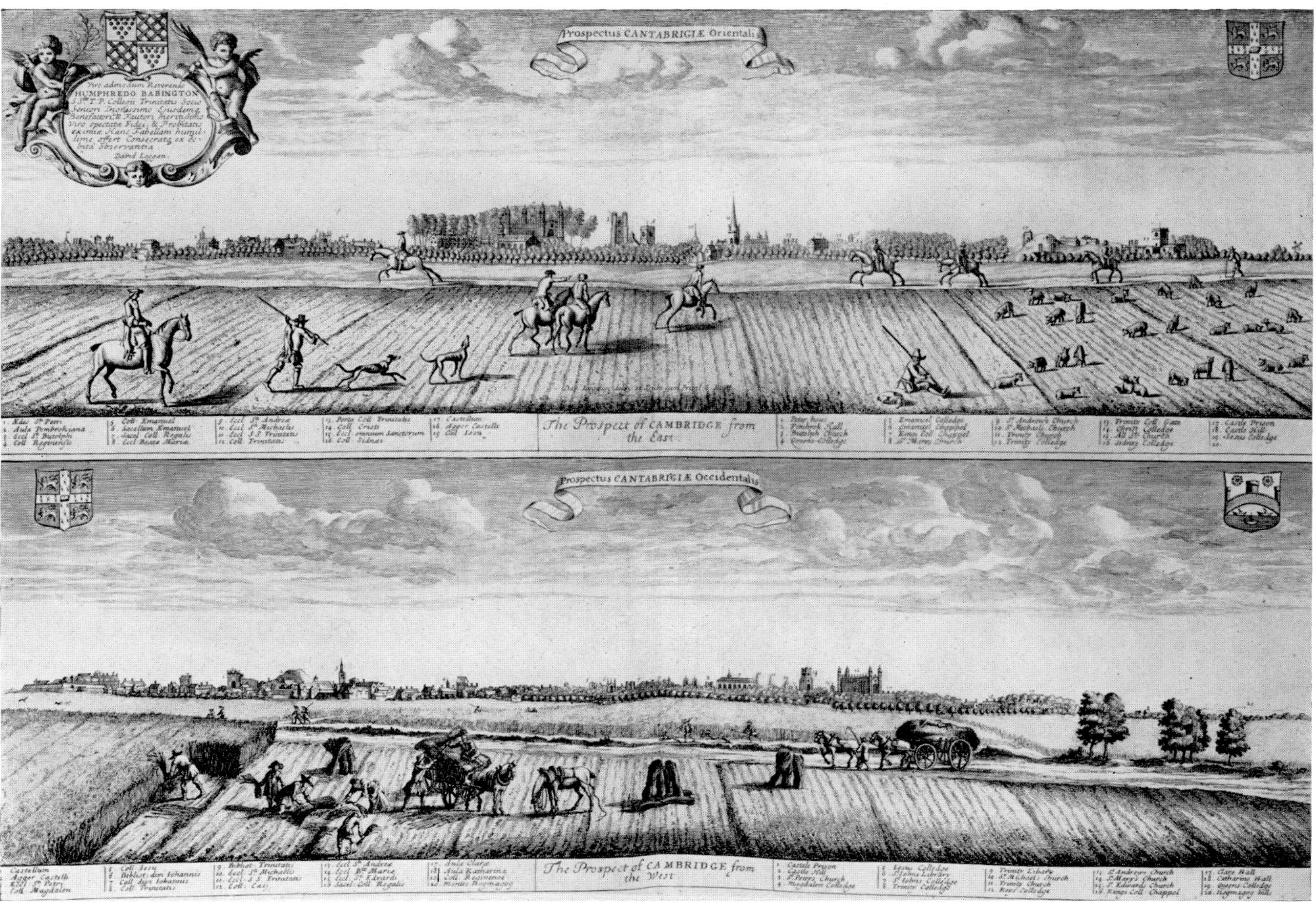

Unenclosed fields near Cambridge during and after harvest, c 1688. *Note the sheep grazing on the stubble, in accordance with a custom that prevailed for very many years after this date and was one of the obstacles to improved rotations.* (p 17)

A. *Eighteenth-century whalers hunting Greenland whales with hand harpoons in the Arctic.* (p 58)

B. *Whaling in the Californian lagoons. The boats have been lowered after a school of Grey whales and the harpoons are ready. A ship in the distance is boiling oil on the deck.* (p 58)

A. *Single-, double-, and three-handed drilling downwards. Before 1850.* (p 70)

B. *Dolcoath man-engine, Cornwall.* c 1850. (p 76)

PLATE 6

A. *Wallsend colliery, Newcastle upon Tyne,* c *1860. Extracted fire-damp is seen burning from the chimney on the left.* (pp 93, 258)

B. *Dolcoath copper mine showing horse-whim, 'call maidens' breaking large pieces of ore, and hoisting of ore in baskets.* c *1850.* (pp 88, 123)

A. *Removal of water was essential in many underground workings. The above illustration shows pumps erected for draining the Kilsby tunnel in 1837.* (pp 78, 567)

B. *The inside of a smelting-house at Broseley, late eighteenth century.* (p 100)

A. *The great burning-glass constructed for the French Academy of Sciences under the direction of Lavoisier and others. The movable lens served to concentrate the sun's rays still further. The substance to be exposed to the action of the burning-glass was placed on an adjustable support. The operator is wearing dark glasses.* (p 218)

B. *An iron forge in 1772.* (p 116)

Blacksmith's shop, 1771. (p 106)

A. *High-pressure direct-acting engine patented by Trevithick in 1802. This was developed for stationary and locomotive use, eventually superseding the beam engine.* (p 188)

B. *Trevithick's high-pressure engine, 1811. This was used for threshing and was working in Cornwall until 1879.* (p 192)

A. *Large water-wheel at Laxey, Isle of Man, 1854.* (p 209)

B. *Coldron Mill, Spelsbury, Oxfordshire. This mill, erected* c *1800, was used for grinding corn. The illustration shows it as formerly displayed in the Science Museum, London.* (p 212)

PLATE 12

A. *Samuel Clegg's gas-making plant for Ackerman, 1812.* (p 268)

B. *Clegg's gas-making apparatus constructed for the Gas Light and Coke Company,* c *1814.* (p 269)

A. *Murdock's gas-making plant for Phillips & Lee*, c *1806*. (p 266)

B. *Drawing the retorts at the Great Gas Light Establishment, Brick Lane, London, 1821.* (p 270)

PLATE 14

A. *Charging retorts at Beckton, 1878.* (p 270)

B. *Mule.* (A) *Carriage with spindles,* (B) *rollers,* (C) *creel for roving bobbins.* (p 279)

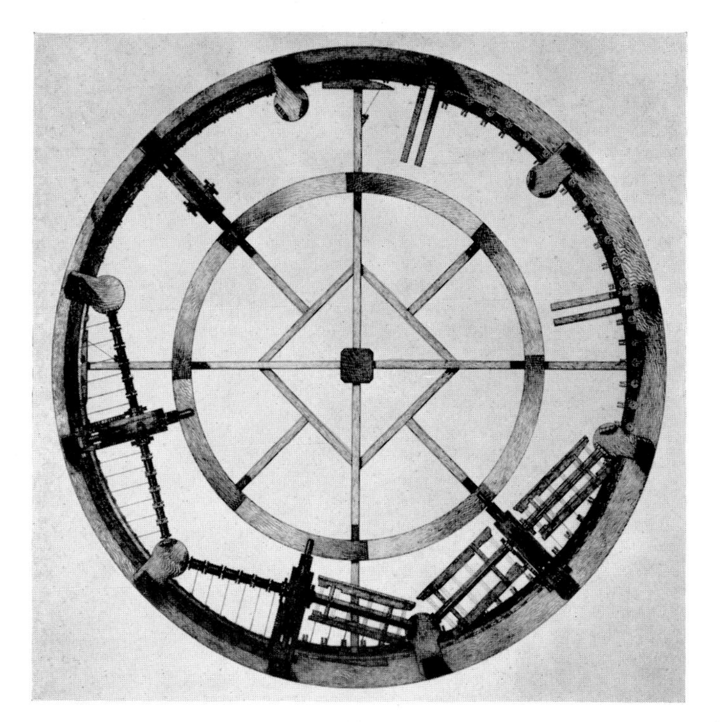

Lombe's throwing machine. The plan (above) *shows the arrangement of the swifts and bobbins in the form of a circle. The elevation* (below) *shows the lower tier with swifts to carry the skeins of silk. The silk was withdrawn from the swifts and taken to the bobbins below, first passing through the wire flyers. As the bobbins and flyers rotated, twist was inserted and the yarn wound on the bobbins. The upper tier shows a similar arrangement, except that the silk is unwound from the horizontally arranged bobbins, and is therefore receiving a second twisting.* (p 311)

PLATE 16

A. *Maiolica: Faenza*, c *1552*. (p 334)

B. *Spanish lustre ware, Valencia. Circular dish painted in lustre, an effect produced by firing in a reducing atmosphere.* (p 335)

C. *Maiolica: Castel Durante. Vase from pharmacy showing shields and coat of arms.* (p 334)

D. *Slip decoration: Staffordshire,* c *1700. Posset-pot in buff earthenware with white and brown slips under a yellow glaze.* (p 331)

A. *Delft wig-stand in manganese purple outline and blue. Dutch, late seventeenth century.* (p 336)

B. *Delft tea-caddy, black enamel painted in green and yellow in imitation of Chinese lacquer. Dutch, late seventeenth or early eighteenth century.* (p 336)

C. *Delft wine bottle with the arms of the Pewterers' Company, inscribed John Smith and Margeri. Lambeth, 1650.* (p 336)

D. *Sèvres biscuit group 'Les trois Contents', modelled by Falconet. 1765.* (p 340)

E. *'Porcelain', Florence, Francesco de Medici, 1575–85. The first 'porcelain' of any sort to be made in Europe.* (p 337)

A. *English soft-paste, Stratford-le-Bow. 'The Piper.'* (p 341)

B. *English soft-paste mug. Derby,* c *1760.* (p 341)

C. *English soft-paste, Chelsea. Group, 'Sportsman and Sportswoman'.* (p 341)

D. *Longton Hall, plate 7·6 inches in diameter,* c *1755.* (p 341)

E. *Longton Hall, mug,* c *1755.* (p 341)

F. *Worcester: dish decorated in black and gilt, 8·5 inches in diameter,* c *1775.* (p 341)

A. *Staffordshire: Thomas Toft slip-decorated dish, 'The Pelican in her Piety'. 17 inches in diameter. Seventeenth century.* (p 345)

B. *Staffordshire: Wedgwood portrait medallion of Joseph Priestley.* (p 353)

C. *Staffordshire: salt-glaze Madonna and Child, 8·3 inches high.* (p 346)

D. *Blocks for making moulds: Chinese shaped spittoon signed by Aaron Wood, 5·7 in; sauce-boat, 3·4 in,* c *1750; bottle, 9·9 in,* c *1750.* (p 354)

A. *Preparing and calcining flint for pottery and porcelain. The flints were broken with an iron mallet* (1) *before being burned in with charcoal* (4). *They were then ground* (2) *and sieved* (3) *before being mixed with clay and water* (7). *When made* (5), *the pottery was allowed to dry* (8) *before being placed in the furnace* (6). (p 347)

B. *Mill-room for mixing ingredients for pottery.* (p 352)

A. *The final stage of buffing or polishing plate glass for mirrors is being carried out with the help of felt rollers on the ends of springs made from strong pieces of hardwood; rouge or some similar polishing medium is applied to assist the process.* (p 362)

B. *Glasshouse scene: Falcon Glass House, Blackfriars. Two furnaces stand on either side of the main chimney shaft. To the left is a 'glory hole' and to the right the annealing chambers.* (p 361)

A. *Vaucanson's drill, in which the position of the tool is adjusted by two worm-screws.* (p 385)

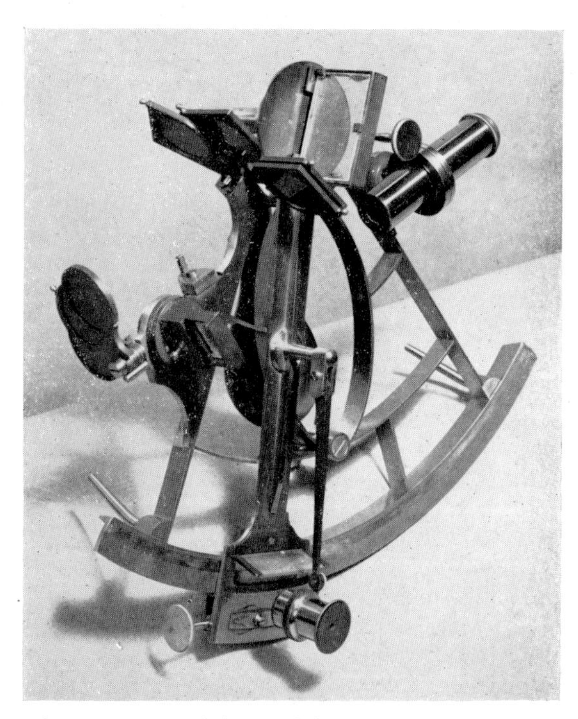

B. *Sextant constructed by Barthelemy Bianchi, mid-nineteenth century. This model represents almost the final form of this type of instrument. It is provided with a micrometer screw for adjustment of the alidade, a lens mounted on an articulated arm for reading the vernier, and coloured screens for reducing the intensity of sunlight.* (p 400)

A. *Vaucanson's lathe for traversing large jobs, with tool-holder driven by a worm-screw.* (p 385)

B. *The hodometer measured distances as it was wheeled along the ground. The distance travelled was recorded on the dial fixed to the handle.* (p 616)

A. *Nasmyth with his steam-hammer, 1856—an improved version of his 1839 hammer.* (pp 116, 431)

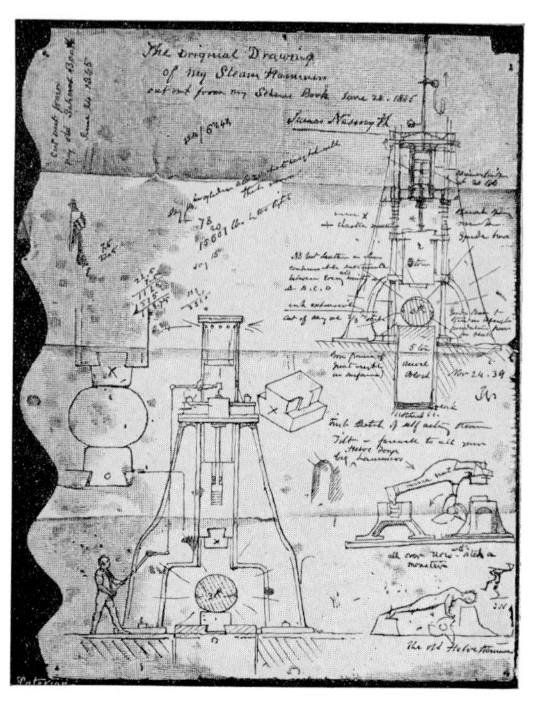

B. *Nasmyth's original sketch of his steam-hammer, 1839.* (p 431)

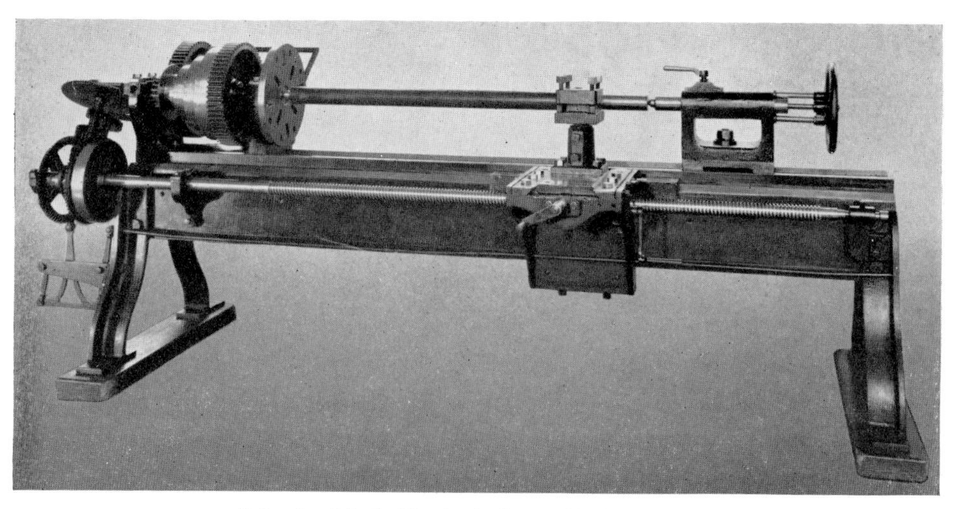

C. *Roberts's original self-acting back-geared lathe, 1817.* (p 428)

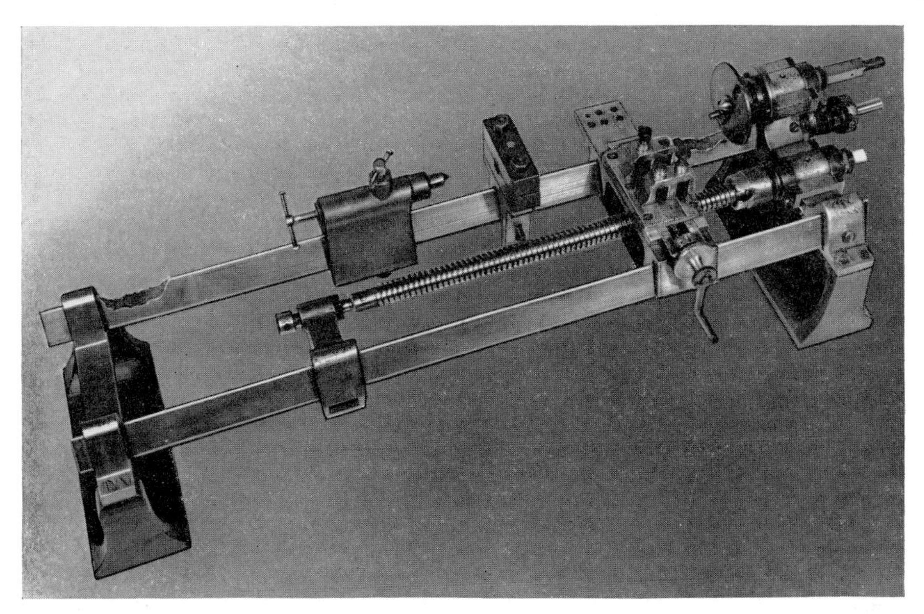

A. *Maudslay's original screw-cutting lathe*, c *1800*. (pp 424, 425, 432)

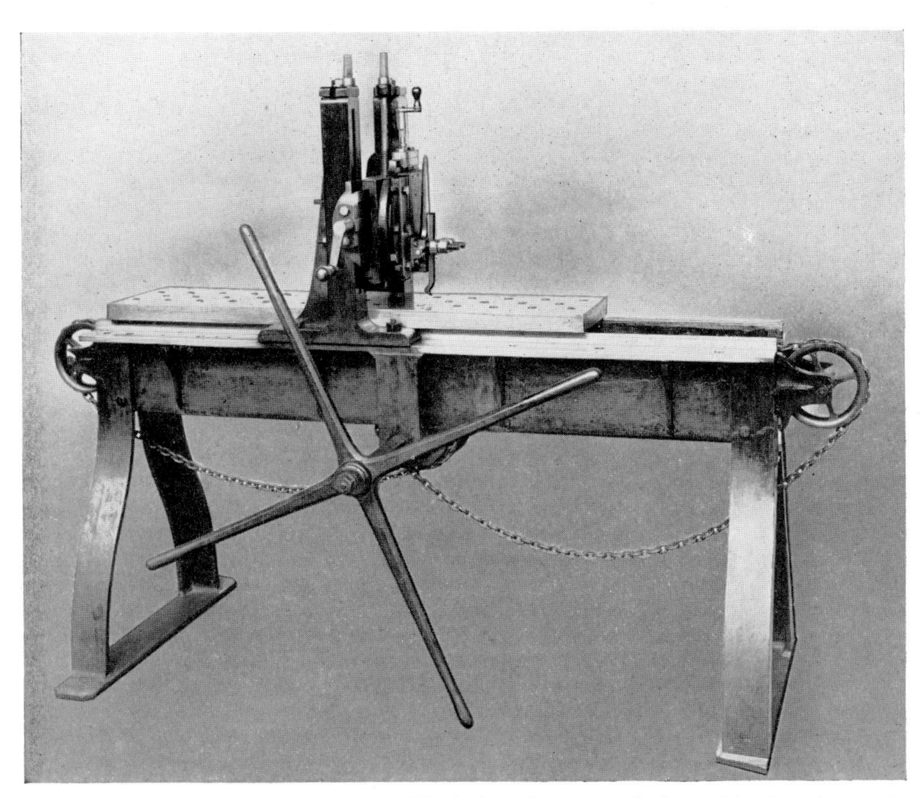

B. *Roberts's planing machine, 1817. This is the earliest extant planing machine.* (p 433)

A. *Brunel's mortising-machine, built by Maudslay in 1803, for cutting the slots in pulley blocks.* (p 427)

B. *Brunel's shaping-engine, built by Maudslay in 1804, for shaping the surfaces of pulley blocks, ten at a time.* (p 428)

A. *Model of Wilkinson's boring mill, 1775.* (pp 421, 422)

B. *Fusee engine, eighteenth century. A screw is being cut by a tool which derives its motion from a lead-screw on the chuck spindle.* (p 420)

A turner's workshop of the eighteenth century, showing the use of the pole lathe and the great wheel. (pp 417, 419, 441)

Telford's iron bridge over the Wear at Sunderland before removal of the centre, 1796. (p 457)

A. *Darby's bridge at Coalbrookdale, the first iron bridge in the world, 1779.* (pp 105, 455)

B. *Burlington House, Piccadilly, designed by Lord Burlington. The building was begun in 1715, and rebuilt in 1866.* (p 470)

A. *The famous factory of Boulton & Watt at Soho, 1798*. (p 183).

B. *The factory of Swainson & Birley near Preston*, c *1830*. *The contrast with Boulton & Watt's factory* (above) *is striking; the fashion of giving factories the appearance of great country houses has disappeared in favour of a more strictly practical design.*

PLATE 32

A. *The Thames Tunnel, begun by Marc Isambard Brunel in 1824. On several occasions the river broke in, and the work was not completed until 1843.* (pp 427, 464)

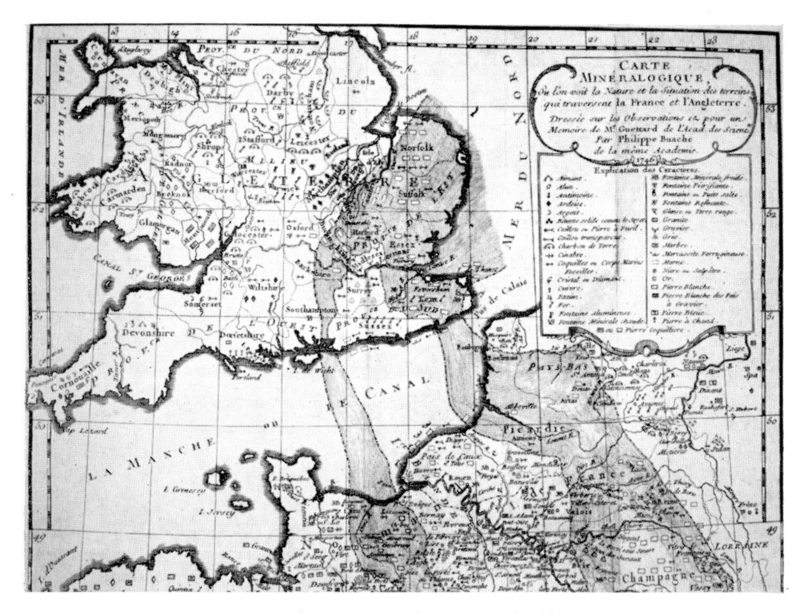

B. *Detail from a mineralogical map drawn by P. Buache 'from the observations of' J. E. Guettard, 1746, showing the key to the geological symbols.* (p 621)

A. *Early road building. The title-page from Gautier's book on road-making.* (p 522)

B. *The Edgware Road at Kilburn, London, in 1750, showing an old stage wagon.* (p 523)

C. *Wood paving in the Nevski Prospect, St Petersburg, which was paved with small hexagons of resinous wood laid on a bed of crushed stones and sand, and covered with boiling pitch.* (p 545)

PLATE 34

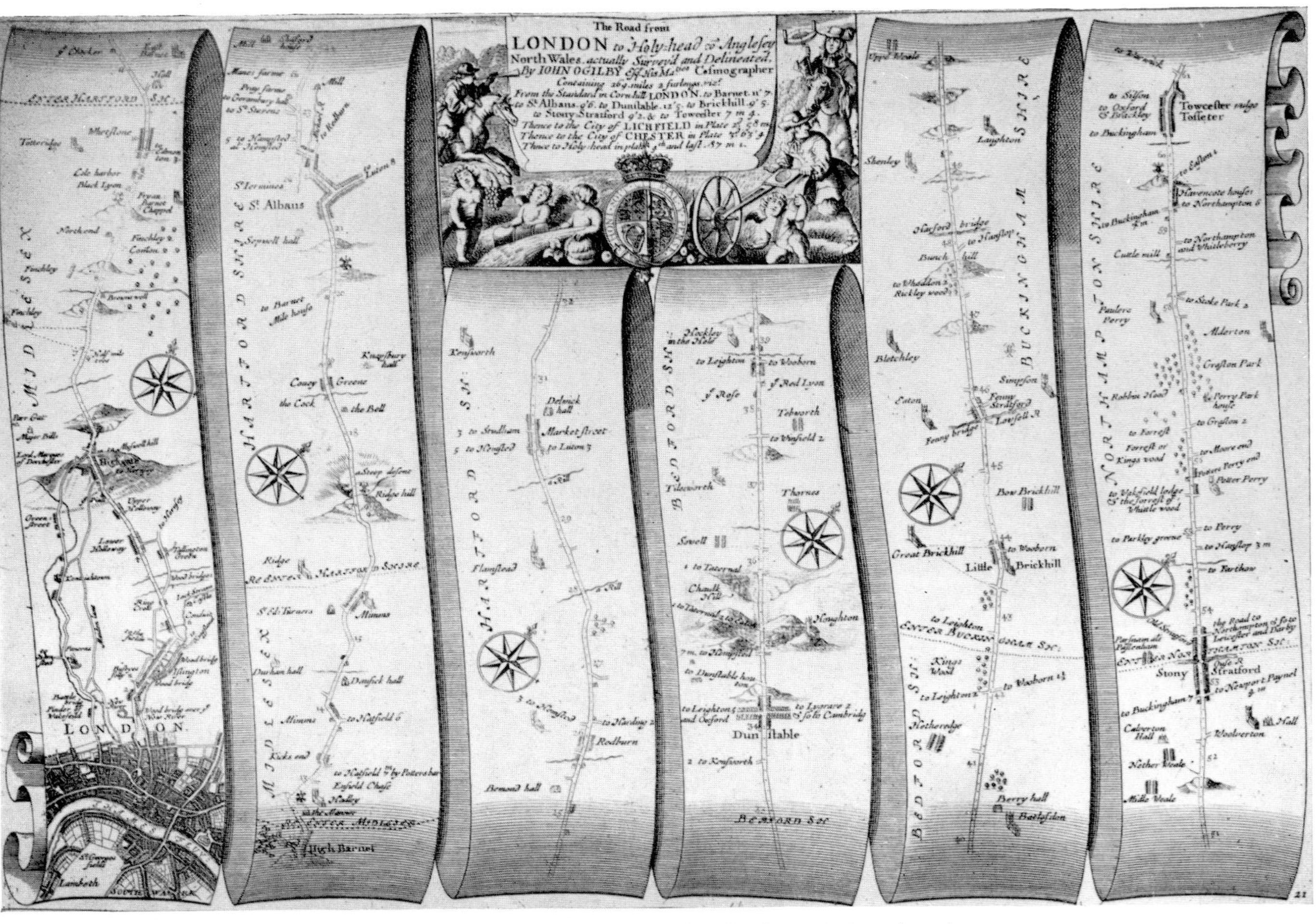

A seventeenth-century map of the road from London to Anglesey. (p 523)

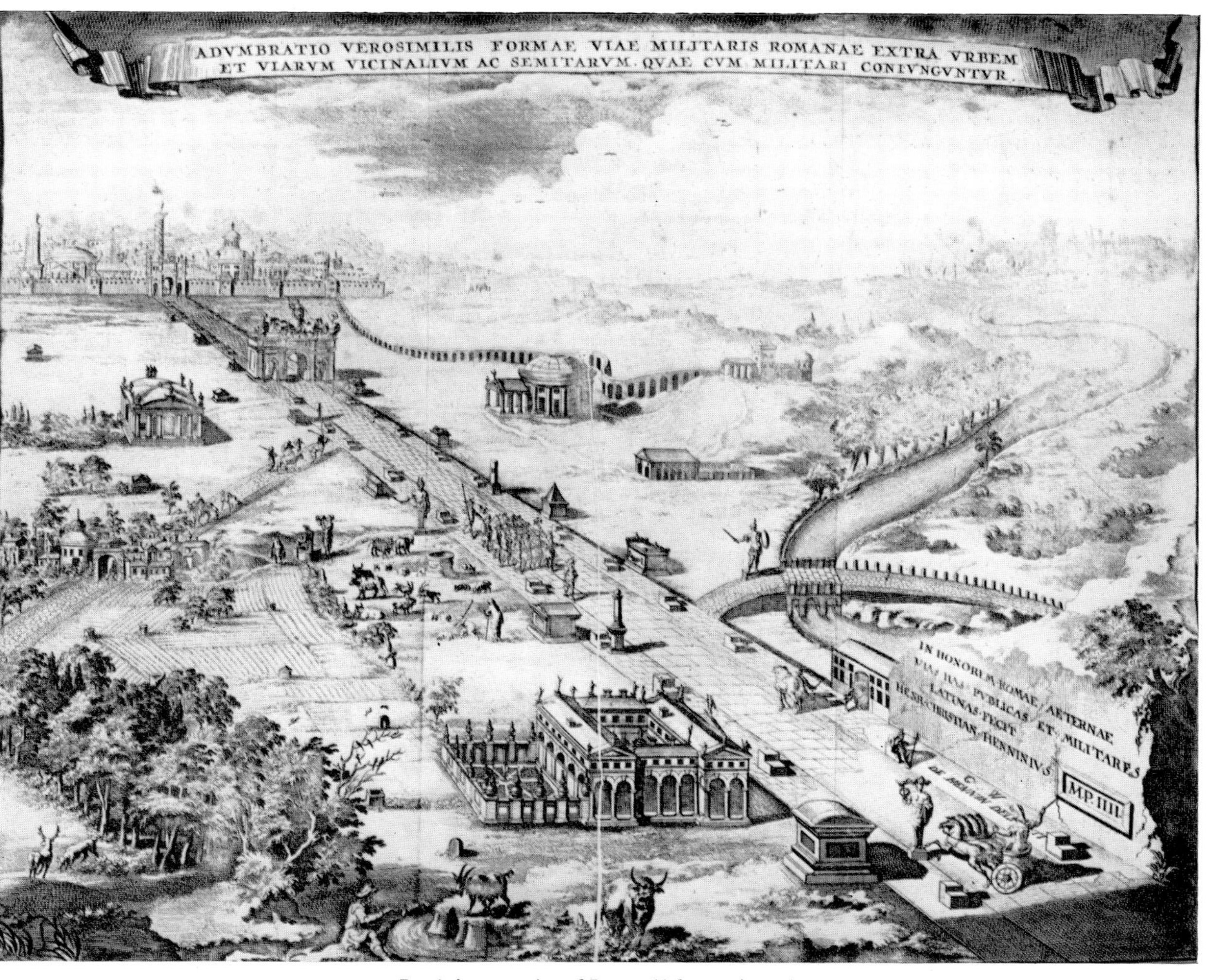

Bergier's conception of Roman highways. (p 521)

PLATE 36

A. *Newgate prisoners repairing roads,* c *1790.* (p 524)

B. *The Devil's Bridge on the St Gothard Pass through the Alps. Early nineteenth century.* (p 529)

The junction of the Staffordshire and Worcestershire canal with the river Severn at Stourport in 1776. (p 566)

A. *The Knoop lock on the Eider canal, seen from the east,* c *1800.* (p 561)

B. *The Suez canal near Kantara, 1869, showing dredgers in action.* (p 562)

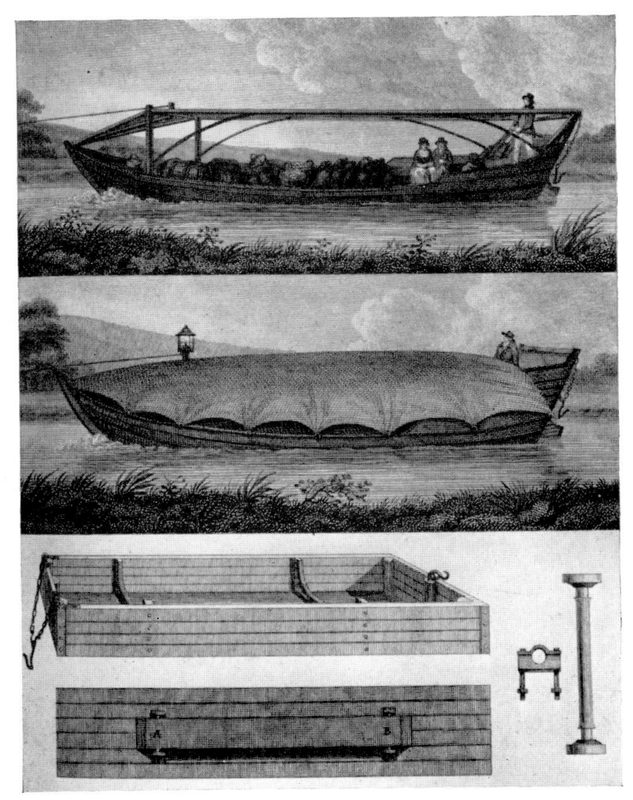

A. *Various boats for use on the canals*, c *1790*. (Above) *The market or passage boat;* (centre) *the dispatch boat;* (below) *a small tub-boat with wheels for running on the rails of inclined planes, such as those on the Bude canal.* (p 571)

B. *Accommodation bridge for a canal*, c *1780*. (p 566)

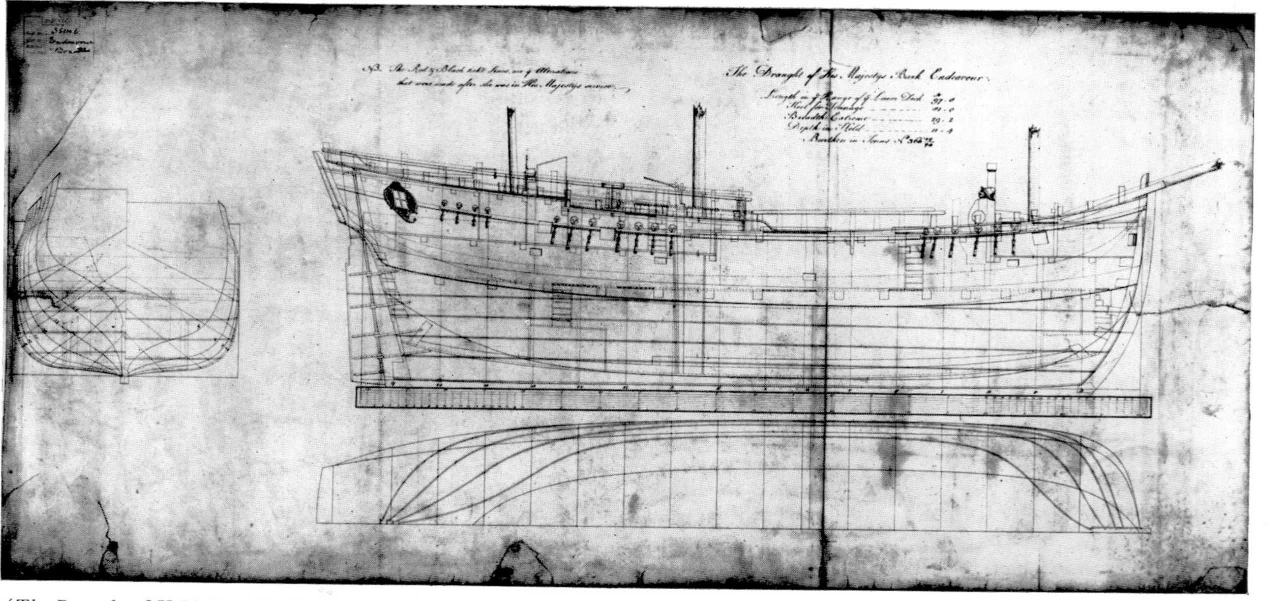

A. *'The Draught of H.M. Bark Endeavour'. The ticked lines on the sheer draught are the alterations made for James Cook's first voyage of circumnavigation. From aft, working forward on the upper deck, will be noticed the tiller and steering-wheel, with the mizzen mast between; the capstan; a pump abaft the main mast; and abaft the foremast a knighthead decorating the anchor winch, which is surmounted by the high gallows of the belfry.* (p 575)

B. *Exploded view of the* Marlborough, *with funnel up and screw down. Although called a three-decker, it will be noticed that she is practically a four-decker, the waist being decked over.* (p 587)

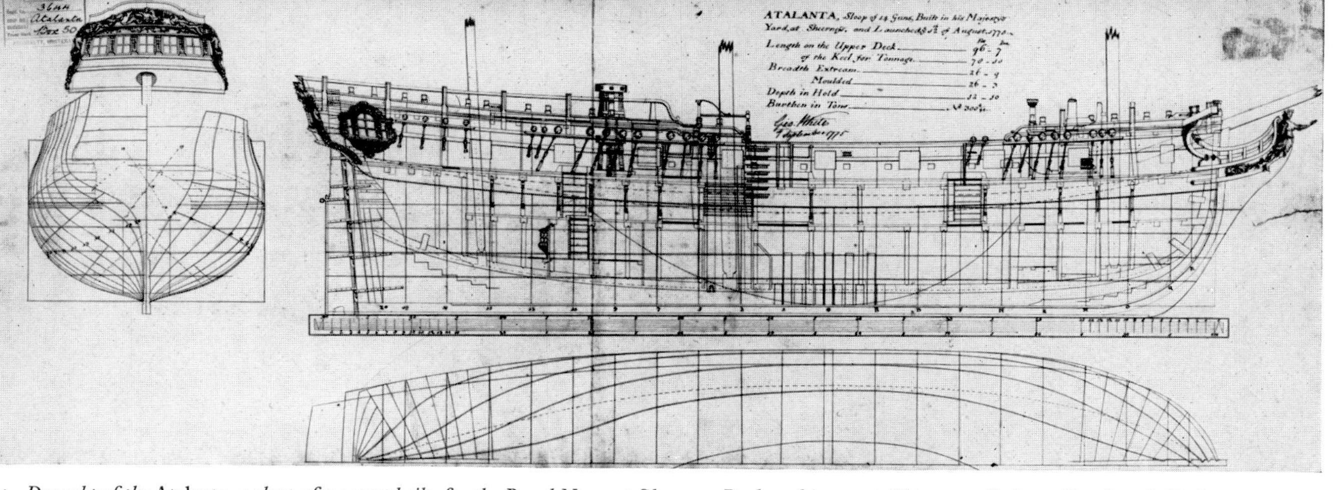

A. *Draught of the* Atalanta, *a sloop of 14 guns built for the Royal Navy at Sheerness Dockyard in 1775. This was a little smaller than the* Endeavour *and had finer lines and the usual beakhead and figurehead which the colliers did not have; note the long poop deck and forecastle with a deep waist between the main and fore masts.* (p 577)

B. *The* Bellona, *74 guns, built at Chatham Dockyard in 1760. A contemporary scale model, unplanked, to show the distribution of the frame timbers or ribs, set closely together and every third frame doubled. The length of her lower gun deck was 168 ft and her beam 47 ft.* (p 584)

A. *H.M.S.* Victory *at sea, late 1790s. By the time of Trafalgar, 1805, the* Victory *had been given a flat, built-in stern without galleries. It will be noticed that she still has the old-fashioned mizzen lateen yard, but the sail is all abaft the mast. By the end of the century the lateen yard had given place to a gaff.* (p 576)

B. *The Honourable East India Company's ship* Atlas, *built in 1812 and mounting 28 guns. The Indiaman with her painted gunports, real and imaginary, was difficult to distinguish from a man-of-war.* (p 576)

A. *The* Ariel *and* Taeping *passing the Lizard in the Tea Race of 1866. Both ships have skysails set on the mainmast. The* Taeping *has double topsails.* (p 592)

B. *H.M.S.* Captain, *1869. Naval steamships remained fully rigged long after merchant steamships were beginning to discard sails.* (p 589)

A. *The* Great Western, *1837, designed by I. K. Brunel. Although she was a wooden ship of 1350 tons, Brunel stressed in his design great structural strength, adequate engine power, and a supply of fuel estimated to last 26 days. Therefore he was able to cut down the ship's rig to that of a schooner, with four masts. She could easily steam at 12 knots.* (p 593)

B. *British four-masted barque, a type which became popular in the 1880s when it became necessary to build rather larger iron sailing ships to compete with steam. The vessel shown here was 287 ft long, with a beam of 42 ft, and of 2081 tons weight.* (p 593)

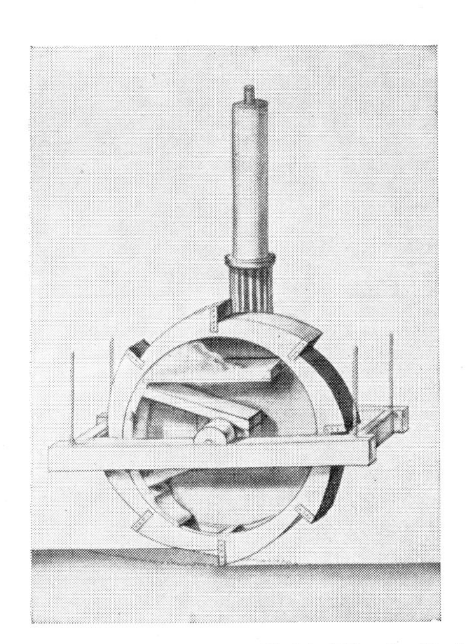

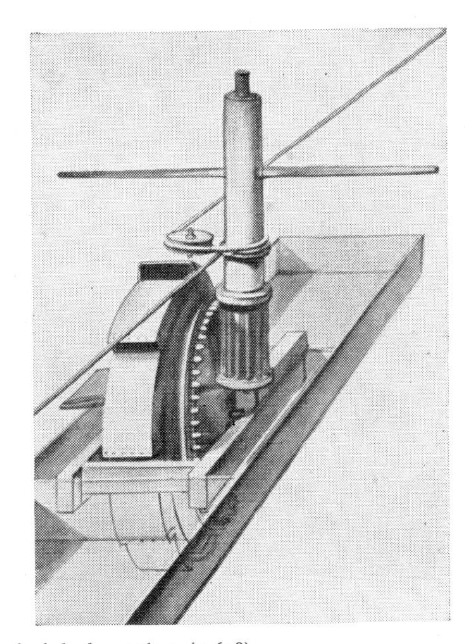

A. *Model of Van der Heyden's wheel-dredger, 1674.* (p 638)

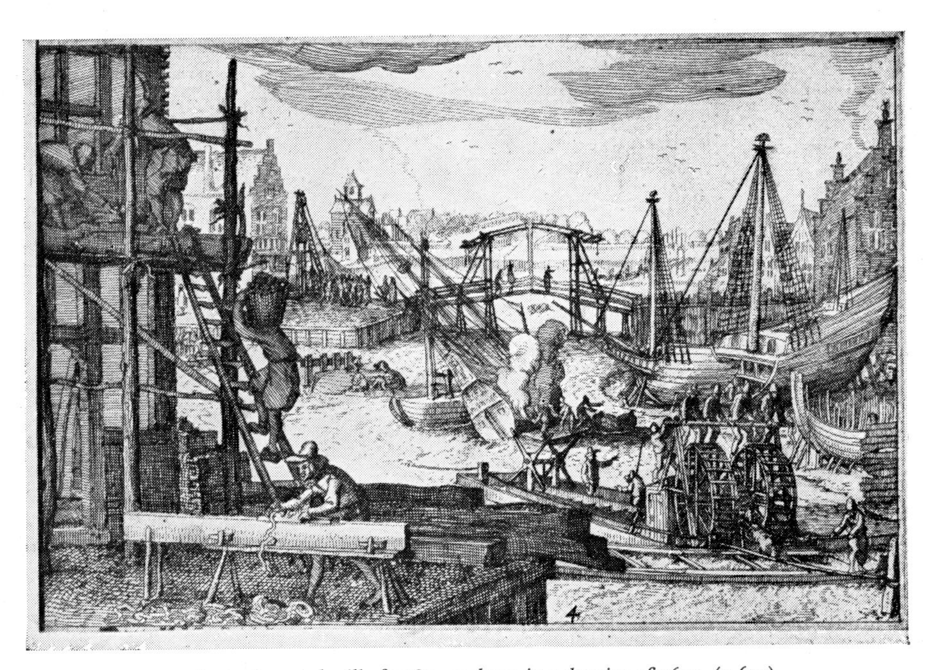

B. *Amsterdam mud-mill of 1589, as shown in a drawing of 1620.* (p 639)

A. *Mud-mill of* c *1730*. (p 639)

B. *The* Great Eastern *under way*, *23 July 1866*. (p 661)

Reproductions of Samuel Morse's telegraphs of 1835 (above) *and 1846* (below). (p 660)

A B C D E F

Many of the trade tokens issued at the end of the eighteenth century, mostly made in Birmingham, show scenes of contemporary technological interest. (A) *A stylized canal boat on the Basingstoke canal, 1789.* (B) *A glass-works illustrated on a Dundee halfpenny token, 1797.* (C) *The inclined plane at Ketley, 1789.* (D) *Mechanical trip-hammer in the works of John Wilkinson, 1793.* (E) *Hand-hammering of iron, 1795.* (F) *Distillation apparatus illustrated on a Perth halfpenny, 1797*